SACRED AND PROFANE

A novel of the life and times of Mozart

Sacred and Profane

A NOVEL OF THE

LIFE AND TIMES OF

Mozart

by David Weiss

WILLIAM MORROW AND COMPANY, INC.

NEW YORK 1968

Contents

FOR
JOHN WILLEY

Author's Note

This book is a historical novel, not a biography or a romance. It is historical because Mozart's life was deeply embedded in the structure of his time, and so the structure of this book is the history of his time. It is a novel because it uses the resources of characterization and story telling. But this work is not a flight of fancy.

All the physical facts are real. Streets, stairways, houses, palaces, cities, furniture, clothes, and all the aspects of living in the second half of the eighteenth century are described as they existed in Mozart's life.

Each event occurs in the correct chronological order. When there is a dramatic coincidence in the narrative, it is not a contrivance of the author but the way the events actually happened. Nothing has been distorted for the sake of vicarious sensation. There are no false love affairs to suggest a romantic titillation. Every work of Mozart's that appears in the book is composed according to the time specified by Köchel. There are many dates and documents and they are accurate. All the people in this novel existed. The narrative moves scrupulously within a framework of historical fact.

Mozart's life is thoroughly documented. There are many contemporary accounts of him, for he was famous from the age of six. An extensive bibliography has grown up about him and most of the physical facts of his life are known. There is his vast correspondence and his father's, which is a magnificent record of their time, place, and emotions, and thus, much of the world of the Mozarts is discussed in their own words.

But there are gaps in Mozart's life, in his feeling and thinking, and in the hope of filling these gaps – as much as it is possible – it was decided that the best approach would be to express his life as a historical novel. Situations, conversations, and motivations had to be imagined and interpreted. Mozart's life was dramatic, full of adventure and struggle, achievement and failure, and lent itself to story telling. Yet

7

even when the novel is imagined and interpreted, it is based on character and probability, with a historical equivalent in mind, so that if precisely this or that did not occur, something similar probably did.

Thanks to the voluminous correspondence of Wolfgang and Leopold Mozart, it is possible to know how they spoke, and so the dialogue seeks to fit their speech without being idiomatic or anachronistic. Then Wolfgang was widely quoted, for he was a witty, pungent phrase maker, and so, whenever it is possible, he is quoted.

During this search for the essence of Mozart, two considerations came to dominate: a respect for the historical fact, and a need to supply the missing details in terms of human behavior. And while it would be presumptuous to assume that anyone has found the whole truth, the one and only truth about Mozart, it is hoped that this work will throw fresh light on his life and character, and his thought and emotion.

Since this is a novel, however, the Köchel listing of his compositions is not used, but when a work is mentioned its title is used or it is named by kind and key as Mozart did in his own thematic catalogue. The term *clavier* is expressed as it was in his time, to indicate any keyboard instrument such as a clavichord, harpsichord, pianoforte, but not the organ. *Pianoforte* is used because it was used in Mozart's time. *Kapellmeister*, which meant leader of the musical establishment, was also an honorary expression, and this title appears both ways, as it did in the period. Forms of address such as "Papa" and "Mamma" are expressed as Mozart did to the day they died. And to evoke the essence of the time the cadences of the period are used as much as it is possible.

Some letters of Mozart and his father are included, for it would be impossible to give a rounded portrait of Mozart without them, as every thoughtful and thorough book about him illustrates. Most of the letters in this book – which are a small portion of what he and his father wrote – are employed as written, with editing. A few have been compressed in the interests of dramatic brevity and impact, and to highlight Mozart's heart and mind. And several are composites or mosaics of Mozart and his father's most moving utterances. But in all instances the contents of the letters are those of Wolfgang and Leopold Mozart.

A number of translations of the letters were read by the author, and he is indebted to *The Letters of Mozart and His Family* by Emily Anderson for the comprehensive picture they give of this correspondence. But wherever a letter is quoted directly, it is taken from *The Life of Mozart* by Edward Holmes. This biography, which also includes much of the correspondence, was published in 1845. Written closer to the time of Mozart's life, it contains the flavor closest to the period and it has several vital letters that were not found anywhere else.

Hundreds of books were read, many maps of the period were studied, and every place that Mozart touched in Salzburg, Vienna,

Paris, and London was visited and revisited, and the four cemeteries where he, his father, mother, and sister were buried. Each composition that appears in the book was heard many times, and most of the works that do not appear in the novel.

Whenever it was possible Mozart's music was heard in public performance as he intended and preferred, and when that was impossible, it was heard on records of the highest quality. The author is grateful to the fine musicians who have expressed Mozart in music. He is especially grateful to the devotion and skill brought to the music of Mozart by Erich Leinsdorf and the Boston Symphony Orchestra, George Szell and the Cleveland Symphony Orchestra, and Robert Casadesus and Lili Kraus. But to list all those who in concert and opera and on records have ably expressed the world of Mozart would be to catalogue most of the outstanding musicians of our time.

This author is indebted to Alfred Einstein's *Mozart* for his precise and penetrating insight into the music; in this observer's judgment the best appraisal of the music itself. He is also indebted to Otto Erich Deutsch's *Mozart, a Documentary Biography,* which contains almost all the documents that relate to Mozart's life; to Erich Schenk's *Mozart and His Times* for many details of value; to John N. Burk's *Mozart and His Music* for his Köchel chronology and his factual evaluation of the music; and to *Mozart and His World in Contemporary Pictures* – which vividly recreates the world of Mozart for the eye.

One of the most valuable contributions to the making of this book was the assistance given by the Mercantile Library of New York and its head librarian, Miss Audrey Eve, who was very helpful until her untimely death in 1967. The Mercantile Library's remarkable research resources were always available for the author's use, and essential to this book.

The author also is indebted to Professor Egon Komorzynski of Vienna for taking him to St. Marx's cemetery where Mozart was buried and for his interesting comments on that dramatic and tragic situation and on Mozart in general; to Professor Geza Rech of the International Foundation Mozarteum in Saltzburg for showing him *The Magic Flute* cottage, the house on the Hannibalplatz where the Mozarts lived, and for his many enlightening ideas about Mozart; and to Professor Hugh Allen Wilson of Union College.

Professor Wilson, in addition to answering important questions about Mozart, Haydn, and Sebastian Bach and the world of baroque music, was kind enough to play their music on the clavichord, harpsichord, piano, and organ to illustrate the vital differences in the playing of and the composing for these varied instruments, so necessary to an understanding of Mozart, the performer and composer.

A special debt of gratitude is owed to Stymean Karlen for creating the poem that opens the book, and for her unfailing feeling for the family relationships of the Mozarts, which was of first importance to the Mozarts.

But now that this book is finished, there is the realization that the feeling and thinking about Mozart began long before the decision to write this novel. This book is the product of a lifetime. And the author's effort has been to write about Mozart as he was in his own work, with clarity and lucidity, and without prejudice, without fear or flattery, but as he was. It is believed that this is the way he would have wished it.

It was his music that kept this story going all these years. If ever a human being's achievement justifies man's stormy and violent existence on earth, it is Mozart's.

David Weiss

New York City
November 1, 1967.

SACRED AND PROFANE is the story of one of the world's great natural resources: Wolfgang Amadeus Mozart. And like David Weiss' penetrating characterization of Auguste Rodin in his best-selling novel, *Naked Came I*, this concentrates on the human being. Mozart's personality was as varied and as deep as his music. He wrote music of a surpassing purity, and wrote letters that were witty, worldly and almost obscene in their awareness of the flesh. He had a tremendous capacity for love and yet he was a pitiless, incorruptible judge of human nature. In this moving novel David Weiss has sought the truth about the child, the youth, the man, the composer, the performer. He has written with feeling but without sentimentality about Mozart who at the age of five was a miracle of nature and at the age of thirty-five was thrown into an unknown grave.

PART ONE

=

Birth

ONE

═

"This one is different."

What Leopold Mozart longed to say, staring at his just born son, was, "*This one must be different,*" but he feared that would sound presumptuous, a defiance of God's will. Yet he repeated, "This one is different," more to himself than to anyone else, as if he were the only person who had to be convinced. And the declaration, made again, made him more cheerful. Now he could almost tolerate his drab, crowded, low-ceilinged bedroom on the third floor of 9 Getreidegasse.

At the instant of delivery Anna Maria Mozart wanted to know but a single thing: would this child live? So many of hers had died, five out of six, she remembered with a chilling sense of horror that no submission to God's will could ease.

The midwife, who had delivered the infant a moment before, now held him hesitantly as if she did not know what to do next. Yet despite her uncertainty, Leopold had hired her because she was the best midwife in Salzburg. Only the midwives could be sure of making a living in Salzburg, he thought cynically; they made more money than the musicians.

When the infant did not move, Leopold was apprehensive. Did the infant have to be mute? All healthy babies cried, he told himself. Leopold Mozart was proud of his good health. At thirty-six he was as busy as any musician in the court of Archbishop Schrattenbach of Salzburg. As assistant Kapellmeister he taught the violin, trained the choirboys, played a violin in the court orchestra, and was a court composer, but he had a sudden fear that if this infant died none of this would survive. Anna Maria was too weakened by the ordeal of the previous childbirths to endure another, and although their Nannerl was learning to play the harpsichord and she was not yet five, she was a girl.

The midwife, realizing that the infant was still alive, gave him a hearty slap, and the child began to cry.

Never had Leopold heard such a welcome sound. God be praised, this sign of life was music indeed.

"Any way you look at him," said the midwife, examining the infant in the glow of the lamp, "he's an ugly one, isn't he."

He was wizened, yes, and wrinkled, thought Leopold, and some of his skin looked red and blotchy, but ugly, no, not his son.

"Yet you are fortunate. Nothing is damaged. Not even the head."

"Give him to me, Frau Albrecht."

Leopold's hands trembled as he felt his son in his hands. But the infant stopped crying, as if comforted by the warmth of his father's caress. And Leopold's trembling ceased and he held the infant lovingly.

Anna Maria said, "He looks so delicate."

"Small, not delicate. Frau Albrecht is right. This one will live."

"Yes," said the midwife. "Praise God, the confinement is over."

Anna Maria lay back on her bed with a sigh of relief. For many hours she had thought she would not live through the pain. Sweat had run down her body although there was snow on the ground and it was January. But now the bed did not feel like a prison. Leopold no longer seemed worried, so she stopped worrying. Instead, her hand felt under the pillows for her small hand mirror. After this seventh birth did she look wretched and old, or younger and lovelier? She studied her face in the mirror. Neither was the case, she decided, she looked the same and was disappointed. One result would have given her the chance to enjoy a well-earned conceit, the other would have given her the opportunity to commiserate with herself. She felt cheated and pushed the mirror back under the pillows. She remembered that when Leopold had married her, they had been called one of the most attractive couples in Salzburg, but that was a long time ago, one year after another marked with pregnancy, and except for Nannerl, and possibly this one, with failure. But Leopold had not changed much, she thought. His features were as regular as ever, his sharp chin prominent and his dark gray eyes keen and penetrating. How proud Leopold must be, with his small vanities, that this one was a boy!

Leopold said, "I will write a mass to celebrate."

"Will the Archbishop permit it?" asked Anna Maria.

"For my own son? Of course! I will compose a mass for His Grace too."

"May I have the child, Leopold?"

He carefully placed the infant in her arms, kissed her affectionately, and stared out of the window on to the small courtyard at the rear of their rooms. The tiny slit of sky made him feel penned in and added to his discontent. He had been trained to take things as they came but some things were difficult to accept. Considering that his father had been a humble bookbinder in Augsburg and that he was the first

15

musician in the family, he had risen remarkably, but there were moments he thought he would never become Kapellmeister – there was such a strong Italian influence in Salzburg. Suddenly this bedroom was too provincial for his ambition. He hated the creaky wooden floors, the scarcity of daylight.

Anna Maria, seeing his sudden somberness, could not endure it and she whispered, "Leopold, you are not hurt by what I said?"

"Why should I be hurt?"

"It will be fitting for you to become Kapellmeister some day. Archbishop Schrattenbach respects you. You do your work very well."

Anna Maria was too good-natured, he thought angrily, she expected the best from everybody, even from Prince-Archbishops, but he knew better. Bowing came easy for some people, but for him it was such a struggle. He was a devout Catholic, he loved his religion – but very few churchmen; he was a strong supporter of Archbishop Schrattenbach and the Empress Maria Theresa – but he resented their favoring Italian musicians; he lived for music and they said they loved music – but how could that make his son different? This was a world created for the nobility and the clergy, no matter how able one was. The nobility and the church dignitaries resided close to the Residenz, the Archbishop's palace, and to the cathedral, his church, and to the other churches clustered around the cathedral.

Leopold knew them by heart: St. Michael's, St. Peter's, St. Cajetan's, St. Erhard's, the Franciscan Church and the University Church which stood behind his home. The aristocrats knew where the power was. They called this compact group of buildings "The Sovereign's Town," and regarded anybody who lived elsewhere as an outsider. Even the part of Salzburg where he lived, while it was on the same side of the Salzach river, was referred to disparagingly as "The Burgher's Town," and no nobleman or church dignitary would have thought of residing in its narrow, crooked, dark streets.

And the rooms in which he lived were uncomfortable, whatever his landlord, Lorenz Hagenauer, said. Hagenauer, who resided on the first and second floors, liked to tell Leopold that no musician in Salzburg had better quarters. But the three flights were hard to climb, the stone and plaster staircase was cold and dark, and the kitchen with its open hearth was so old and crude it made him feel he was back in the Middle Ages.

He strode into his living room. He had asked Doctor Barisani, a friend, to attend the birth of his child, but there was no sign of him and he doubted that the doctor would come, for only the births of the nobility warranted such services. His resentment grew as he glanced out on the Lochelplatz and saw no trace of the doctor. The small square was as black as a tomb. The infant was so quiet his heart sank. It would be a wonder if this child survived. Then suddenly, he heard footsteps.

Silvester Barisani had come reluctantly. Leopold was a friend of his, but good chamber music was hard to find in Salzburg and the Archbishop would have been offended if he had left before the end of the program. As it was, he was doing Leopold a favor by being here at all, for midwives handled every birth in Salzburg except those of the nobility. And Doctor Barisani believed that the survival of a child was accidental, no matter how the physician tried. Yet his long, saturnine face managed a slight smile as he congratulated the Mozarts on the birth, especially of a son.

Leopold cried, "He will live? His chances are good?"

"As good as the rest." The doctor examined the six-foot porcelain stove in the bedroom to make sure that it was giving off the right amount of heat, glanced at the windows to verify that the room was properly aired. But only at Leopold's insistence did he examine the baby.

"Well?" asked Leopold, anxious again – the doctor looked so serious.

"As I told you, his chances are as good as the rest."

"You think he could still die?"

"We could all die – at any moment."

"I know. But our infant mortality is the worst plague of all."

"The baby is small, perhaps a little weak, but otherwise, as I said . . ."

Leopold changed the subject. "Was the program good?"

"They missed your violin. The Archbishop said Brunetti was scratchy."

Leopold grew sarcastic. "Herr Doctor, you mean that for once His Grace could not say the playing was German and thus barbarous?"

"His Grace said the playing was Salzburgian and even worse."

"Did he complain about my absence?"

"A little. You know he likes his music played well."

Anna Maria said, feeling better now that things were returning to normal, "Doctor, you must have some of Theresa's magnificent liver dumplings."

Leopold, before Theresa, their middle-aged maid, served the dinner, pointed out that the infant had the fingers of a musician.

Doctor Barisani replied, "The baby has fingers like everyone else's," but Leopold continued to stare at them as if they had a special life of their own.

The next day Leopold had the infant baptized at the cathedral. He had composed important liturgical works for the cathedral – the center of Salzburg's musical life – and its majestic twin towers, baroque grandeur, and celebrated organ were like home to him. It was bitterly

17

cold outside, and the presence of friends was a comfort. And when the baptism progressed smoothly it allayed most of his apprehensions.

He wrote proudly in the church records: "Johannes Chrysostomus Wolfgangus Theophilus Mozart, born January 27, 1756."

"Father: Johann Georg Leopold Mozart, born November 14, 1719, Augsburg."

"Mother: Anna Maria Pertl Mozart, born December 25, 1720, St. Gilgen."

"Sister: Maria Anna Walburga Mozart, born July 30, 1751, Salzburg."

But as he wrapped the infant in a warm woolen blanket as protection against the freezing weather outside one thing disturbed him. When he stated that his son must become a musician, Abbé Bullinger retorted, "That is immoral. He will become what God wills."

"Of course," said Leopold. One did not disagree with an important churchman, even if he was a friend. Yet he thought that the stocky, middle-aged Jesuit priest was being unfair. And when Bullinger said, "The child is fortunate to be born in Salzburg, it is so beautiful," Leopold thought that depended on how musical the town was for Wolferl.

The first thing Wolferl remembered was the sound of the organ. It was at a church service two years later. There was a thunderous, terrible noise against his ears that made them ache. He turned pale and began to weep.

Mamma was embarrassed, but Papa covered his ears and his crying stopped. Papa whispered, "He is right, Anna Maria, the organ is too loud."

"You are not angry with him?"

"I am proud."

She hugged Wolferl, and he remembered this also.

Soon the child was hearing many sounds. He was past two now, with a large head, blue eyes, blond hair, and a fair skin, and with no signs of ill health, although he was small for his age. He could walk a little – if he held on to something or somebody – but the excitement came from what he heard. There was the table at which he sat and ate, and he liked to eat; there were the windows to look out of and the passersby to see, and he enjoyed that; there was the playing with Nannerl, when she was not taking lessons from Papa, but his happiest moments were when he heard something new. Rain beat on the window and he loved the sound of it. He listened for the wind, although it was often loud and frightening. The ticktock of the clock fascinated him, it was so regular. He could tell by the clatter of the dishes who was washing them. Theresa made very little noise; Mamma made a good deal –

more than he liked sometimes; Nannerl clattered always and occasionally dropped a dish and the abrupt crash brought tears to his eyes.
The night Nannerl dropped a serving plate with a deafening smash
he sobbed as if his heart would break.

Then Leopold took him to the top of the Fortress Hohensalzburg,
which towered over the town. It was a long, hard climb, for only the
Archbishop was allowed to ride a horse up to the ancient castle, and
Leopold had to carry Wolferl most of the way. But as they stood above
Salzburg and the familiar sights Leopold loved came into view, the
Unsterberg, the Bavarian plain, the Salzach river, he felt it was worth
the effort. He thought Salzburg was located as splendidly as any city
there was. He pointed out the flat roofs, the church and convent
cupolas, the dark, narrow streets of "The Burgher's Town," the large,
open squares of "The Sovereign's Town," the grace of the cathedral,
the vastness of the Residenz. It was a beautiful picture and his son
should love it.

Wolferl was interested in other things. Bees buzzed about his head
and he tried to hear what they were saying. Grasshoppers chirped and
he longed to imitate them. He heard a robin and he abandoned himself
to its song. And when the bells echoed in the mountains around them
nothing else mattered. Wolferl rocked back and forth, back and forth.

"What are you hearing?" Papa asked tenderly.

The bells – how he loved them! Ding dong, ding dong, they were
like Mamma's lullabies, sending such a flood of emotion through him.

"Do you like them?"

He nodded yes.

"That's music."

He didn't know what music was, but Papa looked so pleased he nodded again. His apparent awareness was rewarded with a warm hug and
kiss, which made him very happy. He loved music, too – as he loved
Papa – although he still didn't know what it was.

From then on, music filled Wolferl's days. Papa, whenever he could,
worked at home. He taught his private violin pupils there, composed,
had friends in for chamber music, and taught Nannerl, who practiced
daily.

Now that Wolferl could walk by himself, he would toddle into the
music room and sit for hours listening, often under the harpsichord
itself.

Papa told himself it was not surprising that his son was attracted
by the harpsichord, that many children would behave the same way,
but he was pleased. He became accustomed to seeing the child sitting
in a nearby corner or under the harpsichord, listening intently. It made
him want to play accurately so his son would hear music at its best.

19

But when he tried to teach the child to say "harpsichord," the child didn't seem interested. Wolferl didn't know how to tell Papa that when Papa played on this box the sounds sent wonderful sensations through his entire body.

One night Papa played music that was so lovely Wolferl could not contain himself. He had to keep this music with him. After Papa finished on the harpsichord, Wolferl, imitating what he had just heard, hummed the melody. It was the sweetest sound in the world. He wanted to stay up all night. He hated his tiresome bed. He could not sleep until he recalled the entire melody and then, humming it, he fell asleep contentedly. The next morning, when he was able to remember what he had hummed the night before, he was exultant. The tune seemed to carry him wherever he longed to go.

Humming and imitating other sounds became his favorite game. He echoed the bark of their dog, the meow of their cat, the chirp of their canary, the gurgle of the water coming out of the fountain on the Lochelplatz. He became proud of his power to make sounds, and he practiced that often.

And he loved to laugh. This game was easy. When he was a good boy Mamma laughed, Papa did, too, and he joined them. Sometimes Nannerl chimed in but he didn't like hers; Mamma's was soft and gentle; Papa's was deep and resonant; but Nannerl's was thin and shrill. Yet when they all laughed as one it was so pleasing it filled him with love.

A few days before his third birthday, while he was supposed to be sleeping, a sonata Papa was playing at the harpsichord awoke him with a caressing touch. He marveled that music could be so enticing. Unable to resist it, he climbed out of bed and ran into the music room. It was a dangerous journey – he still teetered when he ran and his balance was still precarious – but he had to hear better. He was beside the harpsichord before Mamma or Papa saw him. He reached for the keyboard to touch it, but it was too high.

Mamma laughed at the child's eagerness, but Papa was angry. Papa had toyed with the idea of giving Wolferl lessons on the harpsichord, only to tell himself that the child was too small, too young, and now Wolferl was disobedient, which as a good German father he could not tolerate.

He ordered Mamma to put him to bed at once, and when Mamma did, he slammed the door shut. For an instant Wolferl didn't like Papa. Yet he didn't cry, although the noise jarred him horribly.

Instead, when there was silence he crept out of bed and put his ear against the door and listened. When he discovered that it was the same kind of music as before, it was with rapt attention.

An hour later Mamma opened the door gently and quietly to see how Wolferl was, and he was leaning against the door in a sitting position but sound asleep. She put him back into bed as Papa joined her. Papa was no longer angry. There was a soft smile on the child's face as if he were in the middle of a delicious dream. Suddenly Papa saw a treasure of hope in the sleeping child. He kissed him intensely, but the child did not stir.

The next morning Wolferl remembered nothing but the music. And when he was able to hum the melody, he felt wonderful. He tried it over and over, and then tried it other ways because that was such fun too.

TWO

═

When Leopold told his friends how Wolferl had forced himself to stay up to listen to the music of the younger Scarlatti, no one would believe him.

Abbé Bullinger said, "He only stayed up because he didn't want to go to bed. That's typical childish behaviour."

Doctor Barisani stated that such late nights were dangerous to the child's health. Leopold replied that Wolferl had not had any serious illnesses, and the doctor added, "He will."

Herr Schachtner was even more skeptical. He said, "Next you will be telling me that the child knew *who* he was listening to."

"I didn't say that," said Leopold. "But he knew it was good music."

"He is in love with anything that is new. Most children are."

Leopold didn't answer. It had been his idea to meet the court trumpeter in the Musikant, a small Salzburg inn that catered to musicians, but now he doubted that it was wise. He was surprised and troubled by his friend's skepticism. He didn't expect it in a young musician; Andreas Schachtner was only twenty-seven, a dark, slender Bavarian with a sharp mind. They had become friends quickly, for the trumpeter was also a skillful violinist, a good poet, and well-read, qualities that Leopold respected. So once again he sought to express what he sensed about Wolferl. "The child is always about when I play the harpsichord. He never wants to go to bed then."

"Probably because his bed bores him. That is what drives him to listen to the music. Leopold, there has been much criticism about the way you reported on our music for the Berlin music publisher, Marpurg."

"From the Italians at His Grace's court?"

"Not just the Italians. Perhaps you shouldn't make it so obvious that you want to be a Kapellmeister, here or anywhere else."

"Should I give thanks to heaven because I have to struggle to earn four hundred gulden a year for being an assistant Kapellmeister, and a few extra gulden if His Grace likes the music I compose for the cathedral? You know as well as I do, that I am underpaid."

"No one blames you for wanting to improve yourself. But not at their expense."

Leopold longed to reply contemptuously but Schachtner was someone who could harm him with the Archbishop. Easy enough to say *Homo proponit, Deus disponit,* but His Grace determined every musician's situation in Salzburg. He asked, "Have you read what I wrote for Marpurg?"

"No."

Yet he had an opinion, Leopold thought angrily, everybody had an opinion – even about Wolferl.

"However, I have heard that most of the article is about you, Leopold."

"I'll show it to you. Come to dinner tomorrow, and you can read the article I wrote for Marpurg's periodical."

"Fine. I'm sure it will be as interesting as your *Violin School.*"

"Has my book been criticized too?"

"Oh, no! It is said that its publication has brought honor to Salzburg."

"Because I dedicated it to the Archbishop?"

"Because it is based on sound principles. I read your book as soon as it was published. I use it for all my violin pupils."

Leopold did not believe him. In a sudden moment of despair he thought it was easier to give up, every earthly circumstance was against him. Yet Wolferl *was different,* Wolferl *had to be different*; he could not allow anyone to murder his dream. His son would start taking music lessons as soon as he was able, in another year or two if possible.

Schachtner asked, "How old is Wolferl now?"

"Almost three."

"He is still only a baby."

"Really?"

"Leopold, you are not angry?"

"Should I be?"

"You mean well but not every musically inclined child is a genius."

The next day Leopold had his family wear their best clothes to show Schachtner that they would be able to maintain the social duties of a Kapellmeister's family. He supervised all the preparations.

Mamma wore a simple blue taffeta with white lace trimmings to set off her fair hair and complexion and she was eager for his approval.

"You look lovely, Anna Maria," he said.

"I haven't changed, Leopold?"

"Not much."

"You're sure?" Mamma felt coquettish now that she was no longer going from one pregnancy to another, and these clothes made her feel younger.

"There is no reason to doubt yourself." That was true, he thought, although she was no longer the pretty young woman he had wed. Yet she was still attractive in blue and white. Her constant cheerfulness was worth a thousand kisses. He stated that and she blushed.

"I must look nice," she cried. "You look so nice."

Leopold agreed. He was gratified with the smartness of his white cravat, his gray brocaded coat with its yellow borders. But all he said was, "We must all appear well dressed. Where are the children?"

"Theresa is getting them."

Nannerl was the first to be surveyed. She was excited. She felt like a big girl. It was the first time she had worn grown-up clothes.

Mamma exclaimed, "You look very pretty!" and kissed her.

But Leopold thought she was pretty because she was young and demure, a slender seven-year-old in a simple white taffeta with a tight little bodice. When he kissed her, she curtsied and said, "Thank you, Papa."

"You will play a sonata for Herr Schachtner. Clearly, accurately."

"I'll remember." Then she saw Wolferl trying to clutch her hand. "Doesn't he look silly all dressed up."

"Nannerl!" Papa was stern. "He is a little man now."

She didn't think so, feeling much more grown-up than her brother. But she was silent, for if she disagreed with Papa, he would punish her by forbidding her to play for Herr Schachtner when she yearned to perform and be the center of attention also.

Mamma, on Papa's orders, had taken Wolferl out of the dresses he had been wearing, and had put him in blue knee breeches, white cotton stockings, shoes with imitation silver buckles, and a blue brocaded waistcoat. His hair had been curled in the fashion of the Empress Maria Theresa's children and Mamma thought proudly that he looked like a little courtier. She said, "He could appear at court right now, don't you think?"

Papa wondered if Wolferl had any realization of what he was wearing.

Mamma asked, "Should I put him in simpler clothes?"

Papa deliberated, and then as a plan for the future formulated itself in his mind, he said, "No. He will have to wear them eventually. He might as well learn how as soon as possible."

Wolferl felt very uncomfortable. The knee breeches were too loose, the waistcoat was too tight, and his hair itched. But everyone, except Nannerl, seemed proud of him and so he tried to feel the same way.

The moment Schachtner arrived Leopold led him into his living room to read what he had written for Marpurg's music periodical. But after his friend finished it, he said, "It is comprehensive – about you."

"I only told the truth."

"About yourself."

"I mentioned everyone."

"But there is very little about Eberlin, our present Kapellmeister, or Lolli, our Vice-Kapellmeister, who are ahead of you in rank."

"You are exaggerating."

Schachtner read from the article, " 'Herr Leopold Mozart, first violin, and leader of the court Kapelle.' Ah, Eberlin and Lolli must like that."

"I wrote that Kapellmeister Eberlin is a fine musician, which he is."

"And Lolli?"

Leopold shrugged. He knew that Lolli was supposed to inherit Eberlin's post, but a miracle might happen and he was only helping that along.

"Marvelous!" Schachtner chuckled. "Have you ever read Machiavelli?"

"I have read many things."

"And composed even more, according to what you wrote for Marpurg, more than anyone else in Salzburg." Schachtner read over Leopold's protests: " '*Of the works of Herr Mozart which have become known the ones to be noted are a large number of symphonies, thirty grand serenades, many concertos, twelve oratorios and a great number of theatrical pieces . . .*' "

"Please, you are making my article sound like a piece of sheer lunacy!"

"When Eberlin dies or retires, the enemies you have created will make it difficult for you to succeed him as Kapellmeister."

Leopold retorted sharply, "Enemies? One does not have to make enemies, not in music. They exist simply because you exist, because they want the same patronage you do, because you write music they envy and cannot write. For many reasons. All I did was list some of my accomplishments."

Schachtner smiled skeptically.

"Has His Grace said anything?"

"At the moment he is more concerned with keeping us out of the war between Maria Theresa and Frederick of Prussia."

"We will continue to stay out. We have nothing they need. It is our greatest virtue."

"And you have a secure post here, yet you want another."

"I am His Grace's most humble servant."

"Leopold – Marpurg is read everywhere in Germany. You have adroitly made yourself available without appearing to do so."

Leopold insisted, "That is not true. I hope I will be the choice of His Grace when Eberlin is gone. And why are you so concerned?"

"We are friends. I do not want to see your career damaged."

"Your real reason?"

Before Schachtner could reply Anna Maria interrupted them. Had any of them seen Wolferl? She was disturbed; Nannerl was with Theresa in the kitchen but there was no sign of the baby.

Leopold asked, "Did you look for him in the music room?"

"He is not supposed to go into that room when you are not there."

There was a moment of oppressive silence and then a faint tinkle came from the music room. It rose louder, was muted for an instant, and then continued harmoniously without a quaver. Leopold motioned for Anna Maria and Schachtner to follow him quietly and they tiptoed into the music room.

Wolferl stood by the harpsichord selecting thirds. Ever since he had heard Papa play fluid harmonies on this wonderful box he had yearned to try it for himself. But he had been unable to reach the keyboard until today. Now, however, he felt triumphant. He remembered every step: how he had stretched and stretched, and suddenly it was there, he reached the keys, he pressed down one key and the sound was good. But then the tone of the next key did not fit. His fingers slipped over the keyboard until he found a key that made a tone he preferred and now he struck them in succession. His discovery of thirds and their harmonious intervals gave him great joy. They were his friends, his good, dependable friends. And because he loved them so, he struck them tenderly.

Wolferl was not aware of the others until Papa picked him up. For a second he thought Papa was angry, Papa held him so tightly. Then Papa placed him on the harpsichord stool and told him to continue. But he could not reach the keyboard this way, the stool was too low.

Papa sat him on pillows and this time he was able to reach the keyboard without straining. As he resumed selecting thirds he was not aware of anything else. He sat with such concentration Mamma had to call him several times before he realized that she was calling him for dinner. And although they were having capon and he loved capon, he went reluctantly until Papa said he could play this game tomorrow.

At the dinner table Schachtner exclaimed, "Picking out thirds? He couldn't have done it by himself. You must have taught him, Leopold."

"I haven't taught him a thing."

"And those clothes? He looks like a little footman."

"He will be no footman. You can depend on that."

"So you are going to make a prodigy out of him."

"I am going to teach him to be a musician."

"I hope you won't start him too soon. I was started at five, when I wanted to do other things. I hated it. For a long time I had to be forced to practice. It took me years to learn to like music."

Leopold had stopped listening. He was thinking, Wolferl was his son, not a Schachtner.

THREE

Lessons started the next day in the music room. Leopold made sure that everything was ready while Anna Maria dressed Wolferl. Theresa had fixed the fire and he was pleased that the large porcelain stove was giving off ample heat – no one's fingers would be numb here. She had also polished the harpsichord and it shone brightly. He played a few notes on it to be certain it was in tune for Wolferl and he was gratified with its tone. He did the same with his small clavichord and liked its response. His violin stands were where he had left them on the other side of the room, so he could pace up and down while teaching. But when Anna Maria brought Wolferl in, the child had eyes only for the harpsichord.

The moment he was seated at the instrument he was absorbed, except that he could not reach the keyboard. Papa placed pillows under him but his seat kept shifting. His back ached. He could not sit straight. Papa put his fingers on the keyboard and he cried.

Papa picked Wolferl up to punish him and Mamma halted Papa, saying, "The child is right. He is uncomfortable. You don't practice when you are uncomfortable." She removed the offending pillows, took the family bible out of the bookcase and set it under Wolferl. It was the largest book in the house and the most important; it was wide, thick; it had a fine binding which had been made by Leopold's father.

And it fitted Wolferl's bottom. He stopped crying. And when Papa began to play, he played with him. Mamma was smiling, which meant that she approved of what he was doing. Papa sat close to him now, no longer upset, and carefully demonstrated what to do. It was easy to imitate – he loved to imitate – and he followed Papa happily.

Leopold noticed that when Wolferl hit a dissonance he winced. He moved from note to note with surprising accuracy. He could tell by the look on Anna Maria's face that she still considered Wolferl her baby, but he could not feel that way any more. Wolferl did not want to halt.

28

Yet a minute later as Anna Maria put her arms around him, swaying with him slowly, her lips against his light, soft skin as she sang a gentle lullaby, he fell asleep like any other baby.

Now Leopold taught Wolferl music as he would have taught another child how to speak. Wolferl learned the scales as other children learned the alphabet. What pleased Leopold most of all was the child's love of the harpsichord. Instead of having to encourage him to practice, Wolferl had an urgency to practice as if it were as necessary and natural as breathing. Leopold found it difficult to restrain his own enthusiasm and to restrict the teaching of his son to an hour three times a week, but because Wolferl was so young and Mamma was worried about the strain, Leopold was determined to keep this resolve. It was not easy. Once he corrected Wolferl, the child remembered and did not have to be corrected again. He learned the clavichord now also, with equal facility. He was beginning to read music. He could name most of the keys by ear.

Wolferl had entered a world of new and remarkable wonders. He could not stay away from the keyboard. He marveled that there could be so much pleasure in the world; he could produce music by himself; by some miracle he could make beautiful, caressing tones. And Papa never shouted any more. Papa looked so pleased these days. There were so many keys to strike, so many tones to make. He wanted to hug the harpsichord and when no one was looking he did so.

By the time he was four he was learning minuets. Leopold said special prayers at the cathedral for his son and kept a record of each piece that Wolferl learned. He could no longer go slowly in his teaching, yet Wolferl never objected. He showed his son manuscripts written by himself so that the child could read original scores and learn the rules of composition; he gave him a scherzo to study and the child learned it at sight.

Anna Maria was upset. The instant there was music in the house nothing else mattered to Wolferl. She tried to get him to take daily walks with Nannerl, to have fresh air and excercise, but he preferred the harpsichord.

Nannerl resented that Wolferl was getting more attention. She still remembered how when she had played for Herr Schachtner, he had talked only about Wolferl. She avoided taking him for walks and he was too young to go alone. And she did not want to practice with him.

Papa said she must and she replied, "He is a baby." Nannerl was surprised by her own outspokenness but Papa did not punish her.

Instead he looked preoccupied and said, "He is your brother."

"I can still play better than him. I learned the scherzo a month ago."

But the two children were equal, thought Leopold, except that Nannerl was twice Wolferl's age.

"I can play marches, themes, variations. He can't."

"You are playing them very well." She beamed, and he added, "Would you help me teach them to Wolferl?"

She thought, This is a trap. But Papa kissed her as if she had said yes and led her into the music room where Wolferl was practicing another scherzo. Papa wanted them to play together.

"Papa, you said I would help you teach him."

"That's right. You'll practice duets. You'll lead and he'll follow."

Nannerl stared at Wolferl sitting at the harpsichord. He was still half her size and if he played better she would never get over it.

Papa placed the music before her.

She found herself sitting next to Wolferl, although she was not certain she wanted to. But as Papa had said, he followed her. When they were finished Papa kissed her first, and so did Mamma when Mamma heard how she had led. Nannerl could not be cross, not even with Wolferl.

At the dinner table Nannerl informed Wolferl from her lofty eminence, "Tomorrow I'll teach you how to play a march."

"March?" Wolferl looked puzzled.

"Like you play on a drum."

"Oh. Yes." He tapped his fingers on the table in imitation of a drum.

"You're playing it wrong."

"Wrong?" He stopped beating his fingers on the table; he was bewildered.

"You're half crying." There were tears in his eyes.

"No, I'm not." But he was.

Then, her superiority asserted, she felt sorry for him and informed him, "I'll teach you tomorrow."

The next day Leopold began to teach Wolferl arithmetic and to read and write. They did not get to the harpsichord until late, and then it was briefly. The following few months Leopold concentrated on these subjects and Wolferl applied himself earnestly.

One afternoon Schachtner dropped in to see Leopold and came upon Wolferl sitting on the floor and covering it with figures. Everything was chalked with numbers, the tables, chairs, walls, even the music lessons.

Schachtner wanted to know what he was doing.

"'Rithmetic," said Wolferl, "for Papa."

"You do everything for Papa?"

"For Papa, and God. Next to God comes Papa."

"Who taught you that?"

"Papa. Do you want some 'rithmetic?"

"What will I do with it?"

"Make notes. Papa said it will help me make notes. When I am older. I am five."

Schachtner corrected him, "Four."

"Four, going on five."

"Going on five," Schachtner acknowledged.

"Play with me." Wolferl took a toy drum that Schachtner had given him and said, "Nannerl is teaching me a march. I'll play it and you sing it." He marched into the next room drumming and singing and Schachtner followed him, marveling that the child was playing in time and in tune. The court trumpeter got out of step and Wolferl corrected him. They were in the middle of improvising a new tattoo when Papa entered. Papa kissed his son, then gave him one of his own minuets to read on sight. Wolferl sat down at the harpsichord without another word and began to play.

Schachtner listened carefully. The child was playing his father's music with a gentle, lyric touch. How extraordinary, he thought, but he must not say so, or Leopold would expect the impossible from the child.

Leopold said, "Doesn't he play beautifully?"

"He is skillful," Schachtner said grudgingly.

"He gets better every day. He is the best pupil I have ever had."

"Child prodigies can be a dangerous thing."

"Not Wolferl." He felt that God was speaking to him through this child. But Schachtner, who read Voltaire, would only sneer if he told him this.

Wolferl had finished and now he wanted to play a concerto.

"Concerto?" Schachtner could not hide his amazement.

Leopold said, "I have been giving him compositions of other composers besides myself to study. And since he is so fond of the harpsichord, I have been having him practice a few simple concertos."

"Simple, no doubt, like Scarlatti, Hasse, Telemann."

"Nothing that difficult."

"Papa!" It was Wolferl. "May I play your concerto?"

Leopold looked pleased but his reply was firm. "No. You must practice scales now. You have neglected them recently. For an hour, remember."

Wolferl was disappointed but dutifully began to practice scales.

Leopold escorted Schachtner into his living room. His friend obviously had something important to tell him.

But the court trumpeter had something else on his mind now. "Why did you have Wolferl go back to scales? He is far too advanced for that."

Leopold smiled with gratification and said, "Discipline."

31

"But Wolferl obeys you faithfully. You couldn't have a better pupil."

"So you agree with me that he is different."

"I agree that he is musical, for his age." Schachtner changed the subject. "Have you heard that Eberlin has been ailing?"

"No. He conducted the Kapelle last Sunday."

"He hasn't been feeling well lately, but he has been trying to hide it."

"I am sorry to hear that," Leopold said sincerely, "he is a good composer, almost the equal of Telemann and Hasse."

"When Eberlin goes, you could be the next Kapellmeister. You are our most distinguished composer, next to Eberlin."

"Lolli is a court composer, too."

"You are better than Lolli."

"What about my report for Marpurg? You said that made many enemies."

"It has. But some people think you have a chance to be the next Kapellmeister. Despite Marpurg. Your *Violin School* is well thought of."

"What about His Grace?"

"Archbishop Schrattenbach would like your children to play for him."

"Who told him about them?"

"You have had the children play for Bullinger, Barisani, myself. Didn't you want it to get back to the Archbishop?"

"You are my friends. I wanted your opinion." Leopold asked very seriously, "Do you think their playing will help me become Kapellmeister?"

"If their performance pleases His Grace, it will show that you are a fine teacher. And Barisani says the girl is even better than the boy."

Leopold doubted that, although Nannerl was a fine performer for her age and sex. But the Archbishop was a different matter. When God had given His Grace his sacred office, He had given him great power also. Praise from His Grace could give birth to a plan that had been in his mind for some time. Perhaps Schachtner was a good friend after all. He said, "I will need a few weeks to prepare the proper program."

"His Grace wants to hear them sooner. He has to go to Vienna."

"To look for a new Kapellmeister?"

"More likely, to keep us out of the war between Maria Theresa and Frederick. He is proud that none of their troops have entered the Principality, that he has been able to maintain our neutrality."

"How much time do I have?"

"A week."

"It is too soon. The children are very young."

"Two weeks. But no longer. His Grace has to be in Vienna soon after."

Leopold nodded automatically. There was no choice and he knew it. But he must make no false steps. Many things could displease His Grace.

The sound of practicing had ceased but it was Schachtner who noticed that. He was surprised; he thought Wolferl never disobeyed his father.

"Wolferl may be studying some scores."

Schachtner was curious. They entered the music room and found the child busy with his pen. Wolferl, kneeling on a chair, was scribbling on the table. There were several scores beside him but he ignored them as he dipped his pen into the ink bottle. He was so absorbed in what he was doing that when blots fell upon the paper on which he was writing, he merely wiped up the blots with the palm of his hand and continued with his writing.

Leopold asked, "What are you doing?"

"Writing a concerto for the harpsichord. It will be done soon."

"Let us look at it."

"No, no, it is not ready yet."

"We will judge that. Wolferl, give it to me!"

The child obeyed reluctantly. At first all Leopold and Schachtner could see were the ink blots but gradually they were able to discern notes, a musical structure, and the form of a concerto.

Leopold exclaimed, "See, Andreas, how correctly it is conceived?" Schachtner nodded.

"Only it can't be used, for it is so difficult no one could play it."

"Papa, that is why it is a concerto," said Wolferl. "It must be practiced before it can be performed."

"Can you perform it?" asked Schachtner.

"Well, this is how it goes," said Wolferl. He began, but his playing was uncertain and suddenly he stopped, irritated at his inability to express what he felt. Yet he could tell that Papa liked what he had done; Papa gave him such a warm kiss before sending him off to dinner.

Leopold wrote "Wolfgang Mozart" under his son's composition and knew he would treasure this concerto as long as he lived. God had visited a miracle upon him, there was no gainsaying that now. And he must make sure that this blessing had not been given in vain.

Schachtner said, "That was a fine effort."

"We must remember that he is very young."

"Do you think you will have the children ready for the concert?"

"If it is possible."

33

FOUR

It was two weeks later. Leopold felt that the interval had been fruitful. He had taught the children a duet by Eberlin, a diplomatic gesture he hoped would be praised by His Grace. He had given Nannerl a sonata by Scarlatti for her solo performance – Scarlatti was a favorite of the Archbishop's; Wolferl was to play a minuet by Telemann, who was also well regarded. And he had arranged an encore for each child, a march for Nannerl, a scherzo for Wolferl, each composition by himself.

But now that the day had come Leopold was apprehensive. In the privacy of his humble music room it was easy to nourish dreams, but in the huge and ornate Residenz his children would be under the jealous scrutiny of many who fancied themselves authorities on music. Yet how could he take his children to Vienna if he dared not venture beyond 9 Getriedagasse? If they did not play today a fine opportunity would be gone. He must plunge ahead, he rationalized, whatever the risk.

He hurried into the living room to see that everyone was dressed appropriately. And by the time they walked to the Residenz some of his confidence had returned. He said, standing on the Residenzplatz, "This is one of the largest squares in the world. And the Residenz is a beautiful palace. It represents Italian architecture at its best. It has one hundred and eighty-five rooms, and more are to be built."

Wolferl asked, "What is Italian?"

"The style of the building."

Wolferl did not understand.

"Like the music you play. Like Scarlatti is different from Telemann."

"Oh, yes." That was simple and clear.

"But first you play together."

Nannerl reminded Wolferl, "I lead and you follow."

"Yes. But afterward, you play Scarlatti and I play Telemann."

Leopold said, "No encores, unless His Grace requests them."

"Papa, is His Grace next to God, too?"

34

Nannerl said scathingly, "He *is* God, silly. That is, in Salzburg."

"God's envoy," Leopold said, but he doubted that either child understood. He gazed upward in a silent prayer that all would go well. The winter sun shone on the palace with a silver glow. He interpreted this as a benediction from God and felt less nervous. Salzburg looked lovely.

Wolfgang asked, "Where is the harpsichord?"

"Probably in the Konferenzsaal," said Anna Maria, "where most of the court concerts are held." She smiled, thinking of how much she loved her family. But in the next moment she felt sad, afraid that Leopold was pushing the children too fast, too hard. Nannerl was still too thin and Wolferl was small and frail for his age. Yet she had said nothing. She never told Leopold something he didn't want to hear. Even if it were the truth. He had to be the authority. It was essential to him.

The Mozarts were ordered to wait in the Carabinierisaal. Nannerl was awed by the immensity of the room with its high arched windows, its ceiling frescoes. "It is larger than all our rooms put together."

"Yes," said Leopold, "it is over a hundred yards long." He wondered why they were waiting here. The Carabinierisaal was not the anteroom to His Grace's apartments, but where his bodyguard stood watch.

Count Arco informed him, "His Grace isn't ready yet. He was indisposed this morning. We almost had to cancel the music."

Leopold glanced at the court chamberlain in dismay. Georg Felix Arco was a friend, but in the presence of His Grace it was advisable to be formal with each other. Leopold was disappointed that the Count had dressed all in black, and was wearing his powdered wig down below his ears in an exact imitation of His Grace and to give his face the appearance of length.

"Oh, His Grace is fine now," said Count Arco. He wished the violin teacher wasn't so eager. His Grace disliked eager musicians, especially those who wanted something.

"Aren't the children performing in the Konferenzsaal, sir?"

"Why should they?"

"We do. That is, all members of the court orchestra do."

"But you are professional musicians."

"Where is the concert being held?"

"In the Rittersaal."

"It is a beautiful chamber."

"Quite good enough for an informal concert. Don't you think so?"

"Yes." It was difficult, however, to hide his disappointment.

The great white doors which led into the Rittersaal were thrown open by a liveried footman and the Mozarts were ushered into His Grace's presence. Archbishop Schrattenbach reclined in his imperial chair in gray vestments which matched the color of his wig. There was a luxurious marble table in front of him, and a number of musical scores on it, to show what a connoisseur he was, and a rosewood clock, to remind everyone not to play too long. He seemed to be thinking deeply, but Leopold decided that he was resting after a heavy meal, the real reason they had to wait. His Grace had the proper features for a Prelate, thought Leopold, a sharp chin, a strong mouth, and brown eyes that could become severe instantly.

There were thirty people in attendance, some of whom were Leopold's friends, but they became insignificant as His Grace indicated that the Mozart children should be introduced.

The Archbishop was pleased that the girl's bosom was covered, but he thought their clothes were too lavish for the children of a musician, and he said it was doubtful that a child so young and little as the boy could perform the program listed for him, and Leopold said, "He is five, sir."

"That is still very young to play Eberlin and Telemann."

"He will, Your Grace, splendidly, you can depend on that." But Leopold wished he could sit beside the children, just in case . . .

"It will be interesting to see if he can play as well as they say."

Leopold was dismayed to learn that his children were not the whole program, but just a part, and a small part at that.

Wolferl was full of anticipation. There was happiness in everything, in this great room, in the lovely harpsichord, in Herr Schachtner smiling reassuringly to him, in the other musicians about to play. As the concert started he leaned forward to hear everything. But as the orchestra, conducted by Lolli, played Vivaldi, Lolli's rapid beat did not fit the music. Wolferl was hurt that anyone playing music should make such a mistake. And the music that followed, by Lully, was so full of drums, it gave him a headache. He couldn't stand it and he began to cry.

Papa was dismal, but all His Grace said was, "The boy is a critic."

Mamma dried his eyes and it was a relief when the drums ceased.

A trio followed and he was positive that the first violin was a quarter tone off but they kept playing. He felt sad; Papa had said His Grace was next to God, and his music should be without a flaw. Didn't anyone else know? When the number ended there was loud applause. He felt betrayed; one didn't lie about music whatever other fibs they told. Then he and Nannerl were next. She had him by the hand and was leading him to the harpsichord, whispering, "Don't be afraid, just follow me," but what was there to be afraid of – he had played these pieces many times.

As the children sat down at the harpsichord Leopold noticed that Nannerl was pale but that Wolferl was calm. And once they began their duet she swayed with the music, but Wolferl sat straight on the stool, his countenance grave and thoughtful. He felt they played quite well, precisely as he had taught them. Only one incident interrupted their performance. While Wolferl was playing his solo the Archbishop's pet cat strolled into the room, came up to Wolferl and purred. Wolferl paused, grinned, patted the cat a moment, and then placing it beside him on the stool, he resumed playing exactly where he had left off.

At the end of the program everyone waited for His Grace to applaud. When he did everyone followed, but he did not request any encores.

Anna Maria kissed Wolferl as her reward; Nannerl said, "He was naughty, he shouldn't have played with the cat"; Eberlin congratulated the children on how well they had played his music; but Leopold had eyes only for His Grace. A crowd of sycophants surrounded the Archbishop in a flattering circle: the nobles with their plumes and swords, the churchmen in their velvet robes, the musicians and the others in their simpler dress.

Schachtner looked gratified; Bullinger was impassive, like His Grace; Barisani was laughing sardonically; Lolli was strutting.

But finally, Leopold was able to get a word with the Archbishop, saying, "We were deeply honored, Your Grace, to perform for you."

Now Schrattenbach could not ignore him. He said, "I was surprised that the boy could play at all, his hands are so small."

"He is the most congenial material I have ever had, sir."

"You must be a sorcerer to make him play at such a young age."

"It is the will of God, Your Grace."

"With some assistance from yourself, no doubt."

"I am His humble servant, sir. But sometimes I feel as if He is speaking to me through this child."

Archbishop Schrattenbach wished the violin teacher hadn't assumed such a pious tone but he allowed him to continue, more curious than interested.

"If I might ask Your Grace's permission to present my children in Vienna, to show Vienna the noble state of music in Salzburg."

"I thought you were training your son for my court."

Schachtner, who had been listening carefully, said softly, "If Your Grace will excuse me, perhaps these children could bring honor to Salzburg."

"In Vienna?"

"Sir, you said that the program was well arranged, that it was thoughtful to begin with a piece by Eberlin, our Kapellmeister."

"Yes, their playing was virtuous, Herr Schachtner, although it is bizarre to see a child of five manipulating the keyboard the way he does."

"May I take them to Vienna?" asked Leopold. "Your Grace."

"Mozart, the court chamberlain will transmit my views when I deem it appropriate."

Soon afterward food was brought into the Rittersaal. The Archbishop, nobles, and the clergy sat at the head of the table, while the Mozarts were placed at the foot with the servants and the musicians. It was a custom of the court that always irked Leopold, and now it was very irksome. He had no appetite, and the children were quarreling. Wolferl wanted to play hide-and-seek with Nannerl, but she said it wasn't grown-up and refused.

Wolferl retorted, "I don't like you, Nannerl. I like you best, Papa, you and Mamma, and then Herr Schachtner and God."

Leopold thought his son *was as beautiful as a prince,* his cheeks were red with excitement, he had a lovely clear skin, fine fair hair, full lips, and a broad head. He knew this seating arrangement was not to be questioned, yet he longed to remove his family from the princely lack of courtesy and appreciation. Then there was this stupid Lolli approaching him and declaring, "Your children should study in Italy, Mozart. They need a real harpsichord Maestro to teach them."

Leopold didn't answer the short, fat native of Bologna. The thought of abandoning his children's education to anyone else was unendurable. And Lolli had conducted so badly he should have been hung. He could think of a dozen reasons for disliking the Vice-Kapellmeister.

That evening Leopold put Wolferl to bed himself. This was unusual, but he told Anna Maria that he was doing it as a reward for how well the child had played. He stood Wolferl on a chair as he put his flannel nightgown on him and asked, "Did you enjoy playing for the Archbishop?"

"So-so. He is awfully old, isn't he, Papa?"

"Old?"

"He looked sleepy most of the time. Does he have many clocks? He was watching it all during my playing."

"Very many." Suddenly Leopold was irate because His Grace had not given him any gulden for the performance.

"Does he like notes? Can he name all the notes like I can?"

"I doubt it."

"And does he know exactly how many notes there should be, and where they come in, and how long they should be played? As I do?"

"No."

"Can he play the harpsichord?"

"Not at all."

"Then why does everybody listen to him?"

Leopold shrugged. "Wolferl, do you still love Papa?"

"Yes. Next to God." The child, improvising a tune of his own

38

creation, sang some sounds that had just come into his head, "Oragna figata fa, marina gamina fa." Wonderful sounds, and when Papa looked happy he kissed Papa on the tip of his nose and promised, "When you grow old, Papa, like the Archbishop, I will put you in a glass case and protect you from every breath of air, so that you can always be with me to honor."

Leopold was so touched he could not answer. Tears came into his eyes. He had not been a hypocrite with His Grace. His children were a heritage from the Lord. They must be allowed to spread their wings. He did not leave Wolferl until the child was sound asleep, standing at the window and staring at the dark street, wondering what the future held for Wolferl.

FIVE

—

But the future could not flourish without help, Leopold realized as he waited for the Archbishop's decision. When several weeks passed without any word from His Grace, it was as if there never had been a concert by his children. As he often did when he was restless or unhappy, he arranged a musical evening. He invited Schachtner, Bullinger, and Hagenauer, to hear trios a musical colleague, violinist Wenzel Hebelt, had composed.

The young violinist, who had just been admitted to the court orchestra, considered Herr Mozart the best violinist and teacher in Salzburg, and he wanted his opinion of these compositions.

Anna Maria sat in a corner doing needlework while she waited for the music to begin; Nannerl was in the kitchen helping Theresa prepare cake and coffee for their guests; and Leopold placed Wolferl near the harpsichord and warned him not to disturb anybody. But as Leopold took the first violin, Schachtner the second and Wenzel the third, Wolferl begged to play also, and Leopold replied sternly, "You haven't had any instruction on the violin. You can't play it without learning how."

"To play second fiddle, one does not have to learn."

"That's nonsense! And if you bother us any more, I will have you put to bed as once. Basta! You are bad!"

Wolferl burst into tears and sobbed as if his heart would break.

Leopold's impulse was to punish Wolferl, but he hesitated, for it was not like the child to question his authority. Schachtner put his arms around Wolferl and said gently, "You must learn first. And if you listen carefully and quietly it will be part of learning."

Schachtner's affection halted the tears and Wolferl asked eagerly, "Will I be able to play then? The next trio?"

"Your Papa will decide. Now be a good little boy and no more interruptions. You know we all love you, your Papa most of all."

The others nodded and Wolferl became silent. But when the trio started his chubby features contorted with surprise. Suddenly he blurted out, "Herr Schachtner, your violin is a quarter tone off."

Schachtner glanced over to Leopold, who indicated that he was not sure of this.

"You don't hear it, Herr Schachtner?" Wolferl was bewildered. The music was a living thing; why didn't they feel it as he did?

They resumed from the beginning and suddenly Wolferl was saying, "There it is – he's off," and Leopold said wonderingly, "He's right."

"A quarter tone," Wolferl repeated positively. "I told you, Papa. Can I play now? I won't be out of tune."

Schachtner said, "He can play with me."

Bullinger said, "If he is the prodigy you claim he is, that should be easy."

That was too much to expect, Leopold thought angrily. But he could not retreat now. It would be a dreadful loss of face. He said, "Play with Herr Schachtner, but softly, so you don't interfere."

Wolferl, tenderly holding the miniature violin Leopold had given him as a reward for his performance for the Archbishop, followed Schachtner. Leopold waited for the child to go off. But Wolferl did not. Leopold noticed that Wolferl had copied his violin technique. At the conclusion of the trio everyone applauded.

Excited and proud, the child said he could play the first violin. But now there were mistakes and suddenly he stopped, annoyed at his own scraping – it was more than his ear could endure – and he said, "It's the fiddle. I need another fiddle, Papa."

"Yes, you do," said Leopold, "I'll get you a better one tomorrow." He told the child to kiss everybody good night and then sent him off to bed.

But Wolferl did not fall asleep for a long time. He lay in the darkness and played the trio over and over in his mind. He could hear almost every note and yet, on the first fiddle, he had played it incorrectly. No wonder Papa had sent him to bed. Yet Papa had seemed pleased with him, for Papa had been affectionate. It was confusing.

Bullinger also felt mixed up. To hide his own confusion he became more positive, declaring, "Leopold, you must have given him lessons."

"None, I swear."

"Then how did he learn to play?"

"Watching I presume. Often, when I have pupils I allow him to observe." Leopold was as amazed as Bullinger.

Wenzel had heard nothing about his own work and he suggested that they play the rest of his trios and they did.

As Theresa served cake and coffee, Leopold said, "Wenzel, the trios are agreeable to play and pleasant to hear." He did not add what he really thought, that they were without substance. His mind kept returning to Wolferl. Could he trust these friends? Could he reveal what he actually felt? To find one man in a thousand who was a friend from unselfish motives was to find one of the wonders of the world.

While the others discussed the music, Leopold – deeply moved by what Wolferl had done, the violin was *his instrument* – studied his friends.

Bullinger was the most important. He directed the religious education of the court chamberlain's family and had direct communication with His Grace. The priest was short but robust, with a full, ruddy face, which often had a challenging look. Yet there was amiability in him when he felt at home, and Leopold knew that he enjoyed good music.

Schachtner, too, was someone the Archbishop listened to.

It was Wenzel Hebelt who was the least important to Leopold. Wenzel, round-shouldered, small, had no influence at court. There was a ridiculousness about his desire to please, and Leopold attributed that to self-consciousness. But Wenzel did have one thing in his favor; he was too new in Salzburg, too young, too humble to be a competitor.

The one friend Leopold felt he did not understand was Hagenauer, his landlord and the most prosperous grocer in Salzburg, for Hagenauer seldom spoke and then briefly, yet his round, plump features were always composed and pleasant. He had never seen Hagenauer irritated or upset, and what he found even more unusual, where most merchants regarded musicians as vagabonds, Hagenauer treated him with respect. But what did his friend really feel, Leopold asked himself. No man was always good-natured. It went against human nature.

But when Bullinger stood up to depart, without any further mention of Wolferl's playing, Leopold could not restrain himself. He cried out, "Do you still think I am foolish to want him to play in Vienna?"

"Foolish, no," Bullinger answered, "impractical, perhaps."

"The children will impress," Schachtner said. "Did you see how he took to the violin?"

"Indeed," said Bullinger, "if it is God's will."

"God's will!" exclaimed Leopold. "Is that all?"

Bullinger was shocked; the others were surprised; and Leopold realized that he must not lose his self-control again.

Now, speaking quietly but strongly, he said, "Dear Bullinger, no sensible man, no good Christian denies that everything that happens is the will of God. But that does not mean that I must behave blindly, act carelessly, and make no plans and just wait until something falls out of the sky of its own accord. God Himself would consider that idiotic."

Bullinger did not reply but at least he was not outraged.

"So I must plan for my children's future, or there will be none."

"Granted," said Bullinger. "But that creates problems."

Leopold shrugged. The moment you were born, there were problems.

Bullinger pointed out, "There is talk that young Michael Haydn is coming from Vienna to join our court. That His Grace is concerned about a new Kapellmeister because of Eberlin's poor health. If you are not in Salzburg when the choice has to be made, it will not help your chances."

True, reflected Leopold, and Michael Haydn, although much younger than himself, could be a more serious rival than Lolli. But there was the sensing that Wolferl could achieve so much that he could not, and Vienna was the threshold. Wolferl had a genius that must be asserted, whatever the sacrifices. He asked Bullinger, "What are the other difficulties?"

"If you are to obtain a leave of absence, you must find a substitute."

"Is that what has been delaying the Archbishop's permission?"

Bullinger didn't reply but his expression indicated that was likely.

Leopold felt stricken. No one would substitute for him; it was a situation that had no real value for an ambitious musician.

Wenzel, seeing Leopold's despair, said, "If I offered to take Herr Mozart's place, do you think His Grace might consent to a leave of absence?"

"It is possible," said Bullinger.

Now Leopold hesitated. Was there an advantage to being his substitute after all? Yet Wenzel was not as able a violinist as himself, His Grace might be dissatisfied with Wenzel, but that might be better, that might raise him in His Grace's eyes. He said, "That's nice of you, Wenzel."

"It is an honor."

"But I don't think you can handle all of my duties."

Schachtner said, "I will help out when necessary."

Bullinger said, "That might not be sufficient. A trip to Vienna with two young children will be costly. Leopold, can you afford it?"

Leopold didn't answer. That was humiliating, and he must not be humiliated; he could not endure that – but the priest was right. It was too risky; if his children didn't succeed he would be insolvent.

Hagenauer said, "I will finance the Mozarts."

Bullinger reminded him, "It may cost more than any of us realize."

"I know," said Hagenauer, "but that is not the question. Will you appeal to His Grace for our friend if all the conditions are met?"

"If Herr Mozart wants me to?"

Leopold wondered what services they would want in return, but he was touched by Hagenauer's offer, thinking that the thing men were least eager to give was money. He said, "A tactful appeal to the Archbishop could be useful, if it will not embarrass anybody."

Bullinger smiled. Wolferl seemed to be standing before him and he felt he was seeing now, not the physical, animal child, but a spirit destined to declare itself in music, driven with a mystic sense of inevitability. It made him feel as one with the others, although he could not admit that – it would give them the advantage he held now – but he was able to say, "I will address His Grace through Count Arco." He was embarrassed as Leopold thanked him profusely and embraced the others. He was not certain that Vienna was God's will but he would do what he could. He added, "It may take a while, but an answer should be forthcoming."

Anna Maria thanked the guests for coming. But when they were gone she was silent again. Leopold stood beside her as if he had won a great victory but she was not sure. He thought of the children as a career, she reflected, yet whenever anything troubled Wolferl, he ran into her arms. Traveling would be dangerous; in Salzburg they had many friends.

Suddenly Leopold asked, "You're unhappy, aren't you, Anna Maria?"

"Wolferl is still just a baby really. And it is a long way to Vienna. You have said many times that it is a hard and difficult journey."

Leopold's face set. There was a long pause. Then he stated, "I must teach the children French. It is fashionable in Vienna."

She nodded but her fears remained. She longed to protest but it would anger Leopold, yet a large part of her was disagreeing with him and she prayed that her premonitions would not come true.

A week later Count Arco handed Leopold the following document: "His Serene Highness, Count Schrattenbach, Archbishop and Prince of Salzburg and the Holy Roman Empire, has graciously ordered that court musician, Leopold Mozart, may take a leave of absence by his permission."

Count Arco asked, "Who will the children play for in Vienna?"

The Emperor . . . The Empress . . . Archdukes and Archduchesses . . . Princes and Counts . . . The French and English Ambassadors . . . the thoughts went on and on, but Leopold said, "Friends, musicians, and the nobility."

"And at court?"

Yes! But what do you know of my dreams!

SIX

===

Now that Leopold had the Archbishop's permission, it seemed as if everything was conspiring to prevent the journey to Vienna. He took the children to nearby Munich to play for the Elector, as a trial venture, and that ruler was so noncommittal he was discouraged. He had just recovered from this disappointment and was making travel arrangements for Vienna, when Wenzel fell ill and for weeks there was no substitute.

Shortly after Wenzel recovered, Eberlin died, leaving the position of Kapellmeister vacant. Count Arco announced that Michael Hadyn was joining the court, although no one appeared to know in what capacity. Again Leopold postponed his departure, waiting for His Grace to select a new Kapellmeister. But no one was appointed. There were rumors that Prussia was going to attack Vienna, for the war had been dragging on for almost seven years, but no one knew who was going to be the next Kapellmeister.

There was one consolation. The delays gave Leopold more time to focus on the training of the children, and he did that fervently.

He taught them French, to say their prayers in Latin, to be at home in drawing rooms. He was pleased with Wolferl's growing skill on the violin and with his improvement on the harpsichord and clavichord. Nannerl was still a fine pupil but it was his son's ability to learn that continued to amaze him. When he found the child creating his own melodies on the harpsichord, he gave him the works of other composers to study. This included pieces by Adolph Hasse, Georg Telemann, and Carl Philipp Emanuel Bach. By the time Wolferl was six he knew these pieces by heart. And then he composed three minuets and an allegro for the harpsichord.

Leopold examined these compositions with a new sense of wonder. His son's pieces were not diffuse, which was the usual tendency of learners, but well constructed and to the point. These compositions

45

showed that Wolferl, like himself, regarded music as a precise language in which every note must be measured and say something. He noted that the child had imitated the other composers, but that was natural, and Wolferl had imitated the best, Georg Telemann and Carl Philipp Emanuel Bach.

Wolferl's compositions were placed in a music book and Leopold was so gratified that he wrote on the first page: *"To my dear son Wolfgang Amadee on his sixth birthday from his father Leopold Mozart."*

He told Anna Maria, "The child is learning so fast, not a moment must be lost. We cannot delay any longer. Winter is coming and that will make travel very difficult. And the children are maturing so rapidly that the next year they may be too old, too grown up to create interest. Anna Maria, the younger the child the greater the miracle. His remarkable abilities must be displayed to the world as soon as we can. And Nannerl is almost eleven. Soon she will be too old to be a prodigy."

Anna Maria nodded, thinking that Leopold was really trying to convince himself. It was his own doubts he was arguing against.

September 18th, 1762, the family left Salzburg for Vienna by way of Passau and Linz. Schachtner, Hagenauer, and Bullinger gathered at 9 Getreidegasse to see them off. They were surprised that the Mozarts were going to Passau, it was to the north, not the direct route to Vienna.

But Passau had become part of a scheme Leopold had devised. As he examined his portable harpsichord and his violins, to be sure they were packed securely with the rest of the luggage on top of the hired coach, he did not tell anyone of the letter of introduction he had obtained from Count Arco to the influential Bishop of Passau, Count Thun-Hohenstein, who had important connections in Vienna. He said, "At Passau we can go down the Danube by the water ordinary and avoid the bad roads."

The farewells were affectionate, but he was upset by Bullinger's reminder, "Remember, you have six weeks' leave of absence, no more...."

The rest was erased by the clatter of the horses' hoofs and the creak of the heavy wheels, but Leopold kept hearing, like a dirge of doom, "Six weeks' leave of absence, no more!" It wasn't even time enough to get known properly; he needed six months at least for what he had to accomplish.

But when they rode along the Linzerstrasse and under the Sautter Archway and through the pass that went through the mountains his spirits rose. With all the difficulties, he had gotten away. He longed to shout, We are free, free of the Archbishop and servitude. But Anna

Maria was wiping away her tears and Nannerl was about to vomit and he had to be calm. Only Wolferl was relaxed and happy.

Wolferl loved the motion of the coach, it had its own sound and rhythm. He was proud that its muscular spring did not bother him as it did his sister. And Papa was so triumphant. Papa had told him there was far more music where they were going than in Salzburg, and now he believed that.

In Passau, despite Count Arco's letter of introduction, they had to wait three days before they could see the Bishop, and then he was interested only in hearing Wolferl.

The child was oppressed by the Bishop's residence, a gray, ancient fortress on a hill overlooking the Danube. It was dark and cold and his fingers were numb before he began. Count Thun-Hohenstein was old and fat, and did not look as if he knew anything about music. But when he said that to Papa, Papa whispered that the Bishop was not old, just fifty, and that his opinions were important whether the cleric knew anything about music or not. This puzzled Wolferl. And the Bishop had invited several subordinates to the concert and the child felt as if he were on trial. He did not feel like playing. But Papa was so anxious, he wanted to say, *don't worry*. And once he started, he played his best.

There was applause but when the Bishop gave Leopold just one gulden, he was sure they had failed. He was thinking bitterly that this delay in Passau had cost him many gulden when the Bishop asked, "Are you going to Vienna?"

"Yes, Your Grace."

"I can write my cousin in Vienna, Count Thun, about your boy."

"We would be honored, sir."

"Count Thun and his wife are fond of music. They have more time for it than I have."

Count Herberstein, a canon of the Passau cathedral, who had come to discuss church business with the Bishop, asked, "Herr Mozart, are you taking the water ordinary to Linz and Vienna?"

"Yes, sir." Leopold regarded him suspiciously.

"Your little boy has such good manners. You say he is only eight?"

"Six, Your Excellency, and some months."

Count Herberstein's enthusiasm increased. "I am taking the water ordinary to Linz and Vienna, too. Do you have friends there?"

Leopold hesitated.

"Of course. It is to make friends that you are traveling. At Linz I will introduce you to the Governor of Upper Austria, Captain-General Count Schlick. He is proud of his musical knowledge."

Count Herberstein also persuaded Count Schlick to sponsor a

47

public concert by the children. The program was one the children had played, and their composure pleased the Captain-General as much as it had Count Herberstein. And he was intrigued by their youth. That could create a sensation in jaded Vienna. He told Leopold, "They are attractive. I will be in Vienna next week and I will be glad to introduce them."

"That is gracious of you, sir."

Count Schlick was thinking it would be amusing to outdo Herberstein, and clever, for it should impress the Empress, who had some interest in music.

Leopold was gratified by the knowledge that the children could make money in a public appearance, for their concert in Linz had earned forty gulden, more than he had ever earned for a single performance.

Wolferl was disappointed by the concert for the Captain-General. Nannerl was proud of how she had pleased him, for Count Schlick had praised her charm and had given her a bracelet, but Wolferl doubted that he knew more about music than the Bishop of Passau. Count Schlick had talked during his playing, as had the Bishop, and if not for Papa, he would have stopped. No person who loved music talked when it was being played.

And he was tired of the water ordinary. Papa had spoken eloquently about the magnificence of the Danube, but it was a dirty, ugly brown and rough, windy, and frightening. Hitherto, when he had been afraid he had been able to turn to his beloved music, but the water ordinary was so shaky that Papa had refused to unpack any of the instruments, afraid they would be damaged, and there had been no music for three long days.

Thrown suddenly against the side of the boat by a large wave, Wolferl wanted to cry – he had almost fallen overboard and he had hurt his bowing arm – but he held back his tears, not wanting to anger Papa.

As it was, Papa was upset. Nannerl, terrified by the vicious squall that had struck at twilight, had vomited and Mamma was ashen and saying, "You never know what will happen when you travel."

Wolferl could tell that Papa was annoyed. Papa replied, "Wash the children, Anna Maria. Wolferl, at least, should be able to eat something."

He longed to ask, How much longer to Vienna, Papa? But he didn't dare.

Mamma was bending over him to be sure he was warmly dressed and telling Papa, "Wolferl coughed all last night. He's more delicate than you realize."

48

Papa said testily, "I realize many things. But no one has drowned yet."

Then, as if to confound Papa, a beggar fell overboard. Wolferl forgot his nausea in the excitement, but the beggar was dead when the crew pulled him out of the icy, turbulent water. It was the first time Wolferl had seen death and he didn't know what to make of it. Everything in him felt so alive and the beggar wasn't able to breathe. And Mamma was crying, and Papa was so solemn. Death must be something horrible, cruel, and wicked, thought Wolferl, and he wondered why people couldn't avoid it. Suddenly he was crying too, although he wasn't sure why.

He felt much better when they stopped at Ybbs the next day, so the passengers could stretch their legs and get relief from the stormy voyage.

Papa took them to a nearby church to give thanks to God for their deliverance from the evil weather – Papa had been more worried than he had admitted – but Wolferl was absorbed by the organ.

He had seen and heard organs in Salzburg, but none as magnificent as this one. This great instrument was so towering it lorded it over everything like a God. He yearned to caress the multitude of gold and silver pipes climbing the church walls in a vast trellis. Papa said, "It is one of the finest organs in the world," and the moment their prayers ended Wolferl sat down at the huge instrument and asked Papa how to play it.

As Papa explained, Wolferl followed him. Papa expected the child to flounder, but within minutes he was playing with an accurate touch.

In his imagination he was winning a victory as he played. He was abolishing the fear he had felt on the river. No one could take that away from him, not even death. He was fascinated by the scope and variety of this organ. Some of its tones were so deep, he could believe they were the voice of God. His heart beat faster as he heard the swelling tones. That gave him such energy. He ignored the astonished monks from the monastery that was attached to this church gathering around him and murmuring, "A miracle! A genuine miracle!" This instrument was so responsive. He loved it passionately.

The following morning they reached the outskirts of Vienna. But when the customs official, impatient with Papa's cautious unpacking of the musical instruments, began to tug on them Wolferl was outraged. This was blasphemous. The official was handling his fiddle as if it were a piece of firewood. He cried out, "You mustn't! That's mine!"

The short, stocky, middle-aged customs official didn't believe him. "But it is."

"And, of course, you can play it like a virtuoso?"

Wolferl snatched the fiddle out of the man's thick hands and played.

It was beyond belief, thought the customs officer, but the child was a virtuoso. He fiddled a bit himself, but not like this. He said, to show he had taste, too, "An allegro? By Telemann?"

"A minuet," replied Wolferl. "By Hasse."

"Of course. By Hasse. I should have known."

"But you were close," said Papa. "We are traveling under the official protection of Count Schlick, the Captain-General of Upper Austria. His Excellency is going to introduce my children to the Empress."

This time the customs official was not skeptical. Papa was explaining that this was the reason he had to be so careful with the instruments and the official nodded. He did not bother to examine the rest of their luggage. He wanted an encore. By Hasse, or Telemann, or even Philipp Emanuel Bach. He thought it gracious of the child when his request was met.

An hour later they were in Vienna.

PART TWO

=

Wunderkind

SEVEN

It was love at first sight.

Wolferl stood at the entrance to Vienna and was infatuated by the sounds and sights of the city. Papa purposely paused by the fortifications ringing Vienna to explain to the family that this was where the Turks had been repulsed in 1683, that it was from this time on that Vienna had become a modern city, and perhaps these imposing fortifications were the reason Frederick of Prussia had not attacked the city, and Wolferl sensed that no one was listening. Mamma looked preoccupied, as if her thoughts were back in Salzburg; Nannerl was staring enviously at the elegant ladies in the passing carriages; and he yearned to absorb more of this world. There was so much to see and hear here. He loved the excitement of the city, its pulse and tempo, its variety and vitality, and the crowds.

Papa hired a carriage to take them to their first destination, the White Ox Inn near the Platz Am Hof. As they rode along the Graben – the heart of Vienna – and the crowds increased, Wolferl exclaimed, "Papa, Vienna is so much bigger than Salzburg, there's so many more people!"

"The population has doubled since 1683, from ninety thousand to almost two hundred thousand. Salzburg has only ten thousand inhabitants."

"Are we going to stay long?"

"As long as we have to."

"What's that?" Wolferl pointed to the buttressed church spire that dominated the horizon.

"St. Stephen's" said Papa. "The oldest and greatest church in Vienna. And the center of the city. We will be living nearby."

Their carriage had slowed to a walk, there were so many other carriages ahead of them on the Graben, but this delighted Wolferl – it gave him more time to absorb the city. Despite the gray sky, the unseasonable chill, the Graben was full of promenaders. In Salzburg, thought Wolferl, no one would be on the streets. But here there were many gentlemen in powdered wigs, and ladies in elegant fur-trimmed capes. He heard many languages, and Papa told him that people came to Vienna from all over the world. He saw some soldiers on horseback wearing the Imperial insignia, but no other sign of war, although Papa and Mamma talked often about the war between the Empress Maria Theresa and Frederick of Prussia. Their carriage had to halt to allow these soldiers to pass, and Wolferl heard a man selling tickets for a fireworks display at twelve kreutzer.

Wolferl asked impulsively, "Can I go, Papa?"

"No."

"But he says that children under nine will not have to pay, as long as they come with their parents."

"I said no." Papa looked stern.

Wolferl subsided, but not for long. A beggar held out his hat, asking for groschen from the passing carriages, and Wolferl asked, "Can I give him something? He looks very poor."

Papa was annoyed, but Wolferl was glad when a nobleman in the carriage behind them gave the beggar a kreutzer. Papa said, "Children, poverty is an affliction, a curse from God," and Wolferl wondered why God should want to curse anybody. God punished badness, Papa stressed that, but a curse was something else, like not being able to hear. He could not imagine anything worse. He shuddered at the thought and his eyes filled with tears.

Mamma asked, "What is wrong, Wolferl?"

But how could he explain?

Papa said, "The beggar is wicked, or he wouldn't have to beg."

Mamma hugged him, to protect him from the crowded streets, but he wished she hadn't, it made it harder to hear what was happening around him. He knew most of the sounds of Salzburg, but in Vienna there were so many new ones. He was possessed with a passionate desire to absorb the music of the streets, the voices of the people talking, the haunting intonations of the many languages, the echo of the carriage wheels on the cobbles.

"You like Vienna, Wolferl?" Papa asked, caressing him.

"Very much!"

At the entrance to the White Ox Inn a man offered Leopold "a miracle working relic. A piece of St. Stephen's cross. Only ten kreutzer."

Did this insolent fellow think he was a country yokel? He said indignantly, "That's superstitious nonsense!"

The peddler was not dismayed. He sought to sell this well-dressed man a list of "Wigmakers, tailors, gentlemen of fashion," and when

53

Leopold looked more interested, he offered him another list, "The nobility of Vienna, informative and comprehensive," and Leopold bought it, although he bargained until the price was reduced from twenty kreutzer to ten.

Afterwards, Leopold was disgusted. The list was no better than his own – the money had been wasted! And their accommodations were not what he had requested. They had been reserved for him by a friend in Salzburg, who had advised him that the White Ox Inn was respectable yet not expensive, and close to the palaces of potential patrons. But there was only one room available. There was no space for their small portable harpsichord.

The room had to be partitioned. It was badly lit, so cold the water in the basin froze, and the toilet facilities were poor. The children made jokes about that, and Anna Maria joined in, but Leopold thought it was no laughing matter. He had to share his half of the room and his bed with Wolferl, while Anna Maria did the same with Nannerl.

Leopold did not sleep much. He blamed that on Wolferl, telling Anna Maria that the boy kept digging him in the ribs, but there were other reasons. There had been no word from Count Schlick or Count Herberstein. At the best Leopold expected the worst from people, but this situation was demoralizing. Yet they could not move. This was the address he had given everybody. Was God punishing him for his assuming he could alter fate? And the weather was foul, particularly for early October. It had rained ever since they had arrived. He wondered if the sun would ever shine.

When he heard that the Empress and the Archduke Leopold were going to attend the opera that had just opened in Vienna, he decided to attend. Somehow, he must obtain an audience with her. Although, in the next moment he realized that to even try to attract her attention would be regarded as an offense against the crown. Yet by paying a ducat, far more than the regular cost of a seat, he was able to sit close to the royal box.

He was deeply disappointed when the Empress did not attend. He was forced to focus on the opera, *Orpheus and Eurydice,* by Gluck. At first he was hostile, but gradually he liked the music, which was some consolation – at least his time had not been wasted – and there was a lyricism in the score he thought Wolferl should hear.

As Gluck, who had conducted at the harpsichord, stood up to receive the applause of the audience at the end of the opera, Leopold heard the Archduke say to an aide, "I hear there is a boy in Vienna who plays the clavier like a man." He hurried back to the inn to await a royal invitation.

None came and to relieve his tension he took Wolferl to hear

54

Orpheus and Eurydice. There was another conductor; he was told that the Empress had already heard the opera; and Wolferl was very quiet.

It was the first opera Wolferl had heard and he was puzzled. Papa said that opera was full of action but hardly anything was happening. But the singing was beautiful. Yet the range was quite high; he hadn't believed that anyone could sing that high. And everybody was on pitch. In Salzburg that was rarely true, even during the services for the Archbishop. He did not understand the story of *Orpheus and Eurydice*; Papa was saying that it was the victory of love over death, but that was incomprehensible to him. When Papa stated that they were really ghosts, he asked, "Holy Ghosts?"

Papa smiled, but didn't answer. The Second Act was starting and Papa wanted Wolferl to hear all the music. Wolferl thought that sometimes Gluck's music was so slow it seemed to stand still, but its sound was the sweetest and most delicate he had ever heard. He sat as if in a spell. After the opera ended, he did not want to move, although Papa told him that there were sweets in the foyer.

When Papa put him to bed – Mamma and Nannerl were asleep in their half of the partitioned room – he asked, "Could I write an opera some day?"

"Perhaps."

"Soon?"

"When you are ready." Gluck was almost fifty.

"You know, Papa?"

"Yes?" Wolferl looked unusually reflective.

"Papa, in opera the words sing to each other!" Wolferl spoke as if he were discovering this for Papa. "The words sing pretty, then other words answer prettier, then other words sing a question, then words bring an answer, then they all sing happiness together!"

Wolferl's enthusiasm awoke Nannerl and Mamma. They came into the other half of the bedroom to find out what had excited Wolferl so much.

Wolferl improvised a line of words to music and sang it, saying, "You answer me with words, Papa." But before Papa could, the child sang a line for Papa in a deep voice – like Papa's, then sang in a female voice, "That is Mamma," and then sang in a high girl's voice, "That is Nannerl. Oh, Papa, let us write an opera and sing it tomorrow. I can sing three voices and you can sing your own voice. We'll call it 'Vienna opera'." He listened to the melodies in his mind and became preoccupied.

"Stop dreaming!" Papa ordered, but he couldn't resist asking, "How many instruments do you use in this composition with words?"

55

Wolferl told him the exact number of instruments he would use. They were the same number as Gluck had used. The child was observant as well as intuitive, thought Papa, very good traits for a composer.

Wolferl asked, "Papa, why didn't you and Mamma make me born in Vienna? You knew I would like that. Didn't you?"

Nannerl interrupted, "It is God's will where you were born."

Mamma said, "And it is late. Time for all of us to go to bed."

"Yes," said Papa. "We don't want you to get sick."

Wolferl repeated, "Papa, why wasn't I born in Vienna?"

Papa answered sternly, "Because Salzburg is your home, and you will hear opera there too, someday. Now go to bed. I don't want you to be tired, just in case there is a royal invitation."

Intoxicated by what he had heard, Wolferl slept very little that night. The music of the opera kept recurring to him and he was proud of himself. By the time the night ended he knew several of Gluck's arias by heart.

EIGHT

The next day there was an invitation for the children to perform. It was not from the royal family as Leopold had hoped and expected, but from Count Collalto. Leopold was surprised; he had no letter of introduction to this family. And he was apprehensive, for the children had been unable to practice since they had arrived in Vienna. Yet he accepted at once. Count Collalto was one of the most influential noblemen in the realm.

As they entered the Platz Am Hof, where the Collalto palace was located, Leopold noticed that it was next to the Kirche Am Hof, a famous Jesuit church and one of the oldest in Vienna. He whispered to his family, "Pray to God, for men seldom help each other."

Anna Maria thought he was being too cynical. The steward led them up a magnificent marble stairway and into a music room almost as spacious as the Rittersaal. She loved the high ceiling, the crystal chandeliers.

A slim elegant man standing by the harpsichord introducing himself. "Herr Mozart, I am Count Pálffy, a friend of your host, Count Collalto. I was calling on Count Schlick while I was on my way to Vienna, when he urged me to halt my coach and hear your children."

Leopold noticed that the young nobleman was wearing ruffles of point d'Alençon lace and diamond shoe buckles that must have cost a fortune. He wondered if he was overreaching himself and he was apprehensive again.

"I was enchanted by your children, Herr Kapellmeister," said Count Pálffy. "I have been telling everyone that they must hear them."

"You are generous, Your Excellency," said Leopold, bowing very low.

"Not at all. Count Schlick and Count Herberstein share my sentiments." He introduced the Mozarts to the guests entering the music room.

They were names that Leopold had heard of most of his life: Count Collalto, his host, and a nobleman close to the Empress; the Count and Countess Thun, one of the important families in the Empire; the Baroness Gudenus, famous for her patronage of music; and Count Chotek, the Bohemian Chancellor.

Count Collalto said skeptically, "Mozart, Count Pálffy claims that your children play like adults, but I am sure he exaggerates." He cut short Leopold's answer, and motioned for the children to begin.

Their first number was a duet Leopold had chosen because it was easy, yet pleasing. Then they played solos. Nannerl performed with the greater expression, but it was Wolferl who attracted the most attention.

Baroness Gudenus kissed Wolferl and he wiped it off with his hand. He didn't like her. She had chattered while he had played.

Leopold was sure the nobility was offended – his son was rude – but the Countess Thun said, "Herr Mozart, your son plays even better than our cousin, the Bishop of Passau, wrote us. I hope we will have the pleasure of hearing the children again."

"It will be our pleasure, Countess."

"We will arrange it at your convenience."

Count Collalto asked, "How old is the boy, Mozart, ten?"

Leopold was angry but he replied softly, "Six, Your Excellency, six."

"It is incredible."

"Your Excellency, his age is a matter of record in Salzburg."

The Countess Thun asked Wolferl to sit at the harpsichord with her and explain how he had achieved such a delicate touch with the Telemann sonata he had played. She said apologetically, "I play the harpsichord, but not as well as you do." She was treating him like a grown-up. And she had such a lovely, musical voice, and she was young and pretty.

He heard Count Collalto saying to someone, as if to explain her behavior, "Wilhelmine has just been married. She's very young, only eighteen." But then she was speaking to him again and she had all of his attention. "Wolfgang, the melody in the duet was beautiful. It brought tears to my eyes. I don't remember hearing it before."

"It's by Domenico Scarlatti, the son of Alessandro. It's very melodic."

"Will you play it again when you come to our house?"

"Yes, yes, if Papa lets us."

"I'm sure he will. Thank you, Wolfgang, for a fine concert."

"Thank you, Countess." He would play anything she wanted, he loved her so. If he were older, he would marry her.

Leopold expected a stimulating discussion of music to follow the concert, but Count Collalto was making sarcastic remarks about

58

France losing her American colonies to England, although France was an ally.

Leopold was about to join in the discussion, intending to ask whether Vienna was in any danger from the Prussians – it didn't seem so in this palatial music room – when Collalto's steward informed him that it was time for the Mozarts to leave. No one else was departing, but Leopold hid his dismay. And that eased as the steward handed him lovely lace handkerchiefs for Frau Mozart, a beautiful fan for Fraulein Mozart, a silver watch for the boy, and twenty gulden for himself.

The concert at Collalto's impressed the proprietor of the White Ox Inn. Ordinarily, Otto Heinz set himself above his customers, but the Count was one of the most powerful nobles in the Empire. The stout, red-faced innkeeper found larger and better quarters for the Mozarts, and from then on referred to Leopold as His Excellency, Herr Kapellmeister Mozart, which amused Wolferl. He playfully named his sister Her Royal Mightiness, Fraulein von Annerl, and himself His Royal Rightness, Herr von Ozart, but Leopold did not criticize his son, for a few days after the concert for Collalto, his children were invited to play for the Empress at Schönbrunn.

Leopold wrote Bullinger of the royal invitation, and asked him to have four masses said for the Mozarts in Salzburg, one for each member of the family. Then he concentrated on Wolferl's appearance, believing that his son was the one most likely to attract favorable attention.

Wolferl became a childish replica of young Count Pálffy as Leopold dressed him in lace ruffles, imitation silver shoe buckles, a powdered wig, and a jeweled dagger on his hip like a courtier.

The day of the royal recital he hired a coach and four with a driver and postillion, although it was very expensive. But the children loved the luxury and sat against the blue upholstery as if they belonged there, while Anna Maria – after she recovered from the shock of the cost – enjoyed it, too. They rode through the narrow, winding streets of the inner city and on to the Mariahilfestrasse and out of Vienna. Everyone was excited.

The ride was so pleasant Wolferl hoped it would last a long time. But suddenly, he was silent. Schönbrunn loomed in front of him, a world in itself, and its immensity took his breath away. The great park in front of the palace was vast, and the palace was vaster. He felt intimidated by its size and he exclaimed, "How big it is!"

"It is supposed to be the biggest palace in the world, bigger even than Versailles," said Papa. "Five hundred acres. Bigger than many cities."

"Bigger than Salzburg?"

Papa did not reply, preoccupied by the palatial surroundings.

Wolferl's amazement grew as they neared Schönbrunn. Collalto's palace was tiny by comparison with Maria Theresa's residence. They rode through wrought iron gates, past two tall obelisks crowned with gilded imperial eagles. The closer they came to Schönbrunn, the larger it became. Wolferl was disappointed to discover that what at a distance appeared to be a bright white exterior was actually a muddy yellow-brown. But he was still stirred and he said, "Papa, it is much bigger than the Residenz."

"They say that this palace has fourteen hundred and forty-one rooms and that more are to be added."

"Why does the Empress need such a big place to live in?"

"She has been chosen by God to protect her people and her Empire."

Wolferl wondered if God had such palaces in heaven. He grew uneasy. The immensity of Schönbrunn made him feel very small. This palace was too grand for a harpsichord. Then Papa was warning him and Nannerl and that made him more uneasy. "Remember, you must not speak to Her Royal Highness or any of the royal family unless they address you first."

They were ordered to enter at the rear. A steward informed Leopold, "You are expected in the Mirror Room," and led them toward it without another word. Well! thought Leopold, on the one hand they had to enter at the rear like the servants and on the other day they were being received in a favorite chamber of Maria Theresa. As they trailed the haughty steward through many magnificent rooms, the lavish rococo splendor impressed Leopold despite his determination to be blasé. The exquisite chandeliers, the gilded stuccoed ceilings, the richly ornamented stoves twenty feet high, the parquet floors so clean one could eat off them, were even grander than Leopold had imagined. *His dream was impossible*, he told himself, *to believe one could make an impression equal to this grandiose world was madness. They would butcher his ambitions.*

As he hesitated the steward brought them into the Mirror Room and as he saw the Archdukes and Archduchesses gathered around the Empress and the Emperor, he was sure they were ranged against him.

Maria Theresa and her consort, Francis, sat in the center of the room but everyone else stood. Leopold bowed as low as he could and wondered if the children would be heard, the harpsichord looked so small in this huge chamber. Yet it was a superb setting for Telemann and Scarlatti, he thought, for the Mirror Room was even larger than the Rittersaal and contained seven of the most magnificent ceiling-high mirrors he had ever seen. The walls were a pastel of gold and white, there were two lovely chandeliers – and he hoped the children were calmer than he was.

The children curtsied before the Empress and she turned to Leopold and said, "The boy is very small. How old did you say he was, Mozart?"

"Six, Your Highness. Six, and some months."

Maria Theresa did not look as if she believed him.

Leopold saw Count Schlick and Count Pálffy in the group behind the Empress and Emperor, but they did not acknowledge him. He thought, They are waiting for *her* opinion, they are all unkindly waiting.

But suddenly she was saying, "Mozart, I have been hearing about your children's skills from all sides. Count Schlick, Count Pálffy, the Thuns. I hope they have been accurate."

"We will do our best, Your Highness." He prayed that her interest in music had not been exaggerated. He had heard that she had been gifted with a lovely voice and had studied with Wagenseil, her family's music master and a musician he respected. Yet as she sat coldly and regally, all he could see was the harsh glitter of the diamond tiara in her hair, and that she was the Empress who had warded off as powerful a soldier as Frederick of Prussia. It saturated him with pessimism.

"Proceed," she said forcibly.

Wolferl liked her at once. She resembled Mamma. They looked about the same age, except that the Empress was stouter than Mamma, but they had the same attractive high coloring and vivid blue eyes. And while she seemed stern when he was presented to her, he noticed that this large, round woman softened when she glanced at her own children, several no bigger than himself, and beamed at them in the motherly way that was so typical of Mamma. And Papa had said that in Vienna she was the one he must please.

Suddenly he smiled at her, and she smiled back, without forethought.

Papa lifted him on to the clavier stool, next to Nannerl. He was annoyed. He was old enough to climb up by himself; Papa was doing this to make him seem younger. Papa was nervous – his hands were trembling. *But not mine,* he wanted to shout. *At the keyboard no one had to hold his hand.*

The duet pleased, but when it came time for Wolferl to play alone Maria Theresa suddenly suggested that her youngest child, Archduke Maximilian, who was about the same age as Wolferl, turn the pages.

In the next moment she was chiding herself for being senti-

61

mental, for allowing a Hapsburg to be on the same level as anyone else, but she was proud of her family's musical ability. And because she felt inconsistent, she grew arbitrary. When the Emperor said, "Max is too young," she replied, "He is as old as this Mozart child."

The little Archduke took his place by the side of the harpsichord and Leopold sighed with relief, for the child seemed to know what to do. Maria Theresa was listening intently, and so, everybody else was. Leopold was congratulating himself on his wisdom in programming a sonata by Wagenseil, the Empress' favorite musician, when Wolferl halted abruptly, pointed to the young Archduke turning the pages and said, "He's spoiling it. Isn't Herr Wagenseil here? He understands. He will turn the pages right."

Maria Theresa flushed angrily and Leopold thought she was going to end the recital. But Wolferl smiled at her again, as if she, at least, knew what he was talking about, and she ordered Wagenseil, who was teaching in a nearby room, to be brought here at once.

Wolferl asked Wagenseil with the utmost politeness, "Sir, I am playing one of your sonatas. Will you be kind enough to turn it over for me?"

The middle-aged music master glanced at the Empress, who nodded. When Wolferl finished, he said, "Your Majesty, the boy plays beautifully."

But the Emperor blurted out, "Mozart, is this all the child can do?"

"Your Highness, he can improvise."

The Emperor strode over to the harpsichord where Wolferl sat, eager to continue, and stated, "Child, it is not difficult to play when you can see the keyboard, but to play when it is covered, that would be a feat."

"Yes, sir. What should I play?"

The Emperor placed his royal lace handkerchief over the keyboard and said, "What you just played?"

"Your Highness!" exclaimed Leopold, "that's not improvising!"

"I can play it, Papa," said Wolferl, and before anyone could halt him, he played the entire piece with the keys covered.

"Correctly," testified Wagenseil. "It is amazing."

"Now with one finger," said the Emperor.

Wolferl did.

"And now improvise."

"In what style, Your Highness?"

"Isn't it enough to improvise?"

"That's too easy, sir. Would you prefer it like Telemann or Hasse?"

The Emperor didn't know the difference and glanced hopelessly over to Wagenseil, who said, "Play my sonata in the style of Telemann, if you can."

But after Wolferl finished with Telemann, he went on to Hasse.

The Emperor mumbled, "Do you have any more tricks, boy?"

The Empress said, "He is not a magician. He is a child, although a sweet, talented one, doing whatever you request, even the unmusical things."

"You have enjoyed them, Maria."

"That's not the point." Now she was the Empress, who although she loved her husband and shared their sixteen children with him, had never shared her power. "Francis, he is tired, he needs a rest." She turned to Mamma and said more softly, "Frau Mozart, it must be near his bedtime."

"Yes, Your Highness."

"Frau Mozart, you are fortunate in your children."

"We have been blessed by God, Your Highness."

"He has played enough. He needs his mother now."

"Thank you, Your Highness." Mamma embraced Wolferl.

Then, to show that he had no favorites, he jumped on Maria Theresa's lap and kissed her like a child, saying, "I will tell you a secret."

"What is it?"

"I love you with all my heart."

Mamma, panic-stricken, couldn't move. Everybody was deathly silent.

Maria Theresa said, "You love me as you love your music, child?"

"Like my music." He could not pay her any greater compliment.

"Thank you, Wolfgang." She lifted the little boy off her lap and handed him to his mother.

Wolferl was sad. Maria Theresa had such a nice, large lap, and he was so sleepy suddenly. He did not notice how friendly everybody had become. He was tired. As they approached their carriage he heard Papa whisper disappointedly to Mamma, "Not a ducat, not even a lace handkerchief for all our playing. I was told she was parsimonious, yet you would think . . ." The rest was blotted out by his need to yawn. Nannerl was regarding him disdainfully because he couldn't keep his eyes open, but he didn't mind, he had had such a good time today. And as they rode away and Mamma held him in her arms, he made an astonishing discovery: the Empress' arms were no different from Mamma's. By the time they reached the White Ox Inn, he was cuddled snugly in Mamma's arms, sound asleep.

NINE

===

But Leopold, going from the splendor of Schönbrunn to the simplicity of the Inn, found the contrast dreary. His depression increased as days passed without word from anyone. Just as he was positive that Maria Theresa did not really appreciate music, he was visited by Count Mayr, who introduced himself as a spokesman for the Empress. Now Leopold was pleased that he had had the foresight to dress each day in his best powdered wig, waistcoat, and black silk stockings, clothes of quality.

Count Mayr said, "Herr Mozart, you are still in Vienna?"

"Sir, didn't you expect me to be?"

"Her Majesty expressed the hope that you remain in Vienna, but I was delayed by court affairs and I was afraid I would convey that too late."

"Her Majesty is generous." He wondered: Just how generous? He could not afford to remain here much longer if some money was not forthcoming.

"She would appreciate it if your children played for her children."

"Whatever is the royal pleasure."

"At Schönbrunn again. They will be the guests of the Archduke Maximilian and the Archduchess Marie Antoinette."

"Yes, sir." But who would pay for the many expenses?

"Tomorrow afternoon. Can you arrange that?"

"Tomorrow afternoon? We had several other invitations."

"Her Majesty asked me to express her appreciation with this gift." He handed Leopold a hundred ducats. "I am the imperial paymaster, too."

"Thank you, sir!" Leopold was jubilant. This was far more than he had expected. "We are grateful that Her Majesty enjoyed our music. We will be honored to play for her children."

The imperial paymaster smiled to himself, thinking that Mozart was getting the hundred ducats because Maria Theresa had been moved by the little boy's genuine affection, but it was not something she would like known. He said, "We will expect you tomorrow then?"

"Tomorrow, sir!" Leopold said decisively.

"What about other invitations?"

"I am sure they will be happy to bow before Her Majesty's pleasure."

Count Mayr handed Leopold two bundles of clothes.

"For us?" Leopold was surprised.

"For your children. From the Empress. Gala costumes for the party, and so your children will be at home with the young Archdukes and Archduchesses."

Anna Maria didn't share Leopold's joy. He was flattered by the clothes; she was not. He wrote to Hagenauer and Bullinger, telling them of the hundred ducats and the clothes, and asked the priest to have more masses said for the Mozarts. His gratification was so strong that Anna Maria could not disturb his self-satisfaction, but she felt that these clothes were a patronization, and a hint that they should be more suitably dressed than they had been previously.

The next day Leopold hired a hairdresser to powder and dress their wigs. Anna Maria was surprised. Leopold was always urging economy, and this was an extravagance. But nothing seemed to matter to him now but the appearance of their children. He was proud of how noble his son looked in the lilac colored waistcoat, trimmed with expensive gold braid. He said, "Wolferl's clothes were cut from the finest cloth."

She thought the child looked like a puppet on a string.

He added, "With the jeweled dagger buckled on at his side, his hair curled and powdered, his hat carried in his left hand, his right hand thrust into the opening of his waistcoat, Wolferl looks just like a little Emperor."

Now Anna Maria was sure that Wolferl's clothes had been the Archduke Maximilian's, that Nannerl's white taffeta had belonged to another of Maria Theresa's children, and that added to her distaste for these clothes. Yet when she suggested that their children could be wearing cast-off clothing, Leopold replied, "We trust Her Majesty," which was not like him, for he rarely trusted anybody.

Nannerl exclaimed, "How beautiful my dress is! Papa, Mamma, look at me!" For once, they would have to take her as seriously as Wolferl. But no one replied. Papa was putting the finishing touches to Wolferl's clothes, who looked strange and uncomfortable, while Mamma seemed preoccupied.

Anna Maria was not in a mood for compliments or demonstrations of love. Suddenly she yearned to be alone, to have time for

65

reflection. These gala costumes made the children grown-up. She had a foreboding that from now on, however she mothered them, never again would they be her babies to fondle and protect. But Nannerl looked so hurt, she had to say, "Yes, dear, you look lovely." Yet the pain did not go away. Leopold was telling Wolferl that he must not embrace anyone, it would disarrange his costume, that this party for Her Majesty's children could be another triumph, and she felt like a conqueror whose conquests were being infected with an insidious evil.

They were received at Schönbrunn by Count Mayr, who escorted them through the front entrance and into the Mirror Room with courtesy.

And the Empress was familial. She dispensed with the usual ceremony and introduced the Mozarts to her children.

As Leopold noticed that the Archduke Maximilian was the same size as Wolferl, he realized that Anna Maria was right – their son was wearing the Archduke's cast-offs. Present, too, was the Archduchess Marie Antoinette, who was a few months older than Wolferl; the Archduke Ferdinand, who was eight; the Archduchess Joanna, who was thirteen and the same size as Nannerl, and whose clothes Nannerl was wearing, it occurred to Leopold.

What was unexpected was the presence of the Archduke Joseph, the heir to the throne. In his careful preparations for this royal function Leopold had memorized the age of all of Maria Theresa's sixteen children, but he had not expected any of the older ones to attend. But he recalled that the twenty-one-year-old Joseph was reputed to be musically inclined.

The slender, thoughtful heir to the throne was curious about the boy. His father had been amazed by the child's tricks, his mother by the child's charm, but he had to see for himself. Joseph was proud that he was a skeptic, unlike his pious mother, who despised the Voltaire that he read. He said, "Herr Mozart, I am told that your son has a remarkable ear."

"It is accurate, Your Excellency."

"Can I play, Mamma?" It was the Archduchess Marie Antoinette. "Herr Wagenseil and Herr Gluck say that I am good on the clavichord."

"We would be honored, Your Majesty," said Leopold, thinking that Marie Antoinette, her youngest daughter, was much the prettiest.

"He can tell whether I am in tune." Marie Antoinette pointed to Wolferl.

"No, Toinette!" Maria Theresa was suddenly, abruptly stern. To allow a commoner to pass judgment on a Hapsburg would be unforgivable.

Then, as if to test her authority, Joseph said he would play his violin.

Even more, Maria Theresa wanted to forbid this. But she could not; he was her heir, the next Emperor, it would be too embarrassing.

Wolferl said quickly, "I will accompany him," and sat at the harpsichord. He knew the sonata by Telemann the Archduke Joseph placed before him.

Leopold pretended not to hear what he could hear very well, the Archduke was an amateur and played like one. Joseph might be the next Emperor, thought Leopold, but he had no talent for music. Yet Leopold looked noncommittal and hoped that his son would be tactful.

After several mistakes by the Archduke, Wolferl halted and said, "You are out of tune, sir, and your intonation is scratchy."

Leopold was certain the Archduke would be furious. Instead Joseph said, "Bravo! I have finally found an honest man," and looked amused. The Empress smiled then, too, but Leopold wasn't sure she meant it.

She said sharply, "Joseph, I think we should allow the Mozarts to play by themselves, which is what they have been trained for."

Nannerl cried out, "Your Highness, I can play with my eyes shut!"

Joseph said, "That's only a trick. Can you play music you don't know?"

"At sight?" Nannerl glanced over to Papa for advice.

"Why not," cut in Wolferl, "if it is music?"

"It is music," said Joseph, "by Wagenseil." He placed the sonata in front of the children and asked, "Have you ever seen it before?"

"No," said Wolferl. "But we can play it, can't we, Nannerl?"

Nannerl was ashamed to say no, but she was afraid. When Wolferl began, however, she followed him. And as she realized they were playing correctly her tension eased. At the finish she knew that they had pleased. Everybody had become quiet, even the little children like Marie Antoinette, and the Archduke Joseph was shaking their hands, which was a great honor, and addressing Papa as Herr Kapellmeister, who looked very proud.

Wolferl adored the Viennese cakes full of whipped cream that Marie Antoinette gave him. She was so pretty and vivacious he couldn't take his eyes off her. She said he must see her clavichord, and maybe he would like to play on it, and he was thinking that she must be very nice to kiss.

She asked him, "Do you have your own park? To play in?"

"No." Wolferl wondered why that mattered.

"We do. But you have your own hunting park, don't you?"

"No," he said sadly. With her fair hair, blue eyes, soft skin, and pink complexion he was dazzled when she smiled. But now she was so serious.

She looked a little put out. "We have the largest hunting ground in the Empire. My father is there now, after deer. Do you like hunting?"

He shrugged, wishing she would talk about something he cared about.

"Come," she said suddenly, "I'll show you my clavichord."

The thirteen-year-old Archduchess Joanna joined them, like a chaperone. Wolferl, hurrying to keep up with the bigger children and determined to show that he was grown-up but unaccustomed to the polished parquet floor, slipped and fell. Joanna ignored him, but Marie Antoinette ran to his side and helped him to his feet, consoling him as she did.

At that moment Maria Theresa approached with Mamma, anxious to find out where the children were going, and heard Wolferl say to Marie Antoinette, "You are very kind. Some day I will marry you."

Startled, Maria Theresa asked why.

"From gratitude," he replied, "and because she was good to me. Her sister wouldn't help me, but she did."

After the children were placed in the care of a lady in waiting by Maria Theresa, she motioned for Anna Maria to sit down. Anna Maria was astonished by Maria Theresa's friendliness. The Empress made certain that her chair was higher, with a throne-like back; otherwise they sat almost as equals.

Maria Theresa was curious about the little boy. She was sure she would not get a straight answer from the father; she thought he was too interested in exploiting the child, but she liked the mother, whom she saw as a good German hausfrau. Maria Theresa, trying to be friendly, as much as was possible in her position, asked, "When did it start?"

"What, Your Majesty?"

"His precocity? Charm? Ability?"

"I don't know." Anna Maria looked away, at the gleaming parquet floor, at the glittering chandeliers, at the elegant mirrors, and then came back to the Empress. As she saw her smiling reassuringly, almost like one mother to another, and yet, still the all-knowing ruler, chosen by divine right to rule, she blurted out what she had been wondering about for years. "Your Majesty, where does it come from?"

"Where does *what* come from?" It was Maria Theresa's turn to be puzzled.

"His genius. I'm sure it is that, isn't it, Your Highness?"

"Because he plays well for his age?" Maria Theresa smiled indulgently.

"No, Your Highness, his genius is more than that. As far as music is concerned, everything comes to him quickly."

"It is unusual," Maria Theresa conceded, "and he is a likable child."

"Sometimes, Your Highness, I think his genius is a gift from God."

Maria Theresa did not reply, thinking this was presumptuous, her heritage – the throne – was a gift of divine mercy, but what could the Mozart child have inherited with his ancestors? And almost all musicians were gipsies. She was interested in the child as a mother, not as a patron.

Anna Maria said humbly, "I hope I didn't offend you, Your Highness, but Wolgang has music in him as he has blood in his body."

"Is there any noble blood in your family?"

"I was told my father was of the minor nobility, but I have no proof."

"And on your husband's side?"

"Not that I know of, Your Highness."

"It is strange."

"Your Highness, he has my disposition but my husband's musicality."

"Is Herr Mozart a very good musician?"

"Yes. And so is our daughter. But neither of them are quite like Wolfgang. That is why, Your Highness, I think he is a gift from God."

"That is not possible with his kind of inheritance."

"But he plays as if with the hands of God, Your Majesty."

"I doubt that. Do your children have a thorough religious training?"

"When we are home, they have daily training. My husband was educated in the Jesuit Gymnasium at Augsburg and we are all devoutly Catholic."

"Good. Nothing is more important than a Christian education."

"It is comforting in times of crisis, Your Highness."

"God blesses us in many ways. Particularly in our children."

"Your Majesty, if you will excuse my saying so, Her Excellency, the Archduchess Marie Antoinette, is so exquisite and kind."

"Not always kind. But your boy intrigues her."

"And perhaps she is a gift from God, Your Majesty."

"That is possible," Maria Theresa said decisively. "Sometimes she is frivolous, lazy, even though she is my daughter, but often she is like a little goddess who knows from birth that she is destined to rule."

69

Anna Maria wondered whether it would be correct to ask the Empress a question about her children, just to show a mutual interest, and suddenly she asked, "Your Highness, do your children ever admit they are tired? I want my husband to be pleased but I don't want Wolferl to be tired. And Wolferl says he is never tired. Is that possible?"

"You don't know when to believe him. Children like to be believed all the time, but I am being kind if I believe them half the time."

"Then he loves the traveling even more than his father does."

"That distresses you, Frau Mozart?"

"Yes, Your Highness. At home I can take myself wherever I have to go. But here I have to be led all the time like a child. At home I know what everything looks like. When I travel I never know what the next thing will look like. And there is so much illness about. He is our last child. Of the seven I gave birth to, only he and Nannerl remain, and I can't have any more. If anything happened to them, I don't know what I would do."

"You would go on," Maria Theresa said somberly, "as I've had to go on."

"But Your Highness, you are the Empress, you have to go on!"

Maria Theresa didn't answer. She was thinking there was the war with Frederick the Prussian – the *monster,* she called him, attacking her from the moment she had been crowned. But now, after many years of fighting and crises, there was hope of peace. There was the need for her to marry her children in such a way that would strengthen the Empire. Even her dearly loved Marie Antoinette, not yet seven, had to be wed this way and soon. Yet the Mozarts, except perhaps for the mother, wanted to be famous. What a naive vanity, she reflected.

Anna Maria was telling herself, if people could only trust each other and meet as friends, whatever the differences of rank, when Maria Theresa said, "You are right, Frau Mozart, one must go on whatever our personal feelings. We are not put into the world merely to amuse ourselves. Friendship is something to be careful of and trust must be even more carefully given."

The children were returning with Leopold, and the Empress rose to indicate that the conversation was over.

Wolferl was very excited – so excited Anna Maria wondered how he would be able to endure Salzburg after this – saying, "Mamma, they have their own zoo! Toinette has wolves and lions and bears!"

"Yes, dear," said Anna Maria. "It's time to go now. You must be very tired."

"No, I'm not, honest I'm not."

Anna Maria and Maria Theresa smiled to each other, as if they shared a secret, and then everyone was formal. The Mozarts bowed low before the Empress, and Leopold expressed his gratitude for her kindness and pretended that he did not see her ironic smile. The Empress had given Anna Maria a private audience, that should create a stir in Vienna. Maria Theresa raised her hand and Count Mayr appeared to escort them to their waiting carriage.

Wolferl took Mamma by the hand and as they walked away, she thought of how warm, confiding his fingers felt, how they trusted her, his wonderful fingers, that made so much music and love.

TEN

=

Word of Maria Theresa's approval spread quickly through Vienna. Now there were so many invitations to play for the nobility that often, to fulfill all the requests, the children had to perform afternoons and evenings of the same day. Anna Maria worried about the strain, but Leopold assured her that the children thrived on the activity. Gratified and very busy, he had no time to be concerned. But his greatest gratification was writing Salzburg of his triumphs. Hagenauer replied promptly, informing him that all the good news had been conveyed to the Archbishop, who had seemed impressed but who still wanted to know when Mozart was returning.

Today, several weeks after the second appearance at Schönbrunn, Leopold wrote Hagenauer with care, although the pen and ink were wretched.

"Since I wrote you about the gift of a hundred ducats, the imperial paymaster has informed us that Her Majesty will summon us for further performances by the children. And since she received us with such extraordinary kindness, I cannot disappoint her. From whatever viewpoint I consider the situation, it is evident that we cannot be home before Advent. Even if I were able to leave here in two or three weeks, which is impossible due to the interest of Her Majesty, I must travel slowly so that the children can rest and not fall ill.

"Yesterday we played for the French Ambassador, who graciously invited us to Versailles and assured us that His Majesty, Louis XV, would be delighted with the children. Tomorrow we are to perform for Count Harrach from four to six, and from six to nine for Count Kaunitz, the chancellor. Count Kaunitz is the most influential nobleman at court, and has the ear of the Empress, for he is her chief adviser.

"Now the nobles send us their invitations three, four, sometimes six days in advance, in order not to miss us. The Chief Postmaster, Count Paar, has already engaged us for next week. We have also played for the Thuns, for Count Zinzendorf, who is close to the Empress and who knows everyone in Vienna, and for Count Colloredo, the Vice Chancellor, and for many others. They are enchanted with the children, and marvel at their playing and good manners. The women are more addicted to music than the men, and are taken especially with Wolferl. They pamper him, while Wolferl, may God bless him, is as friendly as if he has known them all his life.

"Everyone gives us something, and since Her Majesty's gift, we have taken in several hundred ducats, although no one has equalled Her Majesty's generosity, the usual gift being ten to twenty ducats for a three-hour performance. Since we can manage on one to two ducats a day, except when we have to hire our own coach, we should come home with a tidy sum and I will be able to repay your kindness. There is still very little talk about the war with Frederick of Prussia, and most of it is to the effect that there will be a peace soon, since neither side is winning.

"If you could be kind enough to ascertain what His Grace is doing about the post of Kapellmeister, it would be much appreciated. I believe I am not asking in vain, since you are my friend. If his choice should be someone else, who knows what I might do?

"Yet I still prefer Salzburg to any other advantages. Again I beg you, tell His Grace, for whose gracious leave of absence we give thanks daily, how popular we are here. Even the Emperor and his heir, the Archduke Joseph, refer to me as the Kapellmeister of Salzburg, and everyone praises me for spreading the fame of His Grace's music, and that it should produce such amazing children as Wolferl and Nannerl.

"I remain ever your true friend."

Hagenauer replied even more promptly that no one had been chosen yet as Kapellmeister, and while the Archbishop had expressed pleasure with the success of the Mozarts in Vienna, he still wanted to know when Mozart was coming back to his post.

Leopold postponed his reply, for there was an invitation from Maria Theresa to attend a gala dinner for her children, and he was hopeful that she would suggest a permanent post for him in Vienna. Instead, while she greeted the family, especially Wolferl, in a friendly fashion, and arranged for the children to play with the Archduke Maximilian and the Archduchess Joanna and Marie Antoinette, there was no talk of music or of the future.

Disappointed, Leopold wondered what had gone wrong. He sat at his desk the day following the dinner and took an inventory of his resources. They had the largest and best quarters in the White Ox

Inn now, and as long as they continued to earn money that was fine, but if that stopped this would be a foolish extravagance. Then he had to decide whether to buy a carriage. That would cost a great deal, and he would have to hire a coachman, yet their own coach would be better for the children's health.

But the expense frightened him and he said to Anna Maria, who had just entered, "I don't relish the honor of feeding the horses and the coachman, whether or not I use them. Still, I am saving ducats elsewhere."

"Yes, Leopold."

"And in one month in Vienna we have earned as much as I earn in Salzburg in a year." Suddenly he realized that she was not listening, which was not like her. He asked abruptly, "What's wrong?"

"I am worried about Wolferl. He has been complaining all day about feeling tired. He doesn't even want to practice."

Leopold stopped estimating his profits. "You are sure of this?"

"In the middle of a sonata by Scarlatti, the new one he was so excited about yesterday, he halted and said he couldn't remember what came next."

"Where is he?"

"In bed. I keep trying to get him to sleep, but he can't."

When Wolferl saw his parents standing by his bed he tried to sit up, saying "Papa, I'm sorry about the sonata but it hurts bad where I sit, on my backside," but the effort was too much and he fell back.

Leopold asked, "Does anything else hurt?"

"I get hot and cold. And I got spots."

Leopold struggled to hide his apprehension – spots were a common symptom of smallpox, most dreaded of all the diseases – and sought to look his calmest as he examined Wolferl. He found spots that were red, lumpy, and painful to the touch. It could be smallpox after all. He shuddered at the possibility. He had heard rumors that an epidemic was spreading in Vienna and he knew the terrifying figures: over half of the population caught the "pox", and of this portion many died, and of those who survived most were pockmarked and disfigured for life.

"Papa, I am so tired," cried Wolferl.

"We'll give you medicine that will make you feel better." He gave him black powder, and margrave powder, common remedies for most disorders.

"Do you think they will help?" Anna Maria asked skeptically.

He shrugged. He thought bitterly, *Homo proponit, Deus disponit.* He hurried to get a doctor before his inner terror overwhelmed him.

Doctor Franke had just graduated from the University and he tried to appear mature, announcing, "The boy is quite ill." He stated

74

that Wolferl should be bled, and when Leopold looked stricken at the idea, he decided that the blood might not have to be drained, but that the boy must take more powders and waters to purge his system. Leopold followed his instructions, and Wolferl grew worse. Leopold asked, "Do you think it is smallpox?" Doctor Franke looked wise and said, "It is in the hands of God."

Doctor Dessau was very old. He constantly adjusted the hairline of his wig, which kept slipping down. He fumbled with his instruments, and his spectacles were dirty. Leopold doubted that this doctor could see the spots. Doctor Dessau also wanted to bleed the boy and when Leopold refused, more powders and waters were prescribed. After Wolferl took them, the pain was terrible. Again Leopold had to ask, "Do you think it is smallpox?" and the doctor wanted to give the child an enema, and Leopold would not allow it, Wolferl had to empty himself too much as it was.

When Wolferl's condition became more alarming, Leopold asked the Thuns if they could recommend a good doctor. Countess Thun replied that she knew a Doctor Bernhard, who was excellent, but that he was out of Vienna, and as soon as he returned she would send him to the Mozarts.

Leopold, deciding that the two doctors didn't know what was wrong with Wolferl and that they were hardly better than fools, waited for Doctor Bernhard, afraid to chance another physician. But as more hours passed without any improvement in the child's condition, he kept remembering what the innkeeper had said when he had questioned the skill of the two doctors.

Otto Heinz had replied, "Over half of the children in Vienna die before their seventh birthday," and had shrugged, as if to add, Why should the Mozart child be any different?

Wolferl did not care for the two doctors Papa obtained. They described his illness in Latin he did not understand, gave him powders and waters that forced him to go to the toilet constantly, and now his whole body hurt. He felt ashamed; he wouldn't be able to play as Papa had planned. And after the visit of the second doctor he could not eat anything, his stomach was too sore. Mamma implored him to take a little broth and he mumbled, "I'm not hungry."

"You must eat something."

"I can't." He could hardly breathe from fear, his head spun; he didn't know where he was. He couldn't hear anything but a dull hammering in his head. He couldn't see Mamma; he had a terrible dread that he would never see her again. Somebody was saying something to him, but he couldn't make it out or tell who it was. In his nightmarish delirium he saw himself sitting at a harpsichord but his hands were tied, there was a ring of harpsichords surrounding him, grinning at him and mocking him, all without keyboards, his hands were free suddenly but there were no keyboards.

His burning sensation ebbed as he became aware that Mamma was wiping the sweat off his face with a tender, cooling touch, and whispering in a kind of lullaby, "Go to sleep, dear, you must sleep."

He wondered if he would fall asleep never to awaken again. She was repeating her words, but he was afraid to fall asleep. He had a horrible feeling that he would not wake up. For the first time he was frightened of death and it had become a reality. He had been told that he had had little brothers and sisters who had died, but it had meant nothing to him. Had their bodies hurt as much as his did, and had they suffered from the same nightmare before death took them, and would he never play again? This possibility was too terrible to contemplate and he started to cry.

Mamma was sobbing, "Dear God, not this one."

He felt better when he saw Nannerl standing nearby, although she looked ill herself, pale and frightened. And when he reached out to embrace her, she avoided him. He did not know that she had been ordered to do so, to avoid catching his contagion. His suffering increased and he fell into another nightmare, crying out, Help me, Papa, help me! But not even Papa seemed to hear him. When he came out of his delirium, he heard Papa saying to the innkeeper, "We had better call a priest," and Papa looked terrible, which was worst of all.

The innkeeper was just about to follow Papa's instructions when Doctor Bernhard arrived. Professor of medicine at the University, he created an air of calmness at once. He didn't rush to examine Wolferl but spoke to him quietly, asking him what hurt, where, how much, and when had it begun? He did not look disturbed until he heard what the two previous doctors had prescribed. Then he muttered, "Fools!" and examined Wolferl.

Leopold cried out frantically, "Should I get a priest?"

"No."

"Are you sure?"

"Who can be sure? But do not bury him yet."

"Is it the smallpox?"

"Who said that?" The middle-aged doctor looked angry suddenly. "The spots. The kidneys."

"And some imbecile made them worse by straining them with the wrong prescriptions. It is not the smallpox."

"What is it then, Doctor?" There was some color in Papa's face now.

"Possibly a touch of scarlet fever. I will return tomorrow. Your son needs rest more than anything else." He gave Wolferl a drug

76

to help him sleep, with such skill that the child lost his fear and fell asleep quickly.

There were no nightmares but a pleasant dream in which Wolferl kept seeing Marie Antoinette. He heard her saying she hated to study the clavichord, which puzzled him, for he loved it. But when she wanted to hear him play, he felt brave again. He could play, for there was no trace of the mocking harpsichords and the clavichord had a beautiful keyboard.

The next day, when he awoke from this deep sleep, there was no sign of Marie Antoinette or the clavichord, but Doctor Bernhard was standing above him reassuringly and he sensed that everyone was in a happier mood.

His rash, pain, and aches vanished in a week, and so did his dreams. Everyone was so relieved with his recovery that he did not have the heart to tell them of his unhappiness that there were no more dreams of Marie Antoinette. He consoled himself with the thought that soon again they would play for the Empress and he would see her then.

There were no more royal requests for the children to perform. Leopold heard from Doctor Bernhard that the Archduchess Joanna had fallen ill and this had caused the Empress to cancel all royal entertainments, but it did not lessen his disappointment. The discovery that Nannerl alone did not attract attention was another disappointment. And even after Wolferl was able to play, there were no invitations from the nobility to perform.

Doctor Bernhard refused to take any fee, but he was delighted to have the children play for him as an expression of their gratitude. He invited close friends from the intellectual elite of Vienna to hear the children, and they liked them very much. And as Leopold, sitting in the doctor's comfortable but unpretentious drawing room, heard the children playing as one he knew he could not turn back, whatever the risks and difficulties.

Then Wolferl was playing alone. Light Scarlatti sonatas, thought Leopold, but *oh, how these little sonatas sing!*

He could shut his eyes and still know it was Wolferl.

Scoff, call me ambitious, but what does anyone know of my dreams? People say I cherish no illusions, but my dreams, Almighty God, speak through my son, speak through him to the hearts of man. Dear God, give him time to reach them. Wherever music is made.

The November wind outside had its own voice, and so would his son.

Anna Maria watched Wolferl anxiously, to make sure he didn't become tired. When Doctor Bernhard congratulated her on the skill of her children, she asked impulsively, "Do you think he is strong enough to play?"

"If he doesn't play too long."

"Will there be any after-effects from his illness?"

Doctor Bernhard hesitated, not wanting to worry her. Then, deciding it would be better if she knew the truth, he said, "His kidneys were strained by the wrong medication, but if he doesn't have any more serious illnesses his kidneys should return to normal."

"He was very sick, Doctor?"

There was silence.

"And he could have died?"

"But he didn't, Frau Mozart. Let us be thankful for that. And he is a remarkable child."

Yet was it worth the risk? November had become fearfully cold. She saw Leopold counting the ducats, and a voice within her cried, Go home!

Instead, when the Thuns invited the children to play for them again, Leopold postponed the departure for Salzburg and accepted hopefully. But the Viennese nobility were absent, only Count Pálffy attended.

After the recital Count Pálffy assured Leopold that the children were playing even better than before.

Leopold answered, "I wish you could convey that to others."

Anna Maria said, "You can't blame people for wishing to avoid anyone who has had a contagious illness."

"But Wolferl did not have smallpox," Leopold said strongly. He and Anna Maria were sitting informally with Countess Thun and Count Pálffy over coffee and pastry, while Wolferl and Nannerl were playing cards with several young cousins of the Thuns.

The Countess said, "Let's be frank, Herr Mozart. Your wife is right."

"The nobility is afraid of pockmarks and rashes?"

"Of course. Aren't you?"

"But it was scarlet fever if it was anything, and that is all gone."

There was a pause and then Count Pálffy said, "We believe you."

"Is fear of catching smallpox the reason for the Empress' indifference?"

"More likely, it is because her daughter Joanna has typhus."

Leopold shuddered. "That's almost always fatal."

Count Pálffy said sadly, "The nature of her illness is not generally known, but my father, as chancellor of Hungary, has been informed."

The Countess said, "The Empress is noted for liking children, but not for liking music."

Leopold said, "Her Highness has supported Wagenseil, Gluck, others."

"When it suits her purpose," said Countess Thun. "But you must not depend on the royal favor. Sooner or later, it will change its mind and its favorites. Your children were the wonder of the moment, the reigning sensation, but now Vienna has another, a circus, a real circus, with puppet shows, conjurers, musical toys, and a large menagerie."

Count Palffy, seeing the disappointment on Leopold's face, said, "You must take the children to Hungary. Our family has many friends there."

Anna Maria said, "Thank you, sir, but we are due back in Salzburg."

Leopold frowned. "That can be altered. We will consider it, sir."

On the Hungarian trip Count Pálffy introduced the children as prodigies to the nobility, but the weather was so stormy that very few people dared to venture out to hear the recitals. Traveling was rigorous. The roads were frozen solid and deeply rutted. They had to stay in public inns, which was another danger. Sanitation was often non-existent, and to relieve oneself became a vital problem and required more ingenuity than planning a program. Clean sheets were a rarity and often they had to sleep in their clothes to protect themselves from the vermin. Even Leopold was troubled by the irregular hours, the wind, rain, and snow, which intensified his gout. After several weeks in Hungary, Vienna was a blessing.

Yet there were no invitations to perform in Vienna as Leopold had hoped. He had also expected that there would be a summons from the Empress, since time had made it evident that Wolferl's illness was not contagious, but there wasn't a word. The Archduchess Joanna had just died of typhus, despite the best medical attention available, and by royal edict the court was in mourning and there were no entertainments of any kind.

So, at the end of December, almost four months after Leopold had taken a six weeks' leave of absence from Salzburg, the Mozarts said goodbye to the Thuns, Count Pálffy, and Doctor Bernhard.

Leopold felt wiser, and proud of the ducats they had earned, but Anna Maria and Nannerl huddled deep in the mail coach, chilled from the cold, while Wolferl looked back longingly at the walls of Vienna.

He would have felt worse, but Papa had assured him that they would be back. *Vienna had become voices now. Marie Antoinette . . . Countess Thun . . . Count Pálffy . . . Maria Theresa . . . Doctor Bernhard . . . Herr Wagenseil . . . Opera. Voices, calling, singing, lulling.* They went on above the rumble of the heavy mail coach, telling him that he must return someday.

ELEVEN

Yet once they were outside Vienna, they rode again on roads frozen as hard as rock. The mail coach that Leopold had taken to save money was drafty and now Wolferl was chilled also, and the only voices he heard were the creaking wheels and the heavy clump of the horses.

Leopold said, "We will be home in a few days," but Anna Maria was skeptical, and it was a week before the familiar landmarks appeared.

They were still traveling westward and all of them had chapped lips, frost-bitten ears, and Anna Maria was praying, Please God, not another dirty, cold inn, when she caught sight of the Unsterberg. Suddenly she was almost cheerful. But twilight was settling over the mountains, and she became anxious again, for darkness came swiftly in winter. The road turned downhill and the pace of the horses increased as if, they too, knew they were near warmth and rest. It became a race against the approaching darkness. A few minutes later they were in Salzburg, and crossing the Salzach, which was crowded with ice. Anna Maria's blood quickened as she saw the twin steeples of the cathedral, a tiny glint of sun still on them. She noticed that Leopold, in spite of his self-control, looked relieved. His expression indicated that now winter could come with all its fury, they were home and still all together. And just in time, thought Anna Maria. The sky was black by the time they drew up to their house. But even in the darkness Salzburg looked beautiful.

Theresa sobbed when she saw them. She looked very hurt.

"What's wrong?" Anna Maria was startled by the intensity of her emotion.

"Nobody wrote me."

"But you can't read."

"Herr Hagenauer would have read your letters to me."

No one answered.

"You didn't even remember me or ask for me."

That was true, but Leopold denied that, saying, "We were busy," but only when Wolferl, distressed by her tears, took her hand and said, "We love you, Tresel," and reached up to kiss her, did her tears stop.

She asked, "Is it true you sat on the Empress' lap and kissed her?"

"Who told you?" asked Anna Maria.

"Everybody in Salzburg is talking about it. Did he, really?"

"Yes," said Leopold. "He was a great favorite at court, and so was Nannerl. Maria Theresa treated them like they were her own children."

Theresa gazed at Wolferl's chubby cheeks, wide forehead, fair skin, and they were unchanged and he had not grown, and yet he was different. He was so sure of himself and she felt she had lost something. She exclaimed, in dismay, "He's no longer a baby!" Theresa considered herself a vital part of the family; she had been with them since the birth of Nannerl, but Wolferl was her favorite, although she tried not to show it.

"Is dinner ready?" Leopold asked. He didn't approve of her emotion; it made her forget her duties as a maid-servant.

"Herr Hagenauer gave us several schwarzreuter."

Leopold loved schwarzreuter, a trout found in the Salkammergut lakes, but he pretended it was nothing or there would be no containing Theresa.

He ordered Nannerl to aid Theresa in the kitchen, and helped Anna Maria change Wolferl's clothes. Then as they sat around the dinner table, eating the best meal they had had in a long time, Anna Maria was full of her old cheerfulness and had everyone laughing.

The next day Leopold was ordered to appear before Count Arco. The court chamberlain demanded to know why Mozart had extended his leave of absence to four months. "His Grace is quite angry about it."

"Illness, sir. Wolferl took several months to recover."

"That long?" Count Arco didn't believe him.

"And I had rheumatism and gout."

"Your boy was very sick, I hear. With smallpox."

"Oh, no sir. Nothing contagious. He was a great favorite of the Empress. His playing amazed all of Vienna, including Her Majesty."

"We will find out. You are certain the boy is all better?"

"As well as you and I, sir."

"You must be positive. There is going to be a gala concert next month, to celebrate His Grace's sixty-fifth birthday, and he would like your children to perform for him as they did for the Empress.

But His Grace doesn't want his court endangered by a contagion."

"No one will be in danger, except from enchantment with his playing."

"I hope so. It will take something unusual to make His Grace forgive the way you disobeyed him."

"Who will lead the orchestra, sir?" And thus, thought Leopold, indicate who would be the next Kapellmeister.

"No one. There will be no orchestra at the gala. Good day, Mozart."

Leopold didn't know what to think and his friends who gathered to celebrate Wolferl's seventh birthday confused him further. Schachtner believed the gala would decide the next Kapellmeister; Bullinger was fatalistic, saying it was in God's hands; Hagenauer said it didn't matter, that the choice had been made already, although he insisted that he didn't know who it was; and Wenzel was certain Leopold would be chosen, since he was the best musician in Salzburg.

The one guest who didn't have any opinions was Michael Haydn, who had been invited to the birthday party by Schachtner. Leopold, curious about a possible competitor, had learned that Michael Haydn was twenty-seven, the younger brother of Joseph Haydn, composer and conductor, who was Kapellmeister for Prince Esterházy, the richest nobleman in Hungary. And he had heard that Michael Haydn was a performer and composer of ability.

Yet, thought Leopold, Michael Haydn was not impressive-looking. He was short and slight, with legs too small for his body, a dark-complexioned young man with square features, a large broad nose, and a shy, rueful expression. He kept drinking wine until Leopold feared he would drown in it. But when he joined Leopold, Schachtner and Wenzel in a string quartet of his own composing, the music sang and he played with a sure intonation.

Suddenly Leopold realized that Haydn might be the best musician here, except for Wolferl. He was surprised to find himself thinking this. The idea that his son was superior to himself already did not gratify him in this moment, but filled him with misery. Then his love for the child forced him to turn away from that.

Afterwards, Haydn discussed his composition with Wolferl, who looked fascinated, and Leopold could not endure this. No one was a better teacher than himself, whatever their other abilities. When Haydn began to drink again, he said abruptly, "Haydn, you should enjoy Salzburg. His Grace has the best wine cellar in the principality."

Haydn was startled but he did not reply.

Bullinger said, "Leopold, I hear that anyone who had the smallpox was forbidden to go near the Vienna court for months."

"None of us had the smallpox. The child was simply exhausted."

"I had it," Haydn said quietly, indicating faint marks on his cheeks. "And so did my brother, Joseph. But we survived it."

Leopold thought the newcomer a fool for making such an admission – it was a horrible handicap whatever anyone pretended; many victims who survived smallpox but not its mutilations went into monasteries.

Not all the music in the air had been played, Wolferl felt, after hearing Michael Haydn's quartet, but he didn't know how to convey this feeling. Yet sounds kept forming in an orderly procession and he yearned to put them down for others to hear. He had an acute physical need to do this. He was annoyed that no one, not even Papa, heard what he was hearing.

He had to write the notes down, or they might be gone forever. The grace and sweetness of Haydn's notes, answering each other with love and happiness, also absorbed him and insisted on being remembered. He hoped that Papa would understand this, but whether Papa did or not, he had to place all of Haydn's notes and his own in the right order. Everybody was discussing the gala, but he wanted pen and ink. That made sense.

Leopold was pleased with the structure of the harpsichord sonata that his son composed, he liked its clarity and precision but he was unhappy that this new piece had so much of Michael Haydn in it, although he thought his son had shown good taste in his choice of a model. Haydn's music had an ease of expression that not even Eberlin had possessed. But his unhappiness remained, for there was nothing of his music in this sonata. He would not allow Wolferl to play this sonata for the Archbishop. He feared that His Grace would recognize the influence of Michael Haydn.

The gala was held in the Konferenzsaal. The optimist in Leopold felt that this acknowledged the Vienna triumphs; the pessimist in him thought that it was simply because His Grace's birthday was a state occasion.

Yet he liked the choice of this room. He had always admired the Konferenzsaal, particularly for music. It was the most distinguished room in the Residenz, far larger than the Rittersaal, almost as wide as it was long, in what he considered true proportion for music, with white stucco walls, a parquet floor of walnut, and the entrance a great stone arch of Unsterberg marble which had been built in 1519.

But now, after Schönbrunn, none of this was as grand as it had been. He sensed that his family felt the same way. Neither Anna Maria nor Nannerl was nervous, and Wolferl was even more poised than before. Yet the affair was of great importance, for all of the court was present and His Grace was announced with the full panoply of his office by the herald.

The Archbishop indicated that he wanted a word with Mozart before the gala, and asked, "How is our young prodigy? Fully recovered?"

"Wolfgang is fine, sir."

"What did your son have?"

"Rheumatism mostly, Your Grace."

"I heard that it was scarlet fever."

"A touch perhaps, sir, but nothing serious. The Empress, may God keep her safe, suffered the real tragedy. The Archduchess Joanna, who when we were at court, graciously took Wolfgang by the hand and showed him through her rooms, died in December at the tender age of thirteen."

"The Empress received you several times?"

"Three, Your Grace. She took a great fancy to Wolfgang."

"I heard she was pleased with the way the boy played."

Leopold said humbly, "You are most gracious, sir." There was a chance he would be chosen after all! "We did our best to bring honor to Salzburg. And everybody loved Wolfgang."

"No doubt."

Leopold wondered whether the Archbishop was being sarcastic, but he could not tell from his expression. He said, "We are profoundly grateful for your kindness in allowing us to display the quality of Salzburg music in Vienna, and we took great pains to be pleasing, Your Grace."

Schrattenbach, who had inaugurated an austerity program in Salzburg, was thinking that the Mozarts were the best dressed of all who were not of the nobility. He decided to review the musician's pay, feeling suddenly that Mozart was overpaid and undependable. He knew he should not be surprised by the violinist's restlessness – musicians were vagabonds.

"Everyone of consequence in Vienna, even the Emperor and the Archduke Joseph praised Your Grace's music for producing such prodigies."

"I know! We have friends there!" The Archbishop's tone was curt but his smile was benevolent as he ordered the concert to start.

After the music ended, Leopold thought that in many ways Wolferl had been the best musician and Lolli the worst.

The Archbishop stated, to show that he was a connoisseur of music also, "The child's hands are skillful. They please the eye, they never seem to hurry, yet they play the fast passages as well as they play the slow ones." He took Wolferl's hand, which was an honor, and added, "His hands are strong. I can see why the Empress liked his playing."

Then the Archbishop motioned for Count Arco to speak. Leopold realized that he had been wrong to believe this concert would decide who would be Kapellmeister, that the decision had been made already.

Count Arco said dryly, "Guiseppe Lolli, Vice-Kapellmeister, has been raised to full rank, Leopold Mozart has been promoted to Vice-Kapellmeister, Michael Haydn has been appointed assistant Kapellmeister."

Leopold's grievance increased as Lolli strutted around the room like a great personage, for Lolli had played the violin with a flourish that had disregarded the tempo of the piece. Haydn looked indifferent, which amazed Leopold. His whole being was of a victim crying out, Why? Why?

Schachtner hurried to his side to console him. Bullinger joined them, reminding Leopold that he had received a promotion, and that Lolli was the natural choice, having been the Vice-Kapellmeister.

Leopold said with a shrug, "It's what I expected, I'm not Italian."

Bullinger said, "You've been away, while Lolli was here."

"You think that mattered?" asked Leopold, although he had a sudden fear that it mattered very much.

"His Grace may well have considered you not dependable enough."

"My dear Bullinger, I would have stayed here if I had been encouraged."

The priest smiled skeptically, but he did not answer.

Schachtner asked, "What are you going to do now?"

"What is there to do? I will thank His Grace for promoting me."

"And afterwards?" Schachtner persisted. "What then? You are not going to remain in Salzburg, are you, which has no genuine reputation for music, when Wolferl is expanding in ability every day?"

Leopold was silent, not wishing to commit himself. Anna Maria was expressing her sympathy, and he cut her short, saying that the appointment was not vital. He was grateful that Wolferl and Nannerl were occupied and didn't seem to realize the gravity of the blow.

Wolferl saw Papa go pale when the announcement was made. He knew Papa was upset; he could tell by the quick, abrupt way Papa was speaking. But His Grace still didn't know much about music. Lolli had been off key and Haydn had played without any of the ease and beauty he had displayed at his party, as if he hadn't cared, but one should always care when one played. Yet the Archbishop had applauded both these musicians.

Then His Grace had taken him by the hand, which was supposed to be an honor, but he didn't like the touch of his hands, they were sweaty, soft, and flabby. Everybody said His Grace was a holy man, but he didn't believe it. Mamma had taught him that a holy man was one who dressed simply, spoke quietly, and ate very little. But the Archbishop wore lavish garments and was eating and drinking with the same immoderation as Haydn. And his voice was unmusical, shrill and loud.

He heard Schachtner, whose mellow voice he liked, whisper to Bullinger, "His Grace acts as if a ten gulden increase in salary is a great expense, when this banquet must have cost hundreds of gulden."

Bullinger said, "He can afford it. This year his income will come to almost two hundred thousand gulden, with twenty thousand more for his private purse. I would not worry about what this gala cost."

Wolferl didn't know what these figures meant, except they seemed to make a big difference to everyone else, causing them to respect His Grace in a special manner. But he forgot all this when Michael Haydn came over to him and said, "Wolfgang, I like your technique very much. You have a fine touch. You have been taught very well."

After everyone had gone to bed the night of the gala, Leopold walked wearily into his living room and sat heavily on his favorite chair. Was this goodbye to his own ambitions? he asked himself. The thought was too painful, yet his mind continued to return to that. He walked to the window but the Lochelplatz was dark. He stood for a long time reflecting. Then suddenly, he found himself crying. He had not cried for many years. In the next moment he was afraid someone would see him. He closed the shutters. Poor Leopold, he said to himself, poor, poor Leopold.

His eyes fell upon Wolferl's last composition, the sonata in the style of Haydn, and he told himself that Haydn was a good composer but that there were better ones in the great world outside. Then his tears were gone and he was planning again. Now he was able to smile wryly, thinking that Schrattenbach was always talking about the spiritual character of his Archbishopric because it saved him money.

Soon afterward, when the Seven Years' War between Austria and Prussia, and France and England ended, and Europe was at peace for the first time in many years, Leopold arranged for the children to embark on a concert tour of Germany, France, and perhaps the entire continent west of Salzburg.

This time His Grace granted him a leave of absence when he asked for it, on one stipulation. Mozart could remain away for as long as a year if that was necessary, but without pay. It added to the risk, but he made the same arrangements with Schachtner, Bullinger and Hagenauer. Anna Maria reminded him that the traveling conditions were arduous, that diseases were common and could infect them suddenly and fatally, that they would still be subservient to the caprices of patrons, some far worse than His Grace, and Leopold replied, "We must not be complacent. We must not rest on our laurels." He knew that the musical expedition he contemplated required audacity and imagination on his part, but he liked this feeling and it lessened his own apprehensions.

On June 9, 1763, the Mozarts left Salzburg again. Spring had been rainy, but today it was clear. The wind was from the south and the city was pervaded with a soft, southern fragrance. It was difficult for Anna Maria to depart, but Leopold and the children were enthusiastic. He didn't even mind that His Grace was at his hunting lodge in the mountains, apparently as an expression of his indifference to their departure. They had their own coach and servant, the nineteen-year-old Sebastian Winter. They were much better equipped for traveling than they had been when they had left for Vienna the previous September. The usually skeptical Leopold felt almost hopeful about the future.

Wolferl was thinking how everybody had said to him after Vienna, "You must be glad to be home," but he hadn't been. There had been variety in Vienna, but in Salzburg he could tell in advance what was going to happen, especially in music, and he had been bored. Now, however, they were going to Paris, and perhaps to London. How could anyone be bored in these famous cities! Papa was right. Of course they would be a success.

And so, the Mozarts set out to conquer the world. Nannerl was not quite twelve and Wolferl was not quite seven and a half.

PART THREE

===

The Grand Tour

TWELVE

When the Mozarts departed on the same road by which Leopold, as a hopeful student of eighteen, had wandered into Salzburg many years ago to study law and philosophy at the university – courses he had not completed – Anna Maria still had many misgivings. She said to him, "The children are too young to realize the dangers, but I am not," and he replied, to hide his own anxieties, "I will take them to the American colonies if it will get them the proper recognition."

A few hours later the coach that Leopold had purchased with such care broke down. A rear wheel shattered, forcing the driver to bring the heavily loaded vehicle to a jarring halt. While the driver jumped off his seat to calm the panicky horses, Leopold hurriedly ordered everyone out of the coach before the damage became irretrievable, cursing the impoverished nobleman who had sold him this defective coach.

Wolferl was regarding the accident as an adventurous joke, but Nannerl was as frightened as the horses and Anna Maria was quite upset. Leopold wondered if this journey was an act of insanity as she implied. Many friends had warned him about the difficulties, and he had expected difficulties, only not so soon! He stared at the damage, trying to collect his wits, and to decide what to do next. This part of the road was uninhabited, they were a long way from their destination, Munich, and hours distant from the nearest community, the small village of Wasserburg.

He turned to the driver for help, and the jack-booted driver, wrinkled and weather-beaten, who had been hired to take them as far as Munich, gazed cynically at the broken wheel and said, "It is irreparable."

"What can we do?"

"We need a new wheel," said the driver, and went off to feed the horses.

Then Sebastian Winter, whom he had hired also with care, wandered away to relieve himself. Leopold grumbled, "It is bad enough to have the honor of feeding the horses and the driver, now I have a servant with a weak bladder."

But Sebastian returned with good news. While looking for a place to relieve himself, he had stumbled upon a mill and they had a wheel. The owner was willing to sell it, for twice what it was worth.

Leopold, determined not to be cheated, saw that the wheel was too small for the coach. Yet there was nothing else available. He informed Anna Maria – who said they should return to Salzburg – that they must be thankful for even this poor help. He bought the wheel and discovered that to fit it into the hub, he had to cut down a tree and tie the trunk against the wheel so that it would not roll away. The driver and Sebastian were useless, and Leopold had to do the repairing himself. Finally, however, the new wheel was fastened, although the coach tilted precariously.

They proceeded to Wasserburg at a snail's pace, Leopold and Sebastian walking beside the coach, for the new wheel could not support all of them.

Wasserburg was a tiny village with an old castle and an older inn. There was no one living in the castle. There was not a single nobleman in the vicinity to perform for, and to pay for their lodgings. The inn was the worst Leopold had ever seen. But when he spoke of continuing to Munich, he was told that it would take all night, that the road was unlit and unprotected and not even a gentleman's sword was enough to ward off the robbers who infested the countryside after dark. The smith said the new wheel could collapse at any moment, and that it would take at least twenty-four hours to put their coach in safe traveling condition.

The inn served only preserved veal, coarse bread, poor wine. Their rooms were cramped, without any heat.

No one slept that night, and the next morning even Wolferl was irritable. Although it was June, he was chilled, and several of his fingers were numb. Papa was informed that it would take still another day to fix the coach, and Wolferl stretched wearily across the bed, unable to nap as Mamma suggested, and wondered how they could endure another night.

Then Papa had interesting news. He had found the local church and it contained an excellent organ. Wolferl's fatigue vanished. He hurried with Papa to the church, and was surprised by the look of dismay that appeared on Papa's face, who said, "This organ can only be played with its pedal. You have never played an organ with a pedal. You didn't use one when you played at Ybbs."

"Show me how."

"You are too little."

"I can reach the pedal if I stand." He wondered why Papa looked skeptical. Or why Papa, after showing him how to use the pedal, was startled when he shoved the stool away and played standing at the organ, at the same time working the pedal. The pedal was there to play, not to worry about. The pedal gave the music fullness. He was delighted that his feet could make lovely sounds too. His fingers were no longer numb.

When Papa told Mamma, "He played the pedal as if he had been doing it all his life," and they were surprised, he was surprised. The pedal was natural to the organ and thus to himself.

After the coach was repaired and Leopold was assured that it was as good as new, he told Anna Maria, "The broken wheel wasn't the disaster I thought. Wolferl's facility with the pedal is a fresh demonstration of God's grace."

But Leopold was determined to help God. In Munich he went to the best inn, and put an advertisement in the largest newspaper, wording it in the form of a letter from a music critic in Vienna:

"Lovers of Music: I am happy to have the honor of imparting news to you which will soon arouse the greatest admiration in all of Germany, and in distant countries. I speak of the two children of the famous Mozart, Vice-Kapellmeister at Salzburg. Imagine a girl eleven years of age who plays the most difficult sonatas on the harpsichord and clavichord with exact execution, incredible ease, and the best of taste. This alone is enough to fill many with astonishment.

"But we are utterly amazed when we see a boy seven years of age at the harpsichord and hear him playing, not like a child, but in the most manly way. And also to hear him improvising for hours, and accompanying at sight. Tell me, does this not exceed all imagination? Yet it is the truth. What is more, I saw him cover the keyboard with a handkerchief, and play just as well on the cloth as though he could see the keys. I have also seen and heard how, when he was made to listen in another room, single notes were played on every imaginable instrument, and he named the note in an instant. When he heard a bell toll or a clock strike, he was able instantly to name the tone of the bell or of the time-piece.

"These extraordinary children had to appear twice before the Empress, and then again for the young princes and princesses of the imperial family. They were invited to perform for the highest nobility, and everywhere rewarded with the most distinguished presents."

Then he made discreet inquiries concerning the whereabouts of the nobility, and when he learned that Prince von Zweibrucken, whom he had met in Vienna, was staying at Nymphenburg palace, the summer residence of the Elector of Bavaria, Maximilian III, whom the children had played for before the Viennese triumphs, he drove out to the palace. He had the family saunter in the garden in front of the palace windows, and as he hoped Prince von Zweibrucken saw them and motioned for them to enter, asking, "Does the Elector know you are here, Herr Mozart?"

"No, Your Excellency. We just arrived."

"Oh, yes, I remember seeing something about that in the newspaper." Excited that the Mozarts were *his* discovery, the Prince sent a courier to the Elector asking the ruler of Bavaria if he would like to hear these marvels of nature, the Mozart children, and told the Mozarts to wait for a reply. A footman returned quickly with orders from the Elector for the children to perform at a concert at eight o'clock this evening.

As Leopold expected, Nannerl was liked and Wolferl was a great success. But the Elector did not hear them, for he had gone hunting that afternoon and had not returned. And they were not paid anything.

Duke Clemens of Bavaria, the wealthiest nobleman in the realm except for the Elector, invited the children to play at his palace. They performed for four hours, but again there was no money or presents.

The Elector, when he finished hunting several days later, insisted that the children play for him – not to be outdone by the Duke – only he wasn't sure when. He had another engagement to go hunting, there was a Molière play he had promised to attend. A week passed before he was able to hear them. Then he praised their musicianship, and kept them playing for five hours, but again they were bowed out of the palace without any recompense.

Leopold was depressed. The inn was costly, and for the sake of appearances they had to live like the nobility. He was told that the Elector was waiting to see what the Duke would give, that the Duke was waiting to see how generous the Elector would be. At the end of another week Leopold was frantically eager to get away from Munich, his expenses had increased so much. He feared that at the rate they were spending money, they would not have enough to reach Paris, his main destination.

When von Zweibrucken requested another concert at the palace, Leopold replied that it must be their last, that they had to leave the next day to fulfill their obligations elsewhere. The Prince gave Leopold fifty gulden for this concert. Duke Clemens, to avoid being shamed by von Zweibrucken's generosity, gave Leopold seventy-five gulden. A few hours later there was a gift of a hundred gulden from the Elector. They left Munich with a handsome profit, and letters of recommendation from the Elector, the Duke, and the Prince for potential patrons on their route.

At Augsburg Leopold was glad to see his two younger brothers, who were bookbinders, and they were delighted with his visit. Joseph Ignaz and Franz Alois were hospitable and asked the family to stay with them. But Leopold insisted on residing at the best inn again, determined not to be obligated to anyone and to convey the impression of success. His brothers were affectionate to the children, who responded warmly.

Leopold's birthplace was a free city; there was no nobility to solicit for patronage; none of the Catholic nobility knew anyone in Protestant Augsburg; there were no potential patrons available. Yet he could not accept indifference from his birthplace. He arranged for public concerts in the stately Renaissance town hall. He thought this was a stroke of genius. The town hall was the heart of Augsburg, the pride of its citizens.

He felt the children performed well, but the concerts were poorly attended, as he wrote confidentially to Hagenauer: "Thanks for sending me unasked the fine letter of credit. However, I am well supplied with what is necessary, thanks to Munich. But I have been held too long in Augsburg and gained nothing. The town is full of middle-class burghers and they are so full of German thrift they spend little on music. I earned much less than I had expected, for almost all of the people who came to the concerts were Lutherans."

He was proud of the story that appeared in the *Salzburger Europaeische Zeitung*, telling how Mozart, Vice-Kapellmeister to the court of Salzburg, had given Augsburg the pleasure of hearing those wonders of nature, his two children. He was hopeful that the Archbishop would be impressed.

Musical, prosperous Stuttgart was his next objective, but at the coach stop of Plochingen he ordered a sudden, unexpected change when he heard that the Duke of Wurttemberg, a lavish music patron, was not at Stuttgart as he had expected, but half a day away by fast coach at his hunting lodge near Ludwigsburg. He hired fresh horses and a new driver, and drove urgently on to Ludwigsburg to obtain an audience with the Duke.

But His Highness was hunting, and would not see Leopold. He was told that no one approached the Duke when the Duke was hunting. Yet he had to stay in Ludwigsburg longer than he intended, for His Highness had confiscated all the available horses for his own use, and Leopold had to pay dearly for the horses he finally hired.

A friend of his, a German violinist who had sought a post in the Duke's orchestra and who had been rejected, informed him, "The Duke has such a passion for Italian musicians, no German has a chance with him. And he is so autocratic and extravagant, it is said that half of his subjects are soldiers and huntsmen, and the other half beggars and outcasts." But what worried Leopold was that Wolferl,

94

usually cheerful, had become homesick for Salzburg, and had cried the morning they had left Ludwigsburg, suddenly wanting to go home.

Wolferl was proud that he was not a baby, although Nannerl said that only babies cried, but if Schweitzingen, Heidelberg, Frankfurt, and all the other places they were going to perform in were like Ludwigsburg, he couldn't help crying, it was such an awful place. And the affection his uncles had given him heightened the absence of it elsewhere. Papa said it was *their duty* to bring fine music to Germany, no matter how undeserving some people were, but it was a great strain to play for stupid people.

Duke Clemens had talked while he played; the Elector had smelled of the stable, a stench he detested; and von Zweibrucken, whom Papa said was a connoisseur, had preferred sonatas by Sammartini to Scarlatti, when anyone with sense knew that Scarlatti was superior. None of them had understood much about music, although they had praised his playing. The Elector had played the cello so gracelessly, it had brought tears to his eyes. If, as Papa said, sins were punished by hell, the Elector should surely end there.

But when he mentioned this to Papa, Papa smiled wryly and warned him not to repeat this to anyone. Tears came again to his eyes and he asked, "Was I bad, thinking that?"

Papa kissed him with an impulsive burst of affection – Papa had been so busy making traveling arrangements he had had little time for affection – and exclaimed, "Not bad. Just indiscreet. But right."

Now Papa confided in him, desiring to teach him to observe men, circumstances, and places as well as music. Papa said, "They play a large part in what happens to a musician, no matter how skillful he is."

Wolferl asked why they hadn't stayed more than overnight in Ulm, for it had a musical establishment, and Papa said, "Ulm is horridly built, old-fashioned, without taste. So are Westerstetten, Goppingen, and Plochingen. Everything about these towns is in bad taste. That is why they have no decent music. But I must say that Wurttemberg is a beautiful duchy, despite the way the Duke ravages it for his hounds and soldiers."

They hurried through Gothic Einzweihingen and Papa whispered to Wolferl, "Completely Lutheran and a dreadful place."

Papa liked Bruchsal, which was Catholic and Baroque, and stopped there, stating, "This town is noble, well worth seeing and resting in."

At Schwetzingen, summer residence of Elector Karl Theodor of Mannheim, who was famed for his patronage of music, they heard a concert by his orchestra and Papa declared, "It is the finest in Germany."

Wolferl already had come to that decision. He was eager to play for these Mannheim musicians. He was sure they would be a sensible audience.

Wolferl played lyrically, subtly creating yet never altering a note. The applause was appreciative, and he could have played on, but Papa halted him after two encores, for there was a command to play for the Elector himself, and Papa wanted him to be at his best.

After that concert he was not surprised when Papa wrote to Hagenauer: "My children have created a sensation in Schweitzingen. The Elector has praised them highly and everyone is astonished by their skill and taste, and say their playing is worthy of Mannheim, in a word, admirable."

It was with genuine regret that Leopold left Schweitzingen. The children had been in constant demand, they had played long, difficult hours, yet neither of them had been ill an instant, which pleased him very much, and soothed Anna Maria, who continued to worry about their health. And the members of the Mannheim orchestra – who the more they played, the more they convinced Leopold that they were the best in Germany – kept telling him how much they respected his children's musicianship.

And he had earned another hundred gulden. But what gratified him the most was when Karl Theodor, hearing Wolferl perform on the violin – which Wolferl had not done hitherto in public, although he practiced regularly – exclaimed, "Herr Mozart, your son is a marvel, and you are a genius to have taught him so well. If your son was not so young and you were not obligated elsewhere, it would be an honor to have you both as part of our Kapelle."

Leopold was still glowing from this compliment and wondering whether he should have tested the Elector of Mannheim's sincerity, when a new tribute occurred in Heidelberg. Wolferl – his fame having preceded him – was invited by the Town Magistrate to play the magnificent organ in Heidelberg's celebrated church, the Church of the Holy Ghost, which was an honor already. Then he performed with such sonority, fullness, and beauty that the Town Magistrate ordered his name and a description of his playing to be inscribed on the organ as a perpetual remembrance.

Thus, at Frankfurt, Leopold had Wolferl play on the organ in addition to his usual program. A large crowd attended, applauded loudly, and the receipts pleased Leopold. While he was being congratulated by Maria Theresa's envoy, Count von Pergen, they were

96

approached by a middle-aged man and his son, who wanted to meet the impresario, Herr Mozart.

Count von Pergen introduced them, "Herr Johann Goethe, one of our imperial councillors, and his son, Johann Wolfgang."

Leopold sensed that the Count did not care for Herr Goethe, yet that this man was influential enough to require politeness. He noticed that the father's features were grim, but that the son's were quite the opposite. While the son's nose was too large and his mouth was too wide for male beauty, his animation gave him an appealing attractiveness and was a vivid contrast to his father's sullenness.

Herr Goethe said, "Herr Mozart, my son is curious about your son. He wonders whether he is actually seven?"

"Only seven." Leopold glanced toward the stage where Wolferl, ignoring the praise of those about him, was looking at Anna Maria for approval and when she blew him a kiss he giggled childishly and blushed.

"It is remarkable," said the younger Goethe. "I am twice his age, I have been practicing music all my life, and I cannot compare with him."

Herr Goethe declared, "My son expects too much. At fourteen he can paint as well as play music. He writes poetry, he can fence, ride. . ."

"Be a complete dilettante," Count von Pergen interrupted cynically.

"No!" His father was horrified.

Leopold hurried to make peace, for his children were waiting for him. "I am sure, Herr Goethe, your son will amount to something." He knew it sounded fatuous, but what else was there to say?

"Hm?" The father did not look at all sure.

His son said, "Herr Mozart, if your son is only seven, why do you dress him up like a little man with his powdered wig and jewelled sword?"

"Does he play like a man?"

"Oh, yes, indeed!" Young Goethe's face was vivacious suddenly.

"Then why shouldn't he dress like a man?"

"But he is a child."

"You are dressed like a man."

"I am fourteen."

"And still a child." But when young Goethe blushed, just as as Wolferl had earlier, Leopold added, "Although precocious, too."

Herr Goethe frowned, Count von Pergen smiled, but neither replied.

Leopold said, to show that he could be a gentleman also, "Master Goethe, would you like to meet my son?" He thought that the boy was better suited to Nannerl actually—there was only two years' difference in age and they were not far apart in class -- and then he told himself that this was absurd, but there was something about young Goethe that was appealing.

The youthful Goethe hesitated and then as the Mozart children approached, he said, "No." What could he say to the little man about his music that had not been said before?

Thus Wolfgang Mozart and Wolfgang Goethe walked past each other and into history.

THIRTEEN

That same evening, when Leopold heard Herr Goethe complain in French to Count von Pergen – so that he would not understand – that 4 gulden, 7 kreutzer were too much to hear two children play, no matter how gifted they were, he was furious. Herr Goethe's snobbish assumption that he did not know French, which all German gentlemen were expected to speak fluently, was discourteous and disgraceful. When the family left their Frankfurt lodgings after another profitable recital, Leopold defiantly scratched upon the windowpane: *Mozart Maître de la Musique de la Chapelle de Salzbourg avec Sa Famille le 12 Août 1763.*

At Aachen several weeks later he felt like writing to Herr Goethe, informing him how the Princess Amalia, after *she heard* the children play, begged him not to go to Paris, but to Berlin with her, where she was sure they would be welcomed with open arms. She was the sister of Frederick of Prussia, and this invitation was an honor. But as he wrote Hagenauer: "Princess Amalia has sought by every means to persuade me to go with her to Berlin. But she has no money, and her court resembles a doctor's entourage more than a royal retinue. Yet if the kisses she bestowed upon my children, particularly Wolferl, were gulden, we would be rich, but as you know, neither the postmaster nor the innkeeper are paid with kisses."

Yet when she continued to insist that her brother, Frederick, would be pleased with the children, he replied humbly, "Your Highness, I am deeply honored, but I hope you will forgive me for having to decline your gracious proposal. Arrangements have been made for the children to appear before the King of France and Madame Pompadour, and I cannot disappoint them."

No such arrangements had been made, but when the family

arrived in Brussels, Leopold sought to obtain letters of recommendation to the French court. After a week passed without any success, he turned to a more immediate objective, the patronage of Prince Karl Alexander, Governor-General of the Austrian Netherlands, and brother of the Emperor.

Prince Karl granted Leopold an audience and stated that he would hear the children in a few days, but nothing happened.

After waiting several weeks without word from Prince Karl, Leopold called a family conference. He was determined to make the final decision, and not to express any of the pessimism that was developing in him, but he was concerned with how Anna Maria and the children felt. They sat in their luxurious suite in the Hotel de l'Angleterre, and the moment he asked Anna Maria what she thought, she said, "We are living too expensively."

"I rented it for the sake of our health and reputation. Otherwise, distinguished personages will not receive us or treat us with respect."

"These rooms are too grand. I don't feel comfortable in them."

"You must get used to this kind of a life."

"I will never get used to it," she said with a rare burst of candor.

"Anna Maria, have we failed so far?"

"You complained yesterday that we have spent too much already."

"But others have paid for these expenditures."

"Others, always others," she said desolately. "Yet you are always telling us that we cannot depend on anyone but ourselves."

"True. But I have earned more than I expected."

"And spent more than you anticipated."

A dead silence followed.

Anna Maria thought bitterly, despite their triumphs they were no better off than when they had left Salzburg. With all the praise no one had offered Leopold a profitable post; no one had given them a feeling of permanence whatever he pretended. And just last night she had dreamed that they were going to their death. She didn't dare tell Leopold – he would ridicule such a malevolent omen. He studied history. He knew about men and how to flatter them. But how could he be sure that things would turn out favorably? *What was, was. What was to be, would be. In the end they would be only wanderers with never a safe place to live in, yet what could she do but follow him even if it brought them to an early death?*

Suddenly, as if this act would dispel such forebodings, she kissed Wolferl and she could feel his loving response. He was such a little boy without his fancy clothes, powdered wig, and jeweled sword. In this moment her need to protect him was overwhelming and she could have thankfully surrendered his genius to a normal childhood. But Leopold would never forgive such behavior. Yet she had to ask, "Would you go home if the children wanted to?"

He looked betrayed, but he said, "Perhaps."

Anna Maria asked Nannerl, "How do you feel about returning home?"

Nannerl hesitated. She adored being treated like a lady, but sometimes she feared they would never see Salzburg again. She said, "I am lonesome for our friends. And I would like to sleep in my own bed for a change." Yet she hoped she hadn't hurt Papa; when she married it must be somebody like him.

Anna Maria turned to Wolferl, "Do you feel the same way?"

"I don't know, Mamma."

"Don't be childish!" Papa said sharply. "You must have an opinion!"

Wolferl didn't know what to answer. He liked that Sebastian dressed him in fine clothes; it was exciting to play for audiences who cared for good music; he longed to see Paris, but waiting was boring and he was tired of practicing. And there was not much to see in Brussels. If he could only compose, but Papa said they must get settled first.

Papa declared, "We've played in the most important musical cities in Germany."

Wolferl asked, "Are we going to play for Prince Karl?"

"Who knows?" Papa said bitterly. "All he does is eat like a pig, drink like a hog, laugh like a hyena, and in the end has no money."

"Why do we stay?"

"Prince Karl has said he will hear you, and I cannot offend him."

"Can't we play for someone else?"

"He will be offended if he is not first." Papa stood up, as the Empress might have done, to indicate that the discussion was ended.

Several days later Leopold triumphantly told the family he had been correct to wait for Prince Karl, who had invited them to attend the Brussels premiere of the opera buffa, *Buona Figliuola* of Nicola Piccinni. He was positive this was evidence of the Prince's favor, but Anna Maria said it was merely an expression of the Governor-General's vanity.

Wolferl felt that Mamma might be right. He noticed they were seated in a box which had a better view of Prince Karl than of the stage.

After the opera ended Prince Karl asked the Mozarts into the royal box and said to Papa, "This is a gorgeous theater, isn't it. I had it brought piece by piece from Verona. It was a great feat to put it together again, but it was worth it, people come from all over Europe to look at it."

"I can imagine," Papa said, trying to sound impressed.

"Would you like to play in it?"

"We would be honored, Your Highness."

Wolferl asked, "But why is it, sir, if you represent the Empress, the opera was Italian, the singers Italian, and the theater Italian?"

Prince Karl said, "What can you expect from a child! Perhaps, Mozart, you should not dress him up like a little man."

Wolfgang still wanted to know why everything about the opera was Italian.

Papa said sternly, "Italian is the language of music, and Italy is the home of music."

Wolferl was not satisfied. *Buona Figliuola* was full of bravura passages, but had none of the melodic ease of *Orpheus and Eurydice*. And the Italian singers had forced their voices to quaver to indicate emotion, turning notes that should have been sustained, and had been so loud! At the climax of the opera he had asked Papa, "Why do they scream so?" and Papa had answered, "Because they are Italian."

Yet now Papa was nudging him to be quiet and saying, "Your Highness, it was a splendid performance, worthy of such a beautiful opera house. It is no wonder your opera house is so famous."

And the more Papa praised Prince Karl, he noticed, the more Prince Karl listened. When Papa stated, "Sire, your musical taste rivals that of your brother, the Emperor, it would be a great honor to play for you." Prince Karl beamed and said he must hear the Mozart children immediately.

Yet Papa scolded him afterwards for speaking when he shouldn't have. They were back at the hotel, Papa was arranging the program for the recital tomorrow for Prince Karl in the latter's opera house, and he repeated, "But I didn't like the performance," and Papa replied, "That is not the point, Wolferl. Prince Karl is an aristocrat and aristocrats live by authority. They are accustomed to command the food they crave, the horses they want, the people who wait on them, the entertainment they desire. And we have to accept this."

"Isn't it wrong to praise bad music, Papa?"

"Not to an aristocrat. How else could one survive?"

The child was still seeking to comprehend this paradox at the concert the next day, and he was surprised that no one else was troubled by it.

Prince Karl liked their playing; he applauded heartily; he gave Papa a hundred gulden. And he recommended the children to other patrons.

By the time they were ready to depart, Papa was able to announce, "I have two hundred more gulden in my pocket than when we arrived here. More than enough to take us to Paris." And other things, as he wrote Hagenauer: "My children have been given many costly presents. Wolferl has been presented with two magnificent swords, one from the Archbishop of Mechlin, the other from General Count Ferraris. My girl has received a gift of Flemish lace from the Archbishop, and all sorts of finery from others. We have enough snuffboxes, gold watches, and rings to set up a shop."

Then Papa turned back to the family and added, "If Paris is hospitable, we will need a separate coach for all our gifts."

"It will be," Nannerl said confidently.

"If it does not consider us provincial," said Papa. "Remember, Paris regards itself as the center of the world. Everything we have accomplished so far could be wasted if we do not succeed there."

F O U R T E E N

―

Their arrival in Paris was auspicious. The Countess van Eyck insisted that they reside with her, and gave them comfortable rooms in her fine, stately house on the rue St. Antoine. She was the wife of the Bavarian minister to Versailles, and the daughter of Count Arco. And though Papa had played for her often when she had been a child, he assumed her hospitality indicated that favorable reports of the tour had reached Salzburg.

Wolferl liked her because she was attractive and affectionate, and because she lent him her new, fine harpsichord and listened to him with rapt attention. Several of the sonatas he performed for her made her quite emotional. When he finished, she called him a darling and covered him with kisses. He could have laughed with joy, except that one thing troubled him. Although she said that his playing made her very happy, her eyes filled with tears when she spoke of how earnestly she had practiced the harpsichord as a child in Salzburg. He sensed that she was lonely and homesick, as he was sometimes, but in the next instant she was exclaiming that Versailles was marvelous, so clever and elegant, and that the great hostesses in the fashionable salons would adore him.

But despite her enthusiasm there were no invitations from Versailles or anywhere else the next few days. Her excuse was that the first request had to come from the King himself and Louis XV was in mourning, but Wolferl was not sure he believed her. He grew restless, for again there was the waiting, the feeling that nothing would happen, that once again they would have to cater to the whims of a nobility interested chiefly in fashion and hunting. He told himself that when he was grown-up, he would not endure these delays and humiliations. Just as he was sensing that Papa was becoming desperate, there were important callers at the door.

It was a brisk, clear autumn afternoon, and Wolferl could tell that these people mattered, for Countess van Eyck introduced Baron Grimm and Madame d'Epinay to the Mozarts with pride and gratification.

Papa, too, looked pleased, and Wolferl – eager to know what Papa and the Countess saw in these callers – observed them carefully. He could not tell how old Madame d'Epinay was – she was too cleverly dressed and rouged to reveal her age – but he enjoyed her elegant posture, her graceful gestures, her musically modulated voice, as if it were an instrument to use with the utmost delicacy. And she did not patronize him, but addressed him as an equal and made him feel capable of accomplishing splendid things.

He was attracted by Baron Grimm, too. Wolferl noticed that this man carried himself excellently, unlike Count van Eyck, who waddled when he walked, that his eyes were sharp and penetrating, and that the Baron spoke extremely well, where the Count was slow of speech and occasionally said foolish things, but nothing the Baron was saying was foolish. Like his companion, his interest was stimulating. It was easy to see why Papa was excited by their visit.

Leopold thought, Friedrich Melchoir Grimm is a man to pay attention to. He had taken pains to learn about this gentleman, for he had heard that Grimm had become the most influential German at the French court. Grimm, son of a humble pastor from Regensburg, had arrived in Paris in 1748 at the age of twenty-five, and in the intervening years had risen in reputation at Versailles, and in all of Europe. Now he was the confidant, associate, and correspondent of the greatest French intellectuals. In addition to becoming secretary to the Duc d'Orleans and a protegé of the Prince de Conti, two of the most powerful nobles in the country, he had become editor of the *Correspondance littéraire* and had assisted Diderot in the writing and compiling of his renowned *Encyclopédie*.

While the literary journal and the *Encyclopédie* represented viewpoints Leopold often differed with – the triumph of reason over religion – he prided himself on being too enlightened a man to ignore their importance. He detested Voltaire's godlessness and was contemptuous of Rousseau's opinions about music, but both writers were among the most widely read in Europe – a word of praise from them would be useful – and they were regular contributors to the literary journal, as were the philosophers Diderot and Buffon. Ordinarily, he had little time for philosophers – he considered them unworldly – but Diderot and Buffon were read by the nobility, too.

The *Correspondance littéraire* had such important subscribers as the Archduke Joseph, Frederick of Prussia, George III of England, Catherine of Russia, and Louis XV, who differed with it often but who was proud that it was enlightened French rationality that was influencing Europe.

Schachtner, who subscribed to this literary journal, had told Leopold that Schrattenbach read it, also, to keep informed on what was occurring intellectually, like every well-read man, although as Archbishop he forbid his subjects to read Voltaire and Rousseau. To appear in its pages was an honor, however one disagreed with its contents.

Then everyone of importance would know about us, Leopold told himself. He reflected philosophically and listened intently to Grimm.

Grimm said, "It is kind of the Countess to introduce me as Baron Grimm, but actually, I am a simple Monsieur, here just to pay my respects to a brilliant musical family."

Leopold asked, "How did you know about us?"

"Your children's reputation preceded you. Our German subscribers have informed us that they are fine musicians. And since Versailles is the center of the arts, we must make something of them here."

Madame d'Epinay said, "We have been told your son plays like a man."

"Indeed!" cried Leopold.

But why should he be so proud, thought Wolferl, that was no great trick.

Leopold said, "I have many letters of recommendation."

Grimm said, "Letters of recommendation, for the most part, are worthless."

"They are a commonplace at Versailles," Madame d'Epinay explained more tactfully. "Although I am sure, Herr Mozart, yours are not."

"Things must be arranged," said Grimm.

Ah, Leopold told himself, a man after my own heart.

"I will set the stage," continued Grimm. "There will be an article in the *Correspondance littéraire,* which will introduce your children to Paris. Then you should be invited to stay at Versailles, and that should be followed with a request to appear before the King himself."

"How can I thank you?" exclaimed Leopold.

"Be discreet. Do not act the bourgeois, show no surprise at whatever you see. In the palace or on the grounds or anywhere. And praise Madame Pompadour if she should play the harpsichord. She fancies herself musical. Ladies command everything at Versailles, and many of them are great amateurs at the clavier, and some play excellently. Remember, Madame Pompadour is of the highest consequence."

"Is there anything else, Monsieur?"

"There will be difficulties. Other musicians will be jealous, other gentlemen will be critical because they did not discover your children."

"Sir, you are an honest man."

Grimm shrugged, but before Wolferl could decide what that meant, Countess van Eyck coughed. At first he thought it was out of politeness, to stop anyone from asking embarrassing questions, then her coughing suddenly was violent and there was blood on her handkerchief. This alarmed Wolferl, and he longed to console her. Only she was saying it was nothing, a brief indisposition, but he could tell that the grown-ups did not believe her, they became so solicitous.

A few days later the *Correspondance littéraire* contained a long, laudatory account of the charm and genius of the Mozarts, in which Grimm, the Voltairian, the nonbeliever, wrote – to Leopold's delight, *"Now in the Mozart children, for once in my life I have seen a miracle!"*

Now the Mozarts were invited to reside at Versailles by the court. They arrived there on Christmas Eve, which they celebrated by attending the Christmas Mass in the magnificent royal chapel so that the children could become acquainted with French choral music. And soon afterward they were ordered to appear at the public court dinner on New Year's Day.

What a fortunate omen for 1764, Leopold thought jubilantly. He forgot his disgust with the expense of residing at Versailles, where every log of wood cost five sous and the stoves had to be fed constantly. As they were escorted through the state apartments he noticed that this residence of Louis XV was even more luxurious than Schönbrunn, yet much of it was also colder and dirtier. But none of this mattered in the pleasure of the moment. The instant the King's two daughters saw Wolferl and Nannerl standing silently and attentively in the public corridor while they passed, they stopped, ran over to them, held out their hands to kiss, and then kissed them on the cheek in return. And the King ordered Wolferl and Nannerl to join him at the royal table. The Swiss guard marched before the children, clearing the way. Leopold felt so honored. Schrattenbach must hear of this.

The Queen, Marie Leszczyinska, daughter of the dethroned King of Poland, curious about *"this miracle of nature"*, insisted that Wolferl stand by her side so she could converse with him while she ate.

"Don't worry," Leopold whispered to an anxious Anna Maria. "She speaks as good a German as we do."

The tall, thin, unattractive, sixty-year-old Queen was amused by the child's attention. She told Louis, who did not know any German, "He speaks like a little courtier. It is a pleasure to have him as a guest."

All eyes were on the conversation occurring between Wolferl and the King and the Queen, for the child was as lively as they were, while the Queen continued to interpret what Wolferl was saying to the King.

But King Louis and Queen Marie were not as good talkers as Monsieur Grimm or Madame d'Epinay, decided Wolferl. He thought, either the King wasn't sure what to say or didn't care to understand the conversation between himself and the Queen. He was disappointed, too, that the royal family were more interested in his reputation than his playing. None of them had heard him perform, yet they were praising him loudly.

When, after the court dinner, Monsieur Grimm took him to meet Madame Pompadour, he hoped that she had better sense. Monsieur Grimm said she was an amazing woman, with great taste.

Her private rooms were the most luxurious he had ever seen. Superb chandeliers of silver and gold lighted their way, but what attracted Wolferl the most was the naked women which were painted on the ceilings.

Papa whispered, "They are the goddesses of love, painted by Boucher, a fine painter and a favorite of Pompadour," and Wolferl could not take his eyes away from them. What flesh! What inviting breasts and buttocks! He had seen nakedness before, in other paintings, but none as voluptuous as these. Papa had shown him nudes by Rubens in Brussels, to educate him, but he thought they were heavy and gross by comparison with Boucher. He longed to examine these female figures inch by inch. He hadn't known that females could be this lovely. They were sensual yet delicate; he wondered if he would ever know such women. Then he blushed at the idea, and could not look at Mamma and Nannerl, as if he was seeing something of them that was shameful. Yet he could not stop looking at these female figures. There was so much pleasure in these women, he could not understand how they could really be evil.

In the next moment Wolferl was irritated, for Madame Pompadour, who was not the most beautiful woman he had ever seen, as he had been led to believe, but who was middle-aged, like Mamma, buxom rather than pretty, ordered him to be placed on a gilded marble table as if he were a baby.

Yet to show that he forgave her, he leaned forward to kiss her and she turned away. Upset, he blurted out to Papa, "Who does she think she is, not wanting to kiss me? The Empress herself kissed me!"

Madame Pompadour flushed, then smiled sharply and said, "Monsieur Grimm, the child is spoiled. Are you sure he is the marvel you say he is?"

"Listen to him perform."

"Has the Queen?"

"You know she prefers cards." Monsieur Grimm's tone grew persuasive. "You could be the first to hear him in Paris."

She hesitated, then said with haughty severity, "Let someone else have the privilege. I am sure they can use the honor more."

And Wolferl said, with the same severity – and Grimm could not tell whether he was mimicking her or matching her – "Madame, will you be so good as to take me off this table?"

She did, although she still did not kiss him, or ask him to play her harpsichord, a present from the King, with her portrait and the King's painted on it.

Leopold expected Grimm to be furious with Wolferl, who in his opinion had been too impulsive. But Grimm, as he escorted the Mozarts to their sedan chairs, said quietly, "She is quite ill, but she doesn't want the King to know. So she dresses every day, and pretends that nothing is wrong with her. Louis does not like ill people around him. It depresses him. But her effort to maintain appearances is almost more than she can endure."

"What is wrong with her?" Leopold asked.

"Consumption. What her doctor calls congestion of the lungs."

"I think the Countess van Eyck has that, too."

"So I have been told. Yet both ladies refuse to go to bed. I suspect their determination to preserve appearances will shorten their lives."

"Are they that ill?" Leopold was shocked. Both ladies dressed in the height of fashion, and were animated and busy.

"Probably. But no one knows for sure, since neither of them will admit to anyone that they are even indisposed, let alone sick."

"Do you think our visit to Pompadour was valuable?"

"Of course. To be invited by her is the ambition of every courtier. It doesn't matter that she didn't hear the children. Everyone will be talking about them. Everyone will be curious. There is time enough for them to play. That will be arranged soon enough now."

"But she didn't want to kiss Wolferl. And he is a lovable child, as you yourself say."

"It is not the French style. If he had kissed her, her rouge would have become blue. Herr Mozart, things are done differently in Paris than in Germany. France is a more refined country, the people are more subtle."

"Pompadour must have been a great beauty, for she is still handsome."

Grimm said, "She was the greatest beauty in France when I met her."

Leopold smiled to himself: he could be French too, when it was necessary.

By bedtime a different feeling prevailed. Wolferl was taken aback by Papa's sudden bitterness. Papa was helping him undress, although he didn't need help any more – but it was one of Papa's ways of showing affection – when Papa said venomously, "Never trust a whore!"

Wolferl, who had come to feel sorry for Pompadour after hearing what Monsieur Grimm had said, was surprised. "Isn't she the King's mistress?"

"She is still a whore. Do not repeat what I tell you, but they make a lot of fuss over a whore. Remember, never trust a whore."

"What about Madame d'Epinay? You said she was Monsieur Grimm's mistress."

"She is different."

But Papa didn't explain why. And when he asked him what the King saw in Pompadour, Papa said sardonically, "His Majesty is devoted to dogs, horses, the hunt, snuff boxes, and prefers the bed to the battlefield."

Several days later there was an invitation to play the royal organ in the royal chapel at Versailles for the King and Queen. An apprehensive Papa told Grimm that Wolferl was more at home on the harpsichord, but Grimm said that since Louis XIV the organ had been considered the *King of the instruments and the instrument of Kings,* and that this was a marvelous opportunity, while Wolferl enjoyed the way Sebastian curled his wig, brushed his waistcoat and hat, and treated him like a little lord. He was informed that the organ he was to play on had been the favorite instrument of François Couperin known as "Le Grand", and considered the greatest French organist, but he didn't share the general veneration, nor was he awestruck. An organ was an organ: it played properly or it didn't.

Wolferl liked its clear tone, although it was a trifle too penetrating for his taste. There was much applause, many flattering comments, but the comment that counted was the King saying to Grimm, "This musical prodigy is all the more worthy of curiosity, for he comes from a country seldom given to producing artists of quality."

Wolferl wondered why the King hadn't said this directly to him.

Grimm explained, "Louis likes young people, but he is afraid of new faces, and to people he doesn't know, he doesn't know what to say."

A few minutes after the King's remark Grimm was asked if the children would be gracious enough to play for the Prince de Conti. Now even Grimm was excited. He told Leopold, "The Prince is the most cultivated man in France. One word of praise from the Prince and your children will be celebrated everywhere." Even allowing for exaggeration, thought Leopold, this was a fine opportunity.

Leopold's optimism increased, for while he was preparing the children for the concert at the Prince de Conti's, there were presents from the King himself: fifty louis d'or, and a gold snuff box, which the King had made.

"This is the greatest approval of all," Grimm told Leopold. "His Majesty is prouder of the snuff boxes he creates than anything else he does."

FIFTEEN

At forty-six, Louis François de Bourbon, Prince de Conti and Prince of the Blood and a favorite cousin of the King, was proud of his musical taste. The slim, elegant aristocrat was the King's private secretary, a supporter of the alliance with Maria Theresa, and possessed the finest musical establishment in Paris. When arrangements were completed for the children to play in his palace he invited the most distinguished nobles, ladies, and musicians in France to hear Grimm's *"miracles of nature"*.

Leopold, although he felt deeply honored by the Prince's invitation, was most involved in the musicians in attendance. But, as always, he carefully observed his surroundings so he could judge the quality of his patron. He was impressed by the Prince's wealth. The drawing room was as luxurious as any he had experienced. The silk tapestries, the exquisite furniture cost a fortune.

He saw many influential courtiers and ladies in the audience. The men in particular, with their powdered wigs, knee breeches of all colors, white silk stockings, and jeweled swords were lavishly dressed, as if in this, at least, they must outdo the ladies. And the Prince was very much the gracious host with his punctilious courtesy and his mistress of the moment, Madame la Comtesse de Tessé, by his side.

Yet all the time he was aware of another presence and it made him uneasy. The musicians did not approach him or the children, but stood apart. He could tell them quickly, for they were dressed modestly, as befitted their lower station, and they wore no swords – they were not allowed.

Nonetheless, he knew the musicians were not ordinary, for the Prince was pleased by their presence. Did they regard the children as enemies, he wondered, as none of them indicated awareness of the Mozarts? Did they resent them? That they might have to compete with children? He could understand their distaste for the situation. In their position he would feel the same way.

He was relieved when Grimm took him by the arm and led him over to the other side of the drawing room and introduced him to the waiting musicians: Jean Philippe Rameau, who had survived many musical enemies, and now, at eighty, was the one French composer who was accepted everywhere, even in Italy; Armand Louis Couperin, related to the great "Le Grand" Couperin, and an extraordinary organist himself; Pierre Gaviniés, who at thirty-seven was regarded as the finest French violinist; the youthful, attractive François Gossec, recently appointed maître de chapelle to the Prince; Johann Schobert, who at twenty-three was a prodigy too, and despite his German birth, the Prince's favorite composer and harpsichordist; and Gottfried Eckhard, not much older, and also of German birth, and a well-known composer and virtuoso on the harpsichord.

Grimm introduced Leopold as maître de chapelle to His Serene Highness, the Prince-Archbishop of Salzburg, yet he sensed that the musicians were not interested in him but Wolferl, skeptical of the child's virtuosity and shocked by his youth. Wolferl was even younger than they had feared, for Schobert, who was profiting the most from his own youthfulness, said, "We are sure you have the best of intentions, Mozart, but. . ."

Leopold felt instantly on guard. He asked, "What's wrong?"

"Your son is very small. He looks about five."

"He is seven," said Leopold, although Wolferl had just become eight.

"Even so, he is so young!" Schobert was irritated.

"It has nothing to do with his playing."

"It has everything to do with his playing. Inevitably, we must make allowances for his childishness."

"No!" Leopold was positive. "He plays like a man."

Schobert smiled cynically, not believing him.

Rameau, who had been listening carefully, said, "I began to perform when I was seven. All the adult musicians hated me."

"But you became a great musician," Schobert said flatteringly.

"Then they hated me more," said the old man.

Leopold turned to Grimm and addressed him formally, although he knew him better than that now. "Monsieur, does my son play like a child?"

Grimm said, "Of course not. But that is irrelevant."

Before Schobert, could reply, they were joined by Prince de Conti, who said, "Herr Mozart, it has been suggested that your children play first, then Herr Eckhard and Schobert, since they are harpsichordists and Germans, too, and finally your son again, improvising on their compositions, since he is supposed to be able to improvise on anything. Is that agreeable?"

But it was a command, not a suggestion, and Leopold had to say yes as he wondered if these improvisations might be too much even for Wolferl.

Wolferl was aware that not until the third portion of the program, when he was to improvise, did the audience really become interested. Then there was an intent silence as he approached the harpsichord. He was grateful that Papa did not lift him on to the stool. But why should Papa, he thought, I am eight now and have been for a few days. He was disappointed that the Countess van Eyck was not here – she would appreciate the way he improvised – but Papa said she was ill. Then, as he began to improvise on Eckhard's sonata, everything else was forgotten. Improvisation was a joyous adventure. He loved creating spontaneously, the excitement of the unexpected. When he improvised the notes came to him without any conscious effort. The feeling of freedom was wonderful. Once he had the melody and the design of the music, the rest was easy.

Leopold was relieved by the ease with which Wolferl developed Eckhard's style, and he marveled at the sureness of the child's improvisation of Schobert's music, as if that structure sprang from his own imagination. For Wolferl was making it unique. Although he was remaining faithful to Schobert's theme, the music was becoming his own. He was developing it with a skill that was remarkable. He had become the music.

The child enjoyed improvising on Eckhard's sonata, it was music that moved easily and melodically, but it was Schobert's that sang, that had a spirit and sparkle which delighted him, which prompted him to be truly expressive. It was music he wished he had composed. He remembered every note Schobert had played, but he varied them when it suited his feeling. And as the music mounted his way, but as lyrical as Schobert's, he felt in a state of grace. It was as if he were in the presence of God.

Yet Schobert said, "I am not impressed. I do not believe the boy improvised. He must have known my sonata, for his improvisation was as accurate as if it had been lying written out before him."

Eckhard said, "I like his improvisation of my work. And he could not have known it ahead of time. My sonata has not been published anywhere."

Schobert said, "Mine has. Throughout Germany, where he played."

Gossec, who competed for the Prince's favors with Schobert, agreed with Eckhard; Couperin, unhappy over the way the King had praised the child's skill on *his* organ, supported Schobert; Gaviniés,

114

as an outsider, had no opinion; the elderly Rameau had fallen asleep during the improvisations.

The Prince was pleased that there was a difference of opinion. This would create a sensation; the affair would be discussed in all the salons. He suggested, "Herr Schobert, why don't you improvise a new composition yourself, and then, let us see if Herr Wolfgang can improvise on that. If he succeeds, you cannot accuse him of knowing the piece beforehand."

Schobert had hardly played a few measures of his improvisation, choosing a very difficult theme, when Wolferl exclaimed, "May I play it, sir!" The composer's theme was new and lively and sang in his ears.

The Prince nodded assent and Schobert relinquished the harpsichord to the child. Then Wolferl sat there improvising on Schobert's improvisation as if he had known this theme all his life.

Schobert's taut features grew more tense, but when Wolferl finished he muttered a few words of praise that Leopold was sure he did not mean.

The Prince said, "Grimm, you are right about the boy. His skill is so obvious it is foolish to question it. Isn't that so, Schobert?"

The composer bowed. "Sir, I grant the child can improvise. But it is still not original. It is based on my theme."

"And his own interpretation," Grimm pointed out.

Schobert smiled suddenly. "Almost like his own composition, Grimm?"

"Yes," said Grimm, but he looked puzzled.

"If he is a genius, as you say he is, he should be able to compose."

Grimm hesitated, but when the Prince de Conti agreed with Schobert, he looked over to Leopold for aid, who didn't know what to say.

Schobert said, "If he were grown-up his improvising would not be remarkable and he would be regarded as merely another competent performer."

Grimm blurted out, for once losing his composure, "Herr Mozart, you did tell me the child composed a concerto when he was six."

"He was younger. But, of course, it was somewhat primitive."

"I composed several sonatas," said Wolferl. "Before we left Salzburg."

"Could they be played?" Schobert asked skeptically.

"Oh yes, yes indeed, sir, they were not difficult."

"Not difficult? Next he will be wanting to do an opera."

"I wanted to, but Papa said I am too young."

"In a few years he will be old enough," Schobert said sarcastically.

Rameau said suddenly, "I was fifty when I composed my first opera."

"Things are different now, sir," said Wolferl. "Papa has promised to let me try one when I am ten."

"Isn't he that now?" said Schobert.

"I told you that he was seven," said Leopold – and before Wolferl could blurt out that Papa was excited, he was eight – Leopold saw their skeptical smiles and added, "You can write Salzburg for confirmation."

Schobert said, "The question is can he compose. Whatever his age."

Leopold, unable to bear Grimm's distress and the thought of losing his support, cried out, "The child is composing right now!"

"For whom?" Schobert asked cynically. "His Majesty, no doubt?"

"Exactly. He is composing a sonata for the King's daughter."

Wolferl was surprised. He was not composing for anybody, but he would like to, especially after hearing Schobert's lovely music.

Prince de Conti asked, "Could he compose a sonata for me, too?"

"We will be honored," said Leopold, and when he saw Schobert's sneer, he declared, "Wolfgang's sonatas will not just be for the harpsichord, but for the harpsichord and violin."

"With your help, no doubt," said Schobert.

"You can watch him if you like," said Leopold.

"It won't bother me," Wolferl assured Schobert.

"No thank you," said Schobert. "I haven't time for such foolishness."

Leopold retorted, "Wolfgang will have these sonatas finished in a week or two," and he saw a look in the Prince de Conti's eyes that said, "I don't believe you," yet the nobleman stated that it would be a pleasure to have a sonata of the child's, no matter how simple it was.

And Rameau, who had listened to Wolferl's last improvisation, said, "The boy does show a profound feeling for harmony. I believe he will compose sonatas that can be played, and I will be honored to hear them."

Schobert declared strongly, "It is impossible. He will fail. It is not only a question of age, but of so many things. His training, his. . ."

Rameau did not allow him to finish. "I will recommend these sonatas to my engraver with His Excellency's permission."

The Prince gave it, and added, "We will expect to hear these sonatas in two weeks," and dismissed the musicians and returned to his guests.

SIXTEEN

What was Monsieur Grimm so anxious about? Wolferl wished their friend would not keep asking when the sonatas would be done. Only a week had passed since the concert at the Prince's palace, yet Monsieur Grimm had stopped by almost every day to inquire how he was progressing with the sonatas. Papa had been polite, but unhappy, yet Papa knew – even if Monsieur Grimm did not – that one could not be hurried in such matters. The form was simple – he could write out a sonata quickly – but he wanted it to be as spirited and graceful as Herr Schobert's and that took time.

And Countess van Eyck was ill in bed and he had to compose quietly, although she insisted that the Mozarts remain as her guests, that his music must not be disturbed. Yet her illness was upsetting. When he was allowed to see her, she was so sickly it was frightening. But she was proud of his triumphs, as if they enhanced her.

"After all," she whispered to him in one of her stronger moments, "we are both Salzburgians." He nodded, but when he returned to his composing he was in a sad mood and he knew that was wrong for these sonatas.

He was still searching for a melody he could trust when Papa said, "Do not be afraid to use what you have already heard. If you like it."

"Even Schobert?" He had liked his music as much as any he had heard.

"Even Schobert."

"But I thought you didn't care for him, Papa?"

"That has nothing to do with his music. I wouldn't give a damn for all the French music we've heard, but Schobert's is German, even if he does pretend to be more French than the French, and that emerges in his music."

Wolferl could hear Schobert's melodies in his mind any time he tried.

"Use a melody you know. Even if you learned it from someone else."

Wolferl took the melody of Schobert's that he liked best and made it his own, and then filled in the details, placing the violin as he remembered Papa did.

Now he heard harmonies which were musical, and he loved them so, and he sat fixed to the keyboard. Their sparkling and changing naturalness was a miracle, and he made the sonata sparkling and lively, and he was fascinated by the motion of the music. He sat composing until Mamma said, "Leopold, doesn't Wolferl know it is dark? How can he see?"

But he didn't have to see as long as he could hear. Mamma lit the candles and called him for supper. He didn't want to go, although he was hungry. He was almost finished with the first sonata, and he didn't want to lose the rest of the notes.

All during supper he kept playing the sonata's end over in his mind, and when he went to bed he couldn't fall asleep for the longest time. He was afraid he would forget the end. His head was so full of music. But the next morning, when he awoke, the notes were there, right in his head, just as he had composed them the night before. It was wonderful.

Papa examined it carefully, then said, "It is playable. That should satisfy them." He sighed with relief. The sonata was childlike in theme, reminiscent of Schobert, although lacking the latter's depth and polish, but it was clear and well constructed, a workable sonata for harpsichord and violin, and his son had composed it.

Wolferl spent the next few days finishing the assignment. He could think of nothing now but the sonatas. It was a game he was playing. He was making the harpsichord and violin sing to each other. He felt a new excitement in making them do his bidding. He continued to put down melodies he knew, and he constructed them as clearly as he could. And he was so caught up in composing, he wrote four sonatas instead of two.

He was not surprised when Papa said, "I like them."

He liked them, too. He knew he would do better with practice, but they were melodic, precise, and lively like Schobert's.

Prince de Conti invited Rameau and Schobert and Eckhard to judge the sonatas in a private session of music. He was amazed that they were playable. He informed Grimm, "You were right, the boy is remarkable."

But Schobert said, "Sir, the child imitated me."

"Oh, perhaps," said the Prince. "Is that a crime?"

Before Schobert could reply, Wolferl blurted out, "It is the best music in Paris," and even Schobert had to smile.

Leopold hurried to say, "Imitation is the sincerest form of flattery, and the theme is his own," and Eckard added, "I wish he had imitated me."

But suddenly everyone's attention was on the aged Rameau, who, leaning on his cane with a painful effort, stood up and said in a quavering voice, "The andante in the last sonata was expressive and original. Herr Schobert is indeed fortunate the child likes his music. I wish he had liked mine that much." He hobbled over to Wolferl, still sitting at the harpsichord, and kissed him on both cheeks.

Wolferl blushed. He felt, despite all the presents and money, he had been given the most precious gift of all.

And when Prince de Conti said, "Herr Schobert, the child had good taste, following your style," the composer made a gesture of magnanimous forgiveness and answered, "I am not embarrassed, sir, if he isn't."

Leopold said, "You do accept that he is a composer?"

Schobert hesitated, but as he saw the Prince frowning, he mumbled, "I bow before superior age and experience."

"Indeed he is a composer, a little virtuoso," Prince de Conti declared warmly. "Monsieur Grimm, you are to be commended for bringing this most agreeably cultivated child to our attention."

The next few days were spent arranging the presentation of the sonatas. Wolferl wanted to present them to the Countess van Eyck and to Madame d'Epinay, since it was the custom to present them to ladies and these two had been kindest to him, but Grimm insisted that they be presented where they would do the most good, to the King's daughter, the Princess Victoire, and to the Prince's mistress, Comtesse de Tessé.

Then Wolferl didn't care what was written, but Leopold was delighted when Grimm composed the dedications. Some of it was effusive, but Leopold was certain his friend knew what he was doing. Leopold was surprised when the Comtesse de Tessé rejected her dedication, saying, "It's too flattering, I don't deserve such praise, it should be more moderate."

Grimm was irritated, but he complied with her wish. Rameau, as he had promised, had the sonatas copied by his engraver – the best in Paris – and then each of the ladies accepted two of the sonatas.

What pleased Wolferl the most was that Papa had him sign them: *J. G. Wolfgang Mozart*, and from that time on Papa called him Wolfgang.

SEVENTEEN

The afternoon the Countess van Eyck died was an oppressive one. It had rained all morning, the sky was a somber gray, and the news made Anna Maria very sad. She had known for days there was no hope, and yet, hearing the news from the footman, she didn't want to believe it. She was preparing supper for the family, who were rehearsing at the theater for their first public concert in Paris, but now she had no heart to continue. The Countess had been kind, had been home, had been Salzburg. Suddenly Anna Maria was crying to herself. She remembered the day the Countess had left Salzburg to marry van Eyck. Even Count Arco, who rarely displayed emotion, had looked concerned, as if, already, he had lost his daughter. How terrible it would be for him, she thought sadly. Count Arco, who had so much power in Salzburg, had been unable to do a single thing to save his daughter.

Would he have guilt about allowing his child to wander so far from home? To die in a strange land? What if, someday, this happened to them? Anna Maria shivered. There was something unholy about this, something profane.

Wolfgang was surprised by Mamma's affection that evening. She always kissed him when he was away from her for a few hours, but tonight she held him as if she must not let go. Then she took Papa aside to tell him something he was not surprised to know, and Papa looked shocked and pale.

And when he asked, "How is the Countess?" Papa gave Mamma a warning glance and Mamma said, "She has gone away."

"Where?"

"We will tell you later," said Mamma.

They put him to bed early, as if they wanted him out of the way. But he could not sleep, sensing that something dreadful had happened.

He bumped into Nannerl, on his way to the toilet, and she didn't make any jokes as she usually did, but looked as if she had been crying. However, she answered his, "What is wrong?" with, "You are too young!" and at that moment he hated her. He was surprised by his feeling; he hadn't thought he could ever hate his own flesh and blood, but she wasn't giving him any more attention, lost in her own reveries.

The next day they moved out of the Countess' house, and then he was left in the care of Nannerl while Papa and Mamma disappeared for the afternoon. Nannerl would not tell him where they had gone, although she obviously knew. That night, even after they had returned, he kept dreaming that he was lost – where was Papa? Mamma? He awoke in a cold sweat, with Mamma, disturbed by his tossing, at his side, and singing a lullaby to him in her light, sweet voice until he fell asleep.

When he awoke the next morning he still wanted to know what had happened to the Countess, and Mamma said, "She has taken a long journey."

"But why do you look so sad? Will I ever see her again?"

No one answered, all of them busy suddenly with unimportant things.

He sat by the window in their new rooms near the rue et porte Saint-Honoré, where he and Nannerl were to perform, and saw nothing but the Countess' face. He refused to eat his supper, which was unusual, but nobody insisted, not even Papa. The weather had become dreadful, with sudden, stormy gusts of rain making the street outside impossible to walk on with any comfort. Yet two men, carrying a torch in one hand and a litter in the other, were plodding slowly and laboriously past the window. There was a long object on the litter and a sheet over it, and he was sure it was a woman, for the outline of the body was clearly visible under the drenched, wind-whipped sheet. He cried out in terror, but even before Mamma reached his side, he knew what it was. She whispered mournfully, "A funeral, a poor woman's funeral, whose family couldn't afford anything better," and now again, all he could see was the face of the Countess and he knew what had happened to her. A sense of horror came over him. He could not understand how she could be without life when he was so full of it.

Unable to sleep, tortured by the harsh clatter of the rain on the roof of his room – it went on as if it would never cease – he made his way in the dark and cold to his parents' bedroom in the hope of finding relief.

Mamma yearned to take him into bed with them, but Papa said, "No, he is not a baby any longer."

"Then you should tell him the truth."

"And ruin the concert."

"You always say he should know what the world is really like."

"The Countess isn't dead?" pleaded Wolfgang, as if, somehow, the saying and the sounding would keep her alive.

"You tell him," said Papa.

"It was God's will," said Mamma, and burst into tears, and the child was stricken with nausea and had to run to the toilet, retching violently.

As Leopold feared, Wolfgang was sick the next morning, and the concert at the theater had to be postponed. It struck him as most unfortunate, for it had been only through the intercession of the Prince de Conti that the public concert had been arranged. French law stated that only those who served the King had the privilege of playing for the public; and it was a privilege Louis XV could take away whenever he wished. But thanks to the Prince de Conti this law had been waived; Monsieur Grimm was taking care of all the preparations; a large profit seemed assured.

Anna Maria was confused. The first doctor she called said the boy had quinsy, but that he couldn't treat it. The second diagnosed his illness as rheumatism and said that the only remedy was time. Then Grimm, seeing that Wolfgang was not getting better, declared that both doctors were fools, that his personal physician would cure the child. This learned gentleman, who was a devout reader of the *Correspondance littéraire*, examined Wolfgang with great care and said, "It is probably an inflammation of the throat and chest." A worried Anna Maria had visions of the child having caught the contagion from the Countess. The physician added, "He should be inoculated against the smallpox. Both your children should."

Leopold refused to allow this, telling Anna Maria, "Inoculation is an aspersion against God. We must leave it to His grace."

Anna Maria, generally more devout than Leopold, was not sure she agreed with him. Inoculation was new, and not like the usual medical practice, but she heard that some of the nobility were having it done to their children. But Leopold was obdurate, and she sought to cure Wolfgang with her love. Gradually the child's melancholy vanished and in a few days he was able to get out of bed and resume his music.

The first public concert was such a success, Grimm arranged another. This was very profitable also, and when Leopold decided to go to London Anna Maria was surprised. Moreover, the children had performed at Versailles again; there had been other recitals for the nobility; the great salon ladies, who determined French taste, were especially taken with Wolfgang, who they said was unusually charming and refined. And the children had earned more money here than anywhere else and the presents were lavish.

Leopold told her to start packing and she said, "We should remain in Paris. We have been welcomed very warmly here."

"No, we cannot stay. French music, all of it, is not worth a sou."

"You didn't mind Wolfgang learning from Schobert's music."

"A German. I hope that in ten to fifteen years there will be no such thing as French taste in music."

"You said the dances at Versailles were quite grand."

"And corrupt. There is so much extravagance at Versailles, that actually, only a few are rich. Even most of the nobles are overwhelmed with debt. Practically all of the country's wealth is owned by a few bankers and financiers, and their money is spent chiefly on Lucretias, who, however, do not stab themselves."

Anna Maria did not smile at his sarcasm as he expected. Instead, thinking that despite his criticism of France, he was being as French as Monsieur Grimm, whom he admired, she became more serious. "Everyone I talk to says England will be detrimental to the children's health, that it is always rainy and foggy there. Wolfgang is not strongly built, his lungs are small, and he could have caught some of the contagion from the Countess. She was spitting blood even when we met her."

He was silent. He could not tell her one of his main reasons for leaving. The memory was as vivid, however, as if it were just happening.

A few days ago he had taken Wolfgang to Versailles to hear and see the French minuets, particularly those composed by the Italians. The French dancing masters were the best in Europe, whatever the quality of their music, and Wolfgang should be acquainted with their work.

Wolfgang was fascinated by the harmonious and hypnotic effect of the French *Danses à Deux*. The child wanted to participate, he loved the graceful, rhythmic flow of the music and the dancers, but Papa said he was too young to dance. So, in his mind, he composed his own accompaniment, and imagined himself dancing to it. Then suddenly, he had to go to the toilet. Papa led him down a long corridor searching for one, thinking that for a civilized place like Versailles, the toilets were difficult to find. They heard a sound, thought it was what they were looking for, and came upon a couple copulating in a dark, dank gallery. They could only see the man's powdered wig bobbing up and down in the darkness, but Papa could tell from the noise what was happening and so could Wolfgang, although he had never witnessed the act before. The woman could

123

not contain herself, while the man cursed them with a nauseating obscenity.

Wolfgang was dazed. He was unable to relieve himself, as if, somehow, that was suddenly unclean, although Papa, Mamma, and Nannerl were always making jokes about that. He didn't say a word. He knew there was a thing called sex and that men and women made children, but this was different than he had imagined. He had visualized it as something charming, elegant, lovely, but this was as ugly and dirty as the filth on the Paris streets, where, if they did not travel in a sedan chair, they trod on dead animals, garbage, decay, human excrement, and had to pretend none of it was there.

He couldn't sleep that night. The grotesque noise of the couple rang in his ears. Love should be attractive, music said so, Papa and Mamma said so, and then he wondered, did they make such dreadful noises? The idea was horrible. And he hated the way he was suffering.

The pain of Wolfgang's reaction flooded over Leopold now. Suddenly, abruptly, he said to Anna Maria, "Versailles is a sewer!"

She wanted to know why, and he said, "There is no piety here. The only miracles that are performed here are by those who are neither virgins nor saints, and they are all performed by their bodies. Indeed, it is impossible to tell who is the mistress of the house, or whose mistress. Everyone lives according to their fancy, and if there is not a special mercy from God, France will suffer the fate of the Persian Empire."

He would not explain further. He started packing.

Grimm assured Leopold that England would welcome them with open arms. Leopold agreed, although Nannerl, who was becoming very much the young lady with her elegant French capes, did not want to leave. But Anna Maria noticed that Wolferl was glad to go. She wondered if it was because of the Countess, whom he had loved so. Suddenly a voice within her was crying out to Leopold: *Go back, Salzburg is our root, our future is there.*

He ignored the entreaty on her face. He and Grimm were kissing each other on both cheeks like good Frenchmen and swearing eternal friendship. Then their hired coach was at the door, and they were on their way again.

The next day Madame Pompadour died.

EIGHTEEN

Soon after the Mozarts arrived in London, the children were invited to play by George III and his German-born wife, Charlotte. Grimm had informed the King, who was one of his subscribers, when and where *"those miracles of nature, the Mozart children,"* would be in London, and had praised them again in the *Correspondance littéraire*, and this had aroused the royal curiosity.

The trip from Paris had been difficult, and Sebastian Winter had quit, afraid to venture across the English channel. But London itself was exciting, and the lodgings Grimm had recommended at Mr Cousin's, a hair-cutter in Cecil Court, St. Martin's Lane, were clean, comfortable, and close to the royal residence, Buckingham House.

Wolfgang was disappointed by the plainness of this palace. Papa, to make sure he was aware of the prestige of the occasion, informed him that England had just defeated France in the Seven Years' War, and had become the most powerful nation in Europe and had seized many of the French colonies in America, yet Versailles was far more magnificent.

And the King's dowdy appearance surprised Wolfgang. The humblest courtier at Versailles was more lavishly dressed. George III wore a plain wig, a sober waistcoat, and gray stockings. He was almost as young looking as Schobert, with a florid complexion, slanting forehead, and a round, receding chin. Queen Charlotte was a small, homely woman, simply dressed, without any of the frills of the French ladies.

After the usual opening duet with Nannerl, the King said he would like the Queen to play with the boy. Wolfgang looked hesitant, and George III added proudly, "It is her own harpsichord. She brought it with her as a dowry. She is an accomplished musician. Her private music master, Johann Christian Bach, says she is the best pupil he has."

Wolfgang didn't think much of Bach's judgment as they played a duet. She couldn't compare with Nannerl. Halfway through a sonata by Handel, he had to halt to correct the position of her fingers. This upset Papa, and the King flushed and for a moment it seemed he might lose his temper.

But when the Queen said, "The boy is right," the King subsided.

A little later Wolfgang warned her that she was hurrying her beat, and she nodded. She slowed down and she was delighted that they finished together, and George III applauded loudly and declared, "She plays so well!"

No one differed, although for an instant Papa thought Wolfgang might, for Wolfgang frowned and he could tell that his son did not agree.

The King said, "And now, Mr. Mozart, I would like your son to accompany the Queen on the harpsichord while she sings."

The aria was by Christian Bach, and Wolfgang hoped she could sing better than she played. But her love of music was such a nuisance, for her singing was, if anything, worse than her playing. If she were a professional singer, he reflected, she would not last a performance, she had no stage presence, her voice was small, without color. Yet Bach's music was enchanting. The aria flowed with a natural, easy grace.

George III was very happy, shouting, "Amiable, amiable singing indeed!"

Everyone joined in; the royal judgment was not to be questioned.

George III, pleased with the way his audience had appreciated his Queen's singing, said, "Master Mozart, it is written in the *Correspondance littéraire* that you play the organ like a miracle of nature. Is that so?"

Wolfgang shrugged. He played the organ as it should be played.

"Can you play Handel?"

Wolfgang nodded.

"Splendid! And afterwards, Handel extempore."

But when it came time to improvise Wolfgang was troubled. He liked Handel's grave and grand organ music, but he loved Christian Bach's gay and pleasing melody. Drawn by a secret force, his improvisation became more Bach than Handel. The King was beating time with his music roll, and no one dared tell him that he was not in time, and when a page grew drowsy the music roll came down on the small powdered head. Wolfgang tried to return to Handel, but now Bach possessed a sweet, enticing flow he could not resist. He saw Papa look startled, then alarmed; Nannerl was grinning as if it were a great joke; no one else, not even the Queen, seemed to know the difference. Then he saw a tall, handsome man, dressed like a great and fashionable gentleman, standing in the doorway and listening so intently he sensed it was Johann Christian Bach himself. That filled Wolfgang with a passionate desire to please this composer, as this composer's music pleased him. By the end of the improvisation it was completely in the style of Bach.

The King nodded emphatically to signify his approval and stated, "No one will ever surpass Handel. He is first among all musicians. Anyone who thinks differently is a fool and a barbarian. Correct, Bach?"

Bach, who had moved in from the doorway once the improvisation was finished, said, "Naturally, Your Highness."

"Do you like the way the child played Handel?"

"He is a fine organist, sir."

"Grimm is right. He played Handel extempore without a mistake."

Papa, grateful that no one but Bach knew what Wolfgang had done – but such a risk – said, "We are your most obedient servants, Your Majesty."

Bach said, "Sir, may the boy play a sonata with me?"

"At sight?" The King was skeptical.

"I am certain he can. With your permission, sir."

Wolfgang cried out, "Please, Your Higness, Please!"

"You are such a little boy to play with a grand musician like Bach."

"I will manage, sir."

Bach placed Wolfgang between his knees and played a few bars, which the boy continued, and then playing in turn, they performed the complete sonata perfectly, as if by one pair of hands.

Christian Bach said nothing about how Wolfgang had improvised his music rather than Handel's until father and son came to his studio near the palace. Then he took that as a compliment to himself rather than a joke against the King, and told Leopold, "I will be delighted to introduce your children to musical London."

Wolfgang loved Bach's fashionable studio which was adorned in the style of Versailles and looked out on Green Park. It contained a clavichord, harpsichord, organ, and pianoforte, and he noticed that Bach, unlike most musicians, dressed like a great lord even in his studio.

Leopold wasn't sure he liked his son's absorption in Bach. Yet this composer, performer, and music master to the Queen knew the musical world of London and was one of its most celebrated musicians.

And he had a reliable background. He was the sixth generation of musicians in his family. His father, old Sebastian Bach, although a Lutheran and a cantor, had been a musician with a sound training and had fathered a number of excellent musicians. But Leopold had never met the father, for Lutheran and Catholic Germany were divided as if there were a wall between them. Yet while the Lutheran church music of old Sebastian Bach, dead fourteen years, was never performed in Catholic Salzburg or Vienna, he was acquainted with the music of several of his sons, who were better known. He had taught Wolfgang the sonatas of Carl Philipp Emanuel, and the organ music of the oldest son, Wilhelm Friedemann.

But it was Christian Bach whom he had heard the most about. How the youngest of the eleven sons of old Sebastian had left Germany for Italy to study music with Padre Martini, the most renowned of all the Italian teachers, and had become a Catholic so that his operas would be performed in Italy. And now, with Handel dead, he was the most popular musician in Protestant England, although he was still a Catholic.

Was there such a preference for German music in London? Leopold wondered.

Then, as if Bach had read his mind, he said, "Herr Mozart, there is no English music now, only Italian and German, Piccinni and Handel."

"And Christian Bach." Who, he thought, was a little bit of both.

"Thank you, but one must not take anything for granted."

"I don't. Believe me, I don't." He studied Bach's grand clothes, his full face, dominated by keen eyes and a large forehead, seeking to judge this musician's interest in Wolfgang.

Wolfgang was examining the pianoforte. He had seen several in his travels and had played briefly on them, but this one seemed better than the others and he wanted to try it. He looked over to Bach for permission, who said, "It is up to your father."

Leopold said, "I've had Wolfgang study sonatas of your brother, Carl Philipp Emanuel. I found their style expressive and pleasing, but essentially for the harpsichord. And the few compositions I discovered of your father's were always for the organ."

"My father was a little old-fashioned, especially when it came to the pianoforte, but it is the coming instrument."

"It hasn't been used anywhere we have been."

"It is not yet fashionable."

"That can't be the only reason."

"People are afraid of it. The pianoforte is new, different, and so, has no prestige. You saw how proud the Queen is of her harpsichord."

"Have you played it in public yet?"

"No. London is not ready, but it will be one of these days." Bach added, "I think that once the public hears the pianoforte and it is improved a little more, it will displace the harpsichord."

"Immediately?"

"It may take ten years, perhaps twenty, but I am confident that eventually it will be the favorite solo instrument."

"Why?" asked Wolfgang, fingering the small, compact, square

pianoforte. The instrument was clothed in a fine mahogany, but it was not as pretty or as large as the royal harpsichords he had played on.

"Because it has a richer, more dynamic, varied tone than a harpsichord."

"Then why isn't it used?"

"Herr Bach just told you," Lepold said impatiently.

"Are they the only reasons?"

Bach said quietly, "People fear new things."

"Even in music?"

"Yes, Wolfgang. Especially in music."

"Papa, may I play the pianoforte?"

Leopold, feeling he had no choice, reluctantly gave his permission.

Bach placed one of his sonatas on the pianoforte and nodded for Wolfgang to start. For once, however, the child was hesitant. Despite his curiosity about *this* pianoforte and his desire to follow in the footsteps of his new friend, the fear that he might disappoint him was almost too much to endure. Then the pianofortes he had tried before had been displeasing, too loud, too resonant, and too unreliable. Yet he could not turn back.

He began slowly, tentatively. As he expected this pianoforte was also louder and more resonant than he liked. He missed the bright crisp clarity of the harpsichord. The tone was not always finished when he struck a note. He felt he could not trust this instrument, for every so often the tone was also blurred and uneven. He was disturbed by the fortissimo, which was much more emphatic than a harpsichord or clavichord. No wonder musicians called this instrument a "hammer-harpsichord". Yet both Bach and Papa looked pleased with the way he was playing. Suddenly he felt he was performing properly. Note after note developed new nuances.

He lost track of the time; he stopped thinking about harpsichords. Now, as he felt the keys under his fingers, he was full of exciting sensations. It seemed to him that this music came to him not from the mind, but from the body. His touch altered, and the heavier and more sonorous sounds of the pianoforte became dramatic and possessed a living warmth. He forgot that the harpsichord had a cleaner execution, for this pianoforte had more subtle shadings and possibilities. That filled him with joy and he wanted to go on and on. Here was a new language to learn, to speak. The moment he finished Bach's sonata, he asked, "Papa, may I study the pianoforte? With Herr Bach, if you don't mind?"

Leopold nodded, and Wolfgang overwhelmed him with kisses and he was embarrassed, crying out, "You are no longer a baby. Herr Bach can help you and that is all we must consider." But he was surprised when Bach took him aside, so that the child could not hear them, and said that Wolgang should also study with Manzuoli. He exclaimed, "The castrato?"

"Giovanni Manzuoli is the best singer in London. Perhaps in the world."

"Do you know him well?"

"Quite well. He is singing in my next opera," Bach said proudly.

"But Wolfgang has no voice, no ambitions to be a singer."

"You want him to compose an opera some day, don't you?"

"Yes." The sooner the better, thought Leopold, and then they would really amaze the world.

"Then he should learn how to compose for a castrato. All the good operas are written for that kind of a voice."

Leopold knew that Bach was right, yet something in him resisted this suggestion. The castration of boys of Wolfgang's age to give them the adult high tones of a soprano was a fact of life despite its illegality, the threat of ex-communication, and the barbarity of the custom, but it was as if Wolfgang was being plunged into a world he was too immature for.

"And he should learn how to sing correctly."

"He is too young."

"If Manzuoli likes him, he can be helpful in arranging public concerts."

"What about the fact that Manzuoli is a castrato?"

"You explain it to him."

That was not easy. Although Leopold spoke as one musician to another, he felt awkward saying to Wolfgang, "Manzuoli, the great opera singer, is a castrato, which means he was operated on when a boy so that he could not have children but which gave him a voice as high as a lyric soprano."

"Is he a man?"

"In some ways."

"But he can't have any children?"

"That's right."

"Why?"

Leopold started to say because the ducts leading to his testicles had been severed, but he said instead, "You'll understand when you grow up."

"Oh!" Wolfgang was annoyed. He knew that men impregnated women, but adults, trying to hide things from him, were so childish sometimes.

Leopold said, "Manzuoli does have the best voice in London."

"Because he is a castrato?"

"Probably."

130

Bach disappointed Wolfgang also. He expected him to explain why *a castrato was a castrato* – he felt that he and his new friend were kindred spirits – but Bach acted as if Papa had taken care of that and kept talking about the qualities of Manzuoli's voice as if they were incomparable, and yet the castrato was unprepossessing. The Italian's studio was smaller than Bach's, without any of the latter's taste, and while Bach introduced him as London's first *musico*, the male soprano was fat, middle-aged, with a long, large nose, ugly, blunt features, and heavy lidded eyes. He was surprised that Bach bowed as low to Manzuoli as Bach had to George III.

Manzuoli sneered, "What can a child of eight know about music?"

"Try him."

All the questions Manzuoli asked him about the harpsichord were easy to answer, and Wolfgang could see that the singer was growing intrigued, although still skeptical, for he said, "Now sing, boy."

"I can't," said Wolfgang.

"You mean you don't know how." Manzuoli looked knowingly at Bach.

"Oh, I know how, signore, but my voice is no good."

"Ah, a critic. Basta, let me decide that. Go ahead boy, sing, sing!"

"What?"

"*God Save the King*. If you know it. Might as well be patriotic, too."

Wolfgang knew the song, having heard it played at the opening of the recital for George III. Only his own voice was shameful. He wanted to halt after the first few bars. He knew how to produce the proper tones, but his voice was thin, shrill, an undependable treble.

The castrato grinned and said mockingly to Bach, "The boy could use an operation. He is just the right age."

Bach replied quietly, "I didn't bring him here to be a singer, but to learn how to compose operas for the best voices. Voices like your own."

Inevitably, thought Wolfgang, the moment a person was flattered, he was interested. Manzuoli said, "What do you suggest?"

"Let him sing after you. See if he knows how to follow."

Manzuoli did, and Wolfgang followed perfectly until the castrato's voice rose so high he could not continue, and he stood there, enchanted with Manzuoli's singing. The castrato, pleased with the boy's admiration despite his intention not to be, now sang as if he were in the opera house.

The voice was full and strong, the most powerful and voluminous soprano Wolfgang had ever heard, yet with all its strength it was also sweet and flexible, leaping from passage to passage with lightness and ease.

When Manzuoli finished, Wolfgang looked as if he had seen a vision.

Manzuoli asked him questions about singing and he knew he answered them correctly, for the castrato grew animated, while he was thinking that this was the kind of a voice for which one *must* compose.

Manzuoli, delighted with the boy's ability to learn, gave him several free lessons a week, and told Bach, "The child is such a fine pupil, it is a pleasure to teach him. He will never have much of a voice, but he comprehends everything I tell him about singing, even the complexities of voice production. He has such an extraordinary impressionability. The boy soaks up whatever I tell him as if he were a sponge."

"Yes," answered Bach, "I find the same thing, teaching him the pianoforte and composition. He has an exceptional sensitivity to any music he hears, and an exceptional ability to absorb it."

Within a month the greatest accolade any of the Mozarts could give a singer was to say, "He sings like Manzuoli." As the castrato's tutelage increased Wolfgang's knowledge of singing, he longed to compose an opera, but Papa said he was still too young. He also became skillful on the pianoforte, yet Papa refused to allow him to play it in public, since no one else had, and said, "I am not interested in being an innovator."

He was not aware that when he referred to Bach as *"his music master,"* Papa was hurt, although Papa reiterated that *"I am the Impressario and the Master of our Travels,"* for Papa seemed pleased that Bach was teaching him how to compose a symphony and was taking him to hear one of his operas.

It was a gala social occasion. The newspapers announced that "Their Majesties are honoring Mr. Bach's presentation with their presence," but Wolfgang was more impressed with the richness of his music master's score, the ingenuous texture of the various roles, the use of clarinets in the opera orchestra. This was the first time he had heard clarinets in an orchestra, and he thought it was a happy use for wind instruments.

Manzuoli sang the lead – admirably he thought – but there was such a mob at the stage door he and Bach could not reach the castrato to express their appreciation of his performance. Yet the swirl of the crowd around this theater in Haymarket was exciting, and he loved the vitality of the scene, but Bach was saying cynically, "Wolfgang, you must not take these fancy gentlemen too seriously. Now that their taste has been satisfied with the newest sensation, Manzuoli, they are off in search of another pleasure, gambling or dancing probably." But Wolfgang loved dancing.

NINETEEN

Leopold was excited when public concerts by the children were sponsored by Bach and Manzuoli. The programs featured the most sensational aspects of the children's skills, although Anna Maria was dubious, but Leopold had no regrets when the first concert earned a hundred guineas, the largest sum they had ever made. And while there was another recital for George III, on his birthday, it was the public concerts that were profitable. After five more performances Leopold's profits totaled five hundred guineas.

He was jubilant. He had just decided to stay through the winter and into 1765 in spite of Anna Maria's fears about the English weather when he received dismaying news from Salzburg.

Bullinger wrote that the Archbishop wanted to know when Mozart was returning, that he had already overstayed his leave of absence, and that the post of Vice-Kapellmeister could not be kept for him indefinitely.

It was like a prison door closing upon his hopes. He sat for a long time, not knowing what to do. He didn't hear Wolfgang enter his study until his son said, "Bach wants me to play some Handel duets with him."

"So?" He looked at his son with a feeling of irritation.

"At Ranelagh House for a charity for the Lying-in Hospital. Bach says it will be regarded as a patriotic gesture, and after that, there should be an invitation to play at Mrs. Cornelys's."

Leopold came out of his reverie. Mrs. Cornelys, although actually a high-class prostitute, had the most glittering salon in London. Bach was a shrewd one. With one hand the gentry supported the Lying-in Hospital, with the other they filled it with their bastards. He smiled, despite his worry about the Archbishop. He said, "Inform Herr Bach that you will be honored to play with him, especially for such

133

a worthy charity. And as an encore, you would like to play your own sonata, with his permission."

As Wolfgang hurried off to practice his own sonata, he concentrated on his answer to Bullinger and wrote:

"Dear Friend, I am honored by His Grace's interest in our welfare, and I would be grateful if you would be good enough to convey to him our appreciation of his kindness in allowing us to make this triumphant tour through the civilized world. Please assure him that we bring only fresh glory to His Grace's music.

"My girl is esteemed the first female performer in Europe, although just twelve, and Wolfgang, although only eight, now possesses the gifts of a man of forty. What he was when he left Salzburg is but a shadow of what he is at present; he surpasses all that you can imagine.

"He is sitting at the clavier now, composing a sonata for a great public concert, after having spent the afternoon with 'The English Bach', and Manzuoli, the greatest musicians in England, yet he desired first of all, to be remembered to you. Not a day passes, despite the praises of George III, who has been gracious enough to make him a special favorite, that he does not speak affectionately of Salzburg and our friends there.

"The English are so grateful to Salzburg for what they call, 'These miracles from God', that they say Salzburg must be a holy place, although this is a Protestant country. They have rewarded us with hundreds of guineas, and only Manzuoli, the castrato, earns more. We have played for George III on his birthday, we have been invited to play for him on the fourth anniversary of his accession to the throne, and Wolfgang has been commissioned to compose six sonatas dedicated to the Queen.

"Thus, it would be difficult to depart at this time. But once we leave England, we will return to Salzburg as quickly as possible.

"Would you please express our condolences to Count Arco over the death of his daughter. It was very sad. She was most kind to us, and Wolfgang loved her dearly, and is just now recovering from this great loss.

"Above all, we remain the most devoted and humble servant of His Grace, most worthy High-born Prince of the Holy Roman Empire, and we will continue to endeavor to make ourselves worthy of His beneficence."

Leopold felt better. What he had really wanted to write to his friend was: *"Every moment I lose today, I lose forever,"* but that would offend His Grace. It should suffice that this letter should postpone the day of reckoning in Salzburg, and by the time it reached the Archbishop, good things could occur in London. He might even find a more profitable post with a great lord that would free him from Schrattenbach.

To aid this, he arranged for Wolfgang to be a true British patriot at Ranelagh by having him perform an organ concerto by Handel, who had become a British citizen and hero.

The charity concert was a great success. It brought, as Leopold had hoped, an invitation to perform in Mrs. Cornely's fashionable salon.

Leopold surveyed the throng that crowded around her, and doubted that many of these loud, profane noblemen cared for music. Most of her drinking, gambling, whoring friends considered music a frivolous interest, but there were more silk stockings, fancy waist-coats, and jeweled swords than he had seen anywhere else in London. And the women in attendance were mistresses, not wives, and so guineas were spent freely. He felt that his foresight was rewarded when he was given over a hundred guineas for his children's per-formance, which went on past midnight.

At their new quarters – they had moved from St. Martin's Lane to Ebury Street so they could be more comfortable – Leopold frowned when Anna Maria said, "The English nobility's morals could harm the children."

He replied, "They are not as bad as Versailles, which was a sewer."

"And you are sweating profusely, yet you have all the windows open."

"It is summer." He assumed he was sweating because of the activity and the excitement. For his stomach was satisfactory. Diarrhea, in his view the first sign of any disorder, was not present. But suddenly his head felt on fire, yet he had severe chills.

The doctor that an alarmed Anna Maria summoned, said, "Mr. Mozart, your complaint is called a cold. You should wear heavier clothes."

But the next few weeks Leopold was so ill he had to stay in bed while a worried Anna Maria nursed him. London became dreary. There was not any word from Salzburg, and no visits from Bach or Manzuoli.

The musicians, warned that Leopold had a bad cold, assumed it would become consumption and be contagious, and so they stayed away. Without their help, there were no concerts. His money dwindled steadily.

He was surprised to find Wolfgang cheerful these difficult days. No one was allowed to play an instrument, or to visit Bach or Manzuoli because of fear that they might carry the contagion, and Leopold was disappointed that his son was seldom by his side but seemed content in the study.

Wolfgang was composing a symphony. Day after day he sat at

Papa's desk, his short legs straddling the chair, remembering what Bach had said, "A symphony must have a theme, Wolfgang, and a pleasing melody." There were no visitors, he had all the privacy he needed, but there was nothing about him that was stimulating, so he thought of the different journeys they had taken, of all the Kings they had met, and gradually, he invented his own Kingdom and called it the Kingdom of Bach. Certainly Johann Christian deserved one if George III did. He made himself Johann Christian's son, and he liked that idea and that he would be King someday.

There was nothing ugly or dirty in this land, no one ever became ill, the sun always shone brightly and warmly, unlike England. All was well and he was quite happy. He recalled that Bach had stated also, "Music must sing." Bach's sang. And now he had a theme. Absorbed in his Kingdom, he wrote down the notes he remembered Bach had used.

He also put in many contrasts as his King did, and he made them as pretty and pleasing as he could, for his King did. There must be nothing sad. His King's music was never sad. And there was so much to remember, like the clarinets his King had used. Seeing Nannerl watching him curiously, he said, "Remind me to give the horns something good to do."

"Remind yourself," she retorted, restless, unhappy, feeling neglected. Wolfgang got much more attention than she did now, yet he was such a little boy sometimes, proud of this Kingdom he had created but refusing to tell her who the King was, when he knew far less than she did about the world. Papa liked to pretend she was twelve, but she was thirteen, going on fourteen, a young lady, while Wolfgang was still a child. Yet when she saw how deep he was in thought, she did remind him, and she was pleased when he thanked her with a kiss, although she pretended she was too old for such displays of affection.

The symphony was completed soon afterward. And when Leopold felt fully recovered, Wolfgang gave him the composition as a present.

Leopold was deeply pleased by the gift and with his son's skill, but he accepted it casually, wanting the child to regard such composition as natural. He was not surprised that the symphony resembled Bach's music. It was evident that his son still considered Johann Christian the best, the cleverest, the most beautiful of men, yet when Wolfgang handed him the symphony, he also embraced him passionately.

Leopold consoled himself with that memory, and set about to make up for the time that had been lost. He had Wolfgang compose six sonatas for the harpsichord with accompaniment for violin and violincello, and had him dedicate them to the Queen. When she accepted them and sent him fifty guineas and invited the children to play for the court festivities celebrating the fourth anniversary of George III's accession to the throne he was positive that the decision to risk England had been wise.

TWENTY

The King and Queen praised the children's playing, but there were no more requests to perform for them. George III's stern policy towards the American colonies had become unpopular, and in January, 1765, while Wolfgang was celebrating his ninth birthday and Leopold was planning new conquests, riots dominated the streets of London to protest George III's suppression of ancient liberties. They were silenced by orders from the Crown, for the King expected absolute obedience, but the discontent remained. George III fell ill, and all royal entertainments were canceled.

Public concerts became rare because of the political situation. The gentry lost interest in the Mozarts, who were no longer regarded as a novelty or a sensation. Bach was busy with his own career, although he continued to teach Wolfgang, while Manzuoli was planning to return to Italy, after earning a fortune, and neither was able to sponsor anybody but himself now. So, when expenditures began to exceed income, Leopold decided to leave England.

Wolfgang was glad they were leaving. England had become a bore with the slackening of interest in him. Papa had taken him and Nannerl to see the Tower, St. Paul's and Westminster Abbey, Lincoln Fields and the Monument, but none of this compared with composing or performing. Yet when it came time to say goodbye to Bach, he wept and didn't want to go.

Johann Christian had to blink back his own tears. The boy kept saying, "I won't see you any more," and he replied, "Of course you will," and Wolfgang added, "No, you won't, you will never come to Salzburg, what would you do in Salzburg?" and Johann Christian didn't answer, for the boy was probably right. He turned to the father and asked, "You'll come back?"

"Once we are in Salzburg? I doubt it."

"England really likes your children."

"Does it?"

"I'm sure it does. Despite your recent disappointments." Bach, for once in his life, was pleading. "You will return?"

"No."

At the last moment Leopold, instead of going home by way of Paris as had been his intention, decided to go to Holland. He wrote to Salzburg that the Dutch Ambassador in England had insisted that the children play for the seventeen-year-old Prince of Orange, who was to be installed ruler of the Dutch republic on his eighteenth birthday, and for his sister, Princess Caroline, who was pregnant. As he explained to Bullinger in his letter, "You cannot deny a pregnant woman anything, and she is eager to hear the children, but we will be home soon after."

What he could not write was the feeling that oppressed him that once in Salzburg, his independence and future would vanish. His spirits rose when the Prince of Orange and the Princess Caroline greeted them warmly, were delighted with the children, and paid him many gulden.

Three weeks after their arrival in The Hague, there was news of the sudden death of Maria Theresa's husband, Emperor Francis I, from apoplexy. But Leopold could not feel sad as he was supposed to, for Francis' heir, the new Emperor, Joseph II, was far more musical than his father.

The evening Leopold heard about the death of Francis I, Nannerl fell ill. At first he assumed this was just a bad cold such as had afflicted him in England, but when she grew worse he became frantic. None of the doctors he called, although the first was Princess Caroline's and the second was the English Ambassador's, knew what her illness was or what to do. She became so critical he hurriedly called a priest to administer the last rites of the church to her, to prepare her for whatever was the will of God.

Nannerl thought she was going to die. Never had she felt so terrible. And now there was a priest by her side. Now Wolferl would have all the glory for himself. The somber priest was saying joylessly that heaven was a far happier place than this wicked world. He gave her a cross to hold, to comfort her in her agony, and her hands went instinctively to her stomach to ease the cramps which were so excruciating she thought she was in hell.

In this delirium many faces kept appearing, but where was the family? Then she was conscious again, the priest was gone and she saw Mamma standing by her bed, tears streaming down her cheeks, and Papa was next to Mamma, looking dreadfully grim, but what about Wolferl? Didn't he know how sick she was? Before she could ask, their faces faded from view.

As if in a vision, she saw Salzburg. A rainbow formed a halo around the city and the Fortress Hohensalzburg. Her throat ached with the beauty of it, and she thought fiercely, I ought to die, it would serve them right, taking me away when I didn't want to go! His Grace gave Papa one year's leave of absence, not two or three! She saw him sitting by her side, crying like Mamma, his hand groping for hers, and she longed to reach out and say, I love you even more than Wolferl does, but she was too tired.

The terrible stomach cramps were gone, however, and some time later she was able to repeat after Papa, "I love God," almost as much as she loved Papa – that was one place Wolferl couldn't outdo her.

Papa whispered, "You must repent, so you will not be damned in the next world," and she begged forgiveness for being envious of Wolferl, or resenting that they preferred him, and Papa was shocked.

He said, "You mustn't think such thoughts, they're not true."

What thoughts? Where were they? London? Paris? Vienna?

"You must keep up the good work. You are getting better, dear."

"When are we going, Papa? When Papa?"

"When you are better."

Suddenly he felt she was not yet alive, yet not quite dead.

Mamma began to sing a hymn to Nannerl – a Salzburg hymn – for Mamma had sung this to Nannerl almost from her birth. The frail girl slowly opened her eyes and listened. Mamma embraced her, rocking her back and forth as if she was still Mamma's baby and whispered, "You are our Princess."

Now Nannerl improved. She felt restored to her rightful place by their care. Often she was the sole subject of the conversation. But she wasn't sure she was out of danger until Papa complained about his gout. He said she had been in bed a month. She wondered where Wolferl was, and Papa explained, "He is in bed, too," but she was positive that her brother was trying to steal the spotlight again.

Wolfgang was so weary of being ill. On their arrival at The Hague he had gone to bed with the quinsy, and he had scarcely recovered from that when he had to stop practicing because of rheumatism in his hands and then, just as Nannerl was able to get out of bed, he felt so feverish he had to lie down, with nausea and diarrhea and cramps as violent as Nannerl's.

He lay in despair many weeks, unable to touch an instrument. He felt crushed by illnesses. His parents tried to cheer him up by making jokes about the frequency of his bowel movements, the nature of his diarrhea, but he couldn't laugh. He had a feeling of terror that he would never be free of pain or sickness. He was so weak it was humiliating.

The day he felt well enough to want to be on his feet, Papa sighed with relief and said to Mamma, "The last doctor said the children could have had *typhus abdominalis,* and he might have been right." Papa was proud of his knowledge of Latin, but Wolfgang was ashamed of his body. When he tried to stand, he could not. There was no sensation in his feet or toes. It made him feel guilty, although he didn't know why. And not until he was able to walk a week later were Papa and Mamma able to sleep soundly.

At the festivities celebrating the Prince of Orange's installation as ruler of the Dutch Republic, Wolfgang and Leopold played six sonatas for harpsichord and violin, which the boy had composed and dedicated to the Princess Caroline. The Prince gave them fifty gulden, and then after nearly a year in Holland, they went to Paris. Before they left, Leopold – worried that there had not been any further word about Schrattenbach's reactions to the prolonging of his leave of absence – sent the Princess Caroline's sonatas to His Grace with Wolfgang's humble compliments.

Leopold was gratified by the warmth of Grimm's greeting. His friend introduced him again as maître de chapelle to the Archbishop of Salzburg; he arranged for more concerts with the Prince de Conti; and he wrote an eulogistic article about the Mozarts in the *Correspondance littéraire,* where he stressed Wolfgang's developing virtuosity as a composer. It was just what Leopold would have written, and he admired Grimm's good taste.

But after two months in the French capital, Leopold realized there was no permanence here either. Prince de Conti fell ill and canceled all his entertainments. The nobility who had patronized them before now were interested in newer things. Louis XV, with the death of Pompadour, was involved in the search for a new mistress and was even less concerned with music. So once again, when expenses exceeded income, Leopold prepared to move on. There had been a brief thank-you note from Count Arco on behalf of the Archbishop for "the Dutch sonatas", but nothing else.

Monsieur Grimm and Madame d'Epinay came to bid them farewell, and suggested that since Switzerland could be on their way home it might be useful if the children played for their dear and great friend, Voltaire, who was living in Ferny, near Geneva. Leopold thought the writer a godless rascal, but he appreciated his influence as a patron. When he exclaimed, "That is a fine idea!" Madame d'Epinay became enthusiastic.

She said, "I will write him myself."

Grimm said, "Voltaire likes her because she doesn't gush over him."

She said, "He is curious about phenomena of nature like Wolfgang."

Grimm added, "Leopold, I hope you are not pushing the boy too hard. He looks quite frail."

"He had typhoid in Holland. But once we get home, he will do nothing but rest. There will be no more traveling. At least for a while."

"He has such natural wit and charm, it would be unfortunate if it were spoiled by too much precocity."

"I agree." Leopold, to show his appreciation for what Grimm had done for them, gave him an autographed copy of the Dutch publication of his *Violin School*, which had appeared during his stay in Holland, and said proudly, "The Prince of Orange has an autographed copy."

"*Merci! Merci!*" said Grimm. "And good luck with Monsieur Voltaire."

After a month in Dijon and Lyons because of concert engagements, the family hurried on to Geneva. Wolfgang was surprised that Papa was upset by a letter awaiting him in Geneva from Madame d'Epinay, informing him that Voltaire was unable to hear the children because of illness. He knew how that felt. And he was not impressed by Voltaire's fame; he had played for many famous people, one more or less certainly did not matter.

Madame d'Epinay, to show her own sincerity, had enclosed a copy of Voltaire's answer and an angry Papa was reading it contemptuously now. "Your little Mazar, Madame, chose, I am sorry to say, an unfortunate moment to bring harmony into my temple of Discord. You know that I live two leagues from Geneva; I rarely go out. And now Mme Denis is ill; I have been bedridden for weeks, and you want me to see your young harpsichord player. Really, my dear, you ask too much. I am not even convalescing."

Papa swore, "The godless dog! And his wicked whores! They do say he is a hypochondriac. But we could go to Italy. It's very close."

Wolfgang wanted to go to Italy, the most musical country in the world, but some other time, when he wasn't so tired. Yet if he objected to Papa's order, Papa would be even angrier than before.

Mamma understood, saying, "We cannot stretch out our tour much longer. The children are exhausted. One more serious illness could be the last."

Wolfgang could tell from Papa's somber reaction that he agreed with her, but that he couldn't say so. Instead, he declared, "I know the condition of the children better than anyone." When Papa decided to continue on through Switzerland and into Germany, he said it was because at this time of the year the weather was healthier than in Italy.

But Wolfgang wondered whether Papa really wanted to go home, for he stopped at every Swiss and German city where a concert could be aranged, and it was several months before they neared Salzburg.

Then, at Munich, just a short journey from home, they paused again.

They were still there a week later. As if, thought Wolfgang, Papa couldn't take the final step back to Salzburg. Mamma begged him to go, and he sat at a desk examining his travel record. Such drudgery — how could Papa endure it? Yet he was so proud of their travels he kept a record of everywhere they had been, everyone they had played for, all the money that had been earned, and all the music that had been composed.

Papa proclaimed, "Do you realize that since we left London we have played at Dunkerque, Lille, Ghent, Antwerp, Rotterdam, The Hague, Amsterdam, Utrecht, Paris, Dijon, Lyons, Geneva, Lausanne, Berne, Zurich, Winterhur, Schaffhausen, Donaueschingen, Dillingen, and now Munich! That we have. . . ."

Mamma interrupted, "Do you think the Archbishop will be impressed?"

"Don't be sarcastic. Look how much we have earned. How much Wolfgang has composed. Thirty pieces, including symphonies and operatic arias."

"How much have we earned?"

"Enough to live on if the Archbishop should dismiss me."

"Enough for the rest of our lives?"

There was no answer, and suddenly Wolfgang blurted out, "I will play wherever you want me to, Papa. And as much as you want."

"Of course!" Papa gulped to hide his emotion. "We will all work hard."

"But couldn't we go home now? Please?"

Hours later that question still hovered in the air. Leopold re-read his records to reassure himself, but he couldn't forget the entreaty in his son's voice. Yet now that he had risked so much by staying away over three years, he was full of anxiety. But the thought of being treated again like an obscure Vice-Kapellmeister, after mingling with the greatest lords, was too much to endure. In his desperation he wrote Hagenauer: "The plans I have made for my children are my chief concern. God has given them such genius, dear friend, that if I fail them, I fail Him. Every moment that I lose is lost forever, and if I formerly knew how valuable time is for youth, I know it more now. You are aware that my children are used to work. They know that it requires an iron will. But who knows what sort of reception we shall get in Salzburg? Perhaps such a one that we shall be glad to pack up our knapsacks and set off again. I am depending on your wisdom and good heart."

Hagenauer answered promptly: "You still have good friends in Salzburg. Come home, Leopold, and let time take care of everything else."

As they sighted the Unsterberg and Mamma and Nannerl kissed each other with joy, Wolfgang realized why Papa had hesitated to return home. Papa would no longer be the master, make the decisions, and someone else would rule. Wolfgang felt sorry for Papa. But he was proud that he was almost eleven, although Papa kept saying he was nine, yet Papa could count so well.

PART FOUR

=

The Years of
Growing Up

TWENTY-ONE

Was he still Vice-Kapellmeister? This question continued to tantalize Leopold in Salzburg. Part of him feared that he was, and thus, he would be forced to remain in this provincial town; part of him feared that he wasn't, and so, he would have to depend on the uncertainty of public concerts.

Whoever he asked had no answers. He went to the Court Pay Office and there was no money for him. He reported to Kapellmeister Lolli, rehearsing the Kapelle for a dinner concert with his usual bravura gestures, and Lolli didn't bother to greet him or to halt the rehearsal but flung over his shoulder, "Michael Haydn is handling your duties, speak to him."

Haydn said, "I don't need any help," and went on teaching the violin to a group of youngsters, mumbling, "Count Arco gave me these duties."

Count Arco was attending His Grace, who was at his hunting lodge in the mountains. No one knew when they were returning, or seemed to care.

At the welcome-home party at 9 Getreidegasse that Hagenauer gave for the Mozarts, no one wanted to talk about anything but the travels.

Hagenauer asked, "Leopold, was Madame Pompadour really beautiful?"

"Handsome, not beautiful. She reminded me of the Empress."

Hagenauer looked shocked but Leopold smiled at his friend's naïveté.

Barisani asked, "Do the English really sing in their ugly language?"

"In London all opera is sung in Italian."

Wenzel wanted to know, "Did Rameau and Bach really favor the boy?"

146

"Manzuoli, too. When he left for Italy, he invited us to visit him."

"And the presents." Everybody wanted to know about them. "Were they really from Louis XV and the Hanoverian King, George III?"

Leopold proudly brought forth the gold snuff box from the French King and said, "The English give their presents in cash." Then he had Nannerl and Wolfgang march into Hagenauer's living room wearing the most splendid gifts, while he itemized, "A dozen gold watches, two dozen snuff boxes, some of them inlaid with gold and silver, ivory and pearl earrings, four gold rings, a traveling silver writing case with silver pens for Wolfgang to compose with, two jeweled swords, Dutch lace, English hats, Flemish cloaks, French capes, and a toothpick box of solid gold."

As Leopold paused for these marvels to impress his attentive audience, Bullinger said, "These presents must be worth thousands of gulden."

"Louis XV's steward informed me that should I ever have to sell his gold snuff box, the King will buy it back for hundreds of gulden."

Bullinger admired this snuff box, as everybody else had, then said, "You must have made ten thousand gulden on the tour."

Leopold, hitherto cheerful, suddenly was suspicious and melancholy. "Think of the fortune I had to spend keeping up with the nobility. And the expense of the concerts was fantastic. I am not even sure we earned more than I spent."

Schachtner was surprised that Wolfgang had grown hardly at all despite the three and a half years away. As Leopold enumerated some of the great lords the children had played for, Schachtner focused on the children. Nannerl looked as proud as her father, but Wolfgang was bored with the presents. If anything, thought Schachtner, the boy's features were more delicate than before, and the ravages of his illnesses were evident in his pallor and thinness. Yet Wolfgang greeted him with a passionate embrace and was animated when he suggested, "You must show me your new sonatas."

Wolfgang said, "You will like the variations I added."

Before he could get them, Anna Maria cut in. Leading Nannerl by the hand, she said, "Andreas, hasn't she grown?"

"She has become so pretty and tall."

Nannerl blushed and showed him her Dutch lace.

"Beautiful," said Schachtner. "You are a lucky girl."

Anna Maria sent Nannerl and Wolfgang over to the other guests so she could ask, "Is His Grace angry at Leopold?"

"Why should he be angry?"

"Now, Andreas, you know the leave of absence was only for a year."

"I am sure that Leopold was aware of all the rules."

"You are not answering my question!"

"Next time, Anna Maria, heed my advice before, not after."

"You know how strong-willed Leopold is."

As if Leopold had heard himself mentioned, he came over but before he could speak Schachtner asked, "Have you forsaken traveling for good?"

"I think that any sensible musician would be foolish to do that."

"Yet you expect to return as if you have never been away."

"Look how I spread the musical reputation of Salzburg."

"At a price. Nannerl and Wolfgang are very thin and pale."

"So many illnesses," sighed Anna Maria. "But now, they will rest."

"Leopold, how much money did you make? After all your expenses?"

"Why?" Leopold was taken aback by his friend's inquisitiveness.

"So I can judge whether it was worth the risk."

Leopold motioned for quiet, for Count Arco was approaching. The court chamberlain had aged, Leopold noticed; his face had become long and hard.

Without any preliminaries Count Arco stated, "His Grace, Mozart, would like your son to compose the music for the first act of the dramatic oratorio, *The Obligation of the First and Foremost Commandment*. Haydn and Adlgasser are composing the second and third acts. And the child will compose this in the privacy of the Residenz, to make sure that this composition is his own creation."

"Does His Grace doubt that Wolfgang composed the sonatas I sent him?"

His Grace did, thought Count Arco. So the Archbishop was having the child locked up in the Residenz to be sure that no one else would compose the music. "The sonatas were skilful for an eleven-year-old."

"Wolfgang was nine when he composed the French and English ones."

"All the more reason he should not need any help now."

Leopold was silent; Count Arco's tone was too firm to be disputed.

A sad smile appeared on the court chamberlain's face as he said, "Our family are grateful for your feelings about our daughter."

"We were blessed by her friendship," said Leopold. "It was a great loss to all of us, but particularly for Wolfgang, for she was very fond of him."

"She wrote us how appealing he was."

"Countess van Eyck was a great lady. It was an honor to know her."

Other people gathered around them and the Count grew official again. "The oratorio is to celebrate the anniversary of His Grace's consecration, and is to be ready in a month. He expects it to be worthy of the occasion."

"A month from now?" Leopold laughed. "That is plenty of time, sir."

Count Arco said sternly, "I hope your son is a composer. Our Grace will be most unhappy if he has been deceived."

What was Papa worried about? He wasn't. He had passed the same kind of test for Prince de Conti when he had known far less. Wolfgang knew that Papa's prestige and position depended on his composition – it was clear without being said – but Papa shouldn't be nervous, Papa should have more faith in him. The story of the old mystery play was dull, but the score should be simple to compose. He had heard enough oratorios to recall how the music should go. And once he heard a piece of music it was easy to follow its form. But when the door of the anteroom, where he was to compose, closed on him, with only a footman to attend to his wants, Papa looked as if he were being thrown into a prison.

Wolfgang was dismayed by the inadequacies of the anteroom. It had a desk for him to compose on, and pictures of the History of the Flood, but the harpsichord was ordinary, and the atmosphere was oppressive.

Bored with the tedium of the oratorio, he worked on an aria for a male soprano. He grew much more interested in the aria and took it to bed with him, feeling close to it, the only thing he felt close to in the Residenz.

When Count Arco stopped in and asked him how he was progressing, he shrugged. If they didn't trust him, he didn't trust them.

After a few days he asked the footman to open the window. No one else had visited him except Count Arco, who had gotten into the habit of stopping in daily, and Wolfgang hated the solitude. It made him feel melancholy, a mood that suffocated his ideas. But now, the windows open, with Count Arco's permission, he could hear the bells, the voices of the servants taking water from the fountain, the clatter of horses on the cobbled streets. Stimulated by these familiar things, he could hear music in his head. He gave his act of the oratorio Eberlin's content and Handel's form. That should please His Grace. Handel's oratorios were the best he had heard, but His Grace preferred Eberlin's. To make sure his music was singable, he sang it to himself. He still disliked his voice – it was thin and shrill – but he was singing correctly, for he could tell that what he had composed fitted the cathedral choir, who would be singing the oratorio.

Count Arco was surprised that Wolfgang finished the first act in two weeks. He had not thought that the child would be so fast. The music sheets were in a childish, blotted hand, and then Count Arco was sure it was unplayable. He gave it to Lolli to prove this, but Lolli reluctantly said this act was playable. He showed it to Haydn, who had not finished his act, and Haydn said, "It is not original. It is full of Eberlin."

"But can it be performed?"

"Probably. But he has much to learn."

"Could you do better when you were Wolfgang's age?" Count Arco had no intention of taking sides, but the child was remarkable.

"That is not the point."

"For the child it is."

After the performance of the oratorio His Grace said to Leopold, "I'm glad your son lived up to the reports we received about him from abroad."

"Thank you, sir. We hoped and prayed that you would be pleased."

"But next time you extend a leave of absence without our permission, I will not be so generous."

"I am your humble servant, Your Grace."

Schrattenbach was amused. Did the musician think he was this easily deceived? For an instant, the Archbishop wanted Mozart to know he saw through his hypocritical obedience; then he thought, no, he would be placing himself on the same level as this servant and that would be demeaning.

"We are greatly honored, sir, that we have had the privilege of participating in your anniversary."

"As honored as when your children played for Louis XV? George III?"

"More so, Your Grace. Wherever we go, we hope our playing is merely an extension of your beneficence and blessing."

Yet while the Archbishop was smiling, Leopold saw only teeth.

After Schrattenbach was gone and Count Arco was alone, Leopold asked the court chamberlain, "What about my duties, sir?"

"What about them? Isn't there enough for you to do?"

"Yes, yes, of course." To do what? Leopold wondered.

"I hope you have still retained your skill on the violin. His Grace needs performers and teachers, not prodigies." When he saw that the musician looked properly abashed, he became friendly. "Leopold, sometimes you approach matters too intensely. You have unusual children, but then I have unusual children, too, and one of them is dead. Be grateful that you are more fortunate."

"I am, sir. But you do understand why my children deserve the opportunity of playing for the Empress. For Louis XV? George III?"

"Are you thinking of another tour already?" Count Arco was surprised.

"Oh, no! Not now! But I wondered how His Grace would feel should, say a year from now, the Empress wanted to hear the children or requested a composition from the boy. It would be a great honor for Salzburg."

"Another leave of absence might be arranged. Without pay. But remember, it must always be understood that you are in His Grace's service."

"Without pay?"

"That will resume whenever you resume your duties."

"As Vice-Kapellmeister?"

"Should we dismiss Lolli, who is always at the Archbishop's call?"

Leopold was silent. He felt an extreme bitterness. Whatever happened, they would always have an excuse to keep him from the first position.

"I should think that you would be more interested in the opportunities here. You do have good friends in Salzburg."

"Count Arco, I do appreciate all that you have done. Thank you."

"You do appreciate it, Leopold?"

"Of course. Wolfgang told me how you stopped in to see him every day."

"He is a fine boy. Sweet and likable, but a little stubborn, like his father. And you must be careful how you put him in competition with other composers. Once he is a real threat, they will resent him even more because he is a child." Count Arco handed Leopold a gold medal for Wolfgang, the Archbishop's gift for the first act of the oratorio.

Leopold was disappointed that the gold in the medal was worth only twelve ducats, but Anna Maria thought it was a handsome present and Nannerl wished she could wear it instead of Wolfgang, who was more interested in doing a new composition for His Grace.

TWENTY-TWO

At His Grace's request Wolfgang wrote an Easter cantata, and it was approved. He composed two symphonies for Prince von Furstenberg and he was paid for them. He transposed four sonatas of Schobert and Bach into harpsichord concertos, and played them for the Archbishop, who said they were worthy of Haydn. But what excited him was the invitation that came from Maria Theresa the following year to write music for the wedding of her daughter, Maria Josepha, to King Ferdinand of Naples. He felt rested, healthy, eager for a change. He was prepared to compose anything that the Empress desired, but he hoped it would be an opera.

Papa's leave of absence was granted on the terms stated by Count Arco. The whole family was excited by the journey. They left for Vienna with great expectations. But before they could appear at court, so Wolfgang could be told what to compose for the royal wedding, a smallpox epidemic swept through the city.

A week after they arrived there was other ominous news. They were staying in the house of a goldsmith and Papa assembled the family in their small living room to inform them, "The Archduchess Maria Josepha has smallpox. All arrangements for her wedding have been postponed."

"What should we do?" Mamma asked.

"What can we do!" Papa said angrily. "Wait, like everyone else!"

Soon afterward the Archduchess died, and Papa stated, "Now no one will want to hear the children, they are afraid of the pox."

Mamma said, "Shouldn't they be? I hear that it is spreading."

"When there is poor sewage there are cases, but there is no epidemic."

"You could be wrong!" she exclaimed in her fear.

"I'm not wrong. You are just being nervous."

The next day she told him, "The oldest son of our landlord is ill, and it must be smallpox, for no one can see him."

He didn't reply, worried about other things.

Wolfgang didn't feel well himself. His head had become hot, yet his hands were like ice. But if he mentioned these symptoms they would leave Vienna, and he didn't want to do that. And the idea of being ill again, after all his illnesses on the tour, was too terrible to think about. He started to practice on his portable clavichord, although his hands were colder and his head had grown hotter. But he had played only a few chords, and then with difficulty because of his hands, when the landlord asked him to halt, saying that his two youngest children were ill also and needed quiet. He told this to Papa, who tried to see these children to learn what was wrong with them, but no one was being allowed to visit them.

Leopold called on everyone he knew and the answer was the same: *Vienna was besieged by the pox and children were the most infected. Fifty out of every hundred children living in Vienna had it. And of those afflicted half were dying, and of those surviving, half were being pock-marked for life.*

When Leopold learned that eruptions had appeared on the skin of his landlord's children, he fled from the house. But wherever they went in Vienna, there was smallpox. Then Wolfgang felt so miserable, he had to confess this to him. In desperation Leopold took the family to Brunn, ninety miles from Vienna. But smallpox broke out there, too. So they hurried to Olmutz, where Leopold knew some nobles, and which should be safe.

None of the nobles would see the Mozarts, afraid of catching the pox. All the good rooms in the better inns were occupied with well-to-do refugees from Vienna. The only shelter available was one dreary room in the run-down Black Eagle Inn. But there was nowhere else to go. Eruptions had developed on Wolfgang's face, and he was having difficulty recognizing them.

Leopold put his son to bed, and then, leaving him in the panic-stricken care of Anna Maria and Nannerl, hurried out to find a doctor. But no doctors were available. The smallpox had spread to Olmutz and all the doctors were busy. When Leopold returned to the Black Eagle Inn alone, he was more frightened than he had ever been. In the time that had passed Wolfgang's face had swollen and there were red spots everywhere.

The child wondered if Papa knew how dreadful he felt. He couldn't see. He was going blind. He would never be able to compose again. He had failed, the greatest love of his life was vanishing in darkness.

153

It was always night now and in the blackness the voices he heard howled. These inhuman harpies were trying to make hearing the ugliest of things.

Afterwards, Papa told him the only thing that had saved him was the care of Count Podstatsky, Dean of the Olmutz cathedral, who, with unusual kindness, had taken the whole family into his own quarters despite the risk, had his own doctor attend him, and had given them every possible service. But Wolfgang knew it was something else. At the moment the noise in his head had become unbearable, he had forced himself to recreate the music he loved best, a harpsichord sonata of Johann Christian's, and gradually the din had ceased before the deceptively simple sonata, a marvel of elegant, pleasing melody, and his pain had eased. As long as he could hear such harmonies, nothing hurried, nothing slack, every note in the right place, he could endure the darkness. At least, not everything was lost.

Just as Leopold and Anna Maria feared that Wolfgang was permanently blind – he had been unable to see for nine days – he recognized them.

He wanted to know where they were and how long they had been here, and when Papa told him he did not answer, stunned by the length of his illness.

Leopold assured him, "You should have no pock-marks. You have some red spots, but they are disappearing already."

"I don't feel hot any more."

"Oh, you are getting better now."

"Was I that sick, Papa?"

"You frightened us to death." Leopold smiled at his own joke. It was the first time he had smiled since the child had fallen ill. "But we will have you playing and composing soon again."

"As long as I can see."

"Of course you can see!"

Wolfgang didn't believe him, for he asked for the score of the harpsichord sonata he had heard at his darkest moment, and examined it carefully. He had remembered it correctly, yet that was not what reassured him – he had expected that – but that he could read the notes. Papa had not lied to him. He really could see. Then he fell into a sound, nourishing slumber.

Leopold and Anna Maria hugged each other as if they would never let go. Each had the same prayer: that this would be the last illness.

TWENTY-THREE

Several months later the postponed audience at court occurred. And Leopold was encouraged when the new Emperor, Joseph II, came out of his mother's apartments at Schönbrunn and escorted the Mozarts in to her.

Maria Theresa was sympathetic about Wolfgang's illness and expressed gratification that he had recovered fully. But when Leopold spoke of his sadness over the death of her daughter, her face darkened and there were tears in her eyes. Smallpox had been a scourge. She had lost three children, two daughters-in-law, and an uncle to this terrible disease. Yet the Empress, who had aged visibly, stiffened as Leopold spoke of how so many people were terrified of smallpox, and said, "It is foolish to fear the pox. It will come or not, whatever one does."

"Yes, Your Majesty," said Leopold. "We await your pleasure."

"I hear your son is a composer now."

"Many Kapellmeisters do not know what this child knows."

Maria Theresa looked skeptical, but all she said was, "Since the death of my husband, my son arranges all musical matters."

Leopold wondered how much power her son had assumed. It was one thing, he thought, to be elected King of the Romans and to be crowned Emperor of Germany, but it was far more difficult to be the final authority while an autocrat like his mother lived. He had heard that Maria Theresa was still grief-stricken over the death of her husband, yet she continued to take a dominant interest in affairs of state. In the act of appointing her son co-regent she had exhibited and kept much of her power. Even now, as she advocated austerity throughout the Empire, she was still enlarging and beautifying Schönbrunn with a lavish zeal. Then, she had never been interested in opera. Her son, however, might be different, reflected Leopold. He glanced at the new Emperor, who looked very young, although Joseph was twenty-seven, and waited for him to speak.

The Emperor said, "Herr Mozart, your son's compositions have caused many to wonder if he is really the one who created such pieces."

"Test him, Your Highness!" Leopold blurted out. "Please, sir!"

"With a sonata? A serenade? That would not be any great feat."

"What about an opera, sir?"

Joseph was startled. "At his age?"

"He will be twelve in a week, Your Highness. On the 27th."

In a sense, thought the Emperor, this musician was throwing down the gauntlet. For a moment he was irritated, resenting his presumption. But he was also a rationalist, a subscriber to the *Correspondance littéraire,* and Grimm, not one to exaggerate, had lauded the boy. And it could be amusing to see this child in competition with his elders. It could cause a stir. He, Joseph II, could become the talk of enlightened Europe.

"Your Majesty, there is an opera theater available."

"The one that I leased to Count Affligio?"

"Yes, sir," said Leopold, wondering why he always had to tell people, even Emperors, what to do. "One word from you and I am sure that the impresario would be happy to have an opera from Wolfgang Mozart."

Joseph glanced over to his mother but she wasn't saying a word. He didn't really control Affligio – he had leased the royal theater to this impresario because his mother had lost so much money with it – but surely Affligio would listen to him. And his mother was glad to see the Mozarts.

Leopold said, "Think of the excitement, sir, when one evening we witness a Gluck, fifty-four and world famous, conducting his opera, and the next evening a boy of twelve competes with him as an equal."

But how much would it cost? Suddenly Joseph felt cautious, although he would not be producing the opera. He said, "I will think it over."

"One word from you, sir, and it will be an accomplished fact."

The musician was persistent. Joseph frowned. Yet the idea was intriguing. If Affligio did the boy's opera, he would not be blamed if it failed. Yet if it succeeded, he would be acclaimed for his taste. He said, "I will arrange for you and your son to meet Count Affligio."

Leopold was surprised that the impresario's rooms on the Kohlmarkt were as luxurious as Schönbrunn. He did not think that the Count was a nobleman, despite his title. His showy clothes were too obvious in their effort to capture attention. But Affligio was a handsome man, with sharp features, an attractive dark skin, and piercing black eyes. The conversation was in Italian and Leopold sensed that the impresario was testing them to see how well they understood the language.

He said, "I control the opera in Vienna. We must be clear about that."

"Yes, Signore," said Leopold. "We know."

"The Emperor says your son should compose an opera, but he is only twelve. How can I trust him to succeed?"

Wolfgang said in fluent Italian like Papa, "I've written a number of arias. For the King of England, the Empress, and the Emperor Joseph II."

"His Majesty fancies himself musical. However, we will see." He ignored Wolfgang as he addressed Leopold, "I have a libretto by Marco Coltellini, our new Vienna court poet, which I would like put to music. *La Finta Semplice*. Do you know it, Mozart?"

"The Pretended Simpleton," Leopold translated for Wolfgang, but the latter understood the Italian and wondered why Papa went to the trouble. "Signore, isn't it taken from a play by Goldini?"

Affligio frowned. "You have been misinformed. I want it to be in the style of Piccini's *Buona Figliuola*, the most successful opera written."

"I heard it in Germany, when my son made his grand tour."

"In Germany?" Affligio sneered. "It is difficult enough to do Italian opera properly in Vienna, but at least, I have Italian singers." He handed Wolfgang the libretto to read while he settled on terms.

It was agreed that Wolfgang would receive one hundred ducats when he delivered the score, the music to be finished within the next three months, the opera to be performed as soon as was practical thereafter.

Papa seemed willing to agree to almost anything, thought Wolfgang, provided he was commissioned to compose the music. But *La Finta Semplice* was not much of a story, with its low comedy complications and the theme of how a clever woman, pretending to be a simpleton, maneuvred two shy bachelors, one of them her brother, into marrying the girls they loved. Yet before Wolfgang could raise any questions, Papa was thanking Affligio for his courtesy when the impresario had not been courteous at all, and saying, "Signore, I am sure you will share the sentiments of Maestro Manzuoli and Johann Christian Bach when the score is finished."

"Perhaps. Mozart, is your son a virgin?"

"Count Affligio, he is only twelve!" A shocked Leopold drew the impresario aside where they would not be overheard.

"When Manzuoli was only twelve, he was already a castrato. And you claim your son is precocious."

"Indeed. He knows more about music than many renowned composers."

"What about life? He will not be twelve very long. And if you want him to be an opera composer, he will have to write about love. There is nothing else in our theater. Is he old enough to penetrate a woman?"

Leopold didn't answer. He had thought about this often, and each time he had decided to allow nature to take its course, which, in his own mind, meant a putting off to some remote time. But how much did his son comprehend of boudoirs and liaisons?

Affligio said, "Mozart, I think you will be jealous of the first woman to have your son. You will feel cuckolded, very moral, and betrayed."

"I want him to have a happy marriage as I have had."

"You want him to marry his music, that it should be his mistress."

"Come, come, Signore, you are jesting."

"Not in the least. You speak of your son as a prodigy, but for me, *Don Juan* is the extraordinary one. Or doesn't he exist in your son's music?"

"Count, he really is twelve."

"His music is to be played for grown-ups, but he is to be regarded as a child, and so, as a marvel. Mozart, you are a clever man."

How clever, Leopold was not sure. Affligio was almost pleasant now, as if this was one trait he respected. But Leopold took Wolfgang by the hand as they left, holding him so firmly the child winced.

What had gotten into Papa, Wolfgang wondered. He had heard many operas. But Papa looked so anxious suddenly. Yet he had a theme for a soprano that should fit a flexible throat.

As they walked to their rooms, Papa cried out, "I am not sure we should have come here at this time. Vienna may have as many whores as Versailles."

"You don't like the impresario, Papa?"

"Do you?"

Wolfgang was surprised that Papa had asked his opinion. Papa must be very upset. "He doesn't seem much interested in music. Is he a whore?"

"More like a pimp."

But Papa did not explain.

Instead, Papa said, "Some people say Affligio is a professional gambler, others say he is a professional seducer, but perhaps that is what an impresario has to be. Wolfgang?" Papa's seriousness increased.

"Yes?"

"Have you, eh . . ." Papa blushed, then coughed, but that didn't help.

Wolfgang was smiling.

"Do you like any girls?"

"Some."

"Much?" stressed Papa, concerned.

"How much?"

"Wolfgang, this is not a game!"

"As much as Louis XV liked Madame Pompadour?"

"What do you know about that?"

"What you told me."

"I said that she was a whore. That was all."

"And that they had sex together. And he preferred her to anyone else."

"I didn't tell you that. How much do you know?" Papa was alarmed.

"Everybody knows how babies are made. Except children."

"Have you, that is, tried to make babies?"

Wolfgang looked sadly at his father, as a pupil who knew more than his teacher. "You don't understand, Papa. I'm too young to make babies. But I know how."

Papa changed the subject. "We will show Affligio. You will finish the opera in less than three months." The busier Wolfgang was, the better.

All of Wolfgang went into composing. He slept regular hours, he ate simply, and he worked while Mamma watched him carefully to make sure that he did not exhaust himself. Mornings Papa gave him opera scores to study. Afternoons he wrote steadily. And evenings, when he was not tired, he discussed what he had done with Papa.

He was happiest while he was sketching out an aria. He felt the human voice was a wonderful musical instrument, and he sought to have his arias sweet and pleasing. He recalled the vocal music he liked best and some of Bach and Gluck went into his score. However, he tried to find his own melodies. It did not trouble him to use someone else's structure, but he wanted the melodic line to be his own. And his greatest gratification came when an aria was natural and agreeable to his ear. Then his concentration grew intense and he wrote quickly. Often he would sit at the fine marble table that Papa had obtained for him to compose on, the sheets of the score scattered all around him, some on his knees, some in his hand, other pages on the table, able instantly to examine the whole so each part would fit, yet able also to focus on the individual part. And he could tell that Papa approved of what he was doing, for Papa seldom suggested changes.

Two months after Affligio had agreed to do *La Finta Semplice*, the score was completed: an introductory symphonic overture, three acts, twenty-six arias, many recitatives, a total of five hundred and fifty-eight pages.

When it was submitted to Affligio he said he would perform it as soon as possible, although he did not pay the hundred ducats as agreed.

At the first rehearsal Leopold sat with Wolfgang, who had come in eager anticipation to hear his music sung and prepared to make the usual alterations to fit the eccentricities of the singers. And from the moment the singers began, Leopold was aware that their parts had not been studied properly, that none of the singers had rehearsed in advance at the harpsichord as they should have, that not one duet or finale had been practiced together, yet this rehearsal was being given with the complete orchestra. He was certain this was being done to cheapen the music. He could hardly recognize a note. The score sounded confused, strident. Some of the singers were on the verge of laughter. What he had expected to be the proudest day of his life became a purgatory.

Yet Leopold sought to be composed when the impresario approached him after the rehearsal. Affligio smiled broadly as he stated, "The music is uneven, and it is pitched too high. The singers say that if your boy will make some alterations they will be able to sing it."

The alterations were made. And Wolfgang, also at Affligio's request, composed two new arias which were inserted into the first act. But when it came time to rehearse again, Affligio said, "We will have to postpone rehearsals, this music is still too high and the singers cannot sing it."

"I can sing it," Wolfgang blurted out, "and I haven't much of a voice, Signore." Before the impresario could halt him, he sang the first aria. His voice was thin but the melody was sweet and pleasing.

Affligio said, "Mozart, your boy fancies himself a castrato."

"What about the opera?" Leopold was determined not to be diverted.

Affligio shrugged. "I congratulate you."

Leopold wondered if he had been mistaken about the impresario after all.

"You said the boy is an opera composer, and he is."

"So, Signore?"

"Have him revise the two new arias and perhaps we can have the opera done for the Emperor when he returns from Hungary next month."

"Thank you."

"But I must tell you, Mozart, that many people are saying that a large portion of the music has been written by you." Before Leopold could protest against this calumny, Affligio added, "And the music is still too high, too German," and he had Leopold and Wolfgang ushered out.

TWENTY-FOUR

When Leopold heard that Affligio was giving out roles for *Buona Figliuola* by Piccinni, that rumors were being spread throughout Vienna that *La Finta Semplice* by Mozart could not be performed because the singers could not sing it, that the phrasing was too German, that the boy did not understand how to use the Italian language, and had no sense of melody or form, Leopold knew that something had to be done. He wanted to appeal to the Emperor but Joseph was still in Hungary; he thought of approaching Maria Theresa and he was warned that she would regard criticism of Affligio as criticism of her son, and thus, of herself.

So he arranged for a musical evening to disprove the slanders, to be given in the home of Baron Gottfried van Swieten, a new and enthusiastic supporter of Wolfgang. Leopold felt that everyone in Vienna would accept an invitation from this family. Gottfried's father, Gerhard van Swieten, had agreed to attend, and this famous physician was loved by Maria Theresa, as much as she could love anyone who was not part of her family, and she listened to him with a respect she seldom gave to anyone.

Wolfgang, who had been stunned by Affligio's behavior, revived when he learned that the concert was to take place at Gottfried van Swieten's. He liked the young Baron, who was in his early thirties, with a large, strong head like his father, and a vigor that conveyed warmth as well as strength. He also respected the young Baron's passion for music. The latter had studied the harpsichord and violin, musical history and theory, and had composed sonatas and songs. After a few evenings together Wolfgang and van Swieten had developed the habit of answering each other in different languages, for both of them could speak Italian, French, and some Latin and English in addition to German, and both loved to talk in numbers and riddles. One moment they were seriously discussing Telemann, who had just died; the next they were joking about prima donnas who sounded like sows and primo uomo castrati who belched every time they hit a high note and conductors who led operas as if they were half asleep.

Leopold was surprised that his son did not ask who else would be there.

"Why should I ask?" said Wolfgang. "It will make no difference Empress. If anyone could influence Affligio, Leopold told himself, the chancellor could.

Then Prince Dmitri, as he preferred to be addressed, enlightened and aristocratic in the same breath, was such a skillful diplomat that he was an intimate friend of Voltaire and Maria Theresa, although they despised each other, and had retained the friendship of both. A good friend, too, of the Mozarts, felt Leopold, for the Prince had paid the children well for playing for him and had invited them to visit Russia. Even now, Prince Dmitri was approaching him directly, taking a reluctant Prince Kaunitz with him and saying, "Herr Mozart, I am proud that I advised you to take your children to Paris. When will you enrich Russia with their playing?"

Leopold, who had been considering this invitation and who felt in how I play." But he had a secret wish that Affligio would be present. Then he would show this belcher who had composed *La Finta Semplice*.

At the concert the van Swietens insisted that the Mozarts stand by their side in the receiving line to greet the distinguished guests.

An auspicious omen, Leopold decided, and a generous gesture. His optimism increased as he saw Prince Kaunitz, the chancellor, who had been elevated from Count to Prince by the Empress because of his services to her, enter with Prince Dmitri Galitsin, the Russian Ambassador to the court of Vienna. At fifty-eight Prince Kaunitz was a tall, slender autocrat, with a long face, cold pale blue eyes, and was the most powerful person in the Empire after the brave because of the boldness that it took, said, "Sir, we would leave tomorrow if not for the fact that as patriotic Germans, we have a duty to our fatherland."

"When that duty is completed, you must honor Russia with your music."

"We will be honored, Your Excellency," said Leopold, bowing low.

Prince Kaunitz stared intently at Wolfgang, who was talking animatedly with the van Swietens, and said, "I've been told your boy had smallpox."

"Not any more," Leopold assured the chancellor, who was known to fear every draft and contagion, and who had cancelled two previous meetings with the Mozarts because of Wolfgang's illness. "Your

Excellency, the red spots only come out in cold weather." And it was almost summer now, he thought, and very warm, and the chancellor should know that.

Nonetheless, Prince Kaunitz peered at Wolfgang to make sure *he saw no red spots* and only came closer when Prince Dmitri took the child's hand to congratulate him on the completion of the opera, and said, "Kaunitz, the child has a great gift. If I were a German, I would treasure it."

"Oh, we do!" said Prince Kaunitz, "but there are other considerations."

"What considerations?" asked Prince Dmitri.

"We have just gone through a costly war."

"That ended five years ago."

"We are still in debt from it. But I have great regard for the boy's gifts," Prince Kaunitz said hurriedly, to show that he had taste too.

He was joined by the Duke of Braganza, who loved music and who had a pension of a hundred thousand ducats to indulge his love. The Duke agreed with Prince Kaunitz and said, "Herr Mozart, I understand your boy has some of Gluck in his opera. Oh, I mean in the best sense," he added, when he saw Leopold frown. The Duke of Braganza was one of Gluck's foremost patrons, but he had paid the Mozarts to play for him, too. "It is natural for a composer so young to be influenced a little."

Leopold did not reply, for many guests were being received now: Count Dietrichstein, who was the Emperor's most trusted advisor; Fraulein von Guttenberg, who was observing everything for the Empress, and who made sure she was near Count Dietrichstein. As Leopold wondered who was watching who, he bowed to the Countess Thun, Count Pálffy, Father Ignaz Parhamer, who was Father Confessor to the Emperor and a favorite of the Empress, and Doctor Franz Anton Mesmer, a protégé of Doctor van Swieten, and a musical patron and an authority on the use of magnetism in medicine.

The guests became interesting to Wolfgang when he saw court composer Adolph Hasse and court poet Pietro Metastasio arguing with another court composer, Giuseppe Bonno. He wanted to play for these men. Papa said that they knew as much about opera as anyone in Vienna, that Hasse was the one German opera composer who was revered in Italy, and that Metastasio was the finest librettist in the world. But before he could ask any questions of these artists, Prince Kaunitz signaled that the musical test should begin.

Leopold said, "Signor Metastasio, Doctor van Swieten has been kind enough to bring a volume of your librettos from the court library, none of which my son has seen. My son would appreciate if you choose one of your arias, any will do, and he will compose original music for it."

As the stately seventy-year-old court poet laboriously searched for an aria that had not been set to music, Wolfgang felt as if Papa was playing the magician when there was no magic to it. He had a melody in his mind, one that should fit whatever the poet suggested.

"Here, child!" Metastasio was pleased. The lyric he had found would require the most careful phrasing.

Wolfgang stared at it a moment, then wrote the music for the aria, and sang it as he accompanied himself on the harpsichord.

There was silence as he finished, and sudden applause. Wolfgang, without hesitation, played his opera. Papa had told him to do just the first act, that the aristocrats would not have patience for any more, but everyone, even Prince Kaunitz, was listening intently. He ended with a tender aria, which concluded the first act, and sat perfectly still.

Everyone crowded around him and Prince Kaunitz declared, "Quite unusual, I would never have believed it if I hadn't witnessed it myself."

Leopold said, "Is there any doubt, Your Excellency, that he composed the music for *La Finta Semplice* himself?"

"Indeed!" exclaimed Prince Kaunitz. "What do you think, Hasse?"

The elderly Hasse bent forward to examine the music Wolfgang had composed for the Metastasio lyric. At sixty-nine he had composed so many operas to Metastasio librettos he had lost count.

Leopold could hardly bear the waiting. At this instant he hated Hasse for having this power over him.

Hasse said slowly, "The aria is composed with exactness."

Leopold said impatiently, "And it is his own, isn't it?"

"Herr Mozart, is that what worries you?"

"Not me, sir. But Affligio."

"One must not despair if a first opera has difficulties."

Wolfgang blurted out, "But Herr Hasse, why should my opera have difficulties if it is good?"

Leopold started to apologize for his son and Hasse halted him, saying, "It is to be expected. He is a child."

"I am twelve and a half," said Wolfgang. "And it is my opera."

"Is it?" asked Prince Kaunitz.

Wolfgang did not answer now, for Papa was glaring at him to be quiet. But it was difficult to understand. He had written the music with love, yet they had not listened with love. There was nothing to be ashamed of. They were the ones who were inadequate. Their love was at fault, not his.

Countess Thun said suddenly, "If I had written an opera as well as Wolfgang has, I would defend it, too."

"But did he write it?" persisted Kaunitz. "Did he, Hasse?"

Hasse looked up from the score. What was the chancellor's hurry?

He was far from his decline, but he would reply when and how he pleased. Yet he was proud that he had no malice in his disposition, although he felt that Mozart was pushing his son too hard. He said, "Music is music."

"It is late." Prince Kaunitz prepared to depart.

Hasse was a jealous old fool, Leopold thought angrily, and this was his way of being competitive, of destroying Wolfgang.

Hasse said, "One can tell from the opera's style that the child composed it."

"Oh!" Prince Kaunitz paused at the door. "You are sure?"

"Of course, Your Excellency."

"Is it good?"

"He is a child. Remember, sir."

Leopold interrupted, "I appreciate your consideration, Herr Hasse, but Wolfgang is not like any other child."

"Granted. His melodies are often flowing and graceful, although not always new, and his orchestration is correct."

"And the music is singable and playable."

"Yes," said Hasse, but before Leopold could feel jubilant, Hasse added, "There is one difficulty. He composed some of the arias for a Manzuoli."

"His ideal," said Leopold.

"Fine, if a Manzuoli is singing. But for most singers, impossible. And that will make them hate your son, for they will never be able to sing like Manzuoli and his music will reveal that."

Wolfgang said, "Sir, the singers asked that the arias be bravura. But if you want them altered, I can do it. Now, if you like."

"No, no, no!" cried Hasse. That could take the rest of the evening.

"I don't mind," said Wolfgang. "It won't take long."

"Aren't you tired?"

"If you are kind enough to listen, I can be kind enough to please you."

Hasse smiled and took Wolfgang by the hand and sat beside him at the harpsichord and said, "This aria you composed this evening. You wrote it for a castrato, but could you place it for a bass?"

"I would be honored, sir."

No one moved. And when it was finished, Gottfried van Swieten, who had a good bass voice, sang it softly and caressingly.

Hasse said, "The boy is not a master yet, but for his age, extraordinary."

Prince Kaunitz said, "Thank you, Herr Hasse. You have been helpful."

Prince Dmitri said, "It is wicked to hinder this boy in any way."

Then, to Leopold, it seemed as if everyone was expressing

astonishment that anyone would want to prevent the performance of his son's opera.

Wolfgang noticed that Prince Kaunitz had said nothing about Affligio.

A little later the nobility left, but Wolfgang did not mind, for the musicians were staying.

Giuseppe Bonno said, "Herr Mozart, I've read your *Violin School* and in clarity and thoroughness it excels anything on this subject I've seen."

Leopold could have embraced this court composer, he was so moved.

Hasse nodded, "You have taught your son well."

Father Parhamer nodded and said, "The Empress has graciously consented to attend the solemn consecration of the church I am having built at the Orphange on the Rennweg. If little Wolfgang could compose a solemn High Mass for the occasion, it could be dedicated to the Orphanage."

As Leopold indicated how honored the Mozarts would be to comply with this request, Doctor Mesmer added, "And if young Mozart could compose an opera for a party I am giving in the autumn, I would be happy to commission it."

"Why not *La Finta Semplice?*" asked Leopold, suddenly suspicious.

"I have a large mansion, but it is not the Burgtheater," said Doctor Mesmer, "and it is not appropriate for an *opera buffa*. But if he could compose a short German *singspiel*, it could be a happy occasion."

"Yes, yes!" cried Leopold, feeling vindicated. "We are honored by both commissions. They will be ready for each occasion." He bowed low to Father Parhamer and Doctor Mesmer. Now Affligio must heed his complaints.

Affligio bowed even lower when Leopold asked him to resume rehearsals of *La Finta Semplice*, and said, "I would be delighted to, but Signorina Bernasconi and Signorina Baglioni are ill."

A week later Leopold heard that these singers had been rehearsing *Buona Figliuola* for days. He demanded of Affligio if this was true, and the impresario shrugged and said, "You know what rumors are like."

"Is it a rumor that you are not going to perform my son's opera?"

"You misunderstand. I am not against doing *La Finta Semplice*, but it is possible it might not please. I must consider my own interests, as you are. I am doing *Buona Figliuola* to protect myself, as you would."

"Then?"

"If it is successful, we can risk your son's work."

"But last week you blamed the postponement on the illness of the singers."

"Come, come! What is a week? I'll have it done as soon as *Buona Figliuola* is in production."

The next opera that Affligio put into rehearsals however, was another one by Piccinni. And when Leopold hurried to the theater he discovered that the copyist had been ordered to stop copying *La Finta Semplice*, that this opera was not to be done at all.

Confronted by Leopold with this accusation, Affligio said, "It is too bad, but the singers say that although the music is interesting and composed skillfully, it is untheatrical and they cannot sing it."

"But the singers told me that they loved it."

"You know how singers are. They didn't want to hurt your feelings."

"Hasse and Metastasio said that many operas are performed in Vienna which cannot compare to my son's opera."

"Then let them produce it."

"Is this the reward for my son's labor and genius?"

"I warned you that it would be risky to have a twelve-year-old compose an opera. That he doesn't know anything about love."

"What about the hundred ducats you agreed to pay us?"

"Is it in writing?"

"You gave your solemn word, signore."

Affligio laughed, then said, "The Viennese prefer spectacles. The two bulldogs I have that can tear a Hungarian wild bull to pieces will attract more people than any opera by your son. It is my next attraction."

Leopold declared, "I will petition the Emperor."

Affligio was angry suddenly. "Do so, Mozart, and you will regret it."

"The Emperor will listen to me. The Empress is very fond of Wolfgang."

"She is fond of any novelty as long as it does not cost her money."

"You even slander her?"

"And if you insist on seeing the boy prostituted. . .?"

"Prostituted! You are a scoundrel!" Leopold was horrified and furious.

"And you are a fool," Affligio sneered. "It is common talk that you are prostituting your son so that you can be rich."

Leopold hated Affligio; he could have exterminated him; and yet, at the same time, he was stunned by the accusation and could not speak.

"If you should have your boy's opera done at any of my theaters, I will see to it that the opera is laughed at, and then hissed off the stage."

Leopold could not sleep that night. Had *he* been prostituting Wolfgang? He loved his son, and his son loved him. Yet Affligio had said. . .?

When he told Wolfgang the next day that *La Finta Semplice* had been put off for a little while but that a new date would be arranged after he spoke to the Emperor, and that Wolfgang should work on the *singspiel* and Mass, his son looked disappointed but did not protest. He had tried to suggest rather than order, yet he did know best. Was this what they meant?

"Do you mind, Wolfgang?" he blurted out suddenly, although he had resolved not to discuss the subject.

"Mind what?" Wolfgang was thinking of the *singspiel*.

Then Leopold could not ask, afraid of the answer.

"Affligio's lies?"

"You know they are lies, Wolfgang?"

"Of course. Anything he says."

"Do you want to compose the *singspiel* and the Mass?"

Wolfgang embraced Papa fervently, and said, *"Mon tres cher pere,* what difference does it make what I compose, as long as it is music."

Leopold sighed with relief. Affligio had tried to shatter his glory, but Wolfgang was his pride and joy. Affligio was cheap and corrupt, and he never should have forgotten that. He held his son close to his heart.

The next day he requested an audience with the Emperor. It was granted and a week later he presented a long, detailed petition of complaint against Count Affligio. And as he wrote to Hagenauer: "His Majesty was most gracious and assured me that we would have complete justice. He promised me there would be a full investigation, and that Affligio would have to pay us the hundred ducats he owes us for the opera. In addition, I am demanding payment of the expenses the delay has cost us, and I am hopeful that this matter will be settled very soon."

The two Piccinni operas opened, there was an announcement that there would be a great, magnificent, ferocious animal spectacle staged by the incomparable Signor Count Affligio, but there was no word from the impresario as Leopold expected after his audience with the Emperor.

Distressed, Leopold discussed this with Gottfried van Swieten. He said, "Gluck must have changed the Emperor's mind," and van Swieten replied, "I doubt that. While his last opera, *Alceste,* was considered a success, it lost money and that is one of the reasons Affligio was given control of the opera. No, you cannot blame it on Gluck."

"What about Prince Kaunitz? I thought he had great influence."

"He has. But it is understood that no royal money is to be spent on the opera. So, since it is Affligio's money, however he obtains it, neither the Emperor nor Prince Kaunitz can really do anything."

"Suppose I speak to the Empress herself?"

"Don't."

"She likes Wolfgang. She is always affectionate to him."

"As long as it does not cost her anything."

Leopold was not satisfied with Gottfried van Swieten's advice. The one act *singspiel* that Wolfgang put to music for Doctor Mesmer, *Bastien and Bastienne,* based on Rousseau's *Le Devin du Village,* encouraged him to continue his battle against Affligio. For the moment the first aria began in this simple tale of three rustic characters Doctor Mesmer turned to Leopold, who was sitting next to him and exclaimed, "It's music! Music! You say he is only twelve!"

"Yes."

"Amazing! Amazing!"

And while praise of *Bastien and Bastienne* was echoing through Vienna, Wolfgang's music was honored at the consecration of the church at the Orphanage by the attendance of the Empress and the Archbishop of Vienna.

Maria Theresa praised Wolfgang's piety and Leopold was sure his enemies had been defeated. He felt that the Empress was in her best mood – deeply moved and religious – as he was, and suddenly he said, "Your Majesty, then there is still hope for *La Finta Semplice?*"

"Hope?"

He wished she wasn't scowling. But he had to continue. "Yes," he said. "Isn't little Wolfgang's music wonderful?"

She ignored that and congratulated Father Parhamer on how well his orphans' choir had sung the solemn High Mass.

"Thank you, Your Majesty," said Father Parhamer, "but it was because young Mozart led them so well and devoutly."

"Devoutly." She dwelt on that word a moment, as if to digest it.

Leopold wavered. He did not sense any genuine sympathy in Maria Theresa. It caused him to recall what the Countess Thun had said when he had consulted her. "Maria Theresa is a strange mixture. She adores her children, yet she marries them off ruthlessly for political reasons without the slightest consideration for their feelings. And since the death of her husband she lives in funereal gloom, prays four hours a day for salvation, yet should Joseph do something she dislikes she has no mercy but is despotic with him. The only thing they have in common is a distaste for spending money. That influences everything they do."

"I thought having the musical at the van Swietens' would influence her. Didn't the doctor save her life when she had smallpox?"

"She thinks so. And she is grateful. But not so grateful that she would support an opera, even if Doctor van Swieten wrote it."

Yet when Maria Theresa patted Wolfgang on the head as if he were still a little child and looked maternal again, Leopold had to say, "Your Majesty, little Wolfgang makes all his music devout. Even his opera."

"Opera is my son's province," she said, suddenly haughty and brusque. "But the child will get a present for what he has accomplished here."

Leopold was troubled by her curtness, until he received a beautiful present from her a few days later. Yet there was no word from Affligio or anyone else about *La Finta Semplice*. There was considerable talk about the honor that had been conferred upon the Mozarts by the presence of the Empress, and no further commissions. So, sixteen months after they had left Salzburg, Leopold arranged to return home.

TWENTY-FIVE

A few weeks later Wolfgang leaned out of the window of his living room at 9 Getreidegasse, noticing things that he had not noticed before. After the discomforts of traveling, he appreciated the comforts of home.

He was glad to have a firm bed underneath him, to have familiar things within reach, to see old friends, especially girls, who seemed to be growing up as fast as he was. He had just reached his thirteenth birthday and he felt quite grown-up. And it was a fine winter day for Salzburg.

The sky was a bright blue, without a trace of snow, and although it was cold, the usual icy wind that rushed down from the surrounding mountains was absent. The white, fleecy clouds over the Lochelplatz had the ease and naturalness of light, sweet melodies. He wondered what instruments they preferred. He saw one that was no larger than a handkerchief, another that was pointed like the spire of the Franciscan church in The Sovereign's Town, and one that was shaped like the miniature violin he had played.

The sights became sounds. As Wolfgang stared at the clouds he could hear voices calling him. He felt permeated with music. *But most people did not know what they were hearing,* he thought, *or that they were hearing, yet the great thing was to hear.* There was music in everything. Although finally, that was not sufficient. He must listen too, he told himself. Then composition was born within him. And it was as if he had created the creator within himself, and what was necessary was to call on himself.

Patrons talked to him of "his inspiration", and how it must come to him in flashes, like lightning, but they were wrong, it was in him all the time, and *he had to find it,* develop it, and not depend on accident or chance. He was aware also that it was not enough to possess a melody.

Sometimes melodies flowed in such an abundance they threatened to overwhelm him. He must choose. It must be his best. The process of selection was, whatever anyone else said, a matter of taste. He wanted to make up his own mind what to compose next, despite what he had said to his father in Vienna. Yet if he had said anything else, he would have hurt Papa, and he couldn't do that.

He saw Papa coming down the Getreidegasse from the Residenz. The way his father was striding, energetically and cheerfully, he must compose a march for him. He could tell from his father's haste that Papa had vital news, for Papa had gone to see the Archbishop at the latter's request.

But before Papa could speak, Mamma asked, "Will your pay be restored?"

"It is not why His Grace wanted to see me. He spoke warmly about the Mass Wolfgang composed for Father Parhamer. He said he received a favorable report about it from the Archbishop of Vienna."

Wolfgang asked, "What does His Grace want me to compose?"

"Another Mass!" Papa exclaimed proudly. "For the University church."

Mamma repeated, "Leopold, what about your pay?"

"I didn't mention it. But I'm sure it was a mistake, I've never seen His Grace nicer to me. He told me that the Archbishop of Vienna complimented him on the piety of Salzburg music. If he likes Wolfgang's new mass, I think he will have *La Finta Semplice* performed. He might even approve of us going to Italy."

"We've been home such a short time and you're talking of going away again."

"If His Grace grants me leave, I would be foolish to refuse."

"You are owed for three weeks' work, and you talk of his generosity. Do you really think he will pay you?"

"I have already prepared a petition."

"Like the one you presented to the Emperor?"

"Anna Maria, what has gotten into you!"

"I'm tired of traveling. Of illnesses."

"But Wolfgang wouldn't be Wolfgang if he hadn't traveled, if he hadn't met the greatest musicians of his time. As he will in Italy."

Nannerl said, "I want to stay at home for a while, Papa."

"No one said you shouldn't." He turned to Wolfgang and asked, "How do you feel about that?"

Wolfgang hesitated. He was still not sure he wanted to go traveling so soon again, but he couldn't hurt Papa. "Whatever you think."

Papa, who had come home elated by his flattering audience with the Archbishop, was hurt. After so many humiliations from Schrattenbach, he was on the verge of convincing him of his son's genius, and nobody in his family appreciated what he had achieved, except possibly Wolfgang, and he was not even certain of him.

And now Anna Maria was saying something she would not have dared to say ordinarily. "Leopold, don't you think that before Wolfgang goes anywhere else, he ought to go to school and study Latin, Greek, and mathematics?"

"I've taught him Latin, and he is brilliant at mathematics and doesn't need instruction. And when it comes to music, in Vienna alone, in addition to the operas and the mass, he wrote three symphonies, several marches, sonatas for harpsichord and violin, minuets, and Italian arias. Since I started to teach him, he has written over fifty compositions."

Wolfgang asked, "Is that much?"

"Yes. And I am right about His Grace. You will see."

When the Archbishop celebrated Wolfgang's Mass himself, Wolfgang was glad he had obeyed Papa. As a reward, Schrattenbach had an opera stage erected in the Residenz and had *La Finta Semplice* performed there by members of his Kapelle to celebrate his name day.

Wolfgang was disappointed in the singing. They did not compare with the singers in Vienna, but Papa looked so pleased he tried to feel the same way. His Grace applauded loudly at the end of the opera. Wolfgang wasn't certain whether it was because the Archbishop was grateful that the opera was over, or because he really liked it.

Papa explained, "He is learning." Papa was relieved that he had received his back pay, although only after he had petitioned His Grace for it.

Wolfgang was glad his next commission was for two divertimentos. He gave the best music to the violins, and they were performed at the University graduation of the Logicians and Physicians on Menstrual Sunday.

But he liked best the Mass he composed and conducted in St. Peter's church to honor the induction to the priesthood of Cajetan "Dominicus" Hagenauer. Cajetan was the son of their landlord. Until he had studied for the priesthood, he had been one of Wolfgang's favorite playmates.

Cajetan, although ten years older, had shared his air gun with him, and had pumped the organ for him. But now his friend was Father Dominicus and was celebrating his first mass to Wolfgang's music. Their landlord was so proud. Hagenauer called the music the *Dominicus Mass*, and said, "Wolfgang, it is such eloquent music, with so much love in it," and blessed him.

Wolfgang blushed. He had put his heart into this Mass. He had wanted to give Hagenauer, usually self-effacing, a sense of dignity and honor.

This year he also wrote more minuets and marches, a new symphony – to keep in practice, Papa said – but none of this music excited him as much as the operas he had composed. So when Papa stated that they were going to Italy, the home of opera, he was glad, although he was unhappy at the thought of missing Barbara von Molk and Theresa Barasini.

There was no doubt in Papa. As it was, he felt he had waited too long. One evening, almost a year after they had returned from Vienna, he announced, "His Grace has not only granted me leave, he has financed me."

"Schrattenbach is giving you money to go to Italy, Leopold?"

"It is given. A hundred and twenty ducats." He showed it to Anna Maria.

"I would never have thought he would do that."

"I told you I would win him over. He has become fond of Wolfgang's religious music. He says that once Wolfgang's masses develop the rushing Italian style, the boy will make a Maestro. His exact words."

She knew she must be glad for Leopold, it meant so much to him, and she tried to show that by congratulating him with a kiss. But the thought of traveling again still repelled her, and she recoiled even as she kissed him.

He had more startling news. "Just Wolfgang and I are going." He stated that decisively so there would not be any arguments, or change of mind.

Her eyes filled with tears at the thought of separation.

"You've been saying you don't want to travel for a while. And His Grace has given only enough for the two of us, since we are in his employ."

"His employ!" exclaimed Mamma.

"Now we must call Wolfgang 'Herr Konzertmeister'."

Wolfgang, who had been feeling stricken at the idea of being away from Mamma and Nannerl, said unbelievingly, "I am a court musician?"

"Why not? You are qualified."

Wolfgang knew that, but there were other reasons. "You're teasing."

"His Grace has appointed you third Konzertmeister."

"Unpaid, of course," said Mamma, startled out of her tears.

"Only while he is away. When he returns from Italy, the moment he performs as a Konzertmeister, he will be paid."

"How much?" asked Wolfgang.

"It hasn't been specified, but the usual fee is a hundred and fifty gulden. His Grace wants to keep you attached to Salzburg."

"But Papa, one of the reasons you wanted to go to Italy was to find new opportunities. You have said that many times."

"To ourselves. What His Grace doesn't know, he doesn't know."

Mamma said, "He knows. He is also sure you will return, as you always have."

"Just so you are sure, Mamma," Papa said affectionately.

Parting was almost more than Wolfgang could endure. He was grateful that Papa told Mamma and Nannerl that they must not come downstairs, for Papa was afraid there would be so many tears they would not be able to leave. Papa said that he must be controlled, like a man.

But as he followed Papa to the stage coach that was waiting for them, he was missing Mamma already and she was still in view, standing at the center window of the living room. Yet Nannerl, who had seemed indifferent to their departure, as if she were relieved that she didn't have to go, was nowhere to be seen. He had a sudden moment of panic; she didn't care; she was glad to see him go. Then he saw her waving to him frantically. But why was she standing at the side window. In the next instant he realized it was to be closer. Her blond hair had darkened the last few years, she resembled Mamma more, but once again she was the sister he loved.

Mamma leaned out the window, although it was December and very cold and cried, "Throw me a kiss."

Papa did, shouting, "A thousand, thousand kisses," but he looked sad.

Wolfgang, however, suddenly ran upstairs despite what Papa had ordered, and kissed Mamma, then Nannerl, who looked afraid that he would neglect her, and said to Mamma, "I couldn't throw you a kiss."

TWENTY-SIX

The first night away from home was lonesome. So Leopold, in addition to writing Mamma, told Wolfgang to write her. Wolfgang wrote: "Dearest Mamma: My heart is full of pleasure because traveling is so exciting, because it is comfortable in our coach, and our driver is a remarkable coachman who, when the road allows, drives like the wind. Papa will tell you about the details of the journey, for I am writing you so that you will know that I am your faithful and loving son. Wolfgang Mozart."

Leopold had him write Nannerl too, so that she would not feel neglected, and he wrote her in Italian, to show her how well he knew the language: "My dearest sister: We have reached Worgl, Praise be to God. The journey is amusing, and not in the least uncomfortable. How is your cold? Tell Schachtner that I now sing 'Tralaliera', and Papa says that now that I am away from Salzburg, I do not have to put sugar in my soup. My regards to all my dear friends, and to Barabara and Theresa. As Papa says, if we keep well and do not get constipated, little else matters. I kiss your hands a thousand times. Your Italian brother, Kapellmeister of the Counting House."

Leopold was not as optimistic about traveling as Wolfgang. It could take ten dangerous, difficult days to cross the Alps. Even as he informed his son, "Italy is the home of music, the greatest German masters, Handel, Hasse, Gluck, Bach have studied there," he was apprehensive about how they would be received and about the icy roads, the snow-clogged mountain passes, and the avalanches.

The next few days there were many times that Leopold wondered if they should have attempted this trip, particularly in winter. Nothing appeared to worry the effervescent Wolfgang, who continued to be enchanted with the traveling, but just as Leopold would become relaxed, riding through a wide valley in the Tyrol, it would contract into a narrow ravine. Often they drove under overhanging cliffs filled with snow. The drivers he hired were experienced, and they knew when the snow was in a favorable condition and less likely to fall, but they never could be sure.

There was the gorge where the cliffs were only a few feet apart. The snow was thick above them, it seemed to be drifting towards them as they entered the gorge, even the driver looked uncertain and frightened, and Wolfgang was humming an allegro passage that was Italian in its rapid, impetuous gallop. As the driver paused at the start of the gorge, Leopold found himself saying, "Is this pilgrimage to Italy really necessary?"

Wolfgang asked, "Is there something wrong, Papa?"

The driver asked, "What do you think, Herr Mozart? There is a great deal of snow here." The fur-clad driver was pale and tense.

I might be killing all of us, thought Leopold, but the idea of turning back was worse.

They were out of the gorge only a moment when a wave of snow slid off the cliff with a roar and down where they had been. But there was no time to concern themselves with that, for they were riding around an icy mountain road with a perpendicular precipice on one side and a steep, straight-up wall on the other and they could not turn back. The horses slipped on the ice and for a terrible instant Leopold was sure they were falling into the valley below. The sudden jerk of the coach jolted Wolfgang out of his musical reverie; he cried out in fear and Leopold covered his eyes to shield him from the ugly crash, then fondled him.

And long after the driver regained control, Leopold felt dizzy and the rheumatism that settled in his shoulders tortured him, while Wolfgang sat with his hands gripped together until his knuckles were white.

Leopold wondered if he was growing old: he had had such a steady head for traveling before. Whenever they had left Salzburg there had been mountains to traverse. But never so many, or for so long, or so dangerous. He wrote home every chance he got, and that was some comfort.

On Christmas Day, 1769, two weeks after they had left Salzburg, they reached Rovereto, a small city in Northern Italy. There was no ice or snow here and the mountains had become moderate-sized hills. Leopold went at once to the most prominent church to give thanks for their safe arrival, and there bumped into an old acquaintance.

Baron Christiani was delighted to see him. The Baron had fond memories of the days he had been Leopold's violin pupil in Salzburg. And he had heard that Wolfgang Mozart was visiting Italy. He said, "Signor Leopoldo, it will be our pleasure to hear your marvel of nature."

Leopold, not to be outdone, for the Baron, who had been Ecclesiastical Commissioner in Salzburg, now ruled Rovereto for Maria Theresa, replied fervently, "It will be *our pleasure* to perform for Your Excellency."

Wolfgang, when he played the next night for Baron Christiani and the most distinguished residents of Rovereto, could not keep up with this flattery. Baron Christiani cried out, "The boy is a miracle of nature!" His guests shouted, "Bravo Mozart!" And Papa replied, "You are simpatico, it is the nature of this great country," but Wolfgang remembered how Papa had hated Lolli and the other Italians whom Schrattenbach had favored.

The Baron seemed sincere, however. He indicated he could not pay the Mozarts, since they were his guests and such a gesture would be offensive, but that if Wolfgang would play in his church, it would sanctify their lives. He was so insistent that Wolfgang almost believed him and sensed that Papa was determined to.

The organ recital was arranged only for the nobility and the musicians of Rovereto, but as Wolfgang rode to the church in Baron Christiani's sedia, he was surrounded by a crowd which grew with each step the horses took. People came running from all directions. Nuns threw flowers at his feet. Mothers lifted their babies high to see him, and to be exposed to his magic. By the time he reached the church it was as if everyone in Rovereto had come to hear him. The crowd had become so huge he had to enter by the rear, and burly priests had to struggle to get him to the organ. Yet when he played the jammed church hushed to a rapt silence. Many sat with closed eyes and held their breath. But the instant he finished there were ecstatic cries: "Bravo Mozart! O benedetto! O Dio!"

In Verona, he was invited to perform at the Accademia Filarmonica. It was a great honor. No one under the age of twenty-one had ever played in this famous school of music, and many professors of music came to judge him. He played a harpsichord concerto at sight, sonatas that were new to him, and composed a finale to a theme given him by a professor of harmony.

Pietro Mantova, the professor who had tested him, declared, "Signor Amadeo Wolfgango Mozart is as great a miracle as we have had in Verona since Catullus. Only a Dante could sing his praises."

Two Veronese poets took the hint and dedicated a glowing ode and sonnet to Wolfgang. He sat for a lovely portrait in oil, posed by the side of a harpsichord with one of his own compositions on the stand, and dressed in his favorite crimson coat, his fair hair lightly powdered.

Papa was exultant over this adulation. He wrote Mamma that the portrait was splendid, that Wolfgang looked handsome in it and resembled her.

Wolfgang thought the praise superfluous. He had not done anything he had not done before. When he was appointed a Kapellmeister of the Veronese Accademia Filarmonica, he accepted it as inevitable.

His triumphs continued in Mantua and Cremona, but in Milan, their first major destination, there was disappointing news. Count Firmian, Governor General of Lombardy for Maria Theresa, and an old friend and patron, could not see them at the moment, but Leopold was informed that an audience should be possible in a week or two. There was nothing to do but wait, and Leopold tried to lessen his disappointment by going to the opera.

Wolfgang was delighted that they were staying in Milan for a while, for this opportunity to see more operas gave him great pleasure. Possessed with an overwhelming need to express himself – he had been absorbing such a multitude of impressions – he also wrote a long letter to Nannerl. It was January 26th, the eve of his fourteenth birthday, and it was another way of marking the occasion:

"My dearest sister: Now the German clown ceases and the Italian begins. For now we hear nothing but operas. Yet even in *Il Ruggiero*, the great success in Verona, some of the singing is a misfortune. In it is a Baroness who has a tolerable voice and a good figure, but who sings horribly out of tune. The primo uomo, a castrato who sings a little in the style of Manzuoli, has a beautiful and powerful voice, but he is too old. He looks fifty-five and his throat quavers. The prima donna has a lovely voice, but there is such a whispering in the theater one hears nothing.

"An opera in Mantua is beautiful, *Demetrio*, by our friend, Hasse, but again the singing often has a bad odor. The prima donna sings well but too quietly. The second donna has the presence of a grenadier, and a strong voice to match, and most of the time she sounds as if she is angry. The castrato sings lyrically, but strains too much to reach his high notes. The second uomo is too old, and he does not please me. The tenor is better, but he sings heavily, like so many Italian tenors.

"The primo ballerino – good; the prima ballerina – also good, and it is said, not ugly, but I have not been near enough to tell. There is a grotesco who leaps well, but who farts when he leaves the ground.

"Piccinni, who is to write the next opera, is here, and we may meet him. Although he is a Neapolitan, he is in great favor at the moment in Milan. But while he pretends to please, his music is loud and extravagant.

"Of other news there is not much, except Gellert, the Leipzig poet, has just died, and since his death, has written no more poetry.

"I am fine and remain your same old clown. I kiss Mamma's hands a thousand times, and to you I send a hundred loving smacks. Addio. Wolfgang in Germany, Amadeo in Italy."

Several weeks later Leopold was informed that Count Firmian could grant the Mozarts an audience now.

TWENTY-SEVEN

Count Karl Joseph Firmian stood at the window of his audience chamber, alone and thoughtful, waiting for his guests to arrive. Then abruptly he paced the shining parquet floor until he came to the ceiling-high Venetian mirror on the opposite wall. He had served Maria Theresa long and well, and yet, next year, or at the most, in two years, a child would be ruling in his place. Her third son, the Archduke Ferdinand, who would be sixteen in six months, was to be appointed ruler of Lombardy upon his marriage to the Princess of Modena. Yet he still felt in his prime. He stared into the glittering mirror and saw a pudgy, thick-set man of fifty-four with heavy features but no visible signs of decline. And he knew that was irrelevant. Ferdinand was a Hapsburg; Maria Theresa needed no other reason.

She lectured her subjects with pious moral discourses, and built the Hapsburg power by whatever method succeeded. He had no choice. He had to reconcile himself to becoming the second-in-command, or to retirement and obscurity. But if he remained as the Archduke's advisor, as she had indicated she wished, most of the decisions would be his, and he could put in effect the following plan.

If Mozart was established as an example of what a youth could actually accomplish, it should expose Ferdinand for the child he really was. The musician was a year and a half younger than the Archduke, yet he surpassed him by decades. The comparison brought a smile to Count Firmian's face. But there must be no risk; he would disavow all interest in Mozart at the slightest sign of suspicion in Maria Theresa. Yet the idea continued to appeal to him, and he felt daring for considering it. His cheerfulness grew as his chamberlain introduced four of the leading opera composers in Italy, whom he wanted to see before the Mozarts arrived.

Adolph Hasse, Giovanni Sammartini, Nicola Piccinni, and Joseph Mysliveček had arrived separately, but Count Firmian had ordered his chamberlain to admit them together. Each of them had the same startled look: why had they been invited at the same time? At the moment they had received the invitation each of them had assumed he was offered a new scrittura for Milan, but now they suspected something devious.

As the musicians bowed before him, Court Firmian thought there had been no handsomer composer in Italy than Hasse, who at seventy was still attractive, and he wondered how much that had contributed to Hasse's success, for the Italians were great lovers of physical beauty.

Sammartini, who was as elderly as Hasse, seemed to have shrunk since he had seen him a few months ago. Yet this musician had too much influence to be ignored. He had taught Gluck; he was the most important musician in Milan; his operas and symphonies were played everywhere.

At the moment, however, it was the forty-two-year-old Piccinni who was the most celebrated composer in Italy. Small, thin, with an unusually long nose and sharp chin, and a tired, serious expression on his pale face, he could hardly keep still as he waited for the Count to speak.

It was Mysliveček, the Czech, who seemed most ill at ease. At thirty-three he was the least known. His successes had been in Florence and Bologna, which did not matter much in Milan.

Wine was brought in, and coffee for Mysliveček. Piccinni broke the uncomfortable silence, suddenly praising Hasse's latest opera, *Demetrio,* which regretfully, however, he had not seen.

Hasse sighed. "My last opera, perhaps. It has not been successful."

"Oh, no!" exclaimed Piccinni, "that would be a great loss."

Hasse looked as if he didn't believe him, but he didn't say anything.

Count Firmian said suddenly, "The Mozarts are coming, too."

Piccinni wanted to flee; Sammartini was surprised; Mysliveček seemed confused; Hasse asked, "Father and son?"

"Of course. Aren't they always together?"

"Usually. Your Excellency, is the boy to be given the next scrittura?"

"Do you think he should have it?"

"I am not the impresario, sir."

"But you did praise him to Prince Kaunitz? Didn't you?"

"You know I did, Your Excellency."

Count Firmian was amused. This musician was not easily deceived. To reach his present eminence, Hasse, like many other composers in Italy, had also mastered intrigue. Sometimes, the Governor-General thought, the successful musicians would make better rulers than the Hapsburgs. But that would shock Maria Theresa. He asked Hasse,

"Do you think *La Finta Semplice* could have been performed?"

"No one can be sure. No one can ever be sure until the opera is done."

"Maestro Piccinni, your operas were done by Affligio."

"It was not my fault, sir. I had nothing to do with his plans."

"Do you think the boy's opera should have been performed?"

"How can I say, sir? Whatever I answer, it is too embarrassing."

Sammartini said, "His father sent me several of his symphonic scores, which the boy was kind enough to dedicate to me. They are well designed. They produce fine effects, and are written with taste and precision."

Count Firmian added, "I heard him play the harpsichord at the age of six. I have never forgotten it."

Leopold was accustomed to surprises and proud that he seldom lost his composure, but when he saw the other composers he was at a loss for words. He had assumed Count Firmian was a friend he could depend on, but now a note of caution intruded. Wolfgang, however, was so glad to see Hasse, he ran up to him in his enthusiasm, forgetting to bow to Count Firmian first.

Leopold started to apologize for Wolfgang, and Count Firmian waved that aside. "I share his sentiments, Signor Mozart. Signor Hasse is a greater musician than I am." The Count introduced the others.

With what Leopold felt was adroitness, he avoided Piccinni, whom he saw as a little Neapolitan, not to be trusted. He was constrained with Mysliveček, but polite, not sure whether the Czech intended to be competitive. He felt that he was getting along very well with Hasse and Sammartini, especially when Count Firmian joined them and asked, "Does your son still play with his wonderfully light touch?"

"Even more so, sir," said Leopold, his confidence returning.

"Remarkable. Don't you think so, Signor Hasse?"

"Sir, I think Wolfgang can speak for himself."

Wolfgang said, "What would you like me to play, Maestro Hasse?"

"Whatever His Excellency wants."

"Later! Later!" said Count Firmian. "There will be time for that." He turned to Leopold again. "Your son has changed. He looks much older. His face is such a reddish brown."

"From the open air and the open fires, Your Excellency."

"What about an opera?"

"For Milan, Your Excellency?" It could not come this easy, thought Leopold, nothing he desired so much ever came so easy. "By my son?"

"It is possible. Isn't it?"

"Yes, yes, Your Excellency!" cried Leopold. "Isn't it, Wolfgang?"

Wolfgang, who was discussing with Sammartini the symphonies he had sent this master symphonist, was annoyed by the interruption but when he saw Papa's seriousness he became attentive. "What is it, Papa?"

"Would you like to compose an opera for Milan?" Wolfgang, to his astonishment, was hesitating. He wanted to shout, "Are you insane?" but controlling himself with great effort, he said, "Didn't you hear me?"

"I heard you, Papa, but . . ." He saw Hasse waiting for him to continue. "Maestro Hasse, I loved *Demetrio*. I know almost all the arias by heart."

"Thank you, Wolfgang."

His son was sane, thought Leopold. No compliment could have been more graciously uttered or better chosen; it would surely enhance matters.

"But Maestro," said Wolfgang, "hearing it, I had such a sick feeling."

Everybody gathered around him and listened intently.

"There was so much noise during the arias I could not make out the words."

Hasse said, "That is the nature of Italian audiences."

Wolfgang said, "Then they should take a physic and purge themselves."

Leopold shuddered. Wolfgang was right but how could he be so rude!

Wolfgang asked Hasse, "Sir, are Italian audiences always so loud?"

"Almost always."

Piccinni cut in, "It is even worse in Naples. That is why I give my music so much bravura. It is the only way it will be heard."

Sammartini replied that Milan opera audiences were just as bad; Mysliveček said Florentine opera audiences were so energetic they even drowned out the orchestra; Hasse declared that Italian audiences were only engrossed when the passages related to themselves. But suddenly this discussion, which had become wildly animated and difficult to hear, for all the composers were talking at once, came to an abrupt halt when the Count clapped his hands and cried, "Bravo! You have proved the boy's point!" He indicated with a flourish that it was time for Wolfgang to play.

After all the composers applauded Wolfgang's performance, even Piccinni, the Count chose Sammartini to test Wolfgang's ability as a composer.

Sammartini ordered the boy to compose four new arias to texts by Metastasio. Wolfgang did this quickly, and Sammartini examined them and stated, "Your Excellency, they are really well composed." Hasse agreed, then Mysliveček, and finally Piccinni, although reluctantly.

Pleased, Count Firmian congratulated the Mozarts. The boy was making the impression he desired, and he had manipulated the musicians into expressing their approval, however differently they might feel privately.

Leopold said, "Sir, my son would be honored to compose an opera for you."

"For the Archduke," said Count Firmian. "It is not my decision to make."

Leopold was puzzled. The Count's word was law in Milan. But he was like all rulers, reflected Leopold, he never gave a direct answer.

"If your son could give a concert at a reception in my palace for the Archduke's future bride, the Princess of Modena, and her father, the Duke, and they like his music, a scrittura might be forthcoming."

"May God bless your decision, sir."

"You will make sure that the boy is at his best."

Wolfgang started to say, I am always at my best, but Leopold cut him short, saying, "As Your Excellency wishes."

"Good. Wolfgang, what were you going to say?" asked Count Firmian.

"It should be a high and mighty occasion, sir."

"You are not frightened?"

"Why should I be frightened, sir? With my high and mighty thoughts."

When Count Firmian was amused instead of being angry, Leopold suggested, "Your Excellency, Wolfgang would make an excellent first Kapellmeister or Konzermeister. He is already the third in Salzburg."

Count Firmian thought: what a joke, a sixteen-year-old ruler with a fourteen-year-old Kapellmeister!

"Sir, he can hold his own with any musician twice his age."

"An interesting idea. My chief steward will make the arrangements for the concert." Count Firmian indicated that the audience was over.

Sammartini congratulated Leopold on his son's success, then so did Mysliveček and Piccinni, although he was positive that they were annoyed, that Piccinni hated Wolfgang at this moment. But where was Hasse?

Hasse was walking down the beautiful marble staircase with Wolfgang, discussing Wolfgang's favorite dish, sauerkraut and dumplings. Hasse was saying, when Leopold caught up with them, that Wolfgang must be his guest for dinner soon, for such solid, nourishing German cooking.

Leopold said, "We appreciate your invitation, Maestro, but he may not have the time. Wolfgang will have to practice very hard for the concert."

"You must not be so possessive about him, or you will spoil him."

"Is he spoiled now?" demanded Leopold.

"No, but that does not mean that he cannot be."

"He needs guidance. He is very young still."

"Only in years."

"He wants me to direct him. Don't you, Wolfgang?"

Tired of Papa's relentlessness, Wolfgang longed to shout No. Yet there were tears in Papa's eyes, and he never could resist tears. He hoped that Maestro Hasse didn't notice. He took both men by the hand and asked, "Do you think the Count will give me the scrittura?"

Leopold remembered Hasse's influence then, and said, controlled again, "I am sure Signor Hasse can tell better than we can."

"No one can tell. Not yet. There are many people to please."

Leopold said, "I do think, however, that we pleased His Excellency."

"It is possible," said Hasse. "He is a man of taste."

TWENTY-EIGHT

═══

At the reception at the Palazzo Firmian for the Princess of Modena and her father a hundred and fifty of the leading nobility of Milan attended.

Wolfgang's program featured music composed by himself and Sammartini, Milan's favorite composer. At Count Firmian's request he played the four arias he had written at the audience. The Duke of Modena applauded loudly, the Princess said, "His music is sweet, he is a virtuoso," and then many of the nobility shouted, "Bravo Amadeo!"

Soon afterward Wolfgang was given the scrittura to set to music the first drama to be performed the next opera season in Milan. It was negotiated by Leopold and the Count's steward, Don Fernando Germani. Wolfgang was to receive one hundred cigliatis upon the presentation of the opera, and free lodgings during the period of composition and rehearsal. The libretto was to be chosen by Count Firmian, who had not yet selected a subject, but who leaned to an opera *seria* in the grand manner.

"There is no rush, however," said Don Fernando. This suave and attractive native of Milan was wed to a well-to-do Viennese, spoke German as fluently as he did Italian, had important business connections in Vienna, and was able to perform many services for the Governor-General. "Signor Leopoldo, since you and Amadeo will be traveling in Italy when the libretto is decided upon, we will send it to you wherever you are. The other terms are customary."

He handed them to Leopold, who read: "It is further agreed that Maestro Amadeo Wolfgango Mozart is to deliver all the recitatives by October, 1770, and to be in Milan again the month of November to compose the arias and to be present at all the rehearsals required by the opera. With the usual reservations in case of theatrical misfortunes and Princely intervention – God Forbid."

Don Fernando saw Leopold frowning and said, "Amadeo shouldn't mind composing for the singers directly. Everybody else does."

"He did in Vienna. But Princely intervention, what does that mean?"

"Oh, the Empress, the Archduke, the Governor-General."

"I did hope we would be better protected here."

"You are, my friend. Do not worry. Hasse is for it, and so is Sammartini and even Mysliveček spoke well of Amadeo. Go on to Bologna, Florence, Rome, and Naples as you have planned, and I will watch out for your interests here." He handed Leopold letters of introduction from the Count for Bologna, Florence, Rome and Naples. "They are to some of the greatest and most powerful men in Italy. They should be very helpful."

Leopold embraced the steward emotionally, and he responded just as warmly but added with a sudden note of regret, "There are two conditions."

"What conditions?"

"It will be necessary to obtain the consent of your Archbishop."

"Oh!" Leopold sighed with relief. "That shouldn't be difficult. He should feel honored. Count Firmian's uncle was the Archbishop before him. Archbishop Firmian of Salzburg was my first employer."

"And it must be *an Italian opera*. If it fails in this, the pack will fall on it as on a carcass. No edict will make an Italian public approve of an opera if it is not in the style to which they are accustomed."

"My dear friend, do you think I would take such a risk!"

This time it was Don Fernando who embraced Leopold, crying out, "Of course I trust you! Eh, Amadeo!" He handed Wolfgang a farewell present from the Count, a snuff box of gold and filled with twenty cigliati.

Wolfgang had not been listening. The assurance that he would be composing an opera in a few months had given him so many musical ideas, he was memorizing them so that he could write them down later.

On the way to Parma, when they paused at Lodi for the night, Wolfgang finished the string quartet he had been thinking about during the journey. Lodi, located on the banks of the Adda river, was full of Renaissance monuments and they stayed on the magnificent cathedral square, but he could feel nothing but the music he was composing, the first of this kind he had done. Papa scolded Wolfgang for waking him up – he had risen in the middle of the night to complete the quartet. So, from then on, he developed the habit of memorizing his musical ideas wherever he was – in bed or in a stage coach or in a sedia, or even in a concert when he was not playing – and jotting them down afterwards. He enjoyed the power and pleasure this gave him so much that it became a game. He discovered that often he could remember a theme or passage for a long time.

At Parma they were invited to dinner by Lucrezia Agujari, the most famous soprano in Italy. Hasse, for whom she had sung, had written her saying that he would regard it as a great favor if she sang for the Mozarts; he hoped that she would sing in Wolfgang's opera, which should insure its success.

Known as "La Bastardella" because she was the natural child of a nobleman, Wolfgang was very curious about her appearance. Due to her birth, he expected her to be more seductive, more scandalous than any of the other sopranos he had met. He was disappointed that she was not beautiful, that she limped, and that she was already married.

But when she sang he forgot everything else. He sat fascinated as he noted that the lower part of her voice was full and deep like an organ while her upper register was clear, natural, and perfect. He felt in heaven when she agreed to sing his arias.

And as she sang his music he no longer related to her as a woman but as an instrument. He wanted to be critical and dispassionate, and he exulted. Her intonation was true, her execution was flawless, she was pathetic and tender one moment and grand and majestic the next.

Wolfgang was still so excited that he had to write to Nannerl: "We heard La Bastardella and she is amazing. She has an incomparable voice, the most flexible throat I have ever heard, and a fantastic range. She sang the following notes and passages in my presence."

He wrote them out for his sister so she could comprehend what he meant.

The more he recalled how superbly she had sung, the more he longed to compose for her. They were in Bologna now, and Papa was telling him that this city in the Po Valley possessed the finest musical academy in the world, and he kept hearing her high tones. Leopold was excited, for Field-Marshal Pallavicini, for whom Count Firmian had given him a letter of recommendation, was granting him an immediate audience.

Field-Marshal Pallavicini, a romantic figure in flowing robes and a silver colored wig, read Count Firmian's letter with genuine interest and said, "Signor Mozart, the Governor-General speaks of you and your son's ability with the greatest warmth, and I hold in high regard his approval. I will be happy if Signor Amadeo would be good enough to play at the reception I am giving tomorrow evening at my villa."

Leopold doubted that there was enough time to prepare a program, but Wolfgang assured the Field-Marshal, "Sir, I can play whatever Your Excellency prefers, Sammartini, Hasse, Johann Christian Bach."

"Or Amadeo Mozart," suggested Field-Marshal Pallavicini.

The Field-Marshal's carriage called for them, and at the reception there were Princes, Dukes, Ambassadors, and Cardinals, but Wolfgang was excited most by the presence of Padre Martini. Ever since he could remember he had heard about this Franciscan Father, the most learned musical scholar in Europe, the authority accepted by everyone as the final word. He was surprised to see him here, for Padre Martini was supposed to never go to concerts. He was disappointed that this musician, whom he had expected to be noble-looking like Hasse, was smaller and more shrunken than Sammartini.

The concert included an orchestra and two castrati, but it was Signor Amadeo the guests clamored to hear. After he played the harpsichord alone, then with the orchestra in a concerto, he accompanied the castrati in the arias he had composed for Count Firmian, and finally he was asked to conduct the orchestra. The music which began at seven-thirty did not end until eleven-thirty, and then only because Padre Martini was tired.

Wolfgang felt he could have continued indefinitely. Extraordinary feats could be performed for such an appreciative audience. Countess Pallavicini had invited many lovely ladies, and they were extravagant with their compliments. Some allowed him to kiss their hand, others fondled him, and several embraced him. But his greatest pleasure came from his hostess.

When Countess Pallavicini, who was disturbingly beautiful with her dark eyes, olive skin, and shapely breasts, kissed him as a reward for his performance, he was intoxicated. Her hand lingered in his after her kiss. He wanted more, and when she turned to someone else he was unhappy.

He heard their host say, "Signor Mozart, you and your son must stay in Bologna and become part of our great Accademia Filarmonica," and Papa replied, "We would love to, sir, but we have to be in Rome for Holy Week."

Wolfgang was surprised. Papa hadn't said anything before about the necessity of being in Rome during Holy Week; he must have devised a new plan this evening, as he was fond of doing. Wolfgang noticed that Papa's eyes shone as the Field-Marshal said, "Cardinal Pallavicini, the Secretary of State for the Vatican, is a distant cousin and a friend of mine. I will give you a letter of recommendation to him."

Padre Martini paused on his way out of the stately music room and said, "Signor Mozart, I am living in retirement now, but if I could have the pleasure of your company before you depart for Rome, I would be honored."

"Thank you, Most Reverend Father," said Papa, "We will be honored."

"Good night, Amadeo, you should rest well after such splendid music."

Later, however, while Papa wrote a long letter to Mamma about all the good news – Field-Marshal Pallavicini's steward also had given Papa two hundred and five lire for Wolfgang's performance and conducting – Wolfgang could not sleep. There had been so much female beauty at the reception it did not seem fair. At his age he was expected to be chaste, but now he desired the caress of feminine hands; the enticing, flirtatious women had awakened his senses and he could not be indifferent to them. And some of the younger women were only a few years older than himself; he noticed that Italian girls matured sooner than German girls, and he wondered if that was true of the boys who lived here. To ease his discontent, he wrote Nannerl a postscript to Papa's letter: "My dearest and most adorable sister: Speak of the devil and he appears. I am pleased you enjoyed the sleigh ride with Barisani, but one thing troubles me, that you caused von Molk to be so sad because you would not go with him. How many clean handkerchiefs your cruelty must have cost him. You should give him a dose of tartar so he can purge his body of any dirty thoughts. Will you tell Barbara that I did send my songs to her, and that when I return I look forward to going sleigh riding with her, and to having a very good time. Kiss Mamma's hands a thousand times for me, and I send a hundred kisses for your wonderful horseface. Wolfgango in Milan – Amadeo in Bologna."

Once this was written it was as if in his bantering tone he had protected himself. He felt safe again and he was able to fall asleep.

Soon afterward they were Padre Martini's guests at dinner. The priest apologized for the sparse repast, although he was proud of the Bologna sausage he had as a delicacy. "Otherwise, Signor Leopoldo, my doctors force me to eat only cold chicken, a small slice of roast beef, and on fast days a little fish." Leopold replied, "The sausage is remarkable, German in its substance and Italian in its flavor," and Padre Martini was pleased and said, "It is always sensible to eat lightly," and Leopold agreed and answered, "Wolfgang never overeats, for it makes him too sluggish to compose." Just as Wolfgang thought they would never talk about anything else, the priest led them into his study to show them his seventeen thousand volumes of music, the most extensive music library in the world.

But when Leopold suggested that Padre Martini should observe Wolfgang compose, he said, "My doctors insist that I go to bed early. The reception was an unusual occasion. If you could be free tomorrow however, I would like you to meet a neighbor of mine who lives outside of Bologna."

191

"We had planned to be on our way to the Holy City tomorrow."

"He is a good friend of mine. Carlo Broschi."

"Farinelli? The greatest of all castratos?"

"The greatest. He is curious to meet your son."

Wolfgang was curious to meet him. By now he understood why a castrato was a castrato, although Papa had never told him, and he accepted that as a fact of life and hoped that Manzuoli would sing in his new opera.

The next day he sat between Papa and Padre Martini as they rode out to the Villa Farinelli, and he wondered whether there was any real difference between the castrato and the priest since neither was supposed to have any children. But somehow, Manzuoli seemed a person apart from this; Manzuoli was a friend. Yet he kept asking himself: was castration the reason Padre Martini was so reserved?

The Villa Farinelli was as large and sumptuous as the Villa Pallavicini, and Farinelli himself was as fashionable as Padre Martini was austere, yet the two men were very friendly.

Farinelli's waistcoat glittered with precious stones, his white powdered wig was in the latest style, and his shoe buckles were of gold. He was sixty-five, but he looked much younger. He was tall, slender and moved like a courtier. His red lips, which were made up like the ladies of Versailles, were parted in his pale face, and his fawnlike eyes were quizzical as he greeted them and said, viewing Wolfgang, "So this is the boy they are all talking about?"

Papa said, "Would you like him to compose a fugue, sir?"

Farinelli nodded and showed Wolfgang his favorite harpsichord – he had many – and said, "This was given me by the late Queen of Spain, who had it built for Scarlatti, who taught her. You know who he was?"

"I have been playing his music since I was five."

"Then construct a fugue in the manner of Scarlatti."

After Wolfgang did, he sensed that even the reserved Padre Martini was impressed, which gratified Papa. But people made too much out of such things, he told himself, even Papa.

Papa said, "Most Reverend Father, I would like you to consider my son for your esteemed Bologna Accademia Filarmonica when we return from Rome."

"He is too young. We have never admitted anyone under twenty."

"You may never have had anyone before so qualified, Esteemed Father."

"Perhaps. We will see when you return."

Farinelli added, "When I was fourteen, I could not even sing correctly."

Wolfgang said, "I am not a castrato, sir."

"You are too old. Too bad, if all that you are supposed to know about music is true."

Papa said, hiding his annoyance, "Your Excellency, George III thinks it is true, and so does Louis of France and Maria Theresa."

"And anyone who puts their trust in royal favor is a fool."

Suddenly, on the way to Florence, Wolfgang wanted to halt and rest, he was so tired, but nothing was halting Papa. It was as if a frantic wheel turned in Papa that had to go on and on. They were being soaked by heavy rain, buffeted by violent winds, and Papa was pretending the harsh traveling conditions did not exist, saying, "Farinelli is bitter because after becoming the virtual prime minister of Philip of Spain by lifting the King out of his dejection by his masterly singing, the instant Philip died, his stepson, the new King, resenting the castrato's influence, had him exiled from Spain. But we must remember that even then, although he was a musician, he was able to retire very wealthy. As you could, some day."

Papa was distressed that Wolfgang had to stay in bed the first day in Florence, to recover from a cold he had caught during the stormy weather that had afflicted them while crossing the Apennines.

But the next morning he was able to present Count Firmian's letter of introduction to the chief steward, Count Orsini-Rosenberg. Although there were many in the antechamber who were ahead of Papa, the letter from the Governor-General obtained an immediate audience with Archduke Leopold, Maria Theresa's second son, and the ruler of Tuscany. The twenty-two-year-old Archduke remembered the Mozarts very well from Vienna, and insisted that Wolfgang play for his wife, the Infanta Louise of Spain.

The next evening there was a grand concert for the Archduke and his wife. Wolfgang still had traces of his cold, but it had no effect on his playing. Nardini, the finest violinist in Italy, accompanied Wolfgang in sonatas for the harpsichord and violin that Wolfgang had composed.

Never had he heard such tone on the violin as Nardini was producing. It had a richness that seemed to come straight from heaven. And the violinist had such a sensitivity to playing in balance with him. Yet he was sad at the realization that Papa would never be able to play with such a poignant intensity, or with Nardini's technique and skill.

The Archduke said to his wife, "I told you he could play like an adult."

Manzuoli, who was in the audience, congratulated him with a passionate hug, and said, "If it is at all possible, Amadeo, I will sing in your opera."

Later in the week Nardini, who was enchanted with Wolfgang, introduced him to his favorite pupil, Thomas Linley, an English boy who was the same size and age as Wolfgang. They played together so well that from then on, Wolfgang and Thomas were always with each other, practicing as one, performing as one, sharing experiences, planning to tour together; they could play in Italy, Germany, England, and as Thomas refreshed Wolfgang's English, Wolfgang taught him German. It was the first time that Wolfgang knew someone his own age who was his equal and he delighted in it.

When it came time to say goodbye after a dozen happy days, Thomas handed Wolfgang a sonnet, "On the Departure of W. A. Mozart from Florence," which the English boy had paid the poetess, Corilla Olimpica, to write for him. Minutes before Manzuoli had said goodbye, then Nardini, and now Tommasino. Just as he got to know someone, to care for him, to never want to be away from him, there were these wretched farewells.

Tommasino said, "Amadeo, this poem will consecrate your journey," and embraced him, and they both burst into tears.

Papa had to choke back his own tears. Tommasino was handsome and lovable; he would miss him, too. But they must hurry on: to have an audience with the Pope during Holy Week now seemed the absolute necessity.

Thomas Linley escorted their carriage as far as the city gate, and then stood waving and crying until they passed out of sight. Wolfgang sat in the rear of the sedia, and the more Papa reminded him of how successful they had been in Florence, the more the tears streamed down his cheeks, and he continued to stare backwards although now there was nothing to see.

TWENTY-NINE

It was Ash Wednesday when they arrived in Rome and Leopold insisted on visiting St. Peter's at once. He had learned there was to be a performance of Allegri's *Miserere* in the Sistine Chapel this day. He said they must hear it, as if that would speed an audience with the Pope.

By now Leopold was not sure why it had become such a necessity to see Clement XIV, except that it might influence Schrattenbach to grant permission for the Milan scrittura. He had put off writing His Grace, although a month had passed since he had signed the scrittura. Only a month, yet so much that was favorable had happened!

This restored his confidence and by the time they reached St. Peter's he knew what he had to do. He got instructions on how to reach the Sistine Chapel from a Swiss guard, who was impressed by his fine manners and clothes. Waving for Wolfgang to follow him, he led his son through the labyrinthine corridors to the Sistine Chapel and there, very much the courtier, he entered with Wolfgang, although he had no pass, but no one dared to halt such an important personage. The Pope was performing the service at the altar, and Leopold sought a quiet corner. He told Wolfgang to listen to the *Miserere*, "and if you can, write it down."

The *"if you can"* irritated Wolfgang. Did Papa doubt him? So he sat listening, seeing neither the paintings by Michelangelo nor the panoply of the Mass. The score had its own logic and unity and went on in a natural development and he had no difficulty following it. At the start he had seen that it was to be sung by a choir of nine voices, and he had divided that into four and five voices, and when it came to the final nine-part chorus that seemed inevitable. He sensed its intrinsic structure, for it had been devised with a definite need in mind, and by the time it ended he had the whole work in his head. He was doing this more and more with whatever he composed. He was surprised that, after Papa asked him to write down the *Miserere* from memory and he did so, Papa regarded it as a feat and wrote Mamma: "You are aware that the celebrated *Miserere* of Rome is held in such high esteem, that the musicians of the chapel are forbidden, under pain of excommunication, to take any part of it away, to copy it themselves, or to give it to any one. Yet *we have it already*, thanks to Wolfgang, who has put it down note by note from memory, and we could enclose it in this letter to Salzburg, if we did not need it for use here. But we will take it home with us, for since it is one of the great secrets of Rome, we cannot allow it to fall into other hands, and thus incur ecclesiastical censure."

The next day, Holy Thursday, at the foot-washing ceremony in St. Peter's, Leopold strode with assurance through the gaping crowd toward the table where the Cardinals sat. The fluency with which he spoke Italian and German, his splendid garb, his imposing walk, the elegance and richness of Wolfgang's rose-colored moiré and taffeta suit, and the pomp with which the footman he had hired informed the Swiss guards to make way erased every difficulty. He was gratified that many assumed that Wolfgang was a prince, and that he was his tutor. By the time they reached the final row of Swiss guards, they were ushered to the Cardinals' table with a flourish.

Wolfgang, on Leopold's instigation, stood beside Cardinal Pallavicini, whom they recognized from a picture they had seen at the Field-Marshal's villa. The Cardinal, attracted by the boy's aplomb, beckoned to him and asked, "Would you be good enough to tell me who you are?"

"Wolfgang Amadeo Mozart."

"Oh! Are you that famous boy of whom so much has been written?"

"Are you Cardinal Pallavicini?"

"Yes, yes! But why do you ask?"

"Your Eminence, we have a letter for you from His Excellency, Field-Marshal Pallavicini, and we would like to pay our respects."

"He has already written to me about you." The Cardinal motioned for silence as the foot-washing ceremonies began, but he indicated that the boy should stay by his side. After the Pope ended, the Cardinal said, "I must hear you play, as soon as Holy Week is over." As the Cardinal went to dismiss him, Wolfgang, sensing that nothing more was to be accomplished at this time whatever Papa thought, knelt before the Cardinal and kissed his hand and in response His Eminence complimented him on his piety.

Leopold was sorry that something could not be arranged during Holy Week, but he felt better when the Cardinal agreed to hear Wolfgang a few days after it. The concert was given at the Palazzo of

Prince Chigi, who invited the most celebrated people in Rome, and Leopold's program catered to the Cardinal's taste. He applauded warmly and said, "Signor Mozart, I am impressed with your son's devoutness and virtuosity, but it is not often that the Pontiff hears musical virtuosi in his chambers."

"Your Eminence, I have not suggested that."

"Yet it is what you desire, isn't it?"

"Sir, you have honored us with your solicitude."

"Something might be arranged for His Holiness' approval in several months."

"Your Eminence, we have been invited to play in Naples in two weeks."

They were interrupted by Christofori, one of the Papal singers. He did not believe that anyone could have written out the *Miserere* from memory, and he insisted on seeing what Wolfgang had done. Everyone gathered about Wolfgang and Christofori, even the Cardinal, who was frowning.

Suddenly Leopold was afraid that this had offended the Cardinal. But Wolfgang, who looked like a very small boy beside the very tall Papal singer, casually handed him the score and said quietly. "It is correct."

Christofori examined it while everyone stood silently. Cardinal Pallavicini asked, "Did he really write it down accurately note by note?"

"Your Eminence, it is absolutely correct."

Leopold said, "Your Eminence, I promise, no one will see it," and the Cardinal halted him imperiously and stated, "It is not as secret as you think. We have given copies to the King of Spain, to the Empress Maria Theresa, and to Padre Martini." Leopold waited apprehensively as the Cardinal asked Wolfgang, "Child, did you know that it is forbidden to take it out of the chapel?"

"Forbidden? Music forbidden? Your Eminence, it is so beautiful and devout, shouldn't everybody hear it? I did copy it correctly, didn't I?"

"Evidently." He thought the Field-Marshal and Count Firmian had not underestimated this boy's charm and wit. He turned to Leopold and said, "When you return from Naples, perhaps His Holiness will be able to see your son, although he has very little time for music." Then he left, followed by his retinue of chaplains, secretaries, footmen, and valets.

Leopold put off the trip to Naples, for now many more potential patrons wanted to hear Wolfgang. In the next two weeks there were many concerts, and enough cigliatis to pay their way to Naples and back.

He was deeply pleased when Florence offered a scrittura for an opera, and there was a similar offer from Rome. He regretfully declined these offers. And just before they departed for Naples, he wrote Schrattenbach, feeling he could not put it off any longer and that this was the opportune time. He stressed that the Pope intended to grant them an audience soon. He told him of Cardinal Pallavicini's approval, and Padre Martini's praise. He said there had been requests for Wolfgang to compose an opera for Milan, Rome, and Florence, and he asked permission for his son to compose the opera for Milan, and thus, he implied, for the Empress and Count Firmian.

Wolfgang wrote to Nannerl: "My Dearest Diligent Sister: God be praised, I and my leaky pen are busy and healthy, and I wish my sister were in Rome, for she would like this city, it is so regular and orderly. There are lovely flowers everywhere, and people sing on the streets, sometimes as if they were in Chapel, but often better.

"I am happy you enjoyed the minuet I wrote for Signor Pick, who danced it in the theater at Milan. I hope that it is danced better in Salzburg, for Signor Pick farted when he danced. When you receive the contredanse I wrote for you, tell me truthfully what you think of it.

"And if you are not busy with friends who sigh for you, will you send me the arithmetical tables, particularly the Art of Reckoning, for I lost mine traveling. Meanwhile, I have written a symphony since I last wrote you, and I will finish another symphony after this letter is done.

"Oh well, I have just drawn St. Peter with his keys, St. Paul with his sword, and I have had the privilege of kissing St. Peter's foot at his church, and since I have the bad luck to be so little, I, still the same old fool, W.A.M., had to be lifted up. And now we go to Naples, Tra la la.

"Papa says it is the home of opera, but we will see. I kiss you and Mamma a thousand times, and I am your horsefaced Wolfgango in Germania, Amadeo in Italia, and Mozarto – guess where?"

Naples was animated and noisy. The streets teemed with people as if the city were a vast anthill, and everyone seemed to have to speak at the top of their voice as if that were a ritual. Wolfgang liked the liveliness of the Neapolitans, but he disliked the loudness with which they conducted their business. The most ordinary conversation was carried on at a shout. In five minutes he heard more cursing, weeping, and yelling than he heard in a day in Vienna. He was told that opera singing was the genius of the Neapolitans, but their extravagantly emotional performances made him very uncomfortable. They went to the opera at every opportunity – when they were not calling on the Prime Minister, or the Imperial Ambassador, Count Kaunitz, or the

British Ambassador, Sir William Hamilton – but Wolfgang felt that the singers were more interested in spectacle than in substance.

So many of the Neapolitan singers were immoderate, he thought, their execution faulty, their tempo too fast, forcing their voices until they were virtually screaming and ending with a passion that was frenzied. The one opera whose score he liked, by Jommelli – although he felt the subject was too old-fashioned and serious for the theater – was a failure. Operas by Piccinni and Paisiello, which were full of sudden jumps from *piano* to *forte*, of abrupt alternations from high to low to high, of barbarous modulations, were greatly successful. It left him dismayed.

Opera was so much the vogue that Papa was able to arrange only one concert by Wolfgang. And while Papa was pleased with the result, for they were paid many cigliatis and there was an offer of an opera scrittura for Naples too. Wolfgang thought the Neapolitans had no delicacy or taste, for his audience had chatted and moved about during his performance.

He was happier visiting Vesuvius, which was smoking furiously, Pompeii, Herculaneum, the tomb of Virgil, the baths of Nero, and the Mediterranean.

Then while he was wishing that the Archbishop would grant the necessary permission for Milan, and that the libretto would arrive soon – his dissatisfaction with the Neapolitan operas had increased his own wish to compose – there was a letter from Cardinal Pallavicini.

Papa, looking gratified but mysterious, prepared to depart at once.

They left by the fastest mail coach. Leopold declared everywhere that he was the steward of the Imperial Ambassador, and was given the best horses and coaches; at Rome he did not even have to enter the Customs Office, but was bowed on. He did not tell Wolfgang that at the last change of horses, one of the horses had reared and in shielding Wolfgang from possible injury the falling dashboard had gashed his shin to the bone. He was proud that he was a stoic, and that they had sped from Naples to Rome in twenty-seven hours when it had taken four days before. Neither of them slept, and at the inn in Rome Wolfgang fell asleep in his chair. Leopold undressed him and put him to bed without his son stirring. And when Wolfgang awoke the next morning, he did not remember how he had gone to bed. He noticed that Papa was limping, but Papa said, "It is nothing. We must be at the Cardinal's as soon as possible. He invited us to lunch when we return."

"Is that what the letter was about?"

"Well – " Papa had seldom looked so optimistic – "about several things."

At lunch Cardinal Pallavicini addressed Wolfgang as "Signor Cavaliere", which surprised Leopold, who had assumed that the Papal Secretary of State had wanted to see them to arrange an audience with the Pope. The Cardinal, looking as mysterious as Leopold had earlier, thanked them for returning so promptly and said he would see them again soon. Leopold could do nothing but wait, while Wolfgang occupied himself with composing several new arias for Milan. When a week passed without any word Leopold cursed the Cardinal for being so secretive, then himself for allowing his enthusiasm to betray him.

On the day they were asked to appear at Cardinal Pallavicini's residence at the Palazzo Quirinale, Leopold could hardly endure the waiting.

The Cardinal said quietly, although he could not keep the tone of triumph out of his voice. "On June 26, His Holiness conferred the cross of the Order of the Golden Spur upon Amadeo Wolgango Mozart of Salzburg."

"June 26!" Leopold exclaimed in his astonishment. That had been the day they had arrived back in Rome.

"Yes, but we had to wait for the proper documents to be prepared."

"It is a great honor, Your Eminence!"

"The greatest that can be conferred upon a musician."

Wolfgang said softly, "Thank you, Your Eminence."

"You are welcome. This decision was reached only after the most serious consideration. Amadeo, listen!" Cardinal Pallavicini read part of the Papal Patent: "*We hearby make and create thee – whom we understand to have excelled since the earliest youth in the sweetest sounding of the harpsichord – Knight of the Golden Order, by the Apostolic authority.*"

The highest rank of this order, Leopold thought jubilantly.

As Wolfgang knelt at the Cardinal's feet, he placed the beautiful gold cross that hung from a red ribbon around his neck and said, "Signor Cavaliere, you are now a 'Knight of the Golden Spur'."

Wolfgang was pleased that Papa was so pleased.

"Wear it with honor and dignity," pronounced Cardinal Pallavicini.

"He will, Your Eminence, he will! We are indebted beyond words for your kindness!" cried Leopold. How could Schrattenbach refuse him now!

"There will be an audience with His Holiness in a few days."

Three days later Wolfgang, wearing the gold cross of the order, was granted an audience with Pope Clement XIV at his temporary residence, the Palazzo Santa Maria Maggiore. Count Firmian's steward, Don Ferdinando, was present, as if this honor had been bestowed upon his master also, and Cardinal Pallavicini and a number of lay and secular dignitaries.

Leopold was surprised by the importance given to Hieronymus Colloredo, the Bishop of Gurk. Ordinarily Bishops were not treated with such respect, particularly in the presence of Cardinals. He noticed this tall, slender churchman was attractive in a way that was worldly and cynical even for a Roman prelate, and he wondered who his friends were. Then he remembered that Colloredo was a powerful family in Vienna. His mind came back to the moment as the Pope addressed his son as *Chevalier* Mozart, he thought it was a vanity that Clement XIV was speaking French, and he was gratified that Wolfgang understood him. He could not tell if this great honor had changed his son, everyone was so formal – even Wolfgang.

Too formal, thought Wolfgang. He did not assume that these people here were necessarily his good friends, except perhaps, Don Fernando and Cardinal Pallavicini, and even there one could not be certain. He felt as if one should sing on such an occasion, and everybody was so solemn. Papa looked as if this homage indicated that he was crossing into another, better world, but he wondered if he was not trespassing. Melodies bubbled within him, and he wanted to laugh when people called him "Signor Cavaliere". Perhaps he should put that to music. How happy that would be!

That night while Papa wrote to Mamma of his knighthood, he added a postscript to Nannerl in a mixture of German, French, and Italian. "My Dearest Sister: I am astonished to see how well you can compose if you want to. Your song was lovely. You must try to compose more frequently. When you send me those six minuets by Michael Haydn that I like, add something of your own again. Give my best wishes to all my dear friends. I kiss Mamma's hands a thousand times, and you, Signorina, I create a Knight of the Golden Spur. Stay well, for here there is so much noise you cannot hear the music. *Cavaliere* Mozart – Tra la la – Ha Ha Ha."

THIRTY

When Field-Marshal Pallavicini heard that the Mozarts had returned to Bologna and were staying at a local inn, he invited them to be his guests at his villa. He grew insistent when he learned that Leopold was confined to his room because his leg was inflamed and it was painful to walk. He said, "You can stay as long as you like. And your leg will get better."

Leopold hesitated. He did not wish to appear too eager.

"Unless you have to be elsewhere. Venice? Milan?"

"Oh, no sir. I had planned to remain in Bologna for the summer. It is a beautiful city and Padre Martini wants Wolfgang to study with him."

"Then you must spend the summer with us."

"But I still cannot get around very well, sir. My right leg is still swollen and I cannot walk without a cane, and then with difficulty."

"You will have one of my carriages. And servants to help you."

The more Leopold hesitated, the more insistent the Field-Marshal became.

Their rooms were spacious and handsome, with marble floors and high ceilings and windows like Schönbrunn. Although it was August and broiling hot in the gardens outside, it was never too warm inside. And Wolfgang loved the feel of the fine linen on his skin, the comfort of large, separate beds. There were two servants to wait upon them, a valet and a footman, and the footman slept in the anteroom so as to be available whenever needed. He thought, how beautiful to have everything so fresh, clean, and pleasant. He wondered why it couldn't always be this way. He knew that they were not noblemen, whatever the Pope decreed, but that shouldn't make much difference. He could pay for it with his music. He felt so cheerful, and his happiness increased when he saw that Papa was in such good spirits and beginning to walk properly again.

Permission to compose the opera for Milan came promptly from Schrattenbach, who congratulated Leopold on the Apostolic benediction. Shortly afterward, the libretto arrived, and Leopold regarded this conjunction of events as a favorable omen, although the choice of a subject concerned him. Count Firmian had selected *Mitridate, Re di Ponto*, which the librettist, Cigna-Santi, had taken from a Racine tragedy.

Leopold told Wolfgang, "It is in a heavy opera *seria* style and very difficult to do." He sought to simplify the plot for him. "Mitridate's sons, Sifare and Farnace, believing that their father has been slain fighting Rome, woo their father's fiancee, Aspasia. She prefers Sifare, for Farnace has plotted with Rome against his father. When Mitridate discovers what has happened, he orders the execution of his sons and Aspasia. But his sons redeem themselves by attacking the Romans, and when Mitridate is killed Sifare and Aspasia are reunited."

Wolfgang shrugged. He was not impressed with the plot, but it would do.

Greater pleasure came from his growing friendship with Padre Martini. The Franciscan monk was impressed with the Pope's blessing.

Leopold presented Padre Martini with his *Violin School* and in return the monk gave Leopold his *Storia della Musica*, and inscribed it to "*Signor Leopoldo Mozart*," and to "*Cavaliere Amadeo Wolgango Mozart*."

Padre Martini said he would be honored to teach Amadeo, and their afternoons together became a ritual, for Wolfgang worked mornings on his opera, and evenings were spent with the Field-Marshal and other friends.

Now that Wolfgang knew Padre Martini better, the boy saw him as a slight, nervous musico who was caustic with bad music, who was more musical scholar than Franciscan monk, his real god, whatever he professed, music.

Padre Martini gave Wolfgang lessons in the strict polyphonic church music of the past, and was fascinated by the boy's industry.

Leopold gradually realized that Padre Martini was preparing Wolfgang for membership in the Accademia Filarmonica of Bologna, the most respected musical society in Italy. "But no one under twenty has ever been admitted," he blurted out one afternoon to Padre Martini.

The latter smiled and said, "Amadeo is not an ordinary applicant."

"But he has to be in Milan by October for rehearsals of his opera."

"He will be there in time. Be patient."

Leopold tried to follow his advice, for admission to the Accademia was a great honor. He grew concerned however, when the examination was postponed until October, and he hoped that it was worth the wait. As the decisive test Wolfgang was given the antiphon melody of a sixteenth-century Gregorian chant, and ordered to compose the three upper voices in the strict polyphonic style, and locked up in a room alone. Leopold was worried, for this construction was very difficult and not to Wolfgang's taste in composition. He felt better when Wolfgang finished in an hour – many took three hours for this test – and that Padre Martini examined the result.

But he did not like his son's irritation, which was unusual. He was quite anxious by the time Padre Martini made his recommendations. Yet when that was affirmative the vote for Wolfgang's admission to the Accademia with the rank of composer and Maestro was unanimous.

Wolfgang was not as proud as Papa. He had noticed that his composition was full of Padre Martini's corrections. Several days later, when Padre Martini handed him the diploma of the Accademia which made him a member, he said, "I really did not compose the upper voices perfectly, did I?"

"Perfection exists only in heaven. You have been admitted, haven't you?"

"With your assistance, Esteemed Father."

"With God's assistance, child. I merely expressed His wishes."

Wolfgang was still thinking about his mistakes when they arrived in Milan. Papa carried the diploma from the Accademia as if it were a great prize, and told everyone that he had passed the test perfectly, but that was not true. And while he loved and honored Padre Martini as a teacher and a friend, he did not respect his compositions, they were so old-fashioned. He should not have been compelled to compose in the ancient style. He had been forced to put dull things into the Gregorian chant because they had been traditional. The dryness of the colorless sixteenth-century music had bored him, although he had sought to hide this, and so, he had made mistakes. He must not distrust his own feelings any more.

Don Fernando rented lodgings for them, as had been agreed in the scrittura. But the two rooms in the private house were uncomfortable after the sumptuous quarters in the Field-Marshal's villa, and Papa had expected, that with all the honors, Count Firmian would be their host.

The steward sensed their dismay, although they were expressing gratitude for his efforts on their behalf, for he said, "I obtained these rooms so you would be near the theater, and Count Firmian's palazzo is far away."

Not by carriage, thought Papa, but he said, "The rooms are fine. I like the balcony and fireplace. We will have plenty of fresh air and heat."

And one bed for the two of them to sleep in, Wolfgang wanted to protest. He was tired of sharing the same bed with Papa, who was a restless sleeper. But he said nothing.

These things became secondary in the rush of rehearsals. Most of the singers had arrived and were waiting impatiently for their arias, which he was expected to compose for them on the spot. He had to be at their service, to please them, to fulfill whatever was their whim

Yet he had to be alone to create. There was so much to do and so little time to do it: a few weeks to compose twenty arias, an overture, a duet and a quartet – the recitatives had been completed in Bologna. Running back and forth from his rooms to the theater, it was as if he went in opposite directions. He stopped writing home. His fingers ached from composing. His eyes blurred from the strain and the wretched pen and ink.

He longed to compose music that was natural for him, light-hearted and gay, and Papa said that would be too sweet and sentimental for the text. But the plot of *Mitridate, Re di Ponto* was so pompous. He was not sure he could write music to fit its solemnity. He wished he could alter the text, but that was impossible. The poet was in Naples, adapting a libretto for Piccinni, and no one could touch the text without his permission.

There was another difficulty. Wolfgang arrived at the theater with Papa and Don Fernando to hear the prima donna, Antonia Bernasconi, sing her part of a duet he had composed for her and the prima uomo, and she complained, "It does not fit my voice. My arias should be composed by someone else. By a mature composer."

Don Fernando asked, "Have you tried this duet?"

"Why should I try it? Basta, I know what I can sing."

"His Excellency wants Signor Mozart's music sung, not your teacher's, Signor Lampugnani."

"But suppose they have to be rewritten, as is always the case?"

"They will be rewritten," said Don Fernando. "By Wolfgang."

Wolfgang said, "Perhaps this duet is too high for the Signora."

"My part is not high enough. I can sing with any male soprano."

Wolfgang altered her part while she watched skeptically, then gave it back to her, saying, "This should display your virtuosity as you wish."

She said she still could not sing the boy's music, and Don Fernando declared, "Signor Lampugnani was employed as an assistant conductor, not as a composer. If he violates his scrittura, he will not get another."

She discovered that she could attempt this duet, although she added, "The real test will be singing it with the primo uomo."

The next day, the primo uomo, Pietro Benedetti, said, "I cannot sing this with Bernasconi, she has all the high notes when I am the primo uomo."

"Signore," said Wolfgang, "I wrote your part for Manzuoli."

Papa groaned, such a tactless thing to say, but he mustn't speak – he would be accused of interfering and there was too much talk of that already.

Wolfgang was proud of his taste; he had not added what was obvious, Benedetti did not compare with Manzuoli. Believing Manzuoli's promise to sing in his opera, he had conceived this role for his voice. Only Manzuoli had demanded a thousand ducats, and Don Fernando, who controlled the expenditures, said that was absurd, for such a sum they could bring Farinelli, the most famous name in opera, out of retirement. Yet Wolfgang also knew that no singer's aria must surpass the castrato's in prominence or brilliance; this was a rule that was sacred in Italy. He said, "I wrote it for Manzuoli to show how beautifully a primo uomo could sing."

Benedetti sneered, "I do not have to strain to reach my high notes."

Bernasconi retorted, "You can't reach mine."

He shouted, "I am the male soprano here, not Signora Bernasconi!"

She snarled, "I am the true soprano!"

For an instant Wolfgang thought the two sopranos would leap at each other's throat. Then he realized they were playing a game, that it was safer to scream at each other, that claws would draw their own blood.

Benedetti cried, "I am embarrassed by her lack of taste."

Bernasconi yelled, "That is a filthy thing to say!"

Wolfgang said, "You both have taste. That is why I wrote the music the way I did." After all, he was not addressing a herd of swine. "Signore, if you prefer the duet higher, I will be happy to please you."

The castrato stamped his foot indignantly and cried, "Basta! to keep my voice high I would be castrated again!"

Don Fernando halted the prima donna before she could comment and said, "Count Firmian does not want this opera delayed any longer. After Signor Cavaliere Mozart rewrites this duet as he has kindly agreed, rehearsals will be resumed. If not, we will find other singers who can sing this music, Manzuoli and La Bastardella if necessary."

Both singers said with one voice, Thank heaven for such fine music, they just did not want anyone to think that Milan opera was inferior.

Mitridate, Re di Ponto was given its first performance the day after Christmas. Leopold sat proudly in a box and looked down upon Wolfgang seated at the harpsichord and about to conduct the orchestra for his opera. Whatever the reception of the production he had accomplished another objective: his son had become an acknowledged professional opera composer. Count Firmian sat in the royal box; Sammartini and Hasse were in another box; Field-Marshal Pallavicini was in a third box. Leopold longed to cry out in his joy, and then, as the overture was about to start, he noticed that Wolfgang was nervous, which was unlike his son. Wolfgang was to conduct the first three performances and Lampugnani the others; but this was the vital one. Leopold's right arm, his conducting arm, began to ache. He knew it was from rheumatism, yet the pain began to ease when the overture was played smoothly. Then as the arias commenced and his son's conducting gathered a new assurance all the pain vanished.

The duet for the primo uomo and the prima donna received an ovation, and as the curtain came down the two singers pulled Wolfgang on to the stage to share the applause, and Count Firmian stood up and shouted, "Bravo! Bravo! Il Signor Cavaliere Filarmonico!" The audience took that up with a rhythmic chant, and even Sammartini and Hasse joined in.

Wherever they went in Italy, Wolfgang was addressed by that title. After the opera played to full houses for twenty performances, they left Milan and visited Turin, Vicenza, Padua, and Venice, but now it was a vacation, just to be enjoyed, although Wolfgang was acclaimed everywhere.

They returned to Salzburg a year to the day they had met Cardinal Pallavicini. Leopold felt like a conqueror. He was coming home with a new opera scrittura for the carnival season of 1772 in Milan, and there were rumors of a scrittura from Maria Theresa herself.

However, Wolfgang hoped that whatever the opera commission, the text would be more to his liking. Despite the approval of Milan, he did not share Papa's enthusiasm for the music of *Mitridate, Re di Ponto*. Intelligent, yes, and workmanlike, he agreed with that judgment of Papa's, but that was not enough. Then he was in Mamma's arms, kissing her and Nannerl, laughing and crying in his joy, and everything else was forgotten.

THIRTY-ONE

How Wolfgang had grown, Mamma marveled. The clothes that had been made for him in Salzburg were now much too tight and small. Mamma held him at arm's length then, to observe him better, and wiped away her own tears while Nannerl hugged Papa as if she would never let him go.

Papa showed them the gold cross, the diplomas from Bologna and Verona, and said, "We earned all the expenses of the trip to Italy, and I still have what the Archbishop gave me, and in addition to the opera, Wolfgang composed other arias, four symphonies, minuets, several religious scores, a string quartet," and Wolfgang, impatient with what he knew already, asked "Nannerl, does Herr Canary still sing? Can he still make a G?"

"Of course," said Nannerl. "Remember how he used to sing with you."

But he ran into the music room to see for himself, and he was dismayed that the canary refused to sing for him, but huddled in a corner of its cage, afraid, not recognizing him. He started to sing to arouse it, but halted, and when Nannerl, who had followed him, asked why, he cried out. "I can't! My voice has changed. I cannot go high or low. My voice is completely gone. I cannot even sing my own airs!" He looked so plaintive that Nannerl had to console him.

He felt better when he was greeted warmly by Barbara von Mölk and Theresa Barisani. The girls knew of his honors – all Salzburg knew, they said – and at first they were shy, as if he was above them.

Sunday, however, Barbara sat next to him in the cathedral while the Archbishop conducted the services, and when he whispered, "You have become very pretty while I was away," she blushed, yet she was pleased that he had noticed, especially since he was so famous.

He was glad he was close to her; Theresa was plain now by comparison. Barbara's small, fine features were rounded to just the right curve. Her lips were a bit thick, slightly different from the rest of her face, and inviting. Only her rosy cheeks – her Salzburg complexion he called it, caused by the constant wind and rain – was not reminiscent of the Italian girls he had desired. Her eyes seemed to say, "I am glad to see you, I am!"

He said, "Remember, Waberl!" – his pet name for her – "how we used to act out the name of Schrattenbach by making the sound of Sh . . ." She hushed him, but she did not blush, but grinned – this was the Wolferl she remembered.

Yet he had changed, she thought. He had grown, although he would probably never be tall, for he was still short for his age, and he was more attentive and courtly. He had such self-assurance she no longer felt the difference in their ages – she was four years older – and he held her hand all through the services. He did not want to talk about the music he had composed in Italy, except some minuets he had written for her and had sent her. He wanted her to take a carriage ride with him.

She said, "The weather is too uncertain."

He said, "But I am not."

He was annoyed that Schrattenbach wanted to congratulate him on the Pope's honor. But she promised to wait, so he was polite, although impatient.

His Grace said, "You have served me well. Cardinal Pallavicini wrote me about your piety and your music, and said both were a credit to Salzburg."

Wolfgang knelt and replied, "Thank you, Your Grace, I am honored by – "

Papa interrupted him in his need to remind the Archbishop, "Wolfgang is an honorary Kapellmeister in Bologna and Verona now, Your Grace, and as you said, he has brought fame to Salzburg although he is just the third Konzertmeister and unpaid," and Schrattenbach cut him short with acerbity, "I am aware of your son's abilities," and dismissed them.

Papa was distressed, but Wolfgang was grateful, for Barbara was waiting. He was happy that she had kept her word, although she refused to go for a ride. As they strolled along the Salzach, she asked, "Did you miss me?"

"Very much."

"And Salzburg?"

He shrugged. "One city is like another, except Vienna and London."

"Even Milan?"

"Milan likes opera," as if that took care of Milan. He wanted to kiss her, but she backed away.

She added, "I did like those minuets you composed for me."

"And if I composed some more for you?"

209

She did not say yes, but her smile was sympathetic and seductive. "Agreed!" He demanded payment at once.

Barbara noticed that his mouth had become voluptuous, that he was full of hope and desire. She knew she should deny him, it was too soon, she was older, he was still a boy, she was not a coquette. But he was so insistent, she could not refuse him.

The next morning Wolfgang stared into his mirror and thought of how he could improve his appearance. He kept recalling the swing of her hips, her well-developed bosom. Papa was saying that he must resume practicing, and he was thinking of her voice. She was not musical, but she spoke well – he could not endure girls who spoke badly. As he sat at the harpsichord he counted the days until he could see her again.

Every Sunday he went for a walk with Barbara after services. But she never allowed him more than an occasional kiss, even after he composed the minuets for her. Yet when his lips touched hers, although he longed for deeper expressions of emotion, he was stimulated with a sudden intense joy.

The afternoon Papa came home with a new commission, as excited as Papa had ever been, Wolfgang, involved with his dreams of Barbara, could not share his enthusiasm. Papa announced to the family, "I have a letter from Count Firmian, inviting Wolfgang, in the name of the Empress, to compose a serenata to celebrate the marriage of her son, the Archduke Ferdinand, to Princess Beatrice of Modena in Milan this October."

Wolfgang longed to tell Papa of his feelings for Barbara, only he could not endure it if Papa laughed at him.

"The scrittura is really from the Empress herself. It is the greatest distinction we have received so far, and the greatest opportunity." Papa's tone changed from joy to exasperation. "Wolfgang, you aren't listening?"

"I am to do another opera for Milan."

"Serenata! Hasse is doing the opera."

"I am sure he will do a good one."

"Hasse will be your competitor. You must be careful how you praise him."

Mamma asked, "What about Salzburg? Wolfgang is a Konzertmeister now."

"Without pay and without duties! In Italy he is acclaimed everywhere."

"Nonetheless, the Archbishop does pay you, when you are here."

"And is sarcastic when I suggest any commissions for Wolfgang."

"He has not been well. Schachtner says he may not have long to live."

"Yet he seeks to keep us tied to him. But we may outwit him."

"Leopold, Nannerl and I would like to go with you. We miss you so much when you are away."

"That is impossible," he replied sternly. "The traveling would exhaust you. But after Wolfgang and I return from Milan, if he does not obtain a post with the Archduke, we must find new quarters. We can no longer sleep together like soldiers. Nannerl and Wolfgang are no longer children."

"Do you think the Archduke will engage Wolfgang permanently?"

"Anna Maria, we have good and great friends in Italy. And the Empress has always been favorably disposed towards us. Hasn't she, Wolfgang?"

Wolfgang wasn't listening. He was in a corner with Nannerl, asking her to convey his messages to Barbara. She said she would. She was sympathetic, as if this was a bond between them.

Ascanio in Alba was the serenata chosen by Count Firmian, with the approval of Maria Theresa. It placed the marriage of the Archduke in a heroic setting, with the Empress, in the role of Venus, as the matchmaker and heroine. Wolfgang did not care for the libretto, but he did not complain, for Don Fernando told him that the librettist, Guiseppe Parlini, was a favorite of the Count's which was warning enough.

The kind of stage representation did not matter to him at this moment; it was the music and the sentiments that he was to depict that counted. He could not feel heroic about the Archduke, who was a slight, pale boy, or be romantic about the Princess, who was homely by comparison with Barbara, but he could visualize himself and Barbara as the young lovers in the serenata and he sought to convey that with sweetness and grace.

His composing was stimulated by the arrival of Manzuoli to sing the main role. As he and the castrato worked together on the latter's songs, it became another love affair for Wolfgang. Manzuoli's singing was so beautiful it enthralled him. The day Manzuoli sang the finale, Wolfgang could hardly contain his happiness.

Manzuoli said, "Amadeo, this is a lovely song."

Wolfgang's eyes were wet. He had never heard his music sung so divinely.

"And a joy to sing."

"I wrote it just for your voice."

"I hope you will always give me such music to sing."

"Signor Maestro, I will try!"

"Amadeo, if you want me for your next Milan opera, I will be honored."

Wolfgang was ecstatic. "*I* will be honored!"

Manzuoli kissed him fervently on the cheek to seal this compact.

Later that day Wolfgang sat at his desk and longed to write to Nannerl what his exalted heart felt, but it was too private, too solemn. So instead, he joked in his postscript to Papa's letter to Mamma: "My Dearest Sister: We have had to endure terrible heat and the dust has treated us with such insolence that we would have suffocated if we had not been so clever. Here in Milan it has not rained for over a month.

"What you promised – you remember well – you must not forget to do, and I will be very grateful, and I will have more music for her soon.

"The chief news is that the Princess has diarrhea and everyone is worried that the wedding will be postponed, but never fear, they will make her vomit and so it will come out at both ends.

"And so it is with us. Above us there is a violinist, beneath us there is another fiddler, next door there is a singing master who gives lessons at all hours, across the hall is an oboist who never stops practicing. But I like it. It is good for composing. It gives me many ideas. Give Mamma a kiss for me. Manzuoli sings wonderfully. Addio. Your sleepy but faithful brother."

The evening after the wedding Hasse's opera was given for the royal couple. This was the most important musical event, but Leopold thought the opera dull, while Wolfgang was preoccupied with his serenata.

This was performed the following night and Leopold was pleased that it received more applause than Hasse's work. The royal couple were delighted with Manzuoli's arias, and applauded them so loudly they had to be encored. At the finale both of them leaned out of the royal box in the direction of Wolfgang, conducting at the harpsichord, and cried, "Bravissimo, Maestro!" and this was repeated by the entire house.

Archduke Ferdinand ordered *Ascanio in Alba* to be performed again, and several days later he ordered two copies of the score, one for himself, and one for his brother, the Emperor Joseph II. Leopold and Wolfgang were approached constantly on the street by cavaliers and other people who wanted to congratulate the composer.

Gratified, Leopold told Wolfgang, "I am sorry to have to say it, but your piece has destroyed Hasse's opera, and everyone is amazed that a fifteen-year-old could do this. It could lead to great things."

And he felt that the time to approach the Archduke had come when he and Wolfgang were invited to the grand reception Count Firmian gave for the royal couple. There were many guests whom he knew, the Field-Marshal, Cardinal Pallavicini, Hasse, Sammartini, but Leopold had eyes only for the Archduke. He waited until he saw the Archducal pair standing in the music room with Count Firmian, who was showing them through his Palazzo. What an auspicious place for such an audience, thought Leopold. He moved so he and Wolfgang were directly in the Archduke's view, and as he hoped, the Archduke indicated a desire to speak to the Mozarts.

The new Archduchess slipped off her glove and held out her hand for Wolfgang to kiss, which he did dutifully. She smiled graciously and said, "I hope we will have the pleasure of hearing more of your music soon."

"Whenever you wish, Your Highness. Now, if you like," said Wolfgang.

"I would adore it, but we are so busy tonight."

Count Firmian said, "Your Highness, think of how much pleasure you could have with as able a musico as Signor Amadeo at your service."

There was a sudden silence. The Archduchess glanced at her husband for her reply, and he said slowly, "There are many things to consider."

"But it is worth considering, isn't it, sir?"

"Signor Amadeo is a most unusual musico. I heard him play for my mother at Schönbrunn when he was very young. Eight, I think."

"Six, six and a half," said Leopold. "Begging Your Highness' pardon."

Count Firmian said impatiently, "Amadeo is a man now, almost sixteen. Signor Mozart, do you think your son is qualified to be a Kapellmeister?"

Leopold replied, as the Count had expected, "He is already in Bologna and Verona, Your Excellency, and a Konzertmeister in Salzburg."

Count Firmian turned to the Archduke and said, "Sir, Signor Amadeo is passionately loved in Italy. His appointment to your court would add to the great affection in which you are already held."

The Archduke said, "It is an interesting idea." But before Leopold could feel festive he added, "Would he be free to leave Salzburg? Archbishop Schrattenbach is our good friend." He looked to Leopold for an answer.

Suddenly Leopold, although he felt frightened, was furious. In his anger all he could see was Archduke Ferdinand's childish, pimply, bony face, with a nose far too large for his small features. To cater to this child seemed the worst humiliation of all. How dare this boy judge his son! But they were waiting for his answer, yet if he said what he was thinking it would cause a scandal Wolfgang would not survive.

Count Firmian said gently, to indicate his friendliness, "I understand that Archbishop Schrattenbach financed your trip to Italy so that your son could obtain a situation commensurate with his talents."

"Yes, Your Excellency!" exclaimed Leopold. The Count was clever. "We do not possess the proper musical resources in Salzburg, Your Highness," he sighed sadly, bowing to the Archduke who seemed to be listening attentively. "But Milan is a great city, and we would be honored to contribute to the glorious days of your reign."

"What do you propose, Herr Mozart?" asked Archduke Ferdinand.

"My son can gratify your every wish, sir. Play the harpsichord, violin, organ, compose whatever you desire, opera, divertimento, symphony. . ."

"I know. But that does not make a Kapellmeister."

"Your Highness, you saw how skillfully he conducted."

"Charmingly," said the Archduchess. "He looked most attractive."

The Archduke asked, "Amadeo, do you want to be Kapellmeister here?"

Wolfgang was not certain. But Papa was so anxious, he said, "I want to be whatever will please Your Highness." He smiled at Ferdinand warmly and courteously, and suddenly the Archduke found himself smiling back.

But what would his mother say? She had taught him that as a ruler he must never give a direct answer. Hasse was approaching with Cardinal Pallavicini and he used this as an opportunity to change the subject. He congratulated Hasse on the beauty of his opera, and Hasse replied sadly, "It was not beautiful enough for Milan, they preferred the serenata."

Count Firmian said, "The serenata was a noble piece of music."

"Yes," said Hasse, "its beauty lessens the pain of my last opera."

"Your last opera!" cried Leopold. "That would be a great loss, Maestro."

"I wonder. In any event, I am leaving the field to your son."

Leopold asked suspiciously, "What about Piccinni? Gluck?"

"Amadeo will put us all in the shade."

Archduke Ferdinand asked, "Do you honestly mean that?"

"Your Highness, I am too old to have to say anything else." Hasse was amused that the prouder Leopold became, the more unconcerned was Wolfgang. "*Ascanio in Alba* is just a beginning, not an end."

Leopold cried out, "Sir, may I present a petition in behalf of my son?"

"If you wish."

"You will give it your most serious consideration, Your Highness?"

Archduke Ferdinand wanted to answer yes. The chorus of praise had convinced him. But he must consult his mother, although no one must know this, not even his wife. He said in his most haughty manner to show that he was still the last word, "I will give the matter some thought."

The period of waiting became easier for Leopold when Wolfgang was given a present from Maria Theresa as a reward for the serenata, a gold watch with her portrait in enamel. It was even more reassuring when he learned that it exceeded her gift to Hasse for the opera, a simple gold snuff box.

He was surprised that the answer to his petition was brought by Don Fernando. He had expected an audience with the Archduke.

"His Highness has been called away," said the steward.

"And Count Firmian?" he asked, suddenly apprehensive.

"His Excellency had to accompany him."

"So the answer is no."

"My dear friend, Amadeo has earned a great deal of money as a musician."

"Is that what you come to tell me?"

Don Fernando shrugged. "I was told to inform you that the Imperial Treasury has made no provision for any new musical appointments."

"What is the real reason?"

Don Fernando said guardedly, "The Archduke told Count Firmian that he could not use Amadeo because it would be depriving his family's good friend, Archbishop Schrattenbach, of two valued servants."

"And Count Firmian did not object?"

"Count Firmian is your friend. He is disappointed, too. But the Archduke is now the ruler of Lombardy." As the steward saw Leopold's despair, he added, "You could try the Archduke Leopold in Tuscany when you return for the opera the next festival season. He is older than Ferdinand, more mature. He will not fear your son so much."

"Fear?"

"Just a way of putting it. We all love Signor Amadeo still."

Wolfgang, who had just entered, asked, "Then we will be going home now, Papa?"

"Unless we are asked to stay." But the steward became melancholy, and Leopold realized that to remain would be humiliating. Yet if he could have only spoken to someone with understanding, like Maria Theresa.

Archduke Ferdinand had consulted her; he had intended to employ Wolfgang until she had changed his mind by writing him: "You ask me about taking into your service the young Salzburg musician. I do not know in what capacity, believing that you have no need for a composer, or for useless people. If, however, it would give you pleasure, I do not wish to prevent you. What I say is intended only to urge you not to burden yourself with useless people, and not to give such people permission to represent themselves as belonging in your service. It gives one's service a bad name when such people run about like beggars; he has, besides, a large family."

Ferdinand did not tell anyone of this letter. The Archduke wanted everybody, but especially his wife and Count Firmian, to believe that he had made the decision.

Leopold and Wolfgang returned to Salzburg. Anna Maria wanted to know the real reason the Archduke Ferdinand had rejected the petition, and Leopold tried to accept the one that had been given him and said, "The Archduke was unable to employ Wolfgang because he didn't want to offend his family's friend, Archbishop Schrattenbach, by depriving him of two valued servants."

Wolfgang did not believe that. The day after they arrived in Salzburg the Archbishop died.

=

PART FIVE

Salzburg–The In-between Years

THIRTY-TWO

The first audience with the new ruler of Salzburg was an anxious one for Leopold. As he and Wolfgang waited in the familiar and beautiful Rittersaal of the Residenz, he was in no mood to enjoy the lovely paintings on the ceiling or the palatial sense of space. Months had passed since the death of Schrattenbach, it had taken an unusually long time to elect his successor and the court of Vienna had interfered, which was contrary to the custom, and their choice had been viewed by most of Salzburg with suspicion. The new Archbishop, Count Hieronymus Colloredo, the former Prince Bishop of Gurk, was reputed to be a worldly aristocrat who had governed his previous post with severity.

Leopold thought, I must try again in Italy despite Ferdinand's rejection. Inevitably at the memory of the Archduke, he asked himself why he had failed and he could not find an answer. Yet he must attempt Italy once more. And escape from Salzburg. There had been so little music since the death of Schrattenbach hardly anything had been accomplished.

Wolfgang, sitting by his side on the ornate settee, felt different. There had been no improvement in his courtship of Barbara, and there had been no opera in Salzburg and he missed that, but he was full of a new music and a new happiness. It was as if he had discovered the symphony, although he had composed many already. The symphonies he had heard in Italy were different from those he had heard before, and he wanted to follow their form, but to put in his own notes. Papa was worrying about the new Archbishop, so on edge he could not sit still, and a graceful melody was running through his head and it must be memorized before it was lost. How could Papa have stopped composing! He was just beginning, although Papa said that he had composed over a hundred pieces; Papa kept a record of such things, but he could not be bothered. It was not important to think of what

he had done; the joy was in the doing. To celebrate his sixteenth
birthday his own way he had composed a symphony in A Major. And
now, several months later, there was this new theme that demanded
to be heard. He became so absorbed in it that he did not hear Count
Arco summoning him to their audience with the new Archbishop.

Count Arco asked, "Daydreaming, Wolfgang?" He was amused by
the boy's preoccupation. But then, musicians were seldom in the real
world.

"No." He thought, Music is never dreaming, but the court chamberlain was not one to understand this.

"What were you doing?"

When Wolfgang did not reply, Leopold said, "He is composing."

"Here? In the Rittersaal?" Count Arco did not believe him.

"Why not," said Wolfgang. "Is there anything wrong with it?"

Count Arco shrugged, and led them into their new ruler.

Archbishop Colloredo stood behind a brilliantly ornamented desk
in the Audienzsaal studying a large map, and he motioned for the
Mozarts to wait in a corner until he finished. Count von Mölk, court
chancellor and Barbara's father, was showing the Archbishop the
boundaries of his domain and the Archbishop was dissatisfied. His
principality was eighty miles long and forty miles wide, but he had
been promised a larger realm in Vienna.

Count von Mölk looked distressed at the Archbishop's complaints
and explained, "Your Grace, our neighbors are Austria and Bavaria.
We are fortunate to possess what we have."

Wolfgang noticed that the Archbishop was ignoring their presence,
yet his tone had become more autocratic with their entrance. It was
as if he wanted them to overhear what he was saying, so they would
know where the final authority was, and in the same instant he was
placing them in a subservient position. Count Arco stood awkwardly
against the tapestries, looking like a simpleton for bringing them too
early, yet this was what His Grace had ordered, and Papa pretended
to be at ease but stood dumbly by the court chamberlain. Wolfgang
tried to capture the melody that had been in his head while they had
waited in the Rittersaal, but now it was gone. Angry, and that was
rare for him, he found himself listening to what was going on, which
was evidently Colloredo's wish, since his voice had not altered with
their entrance. But Wolfgang pretended that he was not listening,
determined not to give the Archbishop the satisfaction.

Colloredo was asking, "What about our revenues, von Mölk?"

Count von Mölk replied proudly, "Your Grace, our province's
revenue is two hundred thousand gulden a year. There is, also,
twenty thousand gulden for your private purse. And, of course, you
are the absolute master of all the revenues of the principality."

"I know that. Do we have a standing army?"

"We have raised forces of eight thousand men on occasion, although it hasn't been necessary lately."

"But if it were?"

"Your Grace, we haven't been invaded since the sixteenth century!"

"This is the eighteenth. How many musicians are employed now?"

"Eighty, Your Grace, when they are all here."

"We will increase that to a hundred. But no one will be paid who is not here." He looked stern and abruptly dismissed the court chancellor.

However, the expression that Archbishop Colloredo turned to the Mozarts was benign. He motioned for them to approach and stated, "I met you in Rome, when you had your audience with His Holiness. You must remember."

"Of course, Your Grace!" exclaimed Leopold, who had not remembered.

Wolfgang, who had not remembered either, did not answer.

There was a pause as they glanced at each other.

Archbishop Colloredo saw the Mozarts as servants, but perhaps useful, since they were better known in the courts of Europe than most servants. And the father was properly humble, but the boy eyed him with a coolness that was almost impertinence. Too much praise too young, he decided, but he smiled, not wishing to reveal his true feelings.

Vienna must have interfered, Leopold thought, positive that Colloredo was not a pious man. He reproached himself for not having been more aware that Colloredo was the eldest son of the Imperial vice-chancellor, one of Maria Theresa's main advisors, a rich and powerful man.

Wolfgang was conscious that the Archbishop's half-closed eyes suggested indifference, when actually, he was observing everything. It oppressed him, although Colloredo was signaling for him to receive his blessing.

When Wolfgang rose, after kneeling for the Archbishop's benediction, he was uncomfortable. He felt so short. Colloredo stood so he towered over him. Colloredo seemed to want him to feel small. And as Wolfgang looked up he realized that Colloredo was a tall man with long, slender hands, and a thin, narrow face with yellow, veiled eyes.

Count Arco, who had been self-effacing up to now, said suddenly, "Herr Mozart, you are the first musicians to be presented to His Grace."

"I am honored," said Leopold, almost by rote now.

"I am curious how you found music in Italy," said the Archbishop.

"Exciting. Wolfgang was acclaimed everywhere, Your Grace."

The Archbishop stated, "The best music is in Italy."

Wolfgang wondered why Colloredo had asked if he knew.

"Mozart, you may not like it, but you cannot deny that Italians are more musical than Germans. Or do you feel different, boy?"

"Italian music? There is only good music and bad music."

"What do you consider good music, child?"

"Christian Bach's."

"The English Bach?"

"He was born in Germany, sir."

Leopold hurried to say, "And educated in Italy, Your Grace. Bach studied with Padre Martini, who treated Wolfgang like his own son."

Colloredo said impatiently, "We are aware of the ability of the Italians to be enthusiastic. But we will see for ourselves. Mozart, we want your boy to write an opera for my consecration. And if it is worthy, Konzertmeister Wolfgang Mozart will be paid one hundred and fifty gulden annually, when he is in Salzburg." The Archbishop halted their thanks and stated, "Chancellor von Mölk will make the customary financial arrangements."

THIRTY·THREE

The libretto selected to celebrate the consecration of Hieronymus Colloredo as Archbishop was *Il sogno di Scipione*. It was supposed to be by Metastasio, and so it was assumed that it would be worthy of this occasion, but Wolfgang learned that the Vienna court poet had taken it from someone else, and that the someone else had borrowed it from Cicero.

The story was about Scipio the Younger, and it reeked with a flattery and self-righteousness that sickened Wolfgang. He could not regard it seriously, yet Papa said he must, or the Archbishop would be offended.

Wolfgang thought this was the worst libretto yet, there were no singers in Salzburg worth writing for, and the staging was static. It had to be sung as a recital, since there were no facilities for opera production in Salzburg, and Wolfgang doubted that this mattered to Colloredo anyhow.

But Papa wanted him to have the salary – Papa said it would help them bargain elsewhere – and he did his best. He was grateful for the brevity of the libretto and he quickly finished the twelve arias and focused on the instrumental music, for here there was some competence in Salzburg. He wrote the overture as he would have written an Italian sinfonia and that gave him pleasure. What gave him the most pleasure was the performance, for that marked the end of the work.

Archbishop Colloredo regarded the opera with moral approval and declared, "Metastasio is a great poet," and waited for everyone to agree.

And in the large, magnificent Konferenzsaal, where the performance had occurred, everyone agreed and crowded around the Archbishop.

Suddenly Wolfgang stood all alone. Even Papa was by the side of the Archbishop, while Mamma and Nannerl were speaking to Count

Arco. Had his music been that bad? All at once he longed to turn his back on Salzburg. He saw Barbara in the throng about Colloredo; but in Italy he would be the one applauded. He reached the marble doorway, determined to depart before anyone saw his tears – he must not cry, not in public, he was too old to cry, it was not manly – when someone took his arm. He looked around and saw that it was Schachtner, regarding him affectionately. He gulped and sought to choke back his tears but he could feel his eyes becoming misty, although he managed to say, "What do you think of it?"

"Considering the dreadful libretto, it was remarkable that you were able to make any of it musical."

"You are not lying to me?"

"Have I ever?"

"No."

"I particularly enjoyed the music you wrote for the orchestra."

"But the singers were so bad!"

Schachtner was pleased to see that Wolfgang's tears had stopped. He had loved him so much as a child and still did, although they saw each other far less. He said, "You will have better singers in Milan."

"If the Archbishop will let us go."

"He will, as long as you are respectful to him."

"Then you think I shouldn't leave?"

"Not until you pay your respects to him."

"I am just a humble third Konzertmeister."

"You are nothing of the kind, and you know it."

He was touched by Schachtner's interest. When Papa took him by the other arm and brought him before the Archbishop, he bowed dutifully, and thanked Colloredo for allowing him to write an opera for Salzburg. And Colloredo was polite, saying, "I liked the Italian flavor of the music."

It was a relief when Nannerl finally approached him and he was able to be himself. She apologized for the delay in congratulating him, whispering, "Old Count Arco had to tell us how much he had helped you get this commission, he must have put his claws on me a dozen times," and he retorted, "Claws, claws, one has the curse and some have the purse. Tell me, my dearest horseface, was my music any good?"

She grinned and said, "You idiot, your notes did harmonize, even if the singers didn't." She kissed him on the cheek as a reward and he felt better. They strode out of the Residenz hand in hand, counting the steps as they used to, and laughing gaily.

Soon afterward Wolfgang's pay started. But before he could enjoy it, it stopped, for he and Papa were on their way to Milan again, to compose the opera for the carnival season of 1772.

They arrived in Milan in early November. The weather was fine, and Don Fernando provided them with comfortable lodgings and greeted them warmly.

Leopold was suspicious, yet it was difficult to resist the steward, the latter was so friendly. Don Fernando embraced him and exclaimed, "The opera will be superb! *Lucio Silla* has a fine libretto, very dramatic, very gloomy, and many big scenes!"

Wolfgang did not share the steward's enthusiasm, except for several scenes between the lovers. He thought the plot obvious as he memorized how Lucio Silla, a Roman dictator, desired the lovely Giunia, who was engaged to Cecilio, a Roman senator and the dictator's enemy. Lucio Silla condemned Cecilio to death so that he could possess Giunia. Wolfgang was not interested in how the dictator in a burst of nobility forgave Cecilio and allowed him to wed Giunia. He did not believe it.

But the duets for the lovers gave him the opportunity to express his own romantic feelings; he composed this music with passion. Two of the finest artists in Italy were singing the lovers, prima donna Anna de Amicis, and primo uomo Venanzio Rauzzini. Papa said it would be sensible to give them the best music. After Wolfgang recovered from his disappointment that Manzuoli was not singing the primo uomo role as the castrato had promised – Manzuoli had demanded a thousand ducats, which the management had refused to pay – he wrote sensuous and showy arias for the lovers. Pen in hand, he was happy. He scored the romantic passages with tender caresses.

The rehearsals progressed favorably. Mysliveček called on the Mozarts to pay his compliments; Hasse invited them to dinner; Sammartini was honored that they could attend a concert of his music.

By the date of the opening, December 26, the omens were auspicious. But at the Teatro Regio Ducal the opera could not start. Curtain time was listed for five in the afternoon but it was assumed that the performance would wait until half past five to allow the latecomers to arrive. And it was six now, and *Lucio Silla* had not begun. His Royal Highness had not arrived, and until he did the opera could not commence.

Leopold stood in his box and looked at the orchestra where Wolfgang sat at the harpsichord prepared to conduct the first performance of his opera as was the custom, and did not know what to think. The theater was so crowded that not another person could get in. The crush was very uncomfortable, and the air was oppressive. He could feel the tension developing. He could see the singers standing in the wings, already frightened at the thought of singing before such an exalted audience, growing more frightened the longer they waited. The tenor, who was a last-minute substitute from the Cathedral in Lodi, had never sung in a large theater, and the delay increased his fear. Leopold wondered what could have detained Ferdinand? Did it concern them? Had the Archduke been offended by Wolfgang after all? Wolfgang had not behaved as a subject, but as an equal. And now Wolfgang sat at the harpsichord, chatting calmly with the Konzertmeister of the orchestra, while everybody else was restless and nervous.

The Archduke finished his dinner about four, but it was a heavy dinner and he had to rest. Then he remembered that he had to write letters of New Year's greetings and compliments to his mother, and his brothers, Joseph, Leopold, Maximilian and Prince Kaunitz. And he had to write them in his own hand, and he wrote very slowly. But it was the letter to his mother that required the most time. She had written him in a way that needed a special answer. He re-read her letter in an effort to decide what to write her:

"Dear Ferdinand: By now I must duly inform you of the wretched partition of Poland. This dreary affair has stolen from me at least ten years of my life. Yet we had to do it. Otherwise, Prussia and Russia would have taken it all.

"You know I detest Catherine and her immorality, and what I think of Frederick, that Satan, who took our Silesia, who has done his utmost to destroy us. But your brother, as Emperor and co-Regent, admires Frederick no matter what I say, and he persuaded me to acquiesce in this partition on the grounds that it will keep the peace and prevent Russia and Prussia from becoming so powerful that they would threaten us.

"But I was the last to sign this evil treaty of partition, and only because the King of Prussia and the Czarina had signed it already and were prepared to take all of Poland. Joseph wrote me that my signature was good news, but all I can say is: 'I signed'. They put in the document the phrase 'just acquisition', to soothe their consciences, but I had to cross out the word 'just'.

"I am deeply troubled. From the start of my unfortunate reign, in spite of all the adversities and crises, we have taken pride in the just and honorable performance of our duties. This earned us the respect of all of Europe, and even the respect of our enemies. But all that we built over many years has been lost in a single year. Nothing on earth has brought me more anguish than this loss of our good name. Sadly I must admit to you that we deserve it. Even as we have pretended to be honest, we have played the Prussian. And I have not found any peace.

"How I wish I could free myself from this ugly partition which blackens my whole reign. God grant that He will have mercy on me. I am haunted by my part in this sorry affair. It weighs on me like a

225

terrible cross and embitters all my days, days that are unhappy enough without any further burdens. I must raise myself up, or the sorrow of it will cause me to succumb to melancholia.

"I had such a good reputation. And you must treasure yours. I hope this will teach you to behave as honestly as you can in all matters. It is very difficult for a ruler, especially one that is surrounded by enemies. Your devoted and faithful mother, Maria Theresa."

Ferdinand did not know whether to write her a letter of condolence or of congratulations. Despite her sorrow, she had added two million subjects to her empire. He recalled what Frederick had said about his mother's attitude to the partition of Poland, *She wept but she took, and the more she wept the more she took.* It brought a smile to his face, although he did not share his brother Joseph's admiration of Frederick. But it was so like his mother to have moral qualms at the precise moment she exerted her greatest political power. Ferdinand did not express that however, but wrote her that he would follow her advice whenever he could, and that she must not allow herself to succumb to melancholy, for all her children needed her so. He did not leave for the opera until this letter was sealed and posted.

It was eight o'clock when Ferdinand arrived at the Teatro Regio Ducal. By now the discomfort was stifling, but no one had left, for that would have been an insult to the Crown. The long wait had raised the tension of the singers to an overwhelming pitch, yet none of them dared to protest.

Wolfgang, disgusted with the delay, wanted to object, but as he hesitated to start conducting, Ferdinand said icily precise, *We are waiting.*

Wolfgang began, but he could not feel servile as the singers did, and he was unhappy with their singing. They were so nervous, they were close to screaming. The tenor, who was more comfortable in a church choir than in a theater, gestured to a point of absurdity and was too high, as if he had to outdo the male soprano. Meanwhile, the male soprano had asked the Archduchess to applaud him first, on the excuse that it was the custom. This infuriated the prima donna, who sang with an exaggerated effect in her effort to surpass the castrato, although Wolfgang had composed her arias for her remarkable ease of execution. The performance became an ordeal Wolfgang thought would never end. The curtain did not descend until two in the morning and he conducted the last act as if in a pantomime.

He hardly heard the applause; he was certain that *Lucio Silla* was a failure. It was so late everyone was eager to get to bed, and there was no after-theater reception. Papa was very quiet, brooding. Wolfgang was depressed, and he could not think of anything to say.

He was surprised the next day to learn that the opera had become the talk of Milan because of the rivalry of the singers. That evening there was not an empty seat in the theater, and this time it started on time and the singing improved. After a week of full houses *Lucio Silla* was the most popular opera in Milan and was scheduled for many more performances.

Count Firmian gave the Mozarts a private audience. He did not discuss Archduke Ferdinand's rejection, but suggested to Leopold that it could be useful to write the Archduke Leopold about Wolfgang. Delighted with the success of *Lucio Silla*, he felt that the ruler of Tuscany, more musical than his younger brother, would give this sympathetic consideration.

Leopold did, with mixed feelings. By now he could not be optimistic, yet he could not quit. The idea of returning to Salzburg's inferior music appalled him. He wrote Count Arco: "I trust you will express our apologies to His Grace for our delay in returning to Salzburg, but my rheumatism, always troublesome, has become much worse. Not only has it settled in my shoulders, it has spread to my thighs and knees. I cannot walk and I have to write you from bed, and it is very difficult for me to write at all, the pain is so great. But please assure His Grace that we will return as soon as we are able."

The wait became a week, then a month. *Lucio Silla* stopped after twenty-six performances, and still there was no word from the Tuscany court. Count Firmian encouraged them to remain, however, and so they did, impatiently now.

Wolfgang had become friendly with Rauzzini, the castrato who had sung Cecilio. The primo uomo realized that he had the finest music in the opera, that Wolfgang had written his role with Manzuoli in mind, and he was fascinated by the brilliance yet tenderness the boy had given to his arias.

He told Wolfgang, "I would be honored if you wrote something just for me. Something that even the best prima donna would have difficulty singing."

Irresistibly Wolfgang was drawn to the operatic style, although the motet he composed for Rauzzini was for the church and he called it, *Exsultate, Jubilate,* for that had become his mood. Now that he did not have to worry about a bad libretto, poor staging, unbelievable acting, he could stress pure music. It made him feel exultant and jubilant as he wrote of love. Composing swept him headlong then, and he wrote the motet as an instrumental concerto, with the solo part, Rauzzini's, as high as the human voice could go. Only a coloratura of the finest quality would be able to sing this, he thought, or a castrato like Rauzzini or Manzuoli. He abandoned himself to the purity of his love. Love singing. Love all-powerful. Love delicate and as light as air. God was unseen, but they would hear God in his music, a God of love, *a God he could love.*

Rauzzini sang *Exsultate, Jubilate*, with the utmost delicacy, and yet an immense feeling filled the church.

You could hear God in the church, thought Leopold, and suddenly it was as if his son had grown incalculably and he had a vision of the music that Wolfgang would write in his maturity.

Rauzzini was standing by his pew and saying, "Such beautiful sound your boy produces, Signor Leopoldo. His possibilities are infinite."

"And you are a singer of great attainments."

"Thank you, Signor. But I have never sung such lovely music in my life."

He asked Rauzzini to sing *Exsultate, Jubilate*, the following Sunday, and the castrato did so, humbly. It was Wolfgang's seventeenth birthday.

Wolfgang was pleased with Papa's pleasure, but he wanted to ride a donkey as a birthday present.

Had his son realized what he had wrought? There were things in this motet you could not grasp with your hands or ears or any of your senses, thought Leopold, yet there was meaning in every note. God was unseen, but Leopold could hear Him now. It would be very difficult to leave Italy.

A few days later Archduke Leopold rejected Wolfgang Amadeus Mozart's application for employment as his Kapellmeister and court composer.

THIRTY-FOUR

It was as if they had been betrayed. Wolfgang's creation of *Exsultate, Jubilate*, had been one of the happiest things in Leopold's life, a miraculous song formed perfect and true, and he had been told that his son's music was not wanted. It filled him with bitterness against a world that could make such a summary judgment, and confused him. Wolfgang had been praised more in Italy than anywhere else, yet no one had offered him permanent employment. But what could he tell his son? When Wolfgang asked him what had gone wrong, he said, "Perhaps God has other plans for us."

Wolfgang looked skeptical, but said nothing.

Count Firmian expressed his condolences and said he had done his best, but that the Austrian Archdukes seemed to prefer Italian musicians. He hoped that the Mozarts would feel more secure in Salzburg.

So it was decided. Leopold could not linger any longer in Italy. He said goodbye to their friends in Milan, for no one had offered another opera scrittura, which was also a shock – he had assumed they would occur each season – and by March, 1773, he and Wolfgang were back home.

In April, he rented new rooms. He did this without consulting anyone, which restored confidence in his own judgment. He was proud of the rooms on the Hannibalplatz in the new part of the town. After he announced his act to the family he assured them, "They will cost only a few gulden more, and they are wonderful compared to what we have here."

Anna Maria said, "What about the children? Their friends live nearby. It could be hard on them, especially on Nannerl."

"We are not going to Vienna or Milan," Leopold answered impatiently. "We will be just across the river, within walking distance. And as I have said before, our rooms are not big enough. We cannot

229

live as soldiers. Wolfgang is not eight anymore, and neither is Nannerl."

Nannerl asked, "Will I have my own room, Papa?"

"Everybody will have their own room."

They all regarded him with wonder then, even Wolfgang, who up to now had been indifferent.

"We have eight rooms. All on one floor. We will only have to climb one flight of steps. And we have a garden, a yard, and our own concert hall."

"A concert hall just for us?" Wolfgang was excited.

"It is almost as large as the Rittersaal."

"You're exaggerating."

"It is as long. Besides, we cannot stay here any more. This house goes back to 1360, and it is no longer in good condition."

Anna Maria's feelings were mixed. These rooms at 9 Getreidegasse had become like an old dress, not always as warm as it should be, and certainly not elegant or attractive, but comfortable and easy to feel at home in. And she would miss the Hagenauers, but if the new rooms kept Leopold and Wolfgang in Salzburg it could be worth the moving. Yet packing filled her with nostalgia and constantly reminded her of her babies.

The day of the moving Hagenauer, Schachtner, Bullinger, and Haydn appeared to aid the Mozarts. Leopold was pleased. He had hired movers, determined to move in style, but some things could be broken while being carried down the three flights of steps, He was surprised by the presence of Michael Haydn, who was hardly more than an acquaintance.

Inevitably, however, the movers did all the work while Anna Maria supervised as Leopold became involved in a discussion with his friends when Schachtner asked, "What did happen with the Archduke?"

"What Archduke?" asked Leopold, looking innocent.

"Leopold. It was known that you were seeking a post with him."

"I had rheumatism. I could not get out of bed for many days."

Schachtner said skeptically, "I doubt our new Archbishop believed that."

"Does he know?" Leopold halted. Anything else would be a confession.

"No one can be sure what he knows, he does not confide in us, but he is not Schrattenbach, he will not accept your absences so easily. Do you know why the Archduke Leopold did not listen to you?"

"All I know is, Wolfgang was adored everywhere we went in Italy."

Bullinger said, "But really, what have you achieved by all the traveling?"

It was impossible to explain, thought Leopold. If the priest did not understand by now, nothing he would say would add to his comprehension.

Bullinger said, "You are not hurt, are you?"

"Why should I be hurt?"

"You have put so much into Wolfgang."

"His nature is a rich soil. Wherever it is nourished, it flourishes."

"But what about your own career? You've stopped composing, performing."

"I am teaching."

"Only Wolfgang actually. You give very little time to other pupils."

"Only Wolfgang! Don't you realize he has become the equal of any composer?"

Bullinger did not look so sure.

Michael Haydn said, so quietly he could scarcely be heard, "The boy has made amazing progress. His *Sinfonia in D Major* which was played at the last concert for His Grace is as professional an Italian piece as you could find. And it is written with such assurance, as if there were no problems of composition, it is remarkable. He probably has a perfect ear."

Schachtner said dryly, "Do you think our new Archbishop has?"

Bullinger said, "I beg to remind you that this is not his function."

Schachtner said, "That does not stop him from being critical."

Everybody laughed, and Leopold declared, "I do think all of you will like our new quarters."

Bullinger said, "I trust this indicates that you are settling down."

"My dear friend, I have served in the court Kapelle for thirty years."

"Not steadily."

"I have never been off the roster of musicians."

The movers were finished and it was time to go, Anna Maria told Leopold, but where was Wolfgang? Nannerl and Theresa were with her, but there was no sign of their son. Leopold was alarmed and she thought, he was always cradling Wolfgang, even at seventeen, just as maternal as he was paternal.

Leopold said, seeking to appear nonchalant to hide his concern, "He probably forgot something. You know how careless he can be." Yet Leopold was relieved when Hagenauer, who as usual, had said nothing, saw Wolfgang sitting in the sun on a small stone bench opposite the house and holding Bimperl, the fox-terrier puppy Anna Maria had bought for him recently.

"Usually Wolfgang is so playful, and spontaneous," said Schachtner, "but now he looks so thoughtful, almost grim."

Nannerl said, "I'm not sure he wants to move."

"Of course he does," said Leopold.

"He told me that he will miss this house, Papa."

231

"We will all miss it, but he will have more space to compose and play."

Nannerl said, feeling among friends, "He can compose anywhere. He even composes when he goes to the toilet."

Bullinger said, "You must remember that he is still a child."

"After what he has composed!" Leopold was incredulous.

Schachtner said, "He looks more like you now, Leopold, and less like Anna Maria. His face has become rounder, and his fair hair has become almost brown, and his eyes protrude a little."

"From an early illness," said Anna Maria, "but he has no pock marks."

Wolfgang was confused. Papa said he should be in raptures over their new home, but he felt solemn at the thought of leaving 9 Getreidegasse. So he had gone out to the Lochelplatz and to his favorite spot to think things out. The small stone bench of Unsterberg marble, just a niche in the wall across from the entrance to their house, was in the sun at this time of the day and was a comforting place to meditate. It was strange: he did not miss something until he was about to lose it, and then he missed it very much. Things he had taken for granted became splendid and precious. They filled him with happy memories, as if that would keep the rooms alive. Yet he shivered as he remembered winter nights when the stoves had gone out and no one had had the courage to get out of bed and spend a freezing hour starting them. But Mamma would miss her marketing at the market place behind their house, and the gossiping with the neighboring women. Mamma said they had lived here twenty-five years, that she and Papa had not lived anywhere else; they had moved into 9 Getreidegasse as newlyweds. No wonder Mamma had cried the night Papa had said they were moving. He had a desire to put that into a song, and he told himself that would be sentimental, and that made him feel self-conscious, and he never composed when he felt self-conscious. Finally, his greatest comfort came from the little three-foot fountain that had been built into the wall at the entrance to the kitchen. The kitchen itself was an ugly, open-hearth medieval room which he kept away from as much as possible – and anyway it was for women, not men – but he loved the fountain. He could visualize all the important details as he sat: the gargoyle figure, the strikingly sculptured face, the perfect mouth out of which the water came, and the finely carved basin. Yet there was no artist's signature on this work of art, but simply the date of construction, 1657.

Papa stood beside him, "Time to leave, Wolfgang."

There were tears in Hagenauer's eyes and Leopold said jokingly, to hide his own emotion, "We won't be far away. We're not going to Italy now. In a straight line it is less than a mile away. You go down the Getreidegasse, turn left at the Town Hall, cross the river. . ."

Hagenauer interrupted, "I know how to go."

Leopold signaled for the departure to begin. Everybody took what mattered the most to them. Wolfgang carefully held the puppy and the canary; Nannerl proudly bore her first composition book and the gold snuff box that had been given to them by Louis XV; Anna Maria carried Wolfgang's first violin and strands of his blond baby hair; Theresa took the cradle which had sheltered Nannerl and Wolfgang; Leopold held the diploma of the Accademia Filarmonica of Bologna; a copy of the Papal patent that had made his son a knight, and autographs of Wolfgang's first compositions.

There was nothing left for their friends – as if, thought Wolfgang, Papa had arranged that because he did not trust them that much, or did not want to depend on them. However, they insisted on coming along.

A few minutes later everyone admitted that their new quarters were splendid indeed. Papa continued to command, Wolfgang noticed, as he pointed out its favorable features. "We will have the sun all afternoon, and the Hannibalpatz, as you know, is many times larger than the Lochelplatz. It is also a corner house, with eleven windows on the square alone. And Anna Maria, the courtyard is our own, with a garden just for you."

"Good!" she exclaimed, as he desired, and blinked back her tears.

"And the theater is directly across the Hannibalplatz, within view," he said suddenly, seeing his son looking distracted, almost indifferent.

"Fine, Papa!" That was useful, thought Wolfgang. But he really grew interested when Papa showed him the concert hall. He realized that Papa had not exaggerated, it was as long as the Rittersaal and possessed other advantages. The high ballroom ceiling was fringed with stunning gilt stucco, five windows looked out on the Hannibalplatz and there were two on the courtyard side, and the shiny parquet floor was as fine as those in the Residenz. Now he understood his father's tone of conquest.

And as his father led everybody through the rest of the rooms he became aware that Papa, consciously or unconsciously, had imitated the Archbishop. But he was not as certain as Papa, who was accepting the congratulations of their friends, that they would be content here.

THIRTY-FIVE

A few days later a concert was given at the Residenz to celebrate the first anniversary of Archbishop Colloredo's enthronement. At his request it consisted of the three composers he considered most representative of Salzburg: Wolfgang Mozart, Michael Haydn, and Guiseppe Lolli.

Wolfgang was pleased that his work was a divertimento for wind instruments. The music was light, cheerful, and written to entertain.

But Lolli conducted it with such heavy hands, Wolfgang thought God would have to forgive him, he could not. Colloredo seemed satisfied with his music, he stayed until it was finished, but he said nothing to Wolfgang. He was dissatisfied with Lolli's conducting, for he cut short the next number, another divertimento by Haydn, although Wolfgang thought it was worth hearing, and left before Lolli could perform his own piece, a quintet.

Soon afterward Domenico Fischetti was appointed Kapellmeister. A Neapolitan composer whose comic operas Wolfgang had heard in Milan and had found trite and dull, he had been Kapellmeister in Dresden the past seven years.

Yet Lolli was not dismissed, for when Leopold asked to be appointed Fischetti's assistant, the Archbishop informed him that Lolli was the new Deputy-Kapellmeister. Leopold's plea that this decision be reconsidered, that Lolli had become so inept that he would have to perform his duties whatever his rank, was regarded skeptically by the Archbishop, whose reply suggested that the Mozarts had nothing to hope for in Salzburg and would do better to seek their fortune elsewhere.

Shaken by this, the moment the Archbishop left for the summer to see his ailing father in Vienna, Leopold made his own decision to depart.

He told his family, "Gassman, the Vienna Kapellmeister, is so ill the Empress must be thinking of a replacement. With all the music Wolfgang composed for her son, she will surely consider him. But not a word to anyone, this must not get back to Colloredo. Our excuse is that we are visiting old friends, and Maria Theresa has been a good friend."

Leopold felt vindicated in the judgment when the Empress granted him and Wolfgang an audience at Schönbrunn. She was receiving them in the Millions Room, her favorite chamber in the entire palace.

Wolfgang knew he was supposed to be amazed by the lavish splendor of the Millions Room – Maria Theresa had spent a million gulden on this chamber – but he was not impressed. The opulence was arrogant rather than attractive. The profusion of gilt and gold ornamentation oppressed him.

And he was shocked by the change in her. Only five years had passed since he had last seen her, but she had aged far more. She peered through a glass to distinguish them. Her skin was yellow now, and ugly. She had become extremely fat and had lost all vestige of her good looks.

Leopold thought Maria Theresa must have rheumatism, her movements were so stiff and awkward, and her body had swelled so much it looked dropsical. The funereal gloom of her presence was accentuated by the mournful black she wore, the widow's weeds she had never taken off since her husband's death.

As she indicated that they should stand close to her, so she could see them distinctly, Leopold noticed that a box of papers was buckled to her waist. He assumed that they were state papers from her air of preoccupation, but she had been writing to her children.

One letter in particular disturbed her. Troubled by Marie Antoinette's behavior, she kept remembering what she had written her daughter. She had heard so many stories from her envoys in Versailles, whom she had sent there to watch her daughter's conduct, about Marie Antoinette's dangerous hostility to Louis XV's present mistress, Madame du Barry, and her extravagances and frivolity that she had had to write a warning: "... *and if you will not be more tactful and careful, some great misfortune will overtake you, and then it will be too late.*"

Now she had to give the Mozarts, who were hardly better than vagabonds, who would surely want something, part of her precious time when it was the last thing she wanted to do. But Maria Theresa was proud that she granted an audience to anyone who requested it. And she was curious about the boy: was he still a freak? Or had he grown up?

As their faces became clear in her glass, she said, "Herr Mozart, your son looks pale and delicate. You push him too hard with your endless traveling. You expect too much."

"Your Majesty, Wolfgang is the equal of any man alive. Even Gluck."

"Gluck? Your son is still a child. Look how short he is!"

"His operas aren't short. Your Majesty, if Herr Gassman should be unable to perform his duties, Wolfgang would be honored to serve you."

"You should see the Emperor. He is interested in such matters."

"Could I speak to him, Your Majesty? He has always been kind to us."

"He is in Poland."

Because Leopold was disappointed, he tried to be worldly. "You must be proud of him, Your Majesty, for the way he conducted the Polish affair."

She sat wearily, breathing heavily. But when she saw Leopold looking sorry for her, she said imperiously, "We had to take the land to protect the Empire against Russia and Prussia. It was the only way to prevent war."

"It must also have been a great strain on you, Your Majesty."

"It was." She changed the subject. "When you were in Italy, you saw two of my sons. Did they seem well? I can only communicate with my children by letter. I am bound here by my duties. I have no choice."

"They seemed fine, Your Majesty. They were gracious to us."

"It is very hard to see your children leave you one by one."

Wolfgang said, "Your daughter, Marie Antoinette, was very kind to me."

"When?" Maria Theresa did not remember.

"When Wolfgang was a child, Your Majesty, and sat on your lap."

Wolfgang did not wish to be remembered for being the child who had sat on Maria Theresa's lap, but he had treasured the memory of Marie Antoinette's charm and beauty. "She was showing me through Schönbrunn, Your Majesty."

"My daughter was a child then. Herr Mozart, you are fortunate, you have your son with you, but my sons are spread all over the world."

"We appreciate your good wishes, Your Majesty. We do hope that if poor Herr Gassmann is taken away from us, you will consider Wolfgang."

She stood up to indicate that the audience was over.

"Thank you, Your Majesty. It was gracious of you to see us."

Wolfgang did not think so. He doubted that she was as good a friend as Papa said she was. She had to hold on to her high-backed throne chair to keep from swaying and he was sure she had not bent over in years. His last impression of Maria Theresa, as they backed out of the Millions Room, was of a stern-faced matriarch, who could only like people when they did not cost her anything, or were children, particularly her children.

When Leopold was invited to conduct Wolfgang's *Dominicus Mass* in the Kirche Am Hof it eased his disappointment. This was a great honor, for the Jesuit church was old and famous, and next door to the Collalto palace where Wolfgang had played first in Vienna. He had no trace of his rheumatism as he conducted, and he felt he had succeeded in the precious task of performing his son's music, for afterwards Wolfgang hugged him, and said, half teasingly and half lovingly, "Next to God, comes Papa."

The performance was just in time, for three weeks later the Jesuits were expelled from all the Hapsburg dominions by the Empress.

When Colloredo returned to Salzburg the next month, so did Leopold. And when the Archbishop heard that Maria Theresa's seizure of the Jesuit possessions had filled the Imperial treasury, he followed her example.

This amused Leopold, and he said to Schachtner, whom he had invited to his new home to find out whether his absence had been resented by Colloredo, "The Archbishop knows how to find money."

"His father is one of Maria Theresa's most important advisors. He could hardly do otherwise."

"Do you approve?" Schachtner was a free-thinker who read Voltaire and Rousseau, but both had friends who were Jesuits, such as Bullinger.

"The suppression of the Order may have upset the Archbishop. He has had diarrhea ever since he returned from Vienna."

"Why should he be so upset?"

"A new Pope, and the Jesuits could be back in favor again. They were expelled only for political reasons. Did Maria Theresa give you any hope?"

"Of what?" Leopold looked bewildered.

"Virtually everyone in Salzburg knows that Gassmann is so ill a new Kapellmeister will be needed soon. Why else would you see Maria Theresa?"

"Fools are fools everywhere but especially in Salzburg."

"Yet it is true you did apply for the post for Wolfgang? Isn't it?"

"It is true that many people in Salzburg have diarrhea in their mouths as well as in their asses, and when people are attacked both in their heads and asses, their condition is dangerous indeed. Has Colloredo complained about my absence?"

"He has been involved with the Jesuits."

"He would have been better advised if he concerned himself with the cost of living. The way it has been rising, what will happen to us if we have to live on our small pay? We will all be beggars."

"Leopold, did you get any encouragement in Vienna?"

"I presume God has other plans for us."

"No doubt." But Schachtner sounded skeptical.

Leopold's tone softened. "Anna Maria and I would be honored if you could come to the party we are giving to celebrate our silver wedding anniversary."

"I will be honored. But you told me that it was last year."

"On November 21, 1772. Only we couldn't celebrate it then because Wolfgang and I were in Italy for *Lucio Silla*."

"Will you invite Bullinger?"

"Of course. He is a dear friend of ours."

Wolfgang delivered his invitation to Barbara in person. It was as if he held that in his heart as he hurried across the bridge which led into the old town and to her house, his senses at a high pitch. He was in the gayest of humors. He loved the liveliness and excitement of parties and dancing and pretty girls and the playfulness of the music he wrote for such occasions, exuberant, gallant, light – but not slight, he thought vehemently – and he wanted her to share this with him. He longed to sing in his anticipation of the pleasure they were going to have, only he did not trust his voice to express what he felt. It was a crisp, dry, clear November Sunday, the dryness unusual for late autumn. He breathed the air with delight, and he enjoyed the familiar things along the way. He skipped through the Judengasse in The Burgher's Town and along lanes so narrow he could put out both his hands and touch the walls of the houses, and came upon the Residenzplatz, so spacious many carriages could ride through it side by side. The Sovereign's Town was impressive in the bright sunlight. For once he did not question the importance of the Residenz, or the Cathedral, or the Fortress Hohensalzburg.

The von Mölk residence was in The Sovereign's Town and close to the Residenz, so the court chancellor could be within reach of the Archbishop. The square it was on was smaller than the Hannibalplatz, but the house itself was larger, with three stories, fourteen rooms, a mansion in its grandeur, and completely apart from any other building.

Barbara was surprised to see Wolfgang. He had been away for over two months and although he had written her, through Nannerl, he had not known when he would be home.

She was dressed to go out, he noticed. He could not tell whether she was pleased to see him.

She said, "You're back."

"Yes. Yes."

"For long?"

"As far as I know."

She seemed at a loss what to say, and looked away.

There was an unreal air about her, he thought, and some of his excitement evaporated. She was as beautiful as a princess, and as remote. Yet he had to ask, "We are having a party for my parents' silver wedding anniversary. I would love you to come as my guest, Waberl."

She frowned, as if that pet name had become unpleasant to her, and appeared even more ill at ease, saying, "I'm sorry, Wolfgang, but I can't."

"Why not?"

"I have a previous engagement."

"But you don't even know the date!"

"Don't you understand?"

"Understand what?"

"It is foolish for us to see each other."

"Italian fool, German fool, what is the difference!"

"It makes a great difference to me that you are seldom here."

"I am here now, Waberl."

"And I don't like that name. I am not a child anymore."

"Indeed Signorina, Mademoiselle, Fraulein, you are not. You are exquisite, beautiful, charming, diverting, I love your lungs, your liver, your stomach. . . ."

"Wolfgang, stop fooling!"

"I was never more serious in my life."

"So am I." Her tone became positive. "I can't see you anymore."

"Can't?" He stared at her in horror. "Do I have the pox?"

"You know what I am trying to say."

"Then say it."

"I am not clever like you are, but I do know that it is impossible to take you seriously. Just when I begin to care for you, you are off to Italy, or Vienna, or God knows where."

"Is that the real reason?" Wolfgang could hardly breathe, he hurt so.

No, she thought, it was not. Her father had ordered her to stop seeing him. Count Felix von Mölk liked the Mozarts, they were old friends, but he did not want a son-in-law who earned only one hundred and fifty gulden a year and who never knew where the next gulden was coming from. The cooks and valets in the Archbishop's service earned more than that. And while Wolfgang was a likable boy, he was unstable, all musicians were.

She stood there and now her light blue eyes were blank, and her small treble was shrill as she repeated, "Yes, that is the real reason," and added, "I'm sorry, Wolfgang, very sorry," when she didn't sound sorry at all. She sounded like a child, and yet she was not a stupid girl.

"Wolfgang, how you stare! Are you always in the clouds? You can make a girl feel quite uncomfortable."

The loveliest face could look so ugly. But he had to ask, "Who is it?"

"Why does a man always think it is someone else?" she said petulantly.

He had been so elated before, he could not endure losing that feeling. So, in spite of her coldness, he sought to recapture his anticipation. He pleaded, "Barbara, come to the party with me. Please!"

"No," she said, "I'm sorry, but I can't."

"I guess it was my minuets," he said sarcastically. "They were dull."

"Oh, not at all!" she exclaimed. "I loved them."

There was a pause, and then her face became a mask and she said icily, "Will you excuse me? I have an appointment."

"You are lucky. Bravo!" He was at the door when Albert, her brother, entered with Count Karl Arco. Wolfgang knew them both well. At twenty-four Albert von Mölk was pudgy like his father, with fat, puffed-out cheeks, his talk as loose as his bowels, thought Wolfgang.

It was the realization that Barbara preferred Count Arco that caused Wolfgang to stare at him with a new, intense gaze. The thirty-year-old son of the chief chamberlain, a tall, slim man with a bony, angular face and hard, opaque eyes, had just been appointed chief steward, Karl Arco spoke French, although he had never been in France; he regarded himself as an authority on music, although he could not play any instrument and had a poor ear; he liked to advise and instruct even when he was not asked. But he was rich enough to have his own carriage, titled enough to wear a sword, and important enough to be pampered as a wit no matter how obvious he was.

Barbara gave Count Arco a bewitching smile and Wolfgang felt as cold as ice. Fools went on foolishly talking, but he had said too much already.

She moved close to Count Arco, who kissed her hand gallantly, and she said, "Wolfgang, you feel things too strongly, but you will get over it."

He knew he should have said, I have already, but that would have been malicious. Instead he whispered, as quietly and as dignified as he could, "I have some music to compose. I trust you will excuse me."

Halfway back to his house he halted abruptly, overcome with unhappiness. He was still on the west side of the Salzach, in the old town, and it was as if, once he left it, he left it for good. The river was going by him in a torrent like his emotion. He looked up at the mountains, and now he felt shut in by them. They were solitudes rather than presences, and suddenly he hated their silence. He walked quickly then, across the river. The truth was, he thought, she had been a dream rather than a reality.

At the party Wolfgang danced with everybody. Papa and Mamma were so happy, he was determined to be happy too. Many more friends had come than his parents had expected. They were excited by the presence of the von Robinigs, the Haffners, two of the richer families in Salzburg, but they were elated by the entrance of the Countess Lützow and the Countess Lodron.

Wolfgang knew the Lodrons and Lützows liked him – Countess Lodron was the sister of the Countess van Eyck and Count Karl Arco while Countess Lützow was the Archbishop's niece – but these were two of the most influential families in Salzburg. Count Lodron was commander of the army, while Count Lützow was commandant of the Fortress Hohensalzburg.

But the greatest surprise of all to Wolfgang was the entrance of Count Felix von Mölk and his sons, Franz and Albert, with Count Karl Arco, the new chief steward. Wolfgang had not expected any of them.

Nannerl said she was disappointed not to see Barbara, and Albert von Mölk explained, "She doesn't feel well. She has a severe headache."

"Oh, I'm sorry," said Nannerl, "we will miss her."

"She will miss you," said Albert. "But you know, women's troubles."

Theresa Barasini told Wolfgang that he danced very well; Ursula Hagenauer was surprised by his imperious manner, it was unlike Wolfgang; Barbara Zezi, daughter of their grocer, complained that he held her too tight, yet she did not pull away.

Then he was dancing a minuet with Countess Lützow. They were the best couple on the floor despite the difference in age, and everyone stopped to watch and applaud. Except Count Karl Arco who cut in and sought to outdo Wolfgang. Arco was not graceful, Wolfgang thought with satisfaction, and the Countess Lützow was irritated with her new partner.

He heard Count Felix von Mölk saying to Papa, "How your children have grown! Soon they will be marrying, and having their own children."

Papa said, "They have time. Particularly Wolfgang."

"Now that you have settled down, he should meet the right girl."

"Settled down? On my salary?"

"Isn't that why you moved to the Hannibalplatz?"

"I moved here for my family's sake."

Count Karl Arco joined them, for Countess Lützow suddenly had become tired, and he said, "Everyone knows, Mozart, that you are well-to-do."

"Oh, I am?"

Count Karl Arco said, "You must have made a fortune on your tours."

"And what about expenses? Food, traveling, accommodations?"

"My sister put you up in Paris, and that must have happened many times."

"Your sister was a great lady," Papa said warmly.

"I don't see what that has to do with what I said."

"Your dear departed sister was very good to us." He turned to speak to Bullinger, who was standing alone.

But Bullinger laughed and said, "Don't worry about me, Leopold. I am exempt. I am the example of the Archbishop's tolerance."

Count Karl Arco, not to be put off so easily, followed Leopold and said, "Don't you think your son ought to play for us?"

"Why?"

"It is what he does best." Before Leopold could reply, Count Karl Arco approached Wolfgang, who was listening to the Countess Lützow.

She was saying, "You have such nice hands, Wolfgang, firm but gentle."

Count Arco interrupted, "Show us. Play for us, will you, Mozart?"

If Arco only knew his secret thoughts. But the expression that Wolfgang turned to the chief steward was bland as he said, "I don't feel like it."

For an instant Arco gazed at him indignantly, but before he could express his disapproval his sister, Countess Lodron, joined them and said, "I would like my daughters to study the harpsichord. With Wolfgang."

Leopold asked, "What about His Grace?"

"I am sure the Countess Lützow can persuade her uncle to allow it, if she wants to. It won't come out of his pocket. Now don't you interfere," Countes Lodron said to her brother, who was trying to speak.

Countess Lützow said, "I will be happy to speak in Wolfgang's behalf."

Countess Lodron said, "Then it is decided. Wolfgang will teach the girls."

"If he wants to," said Leopold.

"It will be a pleasure," said Wolfgang. "And if the Countess would like, I could teach her, too." Then it could be exciting also.

"Thank you, Wolfgang. We will see how the girls progress."

"They will progress very well, I am sure," said the Countess Lützow. And before Count Arco could cut in she was dancing with

Wolfgang again, and whispering, "You must not despair, Wolfgang, there will be others."

"Countess Lützow, I am very happy."

"Is that why you don't want to play?"

"It will keep me from dancing."

"You dance very well. I have enjoyed dancing with you very much. But you are a musician first, and a gallant second."

Indeed, indeed, he thought, he could be friendly with the Countess, he could even dance with her, but he could not marry her or anyone of her rank.

THIRTY-SIX

═══

By the time Wolfgang was eighteen he had courted a number of girls.

Theresa Barasini, whom he had flirted with before, was his first choice and she was pleased with his company, but after Barbara she had little physical appeal. He spent a few evenings with Ursula Hagenauer, who was more attractive, but they knew each other so well it was as if she were his sister. Luise von Robinig had the kind of appearance he liked, but she was so proper she bored him.

Countess Lützow and Countess Lodron were much more appealing. Permission to teach had been granted through the intercession of the two noblewomen and this added to Wolfgang's feeling for them. Countess Lützow dressed in the height of fashion; her features were still attractive, although her cheeks were hollow and her chin was very sharp. Her conversation was witty, and she was well-informed about music. She gave him many compliments, but always maternally. And while it was a consoling friendship, he would have preferred it to be romantic.

Countess Lodron, not as attractive or clever, had a natural sweetness that reminded him of the Countess van Eyck, and she assumed the role of a patron as if it were an honor. But she also behaved like a moral power, which set limits to his freedom with her.

His nature demanded that he become deeply involved in what he was doing, and none of these activities absorbed him enough to matter. He thought that Salzburg, a small and insignificant church town next to Vienna, Milan, and Paris, was assuming an importance in his life far larger than he liked.

He was grateful for an evening of string quartets that Michael Haydn arranged. He responded happily when Haydn said they would include quartets composed by his brother, Joseph. He had heard quartets by this composer in Vienna and he had been fascinated by their beauty and originality.

And these new quartets by Joseph Haydn were even more excit- ing. He felt them at once. They started simply, they did not sweat, yet they were full of surprises, and unexpected passages that glowed with life and feeling.

"Look at this!" An ecstatic Wolfgang was examining the score of the quartet that he, Papa, Schachtner, and Haydn had just played. "One can surely learn from this. Thank you, Herr Haydn." Suddenly Michael Haydn was no longer a musician who drank too much or was lazy, as Papa said, but one with excellent taste. "Have you any of your brother's symphonies?"

"A few."

"May I look at them?"

Haydn glanced at Papa for permission, who said, "Wolfgang is old enough to choose for himself, and certainly mature enough."

Wolfgang eagerly studied Joseph Haydn's scores. His quartets led naturally into his symphonies. He was elated, as if he had discovered a star brighter and more beautiful than any he had ever seen, and yet he was awestruck by its clarity and intensity. This music had an individual voice, a voice he had to listen to, a strong voice.

He had to ask, "Herr Haydn, does your brother ever visit Vienna?"

"Only when his employer, Prince Esterházy, allows him."

Wolfgang looked incredulous.

"Joseph cannot go even for a single day without the Prince's approval."

"I would love to meet him."

"He would enjoy meeting you."

"You think so, Herr Haydn?" Wolfgang was surprised.

Michael Haydn said softly, "I think he would be delighted."

Wolfgang said humbly, "But I would be the one honored."

In this new surge of emotion he felt reborn. The pain of his failure with Barbara von Mölk, his not finding love elsewhere, gradu- ally vanished as melodies poured out of him. The next few months he divided his work into two categories: the music he wrote for himself, and the pieces he did for others. Colloredo ordered dinner music for his banquets and he dutifully composed gracious serenades. He wrote harpsichord sonatas for the Countess Lodron that were ele- gant and charming. These pieces were applauded, but he felt this music was satisfactory and that was all. His gratification occurred when he created for himself. Then he worked with a new vitality as he com- posed six quartets like those Joseph Haydn had done. Yet this was difficult. He was not sure he could reach Haydn's standard.

As soon as these quartets were finished he handed them to his father, and he was surprised by the latter's reaction. Ordinarily,

Papa accepted his compositions quickly these days, but now, as Papa studied the quartets, he was frowning. "You don't like them?" Wolfgang exclaimed.

Leopold was puzzled. There were qualities in these quartets that he had not seen in his son's music before, phrases of melancholy that troubled him. Yet even the sad, dark themes were written with passages of passionate beauty. But while these pieces were soundly constructed, with Wolfgang's usual clarity and preciseness, there was too much of Joseph Haydn in these quartets, and the imitation was second-rate. He had a sudden feeling that while Wolfgang was no longer a child prodigy, his son had not yet found his own element. Whatever he said, however, must be said carefully.

"What is wrong with them, Papa?"

"Nothing really." He paused, thinking it was often more difficult to express an idea than a musical phrase.

"They are not as good as Haydn's?"

"Joseph Haydn is past forty. His brother tells me that he has been working on quartets for many years. For you, it is a new form."

"And one that in your opinion, I have not mastered."

"That is not what I said."

"It is what you feel. Papa, I am not a little boy any more."

"You have not been for a long time. But why don't you try the symphony again? You have written many, you have mastered the form. The one you wrote in D Major, after we returned from our last trip to Italy, is enchanting. Why don't you write another symphony in that key, using what you learned from Haydn? If I like it, I will see to it that it is played here."

"If you like it?" Suddenly Wolfgang's voice was filled with scorn.

Leopold was shocked. What possessed his son? Did he hate him, too?

"It isn't you, but I am tired of composing for other people's taste."

"Even mine?"

Wolfgang longed to shout. *Even anybody's,* but he could not hurt Papa, that would be devastating. Papa made himself invulnerable outwardly because inwardly he was so vulnerable. "You liked my Italian *Sinfonia in D Major?*"

"I loved it. If you could compose such a symphony as a good, honest German composer, you could express what you feel and still meet with favor."

"With Colloredo's love of Italian music?"

"Put it in the Italian style. Three movements, quick, slow, quick, but with your present feeling. If the Archbishop likes it, and he should, he may agree to the opera scriturra that is pending from Venice."

Wolfgang tried to follow Papa's advice but as the symphony

246

developed it created its own laws. He intended to put it in D Major, but A Major was more natural. He started to make the first movement light and lively, but the *Allegro spiritosa* of the previous symphony became *Allegro moderato*. The thematic development was supposed to be suave and elegant, as was the custom, but by the time he reached the second movement the *Andante* was the most thoughtful he had ever written. In a life where much had become uncertain and unhappy, this symphony was the permanent foundation, the one thing that would not betray him.

He felt like his own man when he finished this work. While the form had Haydn's leanness, it expressed his own emotion. He was so gratified with this, he composed another symphony, this time in D Major as Papa had suggested. Now that he had expressed his inner self, it was more cheerful than the one in A Major. Then in a rush of energy he finished two other symphonies. He handed the four compositions to Papa, hoping that Papa would care for them as much as he did. He thought it was not something to proclaim aloud, but he felt that with these symphonies he had grown up.

Leopold marveled at the simplicity yet severity of these symphonies, as if Wolfgang had extracted from Haydn's quartets the economy he needed, but had gone on to be his own man. And where Wolfgang's quartets had been imitative, his symphonies were original. The A Major, which Wolfgang expected him to like the least, stirred him the most.

The writing of the notes in this score had such an emotional intensity, as if his son's emotion was in the actual making of the notes. The last three movements – Wolfgang had built this work in four movements instead of the three suggested – were written crisply, clearly, without blotting, as if his son had known from the second movement just what he wanted to say.

The shuffling of the scores had an ugly, scratching sound. Why was Papa doing this, wondered Wolfgang, didn't his father believe he had written this music?

Papa said, "I told you to keep a record of all of your compositions. But these symphonies have no number."

Wolfgang shrugged. He had tried for a while, but it had become too much of a bother, distracting him from composing, and anyway, Papa must be keeping a record, Papa always had. He asked, "Are the symphonies suitable?"

"Do you realize these symphonies make thirty that you have written?"

Wolfgang was not impressed. "My early ones were really overtures."

247

"These aren't. I would like to play the Twenty-ninth for Colloredo."

Why was Papa using numbers? What lesson was he trying to teach him now?

"The one in A Major. I am acting Kapellmeister for the next concert. Fischetti is ill, and Colloredo cannot endure Lolli's conducting."

"You intend to perform the entire symphony?"

"As you wrote it."

"But isn't it too long for His Grace? He likes his music short."

"If he has any taste, he should enjoy the A Major."

This symphony was placed first on the program. That was unusual, but Leopold did this so that his son's music would be performed before the Archbishop would grow tired, as he often did.

Colloredo sat so that his tall figure dominated the large audience in the Konferenzsaal, but Wolfgang was most aware of Barbara's presence. He told himself that she had ceased to hold any attraction for him, yet he kept glancing in her direction until she was joined by Count Karl Arco. Then he gave all his attention to his music.

Papa conducted better than he expected, with a vigor and sharpness that set off the music as he had imagined it. By the second movement however, Colloredo was squirming in his chair. And at the moment where the *Andante* contained the pathos he had conceived the Archbishop began to cough. Soon others were coughing, and when the symphony did not end at the third movement as the Archbishop expected, he looked angry.

At the end of the concert Karl Arco had a message for the Mozarts from Colloredo. "His Grace is not interested in experiments. The symphony was too long, too dry. His Grace wants serenades for this kind of evening."

"God bless His Grace and serenades," said Wolfgang.

Was the boy serious? You never knew with him. Karl Arco said sternly, "I doubt if I repeated what you just said, the Archbishop would like it."

"As you wish. I will write music that is brief, easy and digestible."

Leopold wanted to caution Wolfgang to be more careful, but this was too much. His son had composed the finest music of his career and this coxcomb was squalking like a castrated rooster. It was very difficult to bow to Karl Arco, for he had known him since the latter had been in diapers. But he asked quietly, "What about the scrittura we have been offered for an opera in Venice? Do we have permission to accept it?"

"No."

"Why not?" Leopold was shocked while Wolfgang smiled bitterly.

248

"I'm sorry," said Karl Arco, who did not appear sorry at all, "But His Grace is not accustomed to giving reasons."

"Archbishop Schrattenbach always gave us permission."

"Ask him."

"You are fooling."

"Isn't your son, Mozart? Unless that is always his attitude."

It was almost impossible to be gracious but Leopold tried. He said, "Count Arco, naturally we wish to please His Grace, but you must recognize that the best music is what the composer himself feels."

Count Arco smiled slightly as he replied, "Venice is still impossible. His Grace will be doing much entertaining the next few months, and he will need many divertimentos and serenades for dinner music."

THIRTY-SEVEN

Yet when the Elector of Bavaria requested an opera from Wolfgang soon afterward, permission was granted by the Archbishop. Leopold learned that Colloredo acquiesced because he was afraid to offend his powerful neighbor.

Wolfgang was so relieved at the opportunity to get away from Salzburg he did not ask any questions, but started to work on the music the moment the text arrived. Once again he had nothing to say about the libretto, for *La Finta Giardiniera* was the choice of the Elector.

The Pretended Gardeness was the story of a noblewoman, who in her desire to revenge herself upon her husband and to regain him, pretended to be a gardeness and found herself being pursued amorously. Two other pair of lovers from different social worlds were also involved in mistaken identity and romantic entanglements. But at the finale everybody was matched properly, as was the opera *buffa* custom.

Wolfgang thought this libretto was a silly charade but it was also a tale of unrequited love, and this fitted his present mood. And his music must care. Did they think he was creating this score solely for their pleasure! He wrote the romantic arias with tenderness, and with little coquettries, and the music became dear to him. He finished the entire score by the time he and Papa arrived in Munich. He had not waited to hear the singers, as he had done in the past. They would have to make the best of it, he told himself, so much of life was making the best of it.

Leopold was gratified that the rehearsals went smoothly. And the music pleased him very much. The overture was light and charming, and thoroughly professional. The first important aria was enchanting in tone, yet solidly constructed. Then Wolfgang gave the maid a coquettish response that was an effective musical contrast to the poignancy of her mistress.

The bass, who had been teased by the maid, replied in a clever mixture of German, Italian, French, and English. Leopold liked the dramatic humor of this aria, although the libretto was neither dramatic nor amusing.

The music Wolfgang gave the tenor, who sang of unrequited love, had elements he had not heard in his son's operas before. It had a mixture of grandeur and pathos that was very moving.

And the reconciliation duet brought tears to Leopold's eyes. There was a lyricism in this music that was lovely. The melody had a perfection that awed him.

When the dress rehearsal ended, Leopold silently embraced Wolfgang.

After the opening was postponed twice, although the opera was ready, Wolfgang grew nervous. Papa was hopeful that the Elector would like *La Finta Giardiniera* so much he would offer him a position, but the Elector was not in Munich. Many reasons were given for the delay: Maximilian was hunting; he was on a diplomatic mission; he did not approve of the score; he was awaiting the arrival of Archbishop Colloredo, so that the latter could attend the opening, too.

Finally, when Maximilian realized that Colloredo did not intend to be at the opening, he entered Munich. And the next evening *La Finta Giardiniera* was given, without the presence of Colloredo.

The theater was full. At the close of the main arias there was much applause, and when the opera ended the *Bravo Mozart*'s were even louder.

Later Leopold and Wolfgang went to a reception for the Elector, and the Elector approached them and said, "We are old acquaintances. I heard the boy play when he was very little. Twice, as a matter of fact. Herr Mozart, have you met my director of theatricals, Count von Seeau?"

"Sir, we were honored with His Excellency's acquaintance on our previous visits." Leopold had heard that von Seeau had great influence.

Count von Seeau, who stood attentively by his master's side, acknowledged this with a brief nod and said, "Your son's opera was interesting."

Wolfgang was not sure the Count intended this as a compliment.

Leopold said, "Your Excellency, we are happy you enjoyed the opera."

"It exceeded expectations. How old is your son? Eighteen?"

"Nineteen. In a few days. Wolfgang would be delighted to show

His Highness some of his other compositions, divertimentos, symphonies."

The Elector said, "My calendar is crowded at the moment."

"We could wait," Leopold said eagerly.

The Elector seemed to be reflecting deeply, but Wolfgang recalled that all the time the audience was shouting *Bravo Mozart!* the ruler had been taking snuff and blowing his nose. He thought, The Elector has no idea what I really could do. No one has, even Papa. The Elector said, "As you know I love music, but I leave the details to Count von Seeau."

The Elector retired for the evening, saying he had a busy week ahead of him. He had to get to bed early, for he had a full day of hunting planned. On wet days he could make love, but on dry days the hunting was superb and the weather had been unusually dry and mild for January, and might stay that way for another week. The fresh air, the excitement made him feel young again, not forty-seven, and then he did not have to yield to being tired, except from the outdoors. While the opera had been arranged for his pleasure by Count von Seeau, he had returned to Munich only because he had thought Colloredo would attend, which required the courtesy of his presence, but the opera had been very inconvenient.

Papa hid his dismay at the Elector's departure and suggested, "Count von Seeau, my son is a fine composer, as you heard, and he could be available."

"Your son is still in the Archbishop's service, isn't he?"

Papa shrugged. "Supposedly, sir, but that could be altered."

Wolfgang said, "I assure you, sir, I can compose whatever you wish."

"We have a Kapellmeister and composer, Herr Michl."

Who spent most of his time training singers, Papa had heard, which was a dog's life. He said, "Wolfgang could be his assistant."

"We have an overdose of concerts here."

Wolfgang said, "I would be careful in that respect." He knew Papa wanted him to state this, although he did not enjoy expressing this attitude.

Count von Seeau said, "No doubt we would enjoy your other music. Only there would be no audience. The court is leaving Munich, and it will not return for some time. I am sorry, but there is no vacancy at the moment."

"Later?" asked Papa.

"It is impossible to say. There will be fifty gulden for the opera."

Colloredo arrived in Munich the day after the premiere of *La Finta Giardiniera.* Leopold and Wolfgang were positive this was deliberate, to miss the opening. Two more performances of the opera occurred, neither of which the Archbishop attended, although he remained in

252

Munich. And suddenly the Elector returned to greet the distinguished visitor, and had his musicians give a concert at his palace in honor of the Archbishop.

Wolfgang was invited, but not to perform, which worried Leopold. But after the concert ended – which both Leopold and Wolfgang thought was inferior – there were shouts from the audience for "Mozart" to play. And when Wolfgang stood up to acknowledge this, at Leopold's prodding, there was loud applause and bravos. The Elector, sitting next to Colloredo, whispered to Count von Seeau, who motioned for Leopold to approach.

The Count said, "His Highness would be pleased if your son played."

Wolfgang played one of his sonatas on the harpsichord, and he was congratulated by the Elector for his fine performance.

Colloredo said nothing, Leopold noticed; his employer did not even acknowledge them. He heard the Elector say, "Hieronymus, you are fortunate in having such a talented boy in your service." And Colloredo seemed embarrassed, bowing his head and shrugging.

Yet Leopold felt that it would be polite to approach Colloredo, but it was difficult, for the Archbishop was surrounded by the nobility and their compliments. Then Count von Seeau drew him away until they were out of the hearing of the Archbishop, and said, "I have been telling His Grace what a splendid musician he has in your son. I have strengthened your position immeasurably, Mozart. He will want to keep both of you for life."

The Count made this sound like great praise, but Leopold wondered if this was the Bavarian way of getting rid of them. And suddenly he and Wolfgang stood alone, for everyone was following the Elector and the Archbishop into the reception room of the palace.

Several days later, Franz Joseph Albert, the jovial, friendly proprietor of the Black Eagle Inn where the Mozarts were staying, asked Wolfgang to engage in a clavier contest with Captain Ignaz von Beecke.

Wolfgang wanted to refuse, he disliked the idea of a clavier contest, but Papa said, "It is a fine idea. Herr Albert is a passionate lover of music, a friend of many of the leading musicians in Bavaria, who always stay here, when they are in Munich, and he is influential with many of them."

"This hardly qualifies him to make musical judgments."

"That is not the question. Beecke is supposed to be the best clavier player in Germany. If you show how much better you are, and you are less than half his age, it will be a great triumph, and very useful."

So Wolfgang agreed, although reluctantly.

And when he saw the instrument they were to compete on, he wanted to withdraw. Albert's clavier was a new, large pianoforte, when he had assumed it would be a harpsichord. He had played pianofortes a few times since he had studied it years ago with Christian Bach in London, but never in public. Yet he could not turn down a musical challenge.

After the introduction Albert said that Beecke should start, since he was the senior musician, preferably with two of his own compositions.

Wolfgang noticed that his opponent was scrawny, middle-aged, with long fingers that raced over the keys with unusual speed. He thought that Beecke's compositions were wretched, but the audience seemed to like them, for they applauded loudly. And his opponent's execution was so rapid it were as if he was in a race, cantering up and down the keyboard like a conceited ass. Beecke's time was uneven, and in the bravura passages he reeked of self-love. He was called Captain Beecke because he had fought in the Seven Years' War, but Wolfgang thought he should have stayed in the army.

Then it was Wolfgang's turn. As he warmed up he was aware that this was the finest pianoforte he had played on. Yet there were unfamiliar things here. He started slowly, and he stressed preciseness of execution, and gradually he felt at home on the pianoforte and his tone expanded.

Leopold felt that his son looked distinguished in his brown velvet suit, white silk stockings and carefully powdered wig. And his hands, once they recovered from their unfamiliarity with this pianoforte, moved with their usual ease. His son must not undervalue himself. He had become an attractive young man, slighter and shorter than average, but with handsome blue eyes, a fair skin worth being vain about, and a pleasing expression.

After Wolfgang played two of his compositions, Albert exclaimed, "Wolfgang is a marvel. He performed just as ably as Captain Beecke, although he is half his age. But quite differently in style."

Beecke congratulated Wolfgang also, saying, "You have a nice tone."

Wolfgang shrugged. Beecke had played without taste.

Herr Albert declared, "It is a draw."

"Yes," said Leopold. It was evident to him that Wolfgang had wiped up the floor with Beecke. But why was his son so distracted?

Wolfgang had fallen in love. This Spath pianoforte surpassed any he had encountered. And where the tone of Christian Bach's had blurred, here the sound had been clear. But he had not played as skillfully as he should have, whatever Papa said. He had played this pianoforte too much as if it were a harpsichord. He needed more practice.

He longed to discuss this with Papa, but Papa was upset. A

message had come from Colloredo ordering the Mozarts to return to Salzburg at once, and Papa was muttering irritably, "Colloredo is becoming impossible."

"What does he want me to do?" asked Wolfgang.

"I don't know – except that it sounds urgent."

Archduke Maximilian, the youngest son of Maria Theresa, arrived in Salzburg on a state visit a few weeks later, after visiting his sister, Marie Antoinette, the recently crowned Queen of France, and this occasion was honored with the opera *Il Re Pastore* by Archbishop Colloredo's third Konzertmeister, Wolfgang Mozart. The libretto, which was about the kindness of Alexander the Great to young love, had been shared by many composers, but it seemed to Colloredo an appropriate choice to celebrate the visit of the nineteen-year-old Prince. The fact that the libretto was a last-minute choice, that his court composer had to write an overture and fourteen arias in several weeks was of no concern to the Archbishop.

It was healthy for a musician to be prodded, he informed the Archduke, when the latter apologized for his sudden decision to visit Salzburg. A generous ruler was a weak ruler, he thought; it was far better to be decisive. Colloredo was proud of the money he had spent on the opera, he had hired a castrato in addition to his own musicians. He did not increase the composer's pay, or give him a gift for the opera. Anything written by one of his musicians was his property.

Il Re Pastore pleased Archduke Maximilian. After the performance he said, "Any text by Metastasio is certain to be entertaining, and the music fitted, although it was a little too pretty, don't you think."

"Mozart's music is usually too pretty," Colloredo declared, "but he is the best we have at the moment."

Count Karl Arco stood before him, "Does Your Grace wish to speak to any of the musicians? They are waiting."

The Archbishop glanced over to the Archduke, who said, "The castrato was very good. Would you give him twenty gulden for me?"

"I will be honored," said Karl Arco. "Is there anything else, sir?"

"Nothing else," said Archduke Maximilian.

"Nothing, nothing at all," added the Archbishop. As they walked into his private apartments he glanced covertly at his guest, who standing, was much shorter, his youth revealed suddenly. Yet there were rumors that the Archduke was going to be appointed an Archbishop or a Cardinal as soon as he came of age. Colloredo thought, feeling irritation at this possibility, it was not as easy to be a good host as some of his nobles assumed.

THIRTY-EIGHT

Wolfgang had found a new voice. The moment the Archduke left Salzburg and his services were no longer in immediate demand by Colloredo and he had a free evening at home he asked Papa, "May I have a pianoforte?"

Papa said, "Herr Albert told me that his pianoforte cost over two hundred gulden. It is far more than we can afford."

"I cannot afford not to have one. Soon everybody will be playing them."

"What about the violin?"

Wolfgang strode up and down their concert hall, the Tansmeister-Saal, as if to evade Papa's question, but Papa persisted.

"You do not have enough faith in your violin playing. If you would practice the violin with the same enthusiasm and emotion you put into the harpsichord, you could be the first violinist in Europe."

"Will you get me a pianoforte if I practice as you wish on the violin?"

"You don't have to bribe me," Papa said indignantly.

Wolfgang took a piece of fruit that Mamma had placed on the table for them, and repeated, "If I practice the violin as much as you wish, will you get me a pianoforte then?"

"That is not the point. You must want to do it."

"Oh, I do. If I can also practice on the pianoforte."

"For over thirty years I have been giving lessons on the violin. And never have I had a pupil who could play with such expression, with such tenderness, and such indifference."

Papa sounded so hurt that Wolfgang was remorseful. He declared, "If you buy a pianoforte, I will write you a violin concerto. Perhaps two."

Papa could not resist being sarcastic. "It won't be too tiresome?"

"I will write them short and easy, so even His Grace can play them."

256

"Bravissimo! That will make him understand your genius."

"Papa, I will certainly try to follow your advice. And if my simple little violin concerto pleases you, I will be very happy."

Leopold continued to grumble about the cost, but he bought a Spath pianoforte from Regensburg, the very best he could find.

Now Wolfgang practiced both pianoforte and violin. He also taught Nannerl the pianoforte, and she took to it naturally as she had to the harpsichord. And once again they began to play together.

One evening when he could not wait to finish dinner, he was in such a hurry to play the pianoforte duet he had just composed for them, Mamma said, amused by his enthusiasm, "You would even get me to play if you could."

"Why don't you?" he said unexpectedly.

"Don't we have enough musicians in the family?"

Leopold, who had been enjoying the boiled beef that Theresa cooked so well, looked up with a start and was so shocked she softened that by adding, "I meant, Leopold, that three careers in the family are enough."

Nannerl complained, "Mine has hardly been a career the last few years."

Wolfgang said, "You could still be a fine concert performer if you would practice more, but the instant someone courts you, you forget music."

Anna Maria had a sudden pain in her throat. Nannerl was almost twenty-four, and at the thought of her becoming an old maid she could scarcely breathe. She said, "Each thing has its place. We must not quarrel. We are a family."

Several weeks later Papa wanted to know what had happened to the violin concerto Wolfgang had promised to compose for him, and Wolfgang answered, "I am not sure of my theme yet, but I will have one soon that we will be able to play for the court," and Papa seemed appeased. Wolfgang did not tell Papa that he was reading his *Violin School* before he started composing.

The *Violin School* had been a bible in his childhood, but one that Papa had given him as a priest would, selecting parts for him to study and always with a precept about the virtues of hard work. Now he was reading it from cover to cover. Much of the text was rudimentary, yet he realized that much of it was more than just the teaching of technique.

There was a strong point of view, and the final chapters were rich in musical contest, stressing that the violinist, even the virtuoso, must always be at the service of the music. Papa liked to exclaim when his children praised him, "Basta! I am not a Saint!" Yet he had given a devotion to the violin, reflected Wolfgang, that should be canonized in heaven. When he finished the *Violin School*, he regarded Papa with a new respect, and it gave him the impetus to start the first violin concerto.

He put it in B Flat, and he wrote the first movement *Allegro moderato*. Recalling the best violin music he knew, by Vivaldi, Tartini, Boccherini, and Nardini, he wrote in their style, gay and lively.

In the second movement, the *Adagio,* his own nature prevailed and he was the melodist, the music apparently simple in structure, yet warm and rich in tone. He liked the quiet emotion of the theme. It was like the substance of a gentle dream. Yet within it, there was a little stately dance step as if he were courting a great and beautiful lady such as the Countess Lützow with elegance and adoration. He wrote this with passion, but it was always controlled. And it filled his heart with warmth.

After such emotion the third movement was *Presto,* with bravura, ideal for a virtuoso like Nardini, the best violinist he had heard, and within the reach of his friend, Thomas Linley, whom he had never forgotten.

A month after he had begun the violin concerto he showed the finished composition to Papa, who said, "It is a sonorous and serviceable piece."

Wolfgang was surprised, and disappointed. He had expected more. He was sure that his father was dissatisfied with the concerto.

Leopold liked it very much, but if he encouraged Wolfgang too much, his son would be satisfied and stop – his son was lazy when not prodded. He added, "Since you grasp the form now, why don't you write another. With the warm weather Colloredo is more interested in hunting than in music. Give him a march or two, and a serenade, and that will take care of the next couple of months and you can focus on your own work."

Wolfgang composed two marches, and a serenade for the Archbishop, and then began a new violin concerto. He placed it in D, but when he finished he was dissatisfied. It was no better than the first.

Listening wherever he went in Salzburg, he heard nothing that suggested a new theme and yet sightseers crowded the Domplatz and the Residenzplatz. He saw from their heavy black stockings, their thick somber waistcoats, their ugly high shoes that they were from the provinces and that Salzburg was the great world for them. But some of the country girls were pretty, and that stirred yearnings in him. Barbara von Mölk was visiting in Vienna; the only females he enjoyed talking to, Countesses Lodron and Lützow, were at their country estates for the summer.

Up to now Wolfgang had sought to keep his personal feelings out of the violin concertos, but starting the third one, he felt in such a chaos of emotion he had to find some order. Papa was in bed with a summer cold and Theresa was nursing him; Mamma was helping Nannerl with her hair, for Nannerl expected an important suitor; and he was so lonely he was miserable. Yet a lovely air was running through his head. He never could resist a beautiful melody. Inevitably and so naturally that this was no longer a conscious act, he wrote it out. He did this with great care, this was what he truly felt. As he worked with this new emotion he realized that he had been composing to please someone else, and that would please no one.

He was grateful that Papa had not asked to see the second concerto, although he had been hurt by his apparent neglect. This new piece was more suitable for Papa; this was his own music he was writing.

His loneliness vanished as he wrote the first movement of the third violin concerto with symphonic eloquence. The orchestra dominated the opening passages of the *Allegro*. This was *his feeling*, he knew, working day after day in their concert hall, ignoring the summer sun on the Hannibalplatz, the laughter of the children playing in the courtyard behind their house. As this violin concerto in G developed he imagined it as a duet with Papa and himself, Papa was the orchestra and he was the soloist. He gave the orchestra his father's vigor, will-power, and vivacity, and for the most part kept the soloist subordinate. And he ended this movement with a triumphant surge of strength from the orchestra.

The second movement became the most personal music he had composed. He had such a need, such a desire for physical affection. Yet it must not be cheap or coarse. And he could not weep or wail or utter reproaches. His music had to be what he wanted love to be, not what it was. This *Adagio* was the voice of the soloist, his voice. It had to sing. Love sang. That was no illusion, whatever else was. This must be a *love that he could love*. Gone was the constraint that had restricted him previously. He felt his own heart throbbing in the notes he was writing. Everyone had strict orders not to disturb him when he was composing, but he would not have heard them if they had. There was so much music in him, he felt he could do anything. But he must select, refine, clarify. He must use the best of the violin, its sonority, grace and emotion.

For the final draft of the second movement he began slowly, cutting away everything that was not part of the main theme, and gradually music emerged that had the beauty and purity he desired. There were moments of poignancy in the *Adagio*, even somberness, but they did not last, they could not last, life bubbled up in him so. Lovely tones came of their own accord, each note in the proper order. And as they sang, they danced. He rocked back and forth in his chair as he wrote these rhythms. The middle of the second movement

259

flowed into a gracious and elegant minuet that he and the Countess Lützow could dance with a classical and flawless grace, and with just a touch of solemnity and sorrow.

The third movement went swiftly and joyously. He scored it as a *rondo,* and added *Allegro* to accent the tempo, and now the soloist and the orchestra were partners. Each had had their individual say, and now they were speaking as one. He sensed that this was music different from any he had written. Yet that did not mean that it should go on indefinitely. Suddenly he stopped. He could visualize the astonishment on many faces; a concerto was supposed to rise to a towering crescendo.

But he had said what he wanted to say. He played the final passages over in his mind to verify that and "Basta!" he cried to himself, "I am right!" He stared at the last note and began to laugh. It was over.

He ran to the dining room where the family were preparing for dinner, and begged them to hear his new concerto. "Just a few bars!" he exclaimed, "to hear the theme!" He gripped Mamma by the hand and danced her around the room, singing the theme as he did, although he had no respect for his own voice. He felt giddy, light-headed, and full of joy.

"What is the matter?" Mamma asked. "Are you in love again?"

"No, no, never!" he shouted. "Never again!"

"Until next time," said Nannerl. "Who is it this time?"

He blushed, then grinned, and added, "Come, all of you, you must hear the new concerto, it is such lovely music."

Papa signaled them to follow Wolfgang to the concert hall, for it was unusual for him to be this excited over a composition.

Wolfgang said, as he picked up his violin while Papa examined the score of this new concerto, "I will play just a little of the second movement, where the theme is most expressive." He was drunk with emotion, and yet, the instant he began he played with the utmost preciseness.

He had improved, Papa thought gratefully, he had been practicing regularly. Then the music became sovereign and Papa marveled, telling himself that nothing could surpass this melody. This third violin concerto was such a leap from the first two that it was as if it had come directly from God. He said, "It is beautiful. To hear something such as this, so excellent, makes me breathe more deeply. You have made great progress this year."

"You read the second concerto?" Wolfgang asked suspiciously.

"Oh, no, not a note," said Papa. He had studied the one in D when Wolfgang had been at court, but he had kept this from his son, not wishing to upset him with his disappointment. "But this concerto is quite lovely."

And Mamma liked it. Wolfgang could tell by the way she was laughing.

Nannerl asked, "Why did you write it this way?"

He shrugged. He knew, only somehow he could not say it.

"The *Adagio* is very intimate. Like a song to a love that could be, but actually never quite is."

So she had suffered also. He felt quite close to her now, yet he said, "Can man write the impossible?"

"Who knows what is possible," said Papa. "If one has genius."

Nannerl said, "I wish I had someone who would write such music for me."

Wolfgang replied strongly, "I wrote it for no one. No one, but myself." Then he felt embarrassed that he had exposed this.

Papa did not rebuke him as he expected, saying instead, "I hope this is the first of many more violin concertos like this one in G."

"I'll try." A new theme was crystallizing in his mind.

"May I have this new concerto, Wolfgang?"

"To play?"

"To keep."

"Just a moment, Papa." Wolfgang took the score from his astonished father, and wrote at the end of the autograph: *"Concerto di Violino di Wolfgango Amadeo Mozart Salizburgo li 12 di Septembre 1775,"* and handed it back to him with a smile.

THIRTY-NINE

The fourth violin concerto was begun immediately. He put it in D Major, not satisfied with the previous one in that key, marked the first movement *Allegro,* and wrote it with passion from the start. He felt so alive. Papa and Mamma's enthusiasm gave him such pleasure. There was not a composer in the world he envied. He could still feel Mamma's delight when he had danced with her. Where the first movement of the third violin concerto had been symphonic, this one was a dance. He was intoxicated with motion, yet even as he created music that was gay and sparkling, he kept it precise.

By the second movement he was calling this work, "his Strassburg concerto", for he was using an air that was popular in that city. His natural exuberance reasserted itself, and he wrote the *Andante cantabile* as a rich, sensuous love song, without sadness or solemnity. The music for the solo violin became a superb aria. And while the melody continued to throb with emotion, he wrote it in a style, as he told Papa, "as smooth as oil."

He concluded the composition with a *Rondeau* that was both a song and a dance. He ignored the usual stress on violin virtuosity, and again he ended quietly, so that the soloist would not overwhelm the music with a flourish.

Without pausing, Wolfgang plunged into a fifth violin concerto. He used the same structure he had employed in the just finished work, but he placed this piece in the key of A Major and the content was quite different. He sought to speak for the music itself. He composed the score with an apparent simplicity that was interwoven with subtlety and spirit. This work became the tenderest of all his concertos for the violin, yet as lean as a quartet by Joseph Haydn. He told himself, the world might be profane but music such as this must be sacred.

He handed Papa both concertos at the same time. It was December,

1775, nine months after he had promised to write one. Gentle, soothing spring had been flourishing when he had begun and now it was harsh, drab winter; there were several feet of snow on the ground, the sky was gray and he had not seen the sun for days, and he felt forsaken; there was not even an aimless bird outside his window to amuse and please him. Suddenly he was tired, depressed, empty, without a thing to absorb him. He had been on such a great height and now he was so low. He was afraid that Papa would dislike his fifth violin concerto, it was so different from anything they knew, completely away from the traditional Italian flamboyance.

Papa was amazed. It was as if this violin concerto in A Major was the final expression of his *Violin School*. And perhaps, made in heaven. But how to put into words what he felt?

They were in the concert hall – Wolfgang was too exhausted to share this music with anyone else – and each was waiting for the other to speak.

"Really!" Papa exclaimed finally, so emotional he was brusque to hide that. "You didn't tell me that you wrote two!"

"Which is which? Does it matter?"

"You can't put them together. They are so different."

"I did it so you can choose which one to play."

"You didn't compose them for that purpose. Now don't apologize, I won't believe you and it isn't necessary. I am not good enough to play these concertos, and you may not be either, although you could be with practice."

"I will be able to play them. Do you like them?"

"Is that essential?"

All at once Wolfgang longed to be just as contrary. He went as if to tear up the new scores and Papa, refusing to relinquish them, regarded him as if he were insane, and said, "The question is, will Colloredo like them?"

"You remember what happened with the symphonies."

"Of course. But if Brunetti performed one, he might approve. He likes Brunetti's playing, and he favors the violin, since he plays it himself."

"But do you like them, Papa?"

"Who can tell without hearing them? We must not be sentimental. Basta! I must get these scores copied immediately, before you lose them. But under your supervision, or a hundred mistakes will creep in."

"You want Brunetti to play one even though you dislike him personally?"

"What has that to do with it! Our first Konzertmeister is Colloredo's favorite performer, and in his opinion, the best violinist in Salzburg."

Colloredo agreed to hear two of the concertos when Leopold told him that Wolfgang had composed them because of His Grace's devotion to the violin. He thought that the musician exaggerated, but he did enjoy the violin and he was curious about the boy's taste. As Leopold expected, Brunetti chose to play the fourth concerto, while Wolfgang decided to play the fifth – the third was too personal – and Brunetti also planned for the Archbishop to perform a trio with himself and Wolfgang.

The concert was held in the Konferenzsaal of the Residenz in January of 1776. It was a few days before Wolfgang's twentieth birthday, and Leopold, who kept a careful record of such things, felt that now Colloredo would have to acknowledge Wolfgang as the equal of Brunetti.

Leopold saw many friends and patrons in the audience, the Lützows and the Lodrons, the von Robinigs, the von Mölks, the Barisanis, and Schachtner and Bullinger, but he was determined to heed only the music.

The program began with the trio at the Archbishop's command. He stood in front, ostensibly playing the first violin, since he had to be first in everything and no one was allowed to perform with their back to him.

Antonio Brunetti, dark, attractive, tall – one of the few musicians that Colloredo did not tower over – was behind him, but close to him, to cover his mistakes and to lead the trio musically whenever it was necessary. He had arranged a brief caprice by Nardini so that it would be within the Archbishop's reach, and Wolfgang was just the accompaniment.

Wolfgang thought it was unfortunate that Colloredo felt he had to play an instrument. His fingering was all fingernails, he scraped rather than bowed, and his tempo was invented on the spot and like nothing Wolfgang had ever known. After the trio ended with Brunetti leading the final passages without Colloredo, who had lost his place, Brunetti applauded him loudly and cried, "Bravo!" But Wolfgang told himself that if the Archbishop cared about the welfare of his soul he should stop fiddling.

However, he tried to like Brunetti's performance of his fourth violin concerto. The first Konzertmeister, who had been a soloist in Salzburg before Wolfgang had been born, could play excellently when he wished. But too often his execution was careless, yet his style although usually in the old fashioned Tartini manner, could be quite pleasing to listen to, with a rich and strong tone. And Brunetti started well. He played the *Allegro* with a lovely, lyrical feeling, but in the *Andante cantabile* his emotionalism overwhelmed him and he rolled his eyes and swayed as if in the grip of a great passion, playing as slowly and as intensely as possible, and in the *Rondeau* he slurred and was too fast.

Leopold ignored everything but the music. He was aware of Brunetti's mistakes, but at least, the Italian's performance was expressive. He loved the firm, sonorous tone of this violin concerto in D Major. The sound was beautiful, full of grace and delicacy, and he was astonished by the maturity of this composition.

But it was not until Wolfgang played the fifth violin concerto, the one in A Major, that he sensed just how far his son had progressed. This was the finest music Wolfgang had composed. It possessed emotions and subtle variations he had not heard in his son's music before. And he realized that his worry about the possibility of mistakes in Wolfgang's playing had been foolish. Each note was in place. Every passage was played cleanly.

Leopold thought Wolfgang performed so that no one was aware of the difficulties, which was the best kind of execution, while Brunetti had performed so that everyone was aware of the difficulties, and yet the latter had been applauded much more.

And now Colloredo summoned Brunetti and Wolfgang before him and ordered his first Konzertmeister to perform over the second movement of the concerto in A Major, dissatisfied with the way Wolfgang had played it. The spacious chamber was very still as Brunetti played the *Adagio*.

This angered Leopold but when Brunetti finished and Colloredo prepared to comment, he assumed his calmest expression as he joined Wolfgang who had been ordered to wait as if his son were an incompetent school child.

Colloredo asked, "Signor Brunetti, what do you think of the *Adagio*?"

"You want my truthful and impartial opinion, Your Grace?" asked Brunetti, which means, thought Leopold, here comes the lie.

"Naturally, Signor Brunetti. You are our first violinist."

"Your Grace, I was playing before the boy was born."

"Didn't you think the *Adagio* was too slow?"

"Too studied, sir. It should be rewritten."

"That is easy, Your Grace," Leopold broke in, although he was furious. "Wolfgang would be honored to compose a new movement."

"Good. Have him make it a little lighter, and shorter."

Leopold said, "But sir, I wouldn't want to see the piece spoiled."

Colloredo suddenly addressed Wolfgang, "Do you feel the same way?"

Wolfgang, to Leopold's surprise, said, "I will consider it, Your Grace."

Colloredo asked Brunetti, "Signore, what did you think of his playing?"

Brunetti, who had not been in Italy for many years, but became more Italian the longer he was away from his native land, exclaimed with a flourish, "Passabilimente! For Salzburg! For Italy – no!"

Colloredo said, "Mozart, the music is too difficult for your son."

"Forgive me, Your Grace, but I felt he played perfectly."

"You don't understand the Italian style."

"Sir, we toured Italy three times. Wolfgang was acclaimed everywhere."

"We are a generous people," said Brunetti, "but we do not always say what we mean."

"You are quite right," said Wolfgang.

Brunetti looked confused.

"You said my concertos were quite rare but not very unusual."

Colloredo said impatiently, "But that is not the point!"

"What is, Your Grace?" Wolfgang asked politely.

"One can accept just so many excuses," Colloredo stated with an emphasis that was unusual for him. "The best violin performers and composers are Italian. There is not one German who has composed music for the violin like a Vivaldi or a Tartini or who plays as well as a Nardini or a Brunetti. You know practically nothing about the violin. You should go to Italy and study in a conservatory."

Wolfgang said instantly, "May we leave for Italy now?"

Colloredo was outraged. "Of course not! You are needed here!"

The moment they were alone, Wolfgang whispered to Leopold, "Asking our Grand Mufti to hear music, is like asking a man to listen when he is deaf."

FORTY

====

While Leopold was still marveling about the phenomenal fertility that Wolfgang had shown in the creation of five violin concertos in nine months, and which lessened the pain of Colloredo's criticism, Wolfgang embarked on a new burst of composing that struck him as just as miraculous.

It was Wolfgang's way of answering Colloredo's disdain. As his love for the pianoforte increased, he composed a concerto in B Flat for himself, and when he liked the result he wrote a concerto in F for three pianofortes for Countess Lodron and her two daughters. Then, so Countess Lützow would not feel slighted, he composed a concerto in C for her.

At the request of the Haffners, he wrote a serenade for the marriage of Elizabeth Haffner. What started out to be simple chamber music became symphonic in style with eight movements of great variety as he wrote into the serenade a melodic expression of the joys of married love.

Aware of Nannerl's unhappiness over her unwed state, he wrote a *Serenata Natturna* for her twenty-fifth birthday. She was so pleased with his present, kissing him affectionately, he responded with an encore, a divertimento, which he made livelier and gayer.

Countess Lodron, envious of the music he had written for the Haffners, asked for a divertimento for a party she was giving, and Wolfgang composed two for her, full of sparkle, charm, and gallantry.

He liked them so much, he wrote six more divertimentos for himself and for the pleasure of his friends this year of 1776.

The music he composed for Colloredo was a different matter. Each week he had to appear before Karl Arco, who was brief and curt.

One week Arco stated, "His Grace desires several hymns, short and simple, for the cathedral." Another time the chief steward ordered, "Some church sonatas and a Missa brevis for the Archbishop's name day." Other weeks entertainment music was demanded as when Arco said, "His Grace is having company for dinner. He expects a serenade, something that will please, but which will not disturb his conversation or his digestion."

Wolfgang did the best he could, but his heart was not in it, and Leopold felt that Colloredo was a vampire sucking his son's blood, the Archbishop ordered so much music despite his indifference to Wolfgang's ability. At the end of the year Leopold estimated that his son had composed thirty pieces for Colloredo in twelve months, yet without one raise in pay, or an extra gulden, or a word of praise, although their friends and patrons had given Wolfgang presents for the music he had written for them.

Anna Maria thought they should not resent Colloredo so much. One night in January, 1777, while Leopold and Wolfgang were discussing how to free themselves of Colloredo and Salzburg, she said, "We ought to have a party."

"What for?" asked Leopold, annoyed that he had been interrupted.

"For Wolfgang's twenty-first birthday." The three of them were in their concert hall, and Anna Maria had tried to choose the right moment, when Leopold would be in a good humor and listen to her. She had waited until Wolfgang was showing a new composition to Leopold, usually a happy time in her husband's life. "It is a very important birthday."

Leopold looked up from the aria Wolfgang had just handed him and said gruffly, "Wolfgang writes fine music for a castrato, and thanks to Colloredo's stupidity and penury, there is none in Salzburg to sing it."

But a party for her son could make him more satisfied with Salzburg. She said, "We could have a masquerade. Both of you love to dress up."

"What about his career? It is stagnating here."

"The Archbishop has kept us at peace."

Wolfgang said, "Our Grand Mufti is afraid to fight."

"Whatever the reasons, we have had no war."

"Mamma, we have nothing anybody could use. not even a castrato."

"Just the same, we are at peace, although there is talk of a new war between France and England over the American colonies. And Vienna and Berlin are making threatening gestures at each other over Bavaria. We are lucky to live here. If we left, who knows what we would run into."

"A theater where there is opera. Now that Colloredo has closed the court theater, there is no chance of any opera here at all."

"You would miss our shooting matches, Wolfgang."

He grinned. The Sunday afternoons they met with friends and shot darts out of air guns at humorous objects was fun.

"And you like the parties, the masquerades, the being welcome in the Lodron and Lützow palaces. You are in them frequently."

"Anna Maria, I wouldn't take the compliments of Countess Lodron and Lützow seriously," Leopold said unexpectedly. "We can't depend on them."

Wolfgang didn't feel flattered by the Lodrons or the Lützows but at home with them. He asked, "Why? They do like my music."

"Naturally. You have written much music for them, most of it as a gift. But both those grand ladies need the Archbishop's favor. Even when they help you, you must not count on it, or expect it."

Nannerl entered with a letter from Mademoiselle Jeunehomme, the noted French pianist, who was visiting Salzburg to perform for the Archbishop.

The letter, which Leopold read aloud to the others, asked Maestro Mozart to compose a pianoforte concerto for her. It went on to say that she could only pay forty gulden for his concerto, what with the cost of traveling and the small fee that she was receiving from the Archbishop. But she had heard several of Maestro Mozart's compositions in Paris and they were worthy of French taste, and she would be honored to play his music.

Wolfgang said spontaneously, "I could compose it for her as a gift," and Leopold was distressed, even when his son explained, "It would be a gesture of friendship. When we are in Paris, she could do us a favor."

"Nonsense," declared Leopold. "Colloredo is paying her, and she can pay you. You are much too impulsive and generous for your own good."

"What about the birthday party?" asked Anna Maria.

Leopold said, "The party wouldn't be significant enough. But if we could celebrate Wolfgang's twenty-first birthday in our Prince's castle with a new concerto for a famous pianist, it should impress even him."

Now it was as if the three concertos for pianoforte that Wolfgang had written had been practice pieces to prepare him for the assignment from Mademoiselle Jeunehomme. A year of practicing and composing had taught him that here was a musical voice which spoke a language that was poetic yet dramatic, with brilliant varieties of tone and color, and sonorities that were deeply emotional. And the French pianist's interest gave him a prodigious vitality, and a new optimism. Once again he felt he could do anything and the thought of failure was inconceivable. He was not composing for amateurs anymore; she was one of the finest concert artists in Europe.

Yet even as he worked so incessantly that there was nothing in life

269

but this pianoforte concerto in E Flat, he wrote with a controlled eloquence that was tonally subtle and technically precise, that sang, danced, and said what he had to say. He brought the soloist into the first movement at once, almost as a gesture of defiance, and gave the soloist and the orchestra a collaboration that added to the beauty of each part.

After this *Allegro* he composed an *Andantino* which became tragic, but without exaggeration or sentimentality. At the pianoforte he heard clearly. He loved it so much. Other things were dark and confused and painful, but he caressed the pianoforte and it gave back love. He poured life into it, and it poured life into him. He gave the final passages of the *Andantino* a tender sadness, but without heaviness, he could not endure heaviness.

He scored the last movement *Rondo*, and added *Presto* to stress the tempo. The music was spirited and lyrical, a mixture of tenderness and a gaiety, as if, no matter what the momentary sorrows, he had to end with joy and cheerfulness. He was answering triumphantly in the face of the enemy. He composed a variation that was so feminine in essence he imagined Mademoiselle Jeunehomme laughing with pleasure. Then he wrote into the conclusion of the concerto a sense of authority and inevitability that was assured and final. The pianoforte had become a God.

Mademoiselle Jeunehomme liked the concerto on sight. By the time she was ready to perform it with a chamber orchestra conducted by Brunetti, she knew it almost as well as Wolfgang.

She was dark, petite, middle-aged, and he was pleased with her concentration and skill, and he was hopeful that she would play the concerto as he had written it.

Wolfgang was disappointed to learn that her concert was to occur in the castle of the Mirabell before a select, and specially invited audience. This was unusual, for the Mirabell was one of the Archbishop's summer residences. Then he heard that Colloredo considered this castle the perfect example of baroque in Salzburg, appropriate for French taste. Some of his skepticism vanished the day of the musical, for it was a lovely Sunday at the end of January, cold but brilliantly clear. The snow-capped peaks that surrounded Salzburg shone radiantly in the sharp sunlight. Usually Wolfgang did not notice scenery, he was generally so preoccupied with music, but today it stimulated his senses. The handsome gardens and the castle of the Mirabell were just across the Hannibalplatz, and as the family left for the concert Papa said this was a good omen.

Mamma agreed, but Nannerl said she still wished they were going to the Residenz, it was warmer. Wolfgang, who did not like to walk, plodded on uncomplainingly. He was grateful for the nearness of the

Mirabell. They entered its gardens through two high stone walls, and he realized that the gardens, with their many statues, did resemble Versailles.

The entrance into the Mirabell was of magnificent Unsterberg marble, and so were the pillars, the ground floor, and the staircase. He took Nannerl by the hand as they climbed it, feeling affectionate with the many lovely cherubic cupids on the elaborate balustrade. He counted the steps to ease his anxiety. "Thirteen, then a landing, eleven. . ."

She interrupted, "They have increased since you were here last summer?"

"Nannerl, *Cara Sorella Mia,* what would I do without your judgment?"

"What you always do, for all the attention you give it."

"If you had listened to me, you could be playing instead of Jeunehomme."

"And spend the morning vomiting, worrying about it. No thanks, Maestro."

"Your hair does look beautiful."

She smiled, somewhat appeased. "Victoria Adlgasser dressed it for me."

"For the concert?"

"No, silly, for the mass this morning."

Both of them were laughing now, and Wolfgang felt much better, bowing as he declared, "My compliments, my lovely Mademoiselle Signorina Fraulein!"

And as he sat in the rear with his family – nobility such as the Lodrons, Lützows, and the Arcos were the only ones permitted in the front rows – he realized that Colloredo had chosen this place because the latter had thought it suitable for a small tone, unaware that the pianoforte had far more sonority than the harpsichord. Yet this room was almost as large as the Rittersaal, but cold physically, for most of the walls were marble, as was the floor. This was not a chamber for a mellow tone, and Wolfgang wished he were somewhere else.

The first number was a serenade in three short movements, which he had written at Colloredo's request, and Brunetti, who was conducting, was full of deprecating grimaces. Wolfgang grew irritable. It was terrible not to enjoy his own music. He felt he was submitting to his own mutilation.

Two large stoves had been placed in the front so that they could warm Colloredo and the musicians, and the rear of the marble room was cold. A chill rose from the floor and crept into his bones and his body ached. The last movement of his serenade, which had been scored as a *Minuet,* became a kind of death march to Wolfgang.

Brunetti, pumping away with his body and his arms, was just as much of a butcher as Lolli, and even more jerky.

Mademoiselle Jeunehomme caused him to forget all this. She announced that she was playing this concerto in honor of Maestro Wolfgang Amadeus Mozart, and from the first notes she stressed purity of tone and clarity of expression rather than showmanship. She had a wonderful left hand, he thought gratefully, yet she didn't abuse it and try to play faster than anyone else. He found himself playing in his seat, right with her. In the slow second movement she did not miss a note, but with a subtle touch, using delicate rather than bravura sonorities, produced such a luminous tone he loved her. And in the last movement she was firm and secure, suggesting tenderness and lyricism with a sensitive eloquence.

Warmed by her fine performance, he ran up to her without noticing who else was there and exclaimed, "Everything was right! The phrasing, the color, the tempo, the mood! Mademoiselle, you were superb!"

"That's true," he heard a voice agreeing, and to his surprise he saw that it was the Archbishop, standing nearby.

He bent his head from habit, but Mademoiselle Jeunehomme said, after a perfunctory bow, "Thanks to you, Maestro Mozart. If I pleased His Grace, it was because the beauty and charm of your concerto made that possible."

Colloredo grumbled, "He never writes such music for me."

Wolfgang said, "Sir, I am at your service whenever you wish."

"Very well. May I have this concerto?"

"I would be honored. But Your Grace, I wrote it for our virtuosa."

"I am sure she would not mind. Would you, Mademoiselle?"

She looked so disappointed, however, that suddenly Colloredo was courtly, saying, "I would not enjoy depriving a lady of her just deserts."

"Thank you, Your Grace, I am honored by your good wishes."

He smiled cynically but he did not comment.

She said, "This lovely concerto is very much in the French taste. Music such as this could make a great success in Paris."

"No doubt," Colloredo said noncomittally.

"Your Grace, I will be taking back to Paris fine reports of the state of music in Salzburg. It is worthy of a great Prince, sir."

Colloredo nodded amiably, held out his hand for her to kiss, and then returned to his throne to receive his subjects, looking almost genial.

Mademoiselle Jeunehomme asked, "Is this your favorite composition?"

"My favorite is the one I am working on."

"You should suit Paris taste very well."

"As when I was a child."

She thought, He is very young in some ways. He blushed easily, and she was sure he was still a virgin although he was twenty-one. Yet while he was not good-looking, he had charm with his fair hair and blue eyes and unusual vivacity, and he might be a great favorite with the women at the French court. She said, "It is a shame to waste your ability in a provincial town like Salzburg. Have you considered visiting Paris?"

"Oh, yes, yes indeed, Mademoiselle!"

"What has prevented you?"

"I am in the service of the Archbishop."

"In Paris you should suit the public, with your ability to please."

"I do have a good friend in Paris. Baron Grimm. Do you know him?"

"Everyone at court knows him. Why don't you have him sponsor you?"

He was still contemplating this when she was called away, to be the guest of honor at a party the Lützows were giving for her. Then he realized that she had forgotten something. She had not paid him.

Papa, who had joined him, wanted to know why.

He could not ask. Countess Lützow had not invited him to her party. Suddenly Wolfgang, walking out of the cold Mirabell Castle with his family, felt chilled again. He looked in the direction of the Fortress Hohensalzburg, which Count Lützow commanded. It seemed close enough to touch, although actually it was several miles away. The sun had vanished, the sky was a somber gray, and it began to rain. He said critically, "It is always raining in Salzburg. You hear now the Salzburg noise, the rain."

"So it is," said Papa. "Does it upset you, Wolfgang?"

"No, no!"

Papa longed to praise Wolfgang. He was full of emotion. But he did not know how to express what he felt without sounding foolish. His son's will to improve, to learn was prodigious, and they assumed his son had sprung from the earth full grown. He said, "Colloredo seemed almost pleased."

"Perhaps he will grant us a leave of absence after all."

"But please!" cried Mamma, "do not anger him."

Twenty gulden, half of what Mademoiselle Jeunehomme had promised to pay Wolfgang, arrived in the mail a week later. He tried to be content, until he heard that she had received a hundred gulden from Colloredo. He was glad when Papa agreed they must ask for a leave of absence from Salzburg.

FORTY-ONE

===

Soon afterward Wolfgang's request for a private audience with Colloredo was granted. Papa wanted to come with him, but Wolfgang said, "It is better if I see him alone. He will think you are interfering."

"Interfering?" Papa was offended. "Is that what you think?"

"Of course not. But he will think so."

Papa grumbled that this was foolishness but he gave in when his son agreed to present the petition he drew up requesting a leave of absence to allow them to improve their financial situation. The petition was humble and supplicating and Papa felt that it would convince Colloredo, but Wolfgang was not so sure. He thought he would have a better chance to go alone, since he was only a half-servant anyway, but Papa was determined to go with him. One thing puzzled Wolfgang, Colloredo had ordered him to bring the autograph of the concerto composed for Mademoiselle Jeunehomme.

And he was disturbed that Papa insisted he wear the Order of the Golden Spur, which had been bestowed upon him by Pope Clement XIV. There was another Pope now, and he thought that this decoration would be resented by Colloredo. But Papa said it would remind Colloredo, who had witnessed the ceremony in Rome in 1770, how celebrated he had been in Italy. So he bent his head as Papa placed the gold cross on the silk red sash around his neck. But he also put on a cloak, to cover it while walking through the streets of Salzburg, since the Residenz was too close to hire a coach, and who knew what ass would see him with the Papal cross and sneer.

The audience was on a blustery, chilly March day, and it was natural for Wolfgang to keep his cloak tightly closed. And as he entered the Residenz its stone walls and floor were very cold. He noticed that its walls slanted back from the pavement more like a fortress than a palace, and the iron bars on the windows gave him the feeling of a prison. It seemed to press down on him, a heavy, implacable stone that could not be moved.

He was in no mood to count the steps of the staircase, which he had done many times. The longest staircase he had ever seen, it seemed even longer this afternoon. But it would not care whether his music lived or died, and he tried to control his shivering as he climbed up the red marble steps.

Since the memorandum from Colloredo had not specified where he should wait, he entered the Karabinierisaal, the first chamber that led to the Archbishop's rooms, and where his bodyguard kept watch day and night.

He had been here often and he was stunned when an assistant steward, hardly better than a footman, ordered him out. "I have an audience with His Grace," he declared, and the steward, whom he did not know, an Italian newly hired from Rome, who had been in the service of a Cardinal and who looked down upon commoners, replied, "I have no record of it. No one is allowed in here unless the Archbishop gives his permission."

Wolfgang said, "I am Herr Mozart, the musician," and the steward shrugged – musicians were even lower on *his* social scale – and pointed to the door.

"Is Count Arco present?"

"Which one?" The steward paused as he was about to call for the Captain of the Guards to eject this insolent young man.

"The older. Count Georg. The father. The Court Chamberlain."

"He is rarely here. He has virtually retired. Do you want his son?"

"No!" The thought of appealing to Karl Arco was repulsive.

"Then be off. Before I call the guards."

Furious, Wolfgang started down the stairway. Walking was awkward, for wooden planks had been placed over the steps. The planks were down so that the Archbishop could ride up in his carriage without having to walk. It was a privilege allowed only to His Grace. Wolfgang, still seething, heard the clatter of horses in the stone courtyard, and before he could retreat the horses were scrambling up the planks. Caught halfway down the steps, Wolfgang could not ask the driver to halt, it was very difficult to manage the nervous horses on the uncertain footing, and the driver was hurrying the horses, anxious to get this hardship over with.

To keep from being run over, Wolfgang had to cower in a crevice in the wall, the only refuge within reach. It was just deep enough for a human body, it had been designed by the architect for beauty and variety, not for comfort. Yet he could not risk dirtying his clothes or damaging the Order of the Golden Spur or the autograph of the pianoforte concerto. He leaned against the crevice until the pressure of the wrought iron bars made him want to scream. But he had to hold himself rigid and quiet, even when the horses, smelling an alien object, relieved themselves in their fear, and he was surrounded with manure and urine. Trying to remain coolheaded, although he was shaken, he stumbled out of the crevice, almost stepping on the manure in his agitation. That was all he needed, he thought bitterly. He was almost at the foot of the stairway when the steward came running after him, crying, "His Grace wants to see you!"

The Archbishop, who had halted the carriage at the top landing, stared at Wolfgang and said, "What are you doing here, Mozart?"

He did not look up into the yellow eyes but mumbled, "You granted me an audience, Your Grace. I have your memorandum which confirms it."

Colloredo said, "I forgot."

Wolfgang was silent.

"If you want to, I can see you after I change."

"Will it be long, Your Grace?"

The steward looked horrified at such presumption, this musician needed moral rescuing, but Colloredo said, "Are you in a hurry?"

"No more than you are, sir."

"Very well then. Wait."

Wolfgang sat on a sofa in the anteroom to the Karabinierisaal, and wished he could move, but he had been ordered to sit here. This sofa was built in such a way that when he sat back on it his feet dangled and he could not reach the floor, and he thought wryly, this was typical of Colloredo, who used sofas to make a short man feel shorter and a tall man superior.

He waited such a long time, it became interminable. He could not compose as he usually did while he waited, he burned so with anger and exasperation. But at last he was called. Karl Arco came to usher him into Colloredo's presence, and he sought to be calm and dignified. They strode through the Karabinierisaal and Rittersaal and Konfer-senzsaal in silence, and Wolfgang hoped that this would be the last time. When they reached the Antikamera, the anteroom that led to the Audienzsaal, the most splendid of all the chambers in the Residenz and where the Archbishop held most of his audiences, Arco paused and asked, "What is your hurry?"

Wolfgang did not reply.

"And this cloak you are wearing? What are you hiding?"

"I am cold. These rooms are not well heated."

"You will have to take it off. His Grace does not allow anyone to appear in his private chambers in such a manner."

"I can assure you, I am not hiding a dangerous weapon."

"One never knows. I cannot admit you unless you take off your cloak."

Wolfgang took it off slowly, stiffly, but without expression.

For a moment Arco said nothing. Then suddenly he laughed. "You are very grand in that waistcoat. And that cross? You know that only the nobility are allowed to wear decorations in the presence of His Grace."

"It is not a decoration, but a Papal benediction. Clement XV made me a Knight of the Golden Spur when I was in Rome. Because of my music."

"Knight of the Spur," sneered Arco. "How much did it cost?"

Wolfgang's throat was dry and he could not speak.

"Five gulden? And did you get permission to wear it? How much did that cost?" When he noticed Wolfgang's growing anger, he said, "Here, have some snuff. Take a pinch. Or isn't a Knight allowed?" he said jeeringly.

"I asked for the privilege of seeing His Grace, not for your opinions."

"You would be better off if you listened to me."

"What has that to do with my audience?"

"You are very young, Mozart, but you will learn. Do you think the Archbishop has only you to think about?"

"Of course not. What are you trying to tell me, Count Arco?"

"His Grace has just learned that Joseph II is stopping off in Salzburg on his way to visit Louis XVI. The Bavarian Elector is quite ill, and there are rumors that Joseph intends to seize Bavaria when the Elector dies, and wants the help of the French King. If he takes Bavaria, we will be surrounded by the Austrian Empire. He may want to annex us next."

"Is the Archbishop worried?"

"Would you want to become part of the Hapsburg Empire?"

Yes, thought Wolfgang, at least Joseph II is musical, but to say this would be regarded as treason, so he looked distressed suddenly, and said, apparently solicitous, "Then His Grace would no longer be a Prince?"

"So you realize why you must be careful what you say to His Worship?"

"Yes. Thank you, Count. May I see him now?"

Arco directed a footman to show him in, and Wolfgang, taking no notice of the footman or the valet at the side of the Archbishop, who was sitting at his desk, walked straight up to Colloredo, and paid his respects.

Colloredo was surprised, but he stopped writing – he was in the middle of a letter to Joseph II saying how honored he would be to have His Majesty as a guest, when it was the last thing he desired – and he said, "Well, Mozart, what do you want?"

Whatever Arco's reasons, his words had been a warning, and Wolfgang knew he was supposed to be deferential but in his need to be free he could no longer hesitate. "Your help, Your Grace."

"To compose?" Colloredo smiled at that, and so did his valet, footman, and Arco, but not Wolfgang.

He said, "To improve my situation, sir. As is stated in this petition."

Colloredo took it from him, but thought, Such bad manners! He would not have granted this impertinent fellow an audience except that he might need some music from him for Joseph II, since the Hapsburgs had been friendly to the Mozarts and the Emperor fancied himself a musical connoisseur. He did not look at the petition but said, "State your business."

"It concerns a leave of absence. Your worship, I beg you to consider my petition. I do not earn enough. I cannot live on my present salary."

"You were just a child when I appointed you a Konzertmeister. You are hardly more than that now."

"Sir, as a child I earned many gulden. And could again, if I toured."

"Did you bring the pianoforte concerto?"

"Yes, sir."

"Give it to me."

Wolfgang handed it reluctantly to Colloredo.

"What's this! You've dedicated it to Mademoiselle Jeunehomme."

"She bought it, Your Grace."

"But you composed it while you were being paid by me."

"Sir, I have to accept commissions when they are offered. A son owes it to his father to earn his bread as soon as he can."

"And this composition could end up in little pieces." Colloredo went as if to tear it up and throw it into the archiepiscopal grate and Wolfgang could not endure that, and he went to halt him, by force if necessary, forgetting that this could cause his death, the Prince-Archbishop's person was sacred.

Arco blocked his way, whispering, "In God's name, do not anger him more."

Wolfgang recoiled, suddenly remembering that Colloredo also could thrust him into the dungeon in the Fortress Hohensalzburg which was so tiny that the prisoner could neither lie nor sit but had to exist at a perpetual crouch until he became a hunchback for life, if he survived. Wolfgang said, fighting to control himself, "If Your Grace likes my pianoforte concerto, I would be honored to compose a new one for you."

"But not this one?"

"Sir, I gave my word to Mademoiselle Jeunehomme."

Their eyes met and Wolfgang's did not waver, and apparently Colloredo was convinced, which was a poor way, thought Wolfgang, but the Archbishop handed back the autograph, saying, "I will not be so merciful next time."

It was as if Wolfgang had been in the grave and now he was alive again. The score of the pianoforte concerto was a living presence in his hand and he vowed to have it copied, although that was costly and would use up what it had earned. "Thank you, Your Grace."

"I can get many to serve me better than you, Mozart."

"Then you should not object to a leave of absence, sir."

"You are infatuated with music," Colloredo said contemptuously.

"If you will be kind enough to consider my petititon, sir?"

"I have."

"But you haven't even read it, Your Grace!" exclaimed Wolfgang.

"I don't have to," Colloredo said disdainfully. "I know what it contains."

"Then, I have your permission, sir. . ."

"You have my permission to prepare some table music for the presence of His Majesty, Joseph II, when he arrives in Salzburg."

"And not a pianoforte concerto, sir," Wolfgang could not resist saying.

"Who would play it?"

"I would, sir."

"You lack style. No. Compose several divertimentos, short and to the point. I will have much to discuss with the Emperor and the music must not be too loud, or it will disturb us."

"Then may my father and I have a leave of absence?" repeated Wolfgang.

"Your father rather fancies himself an impresario."

"He was very successful when we toured before, sir."

"You were a child. A curiosity. Things have changed. You have served me poorly, but I cannot allow my musicians running around like beggars."

"You said, sir, when we asked your permission to visit Vienna three years ago, that I had nothing to hope for here and that I would do better to try my fortunes elsewhere."

"That is true. But there will be no leave of absence." Colloredo put the petition aside without reading it and his voice became autocratic. "And the next time you are in my presence, do not wear that cross. You are not a Knight, and no indulgent Pope will make you one."

279

FORTY-TWO

The two divertimentos that Wolfgang composed for Joseph II were not performed. The Emperor entered Salzburg incognito, and so there was no public acknowledgment of his presence, and no music. Wolfgang was not invited to the private reception for Joseph II, which he resented, but only the nobility were allowed to be present. There was much speculation whether the Emperor really intended to seize Bavaria and Salzburg, but when nothing happened other matters became more important.

As summer arrived the vital things were whom Colloredo invited to hunt with him, who was his guest for dinner, what they ate and who became drunk. Much significance was given to Colloredo's gout and diarrhea, for then he was very severe. There was excitement when Michael Haydn, playing the organ during a High Mass conducted by Colloredo, hit so many wrong notes it was obvious he had swilled a quart of wine before playing. But talk ebbed when Haydn's situation remained unchanged. Soon afterward there were rumors that Brunetti's mistress was pregnant, and the great question was what Colloredo would do, but when he overlooked it, interest faded.

This provincialism intensified Wolfgang's desire to leave Salzburg. At dinner one evening in July he declared with an emphasis unusual for him, "I must resign from the Mufti's service." This was a step far more drastic than a leave of absence, and he expected an immediate protest.

Instead Papa said, after a thoughtful pause, "Your feeling is understandable, but we must consider all the aspects carefully."

"I cannot any longer. I have tried to be patient, but as you know yourself, a man's reputation lasts very briefly."

"But we both cannot quit, or there will be no income in the family."

Nannerl said, "I could do more teaching."

Papa said, "That would help, but it would not be nearly enough."

Mamma said, "We could economize. I could do all the cooking, cleaning."

Papa said, "Everybody is being excessively noble, but it would be better if we were practical." If his son quit, it could become irrevocable.

Yet Wolfgang was not to be halted now. He said, outspoken in his anger, "There will never be any operas to compose here. But I am an opera composer, and I cannot bury this talent, which God, in his grace and goodness, has endowed me. I say this without vanity, for I feel this more than ever."

"True, but you cannot run about in gipsy fashion. We must plan. If you could get free of the Mufti, and he reconsidered a leave of absence for me, we could find you a position that would permit your genius to grow, to earn enough money to live properly, and to achieve a sound future."

"Charming!" exclaimed Wolfgang. "All we have to do is ask again!"

There was such a bitterness in his son's voice that all the years of unwilling submission and servitude that had accumulated in Leopold welled up in an overwhelming flood. He thought with just as much bitterness that actually Schrattenbach, the supposedly generous Archbishop, had been generous only by comparison with Colloredo. Quickly, before he changed his mind, he wrote a letter of resignation for his son. If he succeeded, he would accompany Wolfgang until his son found the right niche for his genius.

This time neither of them submitted it, but presented it on August 1 through Count Georg Arco, the court chamberlain, who had remained friendly.

Leopold and Wolfgang were upset when there was not any answer from Colloredo for four weeks. Then on August 28 both of them were dismissed.

Wolfgang was elated, but Leopold was stunned. The money that he had earned on the Grand Tour was gone and now, lacking the assurance that there would be a post awaiting him in Salzburg if nothing else developed, he was in a state of shock. And that he had been dismissed so summarily after thirty-seven years of service was inconceivable. He was about to beg His Grace to reinstate him, when he received the following decree from Colloredo: "His Grace has reconsidered his previous decision, and graciously commands Leopold Mozart, if he will conduct himself peaceably with the Kapelle, to return to his employment without alteration in pay."

He learned this was because Fischetti and Lolli were unable to perform their duties, and he was needed to help with the Kapelle.

But this caused a new problem. He could not allow Wolfgang to go alone. He told him, "You don't know how to make travel arrangements, to cope with the difficulties that develop on long journeys." And his son was too impulsive, trusting.

So while it was one of the most painful decisions of his life, Leopold said that Anna Maria must go with Wolfgang.

She did not want to go. She feared that this journey to Munich, Augsburg, Mannheim, and Paris would be dangerous and hard, and there were so many people she would miss, and how could she manage without Leopold?

He had to be heartless then, for he had no choice.

The next few weeks were nerve-racking. There was so much to do, and so many apprehensions. Nannerl acted as if she would never see Mamma or Wolfgang again, and Leopold was worried about money. He did not have enough to finance this expedition, and he hesitated to borrow. The thought of asking was appalling. He was surprised and deeply touched when Schachtner lent him fifty gulden and Bullinger three hundred gulden. Hagenauer had lent him a hundred gulden, as before, but he had expected that; the Jesuit priest, however, had given virtually his life savings.

The day of departure was September 23. Leopold arranged that Wolfgang and Anna Maria should leave at dawn so that they would travel during the maximum hours of daylight, and if there were no accidents reach Munich by the following day. But no one slept. Leopold spent the night packing; Anna Maria kept running to the water closet; Nannerl had a violent headache; and Wolfgang couldn't sit still, he was so excited, preparing the compositions he was taking with him.

Then Wolfgang and Anna Maria were in the coach that Leopold had hired and he was making sure that everything was packed securely and giving them more advice, to hide his own agitation, saying, "You must leave early in the morning so you will not have to travel at night, when it is dangerous, and examine your carriage carefully, especially the wheels. If there is not much rain, have them wetted. And never say in an Inn when and where you are traveling. But your main object is to make money, you must not lose sight of this. Keep up your Latin, Wolfgang, and don't hesitate to play the violin if asked, you must live on whatever sums you earn. Munich and Mannheim are musical cities, and if you can establish yourself there, fine, but remember, Paris is the place to make money and a great reputation, but everything costs money, candles, wood, dressmakers, tailors, wine. . ."

"Indeed," interrupted Anna Maria, having to struggle to keep

282

from weeping, "only death costs nothing, and even that is not true."

Before Leopold could reply, shocked by her burst of pessimism, Bimperl was barking so loudly that she was drowning out their good-byes. The carriage drew away as everyone made a great effort to control themselves so the parting would not be impossibly painful.

Leopold went up the stairs tired and depressed and threw him-self upon his bed. He had struggled to be brave, but suddenly he remembered that in the haste of departure he had forgotten to give his son his paternal blessing. He ran to the window to send that after both of them, but he could not see them going out of the city gate and he realized that they were already gone. He sat for a very long time unable to move. Then he heard Nannerl weeping and he had to con-sole her. But in spite of his attention and affection, she only grew sicker and finally had to go off to bed. He tried to lie down also, but he could not sleep although he was exhausted and drained. He said his morning prayers, and thought, Never have I experienced such a melancholy day.

Wolfgang was jubilant. He kept hearing Papa's last words. "If you establish yourself in Paris, or in Mannheim or Munich, it will be the happiest moment of my life."

Papa had stated also, "Traveling is a serious business, and not a second must be wasted," and had repeated his admonitions about morality, caution, and economy, and had coughed violently when they had departed. Wolfgang's eyes filled with tears until he saw that Mamma was crying. Then he had to be the man in the family, to get her mind off the separation, saying, "You will love Munich. *La Finta Gardiniera* was acclaimed there."

She replied, "I know Munich. I have been there, too."

"Of course!" It was foolish to be apprehensive. Nothing could dampen his exuberance. He felt that now he could do anything in music. He was certain he could serve any position in the world with honor. Life was marvelous, away from Salzburg.

PART SIX

The Quest for Fortune

FORTY·THREE

Wolfgang and Anna Maria arrived in Munich the next day and took rooms in Herr Albert's Black Eagle Inn. He welcomed them warmly and, hearing that Wolfgang had left the service of Archbishop Colloredo, predicted a great future for Wolfgang in music-loving Munich.

But when Wolfgang called upon Count Seeau the next morning, the director of theatricals had gone hunting with the Elector. He persisted, however, as he had promised Papa, and several days later he was received by Count Seeau. Despite the news that he was free of Colloredo and available for Munich, Count Seeau could not promise an audience with the Elector.

It was only when he told a friend in the Munich orchestra, Franz Woschitka, of his difficulty that something positive was suggested.

The cellist said, "I will arrange an audience for you with Maximilian."

Yet, the following morning, as Wolfgang walked with Woschitka toward the palace of the Elector, he wondered if he had been too trusting. The cellist was explaining that although this was an audience it was not a formal one, it was too early for that, it was only nine in the morning, and Wolfgang had a feeling that something was wrong. And he was dismayed and uncomfortable when the cellist had him wait in a tiny room that was hardly more than a passageway and said, "At ten His Highness will walk through here on his way to Mass before hunting."

"And I am to approach him then? Here?"

"What could be better? He won't be able to avoid you."

And although it was several years since the Elector had seen him, he recognized him immediately, approached him, and asked, "What do you want?"

Maximilian was in his hunting dress, looking healthy and amiable, not at all the picture of a man who was supposed to be dying or whose country was threatened, and Wolfgang knelt before him and said, "Allow me, Your Highness, to offer my services."

"Have you left Salzburg completely?"

"For ever, Your Highness."

"How did that happen? Did you quarrel with the Archbishop?"

"Oh, not really, sir. I simply asked permission to tour, and when he refused, I had to quit. But I had planned to leave for some time, for I knew years ago that Salzburg was not the court for me."

"Good God, that is youth for you! Isn't your father still at Salzburg?"

"Yes, Your Highness, and he humbly sends his respects and trusts you will allow me to serve you. I have heard that you need a good composer."

"It is too soon. You should travel, visit Italy, get more experience."

"Sir, I composed three operas for Italy, I am a member and an honorary Kapellmeister of the Academies of Bologna and Verona, the greatest musical schools in Italy. I have my diplomas with me, and both Padre Martini and Pope Clement XIV were gracious enough to honor me, but my only wish now is to serve Your Highness."

The Elector ignored the diplomas that Wolfgang offered for his inspection and muttered, "What else can you do?"

"Sir, invite all the composers here in Munich, choose any you wish from Italy, Germany, or France, and I will compete with all of them."

"Have you offered your services elsewhere?"

"No, Your Highness," Wolfgang said hopefully.

The Elector hesitated, as if deliberating, then remembered that he was late for hunting and said, suddenly curt, "But this is not the time."

"Sir, I can prove that I am capable of serving any court in Europe."

"No doubt, my dear boy, if there was a vacancy."

"Your Highness, may I play for you?"

"I have already heard you."

Wolfgang thought angrily, Maximilian has no idea of what I could do, these powerful lords believed only what they want to believe, but he said, "Sir, I would bring honor to your court."

"I am sorry, but as I said . . ." The Elector walked away irritated, for now he would miss some of the hunting, for he could not skip Mass, much as he wanted to. And everybody followed him until Wolfgang was all alone.

Immediately after Mass the Elector and his court left Munich to hunt, and there was no word of when they would return. With the nobles absent from the city there was no demand for any concerts. But after Wolfgang recovered from the shock of Maximilian's rejec-

287

tion, his natural resiliency reasserted itself. And encouraged by Albert, he had a new plan to stay in Munich, and he wrote Papa about it, although Mamma thought it impractical. "Herr Albert has an idea that seems very sensible. He will assemble ten lovers of music, each of whom will give me five gulden a month in return for whatever musical requests they make. That would come to six hundred gulden a year, and if I lived by myself, I could manage on this.

"I would be very frugal. My board would be of little consequence, for I am invited out often, and when I am not, Herr Albert is delighted to have me to dinner. I eat little, and finish with a piece of fruit and a small glass of wine. And I can always earn my rent by giving lessons.

"Papa, I want to stay in Munich because they have operas. Even with the court absent, it occurs often. I have such a desire to compose opera again, it is almost more than I can bear. It is my great passion and joy. I just have to hear talk of an opera, to be in an opera house, to hear the musicians tuning their instruments, and I am overwhelmed with feeling."

Wolfgang was positive that Papa would grant permission to stay, and he waited eagerly for Papa's answer which came quickly. "No doubt Albert is a good friend, but these would-be patrons, are they music lovers or philanthropists! That you could support yourself alone in Munich is probably true, but what honor would there be in that? How the Archbishop would laugh! You can do that in any place – not only in Munich. One must not make one's self so little, or throw one's self away at such a small price. There is no need of that, for we have surely not come to such an extremity. You must go to Augsburg at once, for despite the protestations of friendship and the compliments, you are just wasting time and money, and our capital will not hold out forever. Your loving father and husband."

The next day Wolfgang and Anna Maria left for Augsburg.

Neither of them felt any resentment, they were accustomed to Papa making this kind of decision. To prove that he was an obedient son, Wolfgang followed all of Papa's advice. As soon as they reached Augsburg, he took rooms at the best inn and visited Papa's favorite brother, Franz Alois, the bookbinder, and asked for an introduction to Langenmantel, the city governor, and the noted clavier manufacturer, Andreas Stein.

Franz Alois, who had not seen them for many years, regarded Wolfgang and Anna Maria as distinguished visitors and said he would be happy to follow Leopold's instructions. Wolfgang and Anna Maria also felt at home with his wife, Maria Viktoria, easygoing, friendly, and their nineteen-year-old daughter, Maria Thekla, whom Wolfgang called Bäsle.

The plump, round-featured Bäsle, with her wide, soft lips and fleshy buttocks and breasts had an animal vitality which Wolfgang found appealing. He enjoyed her impudence, her sense of humor. Bäsle told him that Augsburg was a Lutheran town, although they were Catholics, and he replied, "I will still have to kiss their backsides," and she burst out laughing.

They developed a code between them that mimicked the arrogant and the pretentious, and he was titillated by her body. And she was safe; he could caress her, give her buttocks and breasts a squeeze, and she only giggled. It was easy, uncomplicated; he did not love her, but she did give him satisfactions he had missed up to now, and Bäsle was fun to be with, to see how far she would go, to say the most outrageous things to and only have her grin and be impervious to shock. They understood each other so well. In their private life of jokes, glances, nudges, and confidences they were at ease. Life was such a frolic together.

The day after they arrived Franz Alois took Wolfgang to meet Jakob Langenmantel. Wolfgang, as Papa had directed, presented Papa's respectful compliments, although he thought the city governor pompous, a short, thickset patrician-burgher in an over-powdered white wig.

Langenmantel, the most prominent citizen of Augsburg, remembered Papa as a youth and was acquainted with Wolfgang's reputation. He told Franz Alois to wait in his anteroom and asked Wolfgang to perform for him.

Wolfgang was angry at Langenmantel's patronization of his uncle, and ordinarily he would have refused the city governor's request. But Papa had said he must be gracious with such influential persons as the city governor, so he thanked his uncle for introducing him to this dignitary, and suggested to Franz Alois it would be better not to wait, since he did not know how long he would play. After he played several of his pieces on the Langenmantel clavichord, he halted, saying he had to visit Andreas Stein this afternoon. The city governor, impressed with his playing, said his son would be honored to escort such a virtuoso to the clavier maker.

As Wolfgang approached Stein's house with the son, who had the same thick body, wide neck, and heavy head as the father, he told him, "Don't tell Herr Stein who I am. Let me see if he can tell a virtuoso when he hears one."

The Langenmantel son agreed. "It will be a fine joke if you fool him." But as he introduced Wolfgang to Stein, he said, "I have the honor of presenting to you a virtuoso on the clavier," and laughed loudly.

What an ass, thought Wolfgang, who said at once, "I am only a humble pupil of Herr Siegl of Munich, who asked me to give you his compliments."

The fifty-year-old Andreas Stein said, "But you resemble Herr Mozart!"

"Oh, no! My name is Trazom!" This amused Wolfgang, that was Mozart spelled backwards. "May I try one of your pianofortes?"

"Have you ever played one?"

"No."

"It will be difficult. My pianofortes are different from any others."

"I will not damage the instrument, I promise you."

The moment Stein opened the door of his warehouse Wolfgang ran to a pianoforte and plunged into one of his own sonatas.

Young Langenmantel was quiet, while Stein was fascinated, thinking that this pianist's hands were small but they moved with an ease that was beautiful and their balance of delicacy and strength was astonishing.

And the music was lovely and poetic. The instant Wolfgang finished Stein embraced him, crying out, "You are Herr Mozart! I should have known! No one else could have played with such expression!"

"It is the pianoforte. It is the best I have ever played on."

Langenmantel said, "Would you give a concert for the patricians?"

"Whatever you suggest."

"Come to my house tomorrow and we can distress it further."

Wolfgang was so excited by Stein's pianofortes, he had to ask many questions. Then he had to write what he had learned to Papa. "I must tell you immediately about Stein's pianofortes. Before I heard any of his claviers, I liked Späth's the best, but now I prefer Stein's. When I play *forte*, whether I raise my finger or leave it down on the keys, the tone never jars, never becomes stronger or weaker, or is missing, but is always even, always the same. Stein says he will not sell his instrument for less than three hundred gulden, and the work and skill he has put into them is immeasurable. And his pianofortes have another advantage over any other I have heard, they have an escapement. This is very rare, not one pianoforte maker in a hundred concerns himself with this, yet without an escapement you cannot avoid jarring or distortion and leaving an aftersound when the note is hit. But when you strike the keys of a Stein pianoforte, the hammers fall back the moment they hit the strings, whether you keep the keys down or not. I played one of my sonatas on his pianoforte, and it sounded superbly and went like oil."

He was in such high spirits he was eager to play for Langenmantel, although he did not care for him, but the patrician owned a Stein pianoforte and Papa would be pleased. Yet when he visited him the next day, he was told, "I will have to hear you before I can make a decision."

This was irritating, but Papa had advised him to be dignified and gracious, so Wolfgang said, "If it will suit your convenience."

"Tomorrow then. Send me the scores you intend to play, so I can see if they are proper for our music circle, then you can play with members of the Augsburg orchestra."

"As a trial?" Wolfgang could not repress his surprise.

"To see if you can play with each other. And wear your best clothes."

Anna Maria persuaded Wolfgang to wear the Order of the Golden Spur, although he was reluctant, remembering Karl Arco's jeers. But he did look well, he thought, his sword clean and shiny like a courtier.

Langenmantel greeted him coldly and muttered, "A concert is quite impossible. The patricians have informed me that they do not have enough money for a virtuoso like you." Yet the young patrician wanted him to play with the orchestra he had assembled, and Wolfgang compiled. He was accompanied badly, but Langenmantel said, "We have a good orchestra, don't you think?"

Wolfgang said, "I have heard worse." But not often, he thought.

Langenmantel said suddenly, "I must buy a cross, too. How much did yours cost, Mozart?"

Wolfgang did not reply.

Langenmantel said mockingly, "Can I borrow your cross? I must show it to our goldsmith and find out what it is worth. A Bavarian thaler, or maybe less, maybe it is not gold at all, but copper."

Wolfgang was furious, but he said, "You are wrong again. It is tin."

"Then I won't need the spur to determine its value."

"Of course not. You have one in your head."

"Does your hound wear one, too?"

"No, we give the ones we don't want to our pigs. May I have my sword?"

Langenmantel grew pale, but he ordered his servant to fetch it.

Wolfgang held his sword a moment, as if to use it, feeling capable of killing this sneering patrician with one blow. Then remembering that he was not allowed to use a sword, he was not a noble – as it was, he was exceeding his legal rights by wearing one, and if he used it he would be thrust into a dungeon – he buckled it on. But at the door he turned and said to Langenmantel, "You are swine. Fat swine. Good day."

Wolfgang wanted to leave Augsburg after this incident. He told Herr Stein, whom he had grown fond of, "It makes me regret coming here. To think, that in my father's birthplace I should be treated so rudely. There is no point giving any concerts for such idiots."

Stein replied, "It would be scandalous if one of Augsburg's greatest descendants did not play here. I will get an apology."

Stein was as good as his word. Not only did he obtain an apology from young Langenmantel, there was also a plea that Wolfgang play for the patricians as well as for the music-loving citizens of Augsburg.

This appeased Wolfgang, especially since it gave him more time to spend with Bäsle. The next few days his cousin showed him around the city, as quick to make fun of everything and everybody as he was.

The concert for the patricians took place in the Geschlechterstube, but when Wolfgang was handed only two ducats with the excuse that it was all they could afford, he was disgusted.

There was a different mood at the concert arranged by Stein. He rented the Fugger Concert Hall, the finest place for music in Augsburg; he charged a gulden a seat; he insisted that Wolfgang wear the Papal decoration, saying it was a great honor; he advertised the concert in glowing terms; and he selected first-rate musicians to accompany "Chevalier Mozart".

Wolfgang's performance was applauded enthusiastically, and he was gratified that he earned ninety gulden, but Mamma, who was keeping the records in place of Papa, said it was not as great a triumph as he claimed.

"We have had so many expenses, despite getting the hall and the orchestra free, Augsburg has cost us over twenty-five gulden."

"That is not too bad," he said. "We paid most of our expenses here."

"Papa wanted us to make money, not to spend it."

"Oh! So you are the keeper of the purse now?"

"Someone has to be, Wolfgang. It is no credit to be poor."

"That is why I am glad we are leaving here. Believe me, Mamma, I will be delighted to be in a town again where there is a court."

He was so affectionate then, she could not criticize him any further. And he despised arguing; it made him ill. But there were moments, as they packed for Mannheim, she wished he was more practical. It was one thing to say you could deal with all the difficulties of traveling, and another to actually do so. She sighed, wishing Papa was along. If she had not been watchful, Wolfgang would have forgotten his diplomas in Munich.

Wolfgang's one regret upon leaving Augsburg was the knowledge that he would miss Bäsle. When they said goodbye, his cousin gave him such a hug he thought his back would break. He was glad that no one was looking, it was so intimate.

FORTY-FOUR

At Mannheim music dominated at once. The day after the Mozarts arrived in the capitol of the Palatinate and Wolfgang rented a room at an Inn on the Pfälzischer Hof because it was next to the Elector's palace and close to where the musicians lived, he was invited by Danner, a violinist in the famed Mannheim orchestra to hear it rehearse and exhibit its virtuosity.

Mamma was unhappy with the room, it was in the attic and it was small and chilly, and she was frozen from the long, arduous coach ride, but Wolfgang assured her that these quarters were just temporary.

He quoted Papa: "Mannheim has the best musical court in Germany, and is second only to Paris in taste and prestige. The Elector spends more money on music than any other ruler in Germany, and his orchestra is the finest in Europe. If you play your cards right, you should find a position there."

She pretended to agree with Papa, threw more wood into the stove, and said she would finish unpacking, he must not keep Herr Danner waiting.

As the violinist escorted Wolfgang to the rehearsal he was friendly and in a few minutes it was as if they had known each other for years. The rehearsal had not begun and the musicians had been expecting him, Wolfgang thought, for they were waiting to meet him according to their rank. He felt they were judging him as Danner introduced them: Christian Cannabich, Kapellmeister and director of the orchestra, who at forty-seven, was the most important musician in Mannheim; the Abbé Vogler, Vice-Kapellmeister, court composer, teacher, an ordained priest, and at twenty-nine, the prodigy in Mannheim; Anton Raaff, the great tenor, and now, in his sixties, near the end of his career; Johann Wendling, a flutist renowned throughout Europe, and at fifty-five still attractive; the younger

Friedrich Ramm, a skillful oboist, and a few whose names he did not catch. Most of the musicians who had heard of him were courteous and respectful, but several who did not know him stared at him contemptuously and Wolfgang thought defiantly, They assume because I am young and little that I cannot do anything that is important or mature, but they will soon find out.

They were rehearsing an oratorio by Vogler, and Wolfgang felt that the Vice-Kapellmeister's music was bombastic. Yet Vogler was Elector Karl Theodor's favorite. Then the renowned Raaff sang in a style that was so stilted that he had to struggle to keep from laughing. But he liked Cannabich's conducting and the orchestra. It was the finest he had heard.

He thought how splendid his symphonies would sound in their hands! How much more he could do with a symphony, given the resources of this orchestra! How could he be expected to accept anything less! And Wendling, the flutist, and Ramm, the oboist, were virtuosos; they were educating him to possibilities in their instruments he had not realized before.

Deeply moved, he told Cannabich when the rehearsal ended, "You have created the best orchestra I have heard."

"Thank you, Herr Kapellmeister. From you, that is great praise."

"And Herr Wendling and Herr Ramm were magnificent."

Vogler asked, "Mozart, what did you think of the music?"

He could not sell his soul. He did not answer.

Vogler frowned, but he did not persist, and Cannabich said, "I hope you will honor us with a performance of your music, Herr Kapellmeister."

Wolfgang hesitated, then said, "I am not on a concert tour this time."

Raaff said, "But I have heard extraordinary accounts of your playing."

Suddenly the tenor was an honest, decent man despite his stilted singing, and Wolfgang replied, "Thank you, sir, I will be delighted to play for you. But my chief interest is in a post as a court composer."

Cannabich said, "We already have several composers, including Vogler and myself." When he saw Wolfgang's dismay, he added, "Perhaps something can be done. We should have another opera composer. But that depends on the skill with which you address the Elector. I could arrange an audience for you, but it would be better if you played some music for him first. Would you be interested in playing a concerto with our orchestra?"

"It would be a privilege."

"Bravo! You must have dinner with us and we can work out the details."

There was a vast amount of conversation at the Cannabichs, much music and good Rhine wine and tasty German boiled beef, and what endeared them most to Wolfgang, a zest for laughter. Wendling and his wife, who was a fine singer, were present also, but Wolfgang felt most at home with Cannabich's two young daughters, Rosa and Lisel. They insisted on hearing him play, and they sat on each side of him while he performed one of his pianoforte sonatas, and when he finished they kissed him on the cheek and said he must compose a sonata for them – it would be a great honor.

Lisel was too young to take seriously, but Rosa was attractive and fifteen, so he was told, and an excellent pianist for her age. He said he would compose a sonata for her, when she promised him two kisses as a reward.

Anna Maria rarely had seen Wolfgang happier. She thought, He dotes on the natural warmth of the Cannabichs. Yet, she wondered, was some of their warmth because they had a marriageable daughter?

Ramm, who had come in after dinner, admired Wolfgang's composition, and Wolfgang, who had loved the oboist's lovely pure tone, replied impulsively, "It would be a pleasure to write an oboe concerto for you."

Anna Maria was startled. Wolfgang had said that he did not like to write for wind instruments, they were too unreliable, and Leopold insisted that he be paid for what he composed, yet now he was offering Ramm an oboe concerto as a gift. And all Cannabich had to do was praise his music and he was willing to perform a pianoforte concerto for nothing.

Cannabich said, "Herr Kapellmeister, you play with such emotion, yet with such flawless execution. How could the Archbishop have let you go?"

"I was not dismissed. I resigned."

"Even so, how could he have allowed a musician like you to leave?"

"It was said that this sonata was not well composed."

"How absurd! Who was the idiot?"

"His Grace, Prince-Archbishop Colloredo."

Cannabich exclaimed, "I would never compose for the clergy. What do they know about music! You must play the concerto at our gala for the Elector."

The Jeunehomme concerto evoked such applause that Wolfgang had to play a sonata and improvisation as an encore. Wolfgang was sure that the Elector was pleased with him, for Karl Theodor sat close to the pianoforte.

After the concert Cannabich whispered to Wolfgang, "Now is the time for an audience," and led him up to the Elector before anyone could interfere.

As the conductor approached Karl Theodor, Wolfgang was amused by the contrast. Cannabich was tall, lean, with a receding chin, while Karl Theodor was short and stout, with a large double chin.

Wolfgang kissed Karl Theodor's hand and the latter said, "I believe it is now fifteen years since you were here."

"Yes, Your Highness, it is a long time since I had that honor."

"You play very well. And I hear you wrote an opera for Munich."

"Yes, Your Highness. It is my great desire to write an opera here, and I trust that you will not forget me."

"That might be managed. Are you interested in teaching?"

Although Wolfgang didn't want to teach, he remembered that Cannabich had told him that Karl Theodor was passionately fond of his four illegitimate children, and two of them played the clavier. "Yes, I taught in Salzburg."

"My son and oldest girl play. It would be helpful if you observed them."

"I would be honored, sir."

The next day Cannabich took Wolfgang to the palace. They were good friends by now and he said, "The Elector is so attached to his children, that if they like you, he will probably want to keep you here. However, Vogler is their present pianoforte teacher, so be careful what you say, for Vogler is a clever man, he has convinced the Elector that he is a genius."

Wolfgang and the children liked each other at once, and Cannabich thought it was charming, they got along so well, it was as if Wolfgang was one of them. Then suddenly, this caused the Kapellmeister to wonder if it was wise to encourage his daughter Rosa's interest in this musician. There was no question about the young man's ability, but that did not mean he could earn a living. Wolfgang was impulsive, emotional, direct in a world where it was better to be crafty, intriguing, evasive. But this was anticipating, Cannabich told himself, Wolfgang and Rosa were attracted to each other, that was obvious, yet was that reason enough to encourage him to stay?

Karl Theodor entered and wanted to know what Herr Mozart thought about his children's ability on the pianoforte.

Wolfgang answered, "They play quite well. Considering. . ."

"Considering what? Their teacher?"

Cannabich was looking at him intently and Wolfgang hurried to say, "No. They are well taught, sir."

"But you think they could be improved."

"Sir, I have been playing since I could walk."

"Then you should really understand the problems of teaching children."

"I do, sir. I can do whatever you wish in music. Compose, perform. . ."

Karl Theodor interrupted, "How long can you stay?"

"As long as it may please Your Highness. I am at your disposal."

"For the winter?"

"For whatever time Your Highness prefers."

"What about your mother?"

"We had planned to remain in Mannheim during the winter because of her age. Sir, I want to avoid the hardships of traveling, which in winter, are quite difficult for an elderly woman."

"So you are staying here then?"

"As you wish, Your Highness."

"If you could look in on my children it will be appreciated."

Wolfgang was disappointed that he had not been paid for his playing at the gala, but Cannabich said, "It is more important that the children liked you." The Kapellmeister insisted on celebrating this favorable omen with a party, which went on all night, and which Wolfgang enjoyed very much.

The next day he wrote Papa that Karl Theodor regarded him favorably, and said he must add his good wishes to Mamma's on Papa's birthday.

"I cannot write poetry, I am not a poet. I cannot create light and shadow, I am not a painter. I cannot display with grace and movement my thoughts and feelings, I am not a dancer. But I can speak to you with sounds, for I am a musician. Thus, at Cannabich's tomorrow, I will honor your birthday by playing my congratulations on their pianoforte with a sonata composed just for that occasion. Today however, I can only wish you, my beloved father, what I wish for you every moment of your life: good health, a happy heart, a very long life, and as many years of music as you desire. Heaven only knows how much I love and treasure you, and I humbly hope that you will go on loving me as much as you can, to put up with my occasional mistakes, and my compositions, which God willing, may gain in wisdom as I do. I kiss your hand a hundred times and remain – your most obedient and devoted son."

He enclosed the sonata he had composed for Papa in this letter.

Ten days later there was a fervent response from Papa: "I was deeply touched by your letter, and if I chide you occasionally, please do not be irritated with me, for Nannerl and I have no happiness in Salzburg now except for the letters we receive from you and Mamma.

"The news about the Elector sounds hopeful and let us hope he makes up his mind quickly, for soon it will be too cold for Mamma to travel.

"The sonata is lovely and it gave me great pleasure to hear

Nannerl play it, and it made both of us happy. If you should stay as the teacher of Karl Theodor's natural children, do not be affected by their morals. They can afford things that are not allowed a musician. And it would be wise to move into a private house, for the Inn is too expensive and money can slip away without even being noticed.

"Forgive me if I lecture a little, but remember, not one person in a thousand is a true friend for honest reasons, to discover such a person is to discover one of the seven wonders of the world. I would not remind you of this if I did not have your interests so much at heart. Your lonesome father and husband."

Wolfgang was excited when he was ordered to go to the palace to receive a present for his performance, and Cannabich went with him. But it was as he feared. He was not given money as he desired, but a gold watch.

Cannabich said, "The chain and emblems alone must be worth many gulden."

Wolfgang said, "I would rather have money. I have five watches."

"You have been well paid."

"I rank my patrons by the watches they have given me. And now I must have another watch pocket made for all my clothes, a pocket on each leg of my trousers, so I can wear two watches when I play for a nobleman. Then, at least, that should prevent him from presenting me with another watch."

"Have you heard anything from Karl Theodor?"

"Not a word. I visit the children twice a week, I composed variations for them to practice, and they seem to like them, and we get along splendidly, but there has not been any mention of money."

"You must be patient, and persist."

"Can you do anything, Herr Kapellmeister?"

"You know I admire your ability. But such matters are out of my hands."

Finally Wolfgang informed the children's middle-aged governess, whom he had cultivated, that he could not continue to instruct the children without specific word from the Elector. He said, "I will come next Monday, Countess, and then, if matters are still unsettled, I will go to Paris."

He had not made any plans to depart, but Monday while he was giving the girl a lesson at the pianoforte Karl Theodor entered. When she finished playing the variations Wolfgang had composed for her, Karl Theodor asked, "Do you think she will be able to learn them?"

"Sir, I only wish that I will be fortunate enought to teach them to her."

"I should like that, but wouldn't it spoil her to have a second master?"

"That depends on whether he is a good or bad one."

"How long can you stay?"

Wolfgang sighed. Had Karl Theodor forgotten so soon? But he said as humbly as he could, "As long as Your Highness desires."

"Good. I will consider it."

Wolfgang wrote Papa: *"We have proceeded so far that now I must wait."*

FORTY-FIVE

==

Several weeks later he was still waiting. Karl Theodor did not reappear at any of the lessons Wolfgang gave the children. Desperate and disgusted, so much of their money had been eaten up while he had been detained here, he went to a concert at court to confront Karl Theodor for a definite answer and the Elector avoided him. Wolfgang discussed this with Cannabich, who said, "I am sorry, Wolfgang, but alas, it may all be in vain."

"He might have told me a little sooner."

"He would not have made up his mind now, if you had not prodded him."

"Prodded him? Herr Cannabich, I have been waiting for weeks."

"That is what I told him."

"Then you did talk to him?"

"I tried. But you should stay. You could make a living teaching."

When Wolfgang told Wendling of the Elector's behavior, the flutist said angrily, "Karl Theodor is a fool. We must find a way to keep you here."

Six weeks after the Mozarts had arrived in Mannheim, Wendling arranged for them to move into the home of Court Treasurer Serrarius.

Anna Maria was relieved. She hated the steps to the attic room in the Inn. Many days she had not gone out because she had not been up to climbing the four flights. And it had become bitterly cold. To be able to live in the attic, she had the Inn put coal on the fire when they rose in the morning and when they went to bed. But each fire cost twelve kreutzer. In order to save money, she felt she had to economize since her son did not, she had no fire during the day and endured the awful cold.

Some days she could not write home, her hands were so frozen. She sat in her fur and felt shoes and wondered if this was God's

300

retribution. There were times she was so chilled that even this did not suffice and she thought her soul would part from her body. But Wolfgang had not minded the cold, he had been in the attic so little, with his visits to the palace, the Cannabichs, and the Wendlings. Yet she had not complained, he did not like complaints, or told him of her headaches or of the cold that had not left her. She consoled herself with the thought that their new room was much better, hid her poor health, and wrote the good news home. "Praise be to God, finally we have been able to move out of the Inn and now we have a fine, large room with two clean beds in the home of Court Treasurer Serrarius, and on the ground floor, with all the light and coal we need. In return for this Wolfgang gives his daughter clavier lessons.

"He eats at the Cannabichs and the Wendlings, and to pay for this he teaches Rosa Cannabich advanced pianoforte, and keeps the Wendlings amused. He is also teaching composition to a Dutch officer, De la Potrie, who gives him four gulden for twelve lessons. It is not much, but he hopes to make up for that by composing three concertos for another Dutchman, De Jean, a rich amateur flutist. De Jean had promised to give him two hundred gulden, as long as he keeps the flute concertos short, simple, and easy to play.

"Wendling introduced Wolfgang to the two Dutchmen, and made all the arrangements with them and Serrarius. Raaff, Cannabich, and Ramm say that there is not a musician to compare with Wolfgang, and they love his work. He is in such demand that many days I do not see him from dawn to bedtime. I stay in our room by myself much of the time, for it is so wet and cold these days I am afraid to go out. But we are happier here, although Wolfgang is so busy now, I pray that it does not make him ill."

Mamma was not exaggerating, thought Wolfgang. He got out of bed as soon as the sun rose, and dressed quietly and hurriedly on his side of the partition that separated their beds so that he would not disturb Mamma.

After breakfast, which he made himself, he went to the Wendlings where he had a room and a pianoforte he could use with complete privacy and there he practiced until noon. Then he had lunch with the Wendlings, and afterwards he returned to the music room and composed for several hours. At three he hurried to the Inn on the Mainzischer Hof to give De la Potrie a composition lesson; at four he was home to teach Mademoiselle Serrarius; at six he was at the Cannabich's to instruct Rosa. Later he had supper with them and then someone played. The letters he wrote, and he kept up an active correspondence with Papa and Bäsle, were written around midnight.

Almost everyone in Mannheim was encouraging, although Wendling told him that Karl Theodor had not hired him because

Vogler, who taught the children and who had great influence at court, feared him and had spoken against him.

But he put aside this disappointment, for Rosa loved the sonata he wrote for her, and Ramm was delighted with his oboe concerto. And he was excited by a new plan of Wendling's. It was several weeks after they had moved into the Serrarius house, and he rushed there to tell Mamma. "Ramm and Wendling want me to go to Paris with them. By myself. Would you mind?"

She had not wanted to go to Paris. But if she was acquiescent, who knew what wild plans he would make! She asked, "Who will make the arrangements?"

"Wendling. He has been to Paris many times."

"Why is he going there if Mannheim is such a wonderful musical city?"

"At Lent, when there is no music here, there is a great demand for concerts in Paris."

"But Wendling has no religion and he is proud that his daughter was the Elector's mistress, although Karl Theodor has had many others. Papa won't like you spending so much time in the company of a libertine."

Wolfgang laughed. "You know he is harmless. He is part French, part German, part sophisticate, and part sentimentalist. One moment he loves, the next he hates. He claims he respects nothing, yet he goes into ecstasy over a piece of music, approves of free love and would kill the man who touched his wife. Mamma, since when have you become righteous?"

She could not tell her son her real fears. While he was sharply observant of human foibles, if he cared for someone, his intense emotion caused him to offer them the world even if he had nothing.

When he saw her sudden somberness he cried out, "Don't you feel well?"

"It's the cold, that's all."

"You know that you did not really want to take this journey."

"Wolfgang, you don't always see things as they are."

"One's view depends on where one is standing."

"You seem to be happy with the life you are leading."

"Happy?" He said bitterly. "Happiness exists only in the imagination."

"Aren't you fond of Rosa Cannabich?"

"She said she is fifteen, but I learned that she is only thirteen."

"And Bäsle?" Anna Maria hated to ask this, but having traveled this far, she had to take one more step. "Although she is your cousin?"

He did not answer. Bäsle was his business. But he wondered if she was an invention of himself, his joking, flirtatious, mocking self.

"Don't you wish to get married?" She wanted him to, although not to either of these two girls. Leopold worried about his fickleness, but she was certain that marriage to the right person would settle him down.

"I have too much to do. Compose, practice, perform."

"Where will you stay in Paris?"

"Wendling knows. He is also a very good friend of Baron Grimm."

"You want me to tell this to Papa?"

"He will be more influenced if it comes from you."

Her assent brought a hearty kiss from Wolfgang.

While they waited for Papa's reply, they heard that the Americans had captured Burgoyne's British army at Saratoga and that the French, believing that they could defeat Great Britain now, with American help, were going to sign a treaty of alliance with the American colonies and go to war against the British. At the same time Maximilian, the Elector of Bavaria, died of smallpox, and Karl Theodor hurried to Munich to claim that throne while there were rumors that Austria was going to attack him, and perhaps Prussia. This added to Mamma's anxiety, but Wolfgang, eager to go to Paris now, insisted that the storm clouds would blow over.

Papa's answer was addressed to Wolfgang: "I would have preferred, Wolfgang, if you could have established yourself in Mannheim, for there is talk in Salzburg that Austria may support Karl Theodor in Munich, and if this happens, his musical court will be more important than ever. And Mannheim is less than half as far away as Paris. As it is, although you have been away for just a few months it seems like a century to me. But if Baron Grimm is as good a friend of Wendling as the latter says, and that is possible, for the flutist does have a fine musical reputation, your fortune should be made.

"But Mamma must not be neglected. You must be sure she is able to stay comfortably with Serrarius until the weather is mild enough for her to travel. You must also buy her a better fur to keep her warm until then, and I will arrange for a well heated coach that will take her to Munich, and to Salzburg with the least discomfort. And before you go to Paris, you must have your music copied. That is far more expensive in Paris, and it will be good for you to learn how to save money. As it is, our debts have risen since you left, and if you do not find gainful employment in Paris our situation will be difficult, perhaps desperate."

FORTY-SIX

Wendling sent Wolfgang to the cheapest copyist he knew, Fridolin Weber.

Wolfgang stood at the door of a small house, several arias in his hand – he was not going to entrust his precious music to an unknown engraver until he tried him out – and wondered if he should enter. The dwelling was unprepossessing, grass grew between the cobbles in front of it, the grillwork was rusty, the iron knocker on the door was cracked. But Papa's insistence that he have his music copied in Mannheim overcame his hesitation and he knocked. Almost immediately a girl opened the door.

She was his height, and as their eyes met he noticed that they were dark and attractive. Her features were regular and her nose was sharp; she was pleasant-looking without being pretty, he reflected, and she looked about thirteen. She showed no surprise at his presence, as if visitors were customary, and when he said, "I am Herr Mozart, I would like to see Herr Weber," she led him into a shabby drawing room and said, "He will be honored. If you will be good enough to wait, I will call him."

"You know who I am, Fraulein?"

"Everyone musical in Mannheim does, sir."

"And you are his daughter?" He liked her manners.

"Yes, Herr Kapellmeister. One of his four daughters. I am Constanze."

"Are you musical, too?"

"We all are. My two older sisters sing, my younger sister plays the clavier, and I am a good listener," she said proudly, and left.

Her mother appeared first, followed by the rest of the family. Cäcilia Weber greeted Wolfgang as if it were a matter of considerable importance, and said, "It is an honor to meet such a renowned musician."

And suddenly Wolfgang had the feeling that in spite of the shabby drawing room, which obviously did not belong to the Webers, and the four girls who circled around their mother as if she were the Kapellmeister in this family, he had been in this situation before. Yet the Webers bore little resemblance to most of the people he had met: the Empress and the Emperor, the Archdukes and the Archduchesses, the Kings and Queens, the Princes and the Dukes, the Pope and the Prince-Archbishop, the Hasses, Bachs, and Padre Martinis. He would be twenty-two soon, and some people still regarded him as a child, although he had spent a lifetime in an adult world, and he did not feel like a child at all no matter how Papa and Mamma sought to protect him. And the Webers were plainly not of the great world of power and consequence, and yet somehow, he felt at home here.

They were very friendly. He was glad he had put aside his doubts and knocked. Fridolin Weber was a slight man, pale and worn, but younger-looking than his wife, who must have been a handsome woman, Wolfgang thought, but now was old. She introduced her daughters: Josepha, a large, big-bosomed nineteen; Sophie, who was just a ten-year-old child; and Constanze, but she did not attract him now, for he had just met Aloysia.

The other girls were commonplace in appearance by comparison with her. Aloysia was tall, slender, with a graceful figure. Her dark hair was like black silk, her gray eyes were as pleasing as the sonata he had composed for Rosa Cannabich. She was lovely to look at, and to listen to, her voice soft and well modulated.

When Cäcilia Weber saw his interest, she said, "Aloysia would be honored to sing for you, Herr Kapellmeister. Wouldn't you, dear?"

"Whatever you wish, Mamma."

"But I came to have some music copied, Frau Weber."

"My husband is a fine copyist. Constanze, make Herr Mozart some coffee. He must be chilled, with the cold weather we are having."

Before Wolfgang realized what was happening, Frau Weber seated him at the pianoforte, placed Aloysia by his side to sing one of his arias, and he wanted to protest, he had had enough of amateurs, but the sight of this beautiful girl standing next to him, the touch of her hand upon his shoulder to indicate that he should start, was more than he could resist, especially when she said, "I can accompany myself if you prefer, Maestro."

"How could I be so rude!" How lovely she was! But he was still afraid that when she opened her mouth all this would be dissipated.

The pianoforte was surprisingly good and her singing amazed him. Her voice was warm and pure, although she had much to learn about technique. But her basic tone was never distorted. And she had a fine legato, and her high notes were brilliant. What he could do with an instrument like this! He could hardly take his eyes off her as he accompanied her. There was not a thing about her, except for her technique, that he would change.

Aloysia said, "I am sorry, Herr Mozart, if my singing displeased you."

"Displeased me? It was charming."

"My husband taught her," said Cäcilia Weber. "He has been associated with the Mannheim court as a musician since 1765."

Fridolin Weber said, "It would be a great privilege if Herr Kappellmeister told us what he really thinks of our daughter's voice."

"After you copy those arias, Herr Weber, I could hear her sing again."

"Tomorrow," said Cäcilia Weber. "If you can spare the time, Maestro?"

"I will try," said Wolfgang. "About this time."

Aloysia said, "I can accompany myself if you would just like to listen."

Wolfgang wondered if he should tell Mamma about his new friends, then decided that it would be more sensible to discuss them later, when he knew them better. Yet when Mamma asked him whether Herr Weber was a capable copyist, he retorted, "Excellent! First-rate!"

"But you didn't have time to see examples of his work, did you?"

"I heard one of his daughters sing. He is a good musician."

For twenty-four hours he counted the minutes until he would see Aloysia again. Then he was in her shabby drawing room with her again and he was light-hearted, for she looked even lovelier than before.

He saw his engraved arias waiting for his approval and they had been copied perfectly. He handed Fridolin Weber his two completed flute concertos to engrave and five gulden for the work the copyist had done, although the latter said he mustn't, after all, Herr Mozart had given his daughter precious musical advice without any fee, but Wolfgang said that was different, Fraulein Aloysia had great potential which would be a pleasure to bring to fruition, and he felt benevolent when Fridolin Weber took the money. All that he really saw was Aloysia. She accompanied herself this time while he listened and he was delighted with her artistry.

Now he went to the Webers every day. This worried Mamma; she learned that there were four girls in the family, and that one of them, who sang, had a fine voice, and was beautiful. She was not surprised when Wolfgang told her, "The Princess of Weilburg, the sister of the Prince of Orange, who liked me so much as a child,

306

insists she must hear me again. She is at Kirchheim, a short drive from Mannheim, about ten hours away. She has promised me seven louis d'or for some arias, for she adores singing."

"And Fraulein Weber will do the singing?"

"Oh, she will be properly chaperoned. Her father is going along, and he is copying my music virtually for nothing in return for my help."

"Are you in love with her?"

"She is hardly more than a child. But she has a remarkable voice."

"What about your pupils, and the concertos for the Dutchman?"

"The pupils will be here when I return, and I have already composed two of the flute concertos. I will complete the third when I return. Seven louis d'or is equal to many gulden. I will be back in a few days."

He was gone twelve days. He felt an instant rapport with Fridolin, who knew much about music, and who had the good sense to know when he wanted to be alone with Aloysia. In the carriage they sat close to each other and the touch of her sensuous body, her listening to his every word as if it were the gospel, filled him with a joyous expectancy. And she learned so swiftly. Her voice flowered under his instructions. They could go far together, he thought, and he felt that an extraordinary affinity was developing between him and Aloysia.

Anna Maria was stunned by Wolfgang's announcement that to go to Paris with Wendling was a mistake, his saying, "Wendling is honest enough, but he hasn't any religion, and he has the instincts of a libertine."

"When I said that, you waved it aside."

"I didn't know him that well then."

"What excuse will you give him?"

"Don't worry, I will find something." He handed her two louis d'or.

"You said you were going to get seven."

"I paid half of the Weber expenses. The poor man makes very little, and Aloysia darned my stockings and mended my clothes. I have suggested that they go to Italy where she is sure to make her fortune as a prima donna, if I am with her to guide her. After you return to Salzburg."

Wolfgang wrote Papa of his change of plan, asking his approval and aid: "Wendling is a decent man and a fine musician, but so irreligious he makes me uncomfortable. I am sure you would not want me to spend so much time in such company. The Webers, on the other hand, are a devout family.

"Herr Weber, who copied my work perfectly and who charged me very little, is very much like you, a musician of ability, wit, and discernment, but unfortunately, although he sings, prompts, and copies with skill for Karl Theodor, is paid almost nothing, a situation we know so well. His daughter, Aloysia, although she is only sixteen, sings beautifully, with a remarkable range, and except for some flaws in her acting and vocal style, which I am correcting, is able enough right now to sing in any opera house.

"There are three other daughters, all of whom are musical, and a mother who treats me with great respect, although she runs her family like a grenadier, but it is Aloysia who has the genius.

"The Webers have been very kind to me and I have become quite attached to this oppressed family, and I would like to help them. My idea is that Herr Weber, and his daughter, Aloysia, should go to Italy with me, to seek their fortune in an opera house there. If you could write our friends in Milan and elsewhere, perhaps you could find an opening for a prima donna as Fräulein Aloysia is sure to become. I assure you that with my teaching, she will do me great honor with her singing. In the brief time I have instructed her, she has improved tremendously.

"If this plan materializes, Herr Weber, his daughter, and myself will have the privilege and pleasure of visiting my beloved Papa and sister on our way to Italy. There I should obtain a scrittura for an opera. You know how I yearn to write an opera, it is my most fervent wish, and if Aloysia sings it, I will not be victimized by the singing but honored.

"As for Wendling, I have told him that I cannot go with him to Paris because letters have come which makes my presence needed elsewhere to compose an opera. I pray that you will approve of my plan, Papa dearest. The Webers are like a second family to me, next only to my own, and Mamma admits that Fräulein Weber sings incomparably for her age."

Mamma, without Wolfgang knowing it, added a postscript to his letter:

"You will notice from what Wolfgang writes that when he likes someone he desires at once to give them the world, even at the sacrifice of his own interests. He is right that she sings beautifully, but we must not damage ourselves. I have never been happy about his going to Paris with Wendling, but I said little, for he does not pay attention to me. But the moment he becomes friends with the Webers, he changes his mind at once. Often he prefers the company of others to my company, and if I question him about what he does, he changes the subject.

"Thus, you will have to decide what is the best thing to do. I am still not in favor of his going to Paris with Wendling; indeed, I prefer that I go with him myself when the weather improves. It would not be very expensive if we took the mail coach. Maybe you will receive some encouragement from Baron Grimm. Meanwhile, we are not suffering or spending much money here, and we could remain longer. I am writing this secretly. He is away dining and he must not know what I am doing."

Leopold was shocked by these letters. Everything he had constructed so carefully seemed about to collapse. He had been prepared for many difficulties, but not this. And when he told Nannerl, she wept. He was stern then – someone in the family had to be strong – but in the privacy of his room he wept himself. There were moments he longed to dig a deep pit and hide in it forever. What was going to happen to them? If his son followed his wild idea, his carefully planned career would shatter into many pieces and nobody would remember him. All his hopes for Wolfgang gone with a pretty mouth, a good legato. What a devilish joke!

He walked into their concert hall and sat down at his desk to write his reply to Wolfgang but no ideas came. The Tanzmeister-Saal was the most elegant music room they had possessed and now it was silent and desolate.

He wondered if his family, who thought him so durable, knew how close to breaking he was sometimes. He had as much emotion as any of them, even as much as Wolfgang. Friends warned him that he had put too much into his son, but there was so much to nourish. When his son rewarded him with a new composition, there was such a mastery of music it gave him great joy.

But to have it wasted!

Yet while the lamp burned the letter did not advance. He rose and shambled about the Tansmeister-Saal, and felt like a martyr. His dressing gown was full of holes, his shoes were old – all so this journey could be made. Yet his debts had risen from 400 gulden to 700 in the few months Wolfgang and Anna Maria had been away. And how they would laugh at him in Salzburg, Colloredo particularly, hearing that Wolfgang, the virtuoso, the would-be Kapellmeister had gone off with a would-be girl prima donna.

But he stopped brooding and caught hold of himself when Nannerl entered, and between sobs, wanted to know what he was going to do.

"What is there to do? Stop him. Before he drifts away completely."

"Don't be too hard on him, Papa."

"The moment a pretty face smiles at him he is infatuated."

"Maybe he is lonely. Maybe he wants to get married."

"At his age the heart breaks easily."

"And at my age. What about me, Papa? Am I going to die an old maid?"

"You're only. . ."

"Twenty-six. That's not young for an unmarried girl. Maybe when I cried about Wolfgang, I cried for myself, too."

"You have had gentlemen call on you, and you will again."

She shouted, "Papa, I am just a music teacher. I cannot live on the past." Then she wanted to flee from what she had confessed, even as she blurted out, "Almost all my friends are married," but Papa had his arms around her and was saying, "And you will be, too. You look just like Mamma did when I married her, and she was the prettiest girl in Salzburg, and so are you, and one of these days we will all be together again."

She felt his protectiveness fitting over her, and now she was his little girl who had traveled across Europe at his direction. She kissed him goodnight, promised to be a good girl and went to bed as he suggested.

Leopold sat up all that night composing his reply to Wolfgang's plea. He must sound as if he would aid Aloysia, who obviously wanted to trap his son, even as he proved her inadequacies as a prima donna. As he sent this letter, he prayed that it would bring his son back to earth.

While Wolfgang waited for Papa's verdict with a mixture of anxiety and hope, he prepared his pupils for a farewell concert and devoted most of his time to Aloysia. Wendling, who was amused rather than offended by Wolfgang's change of plan, wanted to perform also, and so did Raaff, and the concert became a gala occasion to honor his music.

Wolfgang knew this should make him happy, but he was disturbed by the lack of money. He handed De Jean two of the three flute concertos the Dutchman had commissioned, and assured the amateur flutist that the third would be completed soon, and De Jean replied, "Don't bother with the third, I won't need it, I'm not sure I can use the two you wrote," and paid Wolfgang only 96 gulden instead of the 200 that had been promised.

He gave the money to Mamma to buy a new fur and to hold the balance, and she asked, "Do you think Wendling had anything to do with this?"

"No. De Jean is a fool."

"Do you still want to go to Italy? You have earned far less money than you expected. And the cost of food is going up everywhere."

"Certainly I want to go. As soon as Papa gives his consent."

Later that day as he waited at the Webers for Aloysia to take her lesson he was not as sure as he sounded. He had given her his word of honor that he would ask his father for help, even as he had had a feeling that Papa would oppose such a venture. Yet he could not go to Italy without his help, he did not have the money, and the thought of being with Aloysia without funds was a situation too humiliating to endure.

Her father appeared to explain her delay, saying, "You know how girls are, Herr Kapellmeister, they like to dress their prettiest for special guests. Have you heard from Herr Leopold yet?"

"No. But he will answer promptly. He always does."

"You will be appreciated in Italy, Maestro. Not like in Mannheim where the petty jealousy of Vogler can destroy your chances with the Elector, or a Cannabich can pretend to do something and do nothing. The difficulty here is, you are too fine an artist for our provincial taste."

That sounded like Salzburg, Wolfgang thought wryly.

"And now that Karl Theodor is in Munich, waiting to see which cat will jump, Austria or Prussia, there is no public music in Mannheim at all."

Wolfgang forgot all this as Aloysia appeared. She wore a low-cut bodice, and as she leaned toward him so that he could kiss her hand and lead her to the pianoforte, it increased his desire to fondle her. But when he moved closer to her, she backed away. Yet she seemed so glad to see him that he swore to himself that she could not be a coquette, then he was not sure. Aloysia appeared submissive to her mother's wishes, yet he sensed that underneath her soft surface there was strength and purpose. She worked with an intensity that was ferocious in its desire.

Her father left them alone as the lesson began, but the moment the singing stopped her mother appeared. This had become a pattern, Wolfgang noticed with annoyance. And today, Constanze entered with Cäcilia Weber. After their first meeting he had been hardly aware of her, she was childish and plain beside Aloysia, yet he felt now, seeing her smile as she greeted him, that she got genuine pleasure in his company. Cäcilia Weber asked, "Maestro, you will let us know as soon as you hear from your father?"

"Certainly. I want to go to Italy as much as Aloysia does. I had three triumphal tours there. And the Pope, Padre Martini, and..."

"We know!" Aloysia cut him short, then said animatedly, "You were a sensation," gave him an angelic smile and ushered him out of the house.

There was a letter from Papa awaiting him in his room. From Mamma's tone, he knew at once that his father had said no. He thought bitterly, any other answer would have been too much to expect. He re-read the following passages, hypnotized by their truth even as he disliked their verdict:

311

"You say you wish to escort Fräulein Weber to Italy and there put her upon the opera stage as a prima donna. Dear son, name one singer who has appeared on the Italian stage without first having performed often in Germany. And even then, they had the most powerful patronage before they achieved this goal, Princes and Cardinals and composers as renowned as Hasse and Gluck. But what madness is this, to recommend a girl of sixteen, and worse, one who has never been on any opera stage. You know better than anyone else that it is not enough to open one's mouth on stage. One has to know where to stand, how to act, to have style. And what about the knowledge of hairdressing, wardrobe, and make-up that every prima donna must have, and which comes only with much experience. No matter how talented she is, no matter how well she is taught, how skillfully she sings, any impresario will regard you as insane, recommending such a novice. Your own great reputation, which I have built so carefully, will be shattered by such an act. You will be ridiculed by the whole world. Even the Mufti will roar with laughter.

"Wolfgang, your proposal sounds like a fairy tale. But I appreciate your kind heart. Your need to aid the persecuted you get from your father. But you must also remember the health and happiness of your parents, and how they have struggled for you, or you will condemn yourself to the devil.

"I will tell you what you could accomplish for Fräulein Weber. Ask Raaff to hear her. Whatever his voice is now, he was a great singer in Italy and still has a great reputation there. If he likes her voice, and it is likely, since you do, and you have the better taste, he could recommend her to the Italian impresarios who respected him in his prime. Until then, she should obtain roles on the Mannheim stage, even if she is not paid, for she will get useful experience and even a reputation.

"But to throw away everything on such a mad venture, and after what all of us have endured for your sake, your sister, too, who has sacrificed her own career for yours! You must not allow anyone to cast such a spell on you. You have gone on this difficult and dangerous journey to find a post equal to your ability, and the earnings you deserve, but above all, to increase your honor and reputation. Some of this you have already achieved. Now however, it is up to you, and you alone, whether you will lift yourself to the greatest height any musician has ever reached and become famous even to posterity or – seduced by a woman – become just another Kappellmeister, forgotten by the world, and die on a dirty straw pallet in a hovel surrounded by ragged, starving children.

"So off to Paris with you! and be quick about it. Find your place with the great people. *Aut Caesar aut nihil.* The very idea of visiting Paris should have kept you from all these foolish ideas. From Paris the glory and reputation of an artist of genuine ability sounds through the entire world. There the court regards musicians of genius with the utmost respect. There you will find the recognition you so richly deserve."

He sat silently until Mamma asked, "What will you do?"

"Go to Paris."

"With Wendling?"

"No. Papa is against that also now. He says you must go with me."

"You won't be sorry, Wolfgang?"

"I hope you won't be, Mamma."

She smiled reassuringly even as a cold chill went through her at the thought of the long and arduous traveling still ahead of her.

But it was Wolfgang who fell ill, who asked Mamma to explain to the Webers that he could not go to Italy, that it was too soon.

She repeated to them what he had said, and added, "He could go next year perhaps, or the year after, when he is established in Paris, but now is not the time."

She told Wolfgang afterwards, "They did not seem surprised by this change of plan, but resigned, almost as if they had expected it."

"Did you tell Fräulein Aloysia that she is going to sing for Raaff?"

"Yes."

"Was she pleased?"

"She smiled, after her mother did."

"You told them that I was sick."

"Yes, and that it was one of the reasons you can't go to Italy now."

At the farewell concert Wolfgang composed an aria for Aloysia that displayed her voice to advantage; he wrote an aria for Raaff which made allowances for the limitations of his voice; he had Weber engrave a copy of a flute concerto so Wendling could perform it, and he paid the copyist for his work; and he arranged for Rosa to play the sonata he had composed for her so that no one would feel slighted.

Cannabich was pleased with the way Rosa had improved under Wolfgang's tutelage, although he did not give him a kreutzer or a thank you.

Raaff was happy with his aria, which stressed his deep tones, which were still secure, and he liked Aloysia's voice. When Wolfgang asked him if he would be kind enough to teach her, he replied, "I will be glad to, but of course, there will have to be a fee."

Wendling liked the flute concerto and wanted to take it to Paris to play, but he did not give Wolfgang anything when the latter said yes.

It was Weber who touched Wolfgang's heart, saying admiringly, "Your flute concerto is a miracle of tonal sweetness and sonority."

"Perhaps, but it is hard to compose for an instrument I do not like."

"Yet the music is impeccable. Glowing, natural, and eloquent."

"I could have scribbled it, but once my work enters the world I don't want to be ashamed of it. So I did my best. I tried to please."

"You did, you did! But why don't you care for the flute, Maestro?"

"I prefer more precise instruments, that can be controlled better."

Weber invited the Mozarts to dinner the night before they left. They could not accept since, as Anna Maria pointed out, they were departing early the next morning by their own coach to take advantage of the precious daylight, but they did visit the Webers in the afternoon.

Constanze served coffee and cake, but Wolfgang, sitting next to Aloysia, was so enchanted with her that he could have subsisted on bread and water.

Aloysia said, "I am sorry about Italy, Wolfgang. I really am."

"So am I. We could have accomplished much together."

"Perhaps we still will. If you should change your mind, I will be here."

"Promise?"

Aloysia kissed him on the forehead and whispered, "I promise," and handed him a pair of mittens she had knitted for him as a farewell gift.

Then it was time to depart and he could hardly endure it. The Webers embraced him; there were tears in Constanze's eyes; and Fridolin gave him the collected plays of Molière as a gift and told Anna Maria, "We owe your son so much, Fräu Mozart. He has been a dear friend. We are eternally grateful for what he has done for us, and we will miss him like a son."

FORTY-SEVEN

━━

The journey from Mannheim to Paris took nine long days. Never had Wolfgang been so bored. All he could think of was Aloysia and that this venture was taking him further away from her. And her mittens, which he wore as a keepsake, were a poignant reminder of this sad circumstance.

Mamma was grateful that for most of this trip the weather was mild and sunny for March, although the last two days a fierce rain and wind soaked and chilled her, and that there were no hostilities along the route, even though France had declared war on England, and Prussia and Austria were making menacing gestures at each other over Bavaria. She sought to keep Wolfgang cheerful by interesting him in the towns they passed through in France, such as Metz, Verdun, and Chalons on the Marne; she jokingly remarked that as Papa had said, it was as if Wolfgang was invading this country to conquer it, but he did not feel like a conqueror, he could not capture the excitement of the Grand Tour.

As soon as they reached Paris he ordered the coachman to drive them to the residence that had been recommended, of a Herr Mayer, a German scrap-dealer on the rue Bourg l'Abbé. Mamma did not care for the location: the rue Bourg l'Abbé was a narrow, short street, only several hundred yards long, and she felt penned in by the street, and by her room, which was small and dark, like a prison. But Wolfgang said – to justify staying here, for he did not wish to waste time searching for new quarters until he felt more settled in Paris – that the Mayers spoke German, which would make her feel at home, and if she wanted to know what a real prison was like, she should see the Bastille, which was nearby. The very thought of its awful presence caused her to shiver. Europe was full of terrible tales of its impregnable walls, its dungeons deep in the bowels of the earth, deeper than the grave, and prisoners who never saw the sun from one year to the next. Her room became better by comparison and she told Wolfgang not to worry, that it would be satisfactory until he got settled.

The next day Wolfgang hurried to pay his respects to Baron Grimm and he was disappointed to learn that their old friend was out of Paris on state business and would not be home for a week. And now, as he stood before the home of Baron Grimm and Madame d'Epinay once more, he wondered who owned this handsome mansion. He had been told that Madame d'Epinay had inherited a fortune from her dissolute husband. He asked himself: Am I attaching too much importance to them? Papa had written, *"If Grimm is in Paris, your fortune is made,"* and he held the address his father had sent him as if it were a treasure and re-read it: *"Monsieur le Baron de Grimm, Ministre Plenipotentaire de Saxe-Gotha, rue de la Chaussée d'Antin,"* and he had a sudden feeling of foreboding. Operatic Paris was split by the supporters of Gluck and Piccinni, and Baron Grimm was reputed to be one of Piccinni's strongest advocates and he disliked Piccinni's music.

The rue de la Chaussée d'Antin was a wide, clean avenue where the nobility lived. It was within walking distance of the rue Bourg l'Abbé, but he had taken a sedan chair to get here, for the streets in between were filthy and if he had walked his clothes would have become soiled.

He had had his hair dressed carefully and powdered; he wore white silk stockings, silver shoe buckles, a simple but good black waistcoat trimmed in gold braid, but not the Papal decoration – he had had enough of that.

He heard someone saying, "If I may take the liberty, sir."

It was Baron Grimm's valet de chambre opening the door for him.

Baron Grimm and Madame d'Epinay greeted him warmly in a large, luxurious drawing room, and Grimm said, "I am sorry, Herr Amadeo, that our meeting here was delayed, but I was in Prussia. Frederick wants me to keep France out of his present difficulty with Austria, in the event he will have to fight the Hapsburgs. France does have an Austrian-born Queen, although sometimes Marie Antoinette is more French than the French."

"I knew her when she was a child, Monsieur Baron."

"When did you last have an audience with her mother, the Empress?"

"After *Lucio Silla* was produced. At the time of the Polish partition."

"Five years ago. Many things have changed. Since Marie Antoinette has become Queen, she is no longer influenced by her mother."

"But if I could play for her, sir?"

"Marie Antoinette is not interested in music."

Wolfgang looked upset and Madame d'Epinay added, "She is pregnant, although that is not generally known, and she is not making any public appearances. I doubt anything can be accomplished at Versailles. But I think we can be of some service to you."

"Thank you, Madame." Wolfgang became aware that Grimm had not changed much, as had most of the people he had not seen since childhood. Still editor of the famed and powerful *Correspondance littéraire,* Grimm had retained his good figure, his well-turned legs, his youthful vigor.

It was Madame d'Epinay who had aged. Yet she seemed determined to preserve the illusion that she was a Mademoiselle, for she dressed in the most provocative, alluring fashion, although she looked as old as Mamma.

Wolfgang said, "If I may suggest, Monsieur Baron, I would like to compose an opera first."

"It is too soon," said Grimm. "Piccinni is the fashion. He and Gluck are all that anyone is talking about. No one would pay attention to you."

Or perhaps too much, Wolfgang told himself, and expose Piccinni for the second-rate composer he was. But he said, "Whatever you think, Baron."

"I do not question your ability. I loved you as a child and I am glad that you are in Paris, where your talents are certain to be known, in time, but at the moment no one but Piccinni or Gluck interests the musical public."

"Then why did you suggest that I come now, sir?"

"Your father desired it. But not everyone will be impressed as they were years ago. You are no longer a wunderkind. Yet your French is excellent."

"Does that matter, sir?"

"It will be useful in the drawing room. The great ladies still control music in Paris. I will send you to the Duchess de Chabot for approval."

Madame d'Epinay said, "She is wealthy."

"And has influence," said Grimm. "Amadeo, you are unfamiliar with the customs of France. Without consulting me, you will be walking blindly."

Wolfgang bowed humbly and said, "Your most obedient servant, Baron." Somebody was breaking wind; he wondered if it was Grimm.

Madame d'Epinay said, "Don't be disappointed if she prefers cards."

"Louise!" Grimm was offended.

"I was just warning Wolfgang. And he should move into this neighbourhood, where he will be near the theaters and the nobility."

"Can he afford it?"

"Of course I can," Wolfgang said proudly, although he was not sure.

Madame d'Epinay said, "I will find clean, large rooms, and where they speak German so your mother will feel at home."

"Do you think I should see Dr. Franklin, the American minister, too?"

"To go to America?" Grimm laughed. "They know nothing of music there."

"But Dr. Franklin is said to be devoted to music. And I have been told that since the alliance he is the most popular figure in Paris."

"You have been told? Listen to me, Amadeo, not to fools. Dr. Franklin is more interested in the ladies than in music. And in lightning rods."

"Whatever you suggest, sir."

But Wolfgang looked so disconsolate – Wolfgang had his heart set on meeting the American, more out of curiosity than any other reason – that Grimm said more kindly, "I will introduce you to Piccinni, if he has time."

"I met him in Italy. Several times."

"He is far more famous now. I would also introduce you to the Chevalier Gluck, but he returned to Vienna, after a meeting with Voltaire."

"Isn't Voltaire a supporter of Piccinni?"

"That does not commit him to ignorance. Gluck is a great man."

"And so is Voltaire?"

"Of course." Grimm was shocked. "You don't think so, Amadeo?"

"I do not like him, or Rousseau. They profess to know so much about music, when they know very little. Why should philosophers have such influence on music?"

"Are you always this outspoken, Amadeo?"

Wolfgang looked innocent as he said, "Sir, isn't truth a virtue?"

"Do you really think so?"

"Standing up or sitting down?"

That broke the tension and Grimm, laughing, declared, "I must also introduce you to Le Gros, the director of the Concert Spirituel, the foremost orchestra in Paris. He is a friend of Herr Raaff and Herr Wendling, supporters of your music. They have spoken very well of your work to me. They were enchanted by the music you wrote for them in Mannheim."

"They are in Paris?"

"I saw them yesterday. You mustn't be impatient, you have time to make your fortune. You are young enough not to have to get established at once."

"When I was here before, Schobert was the most favored

musician, and a few years later he was dead at twenty-seven from eating mushrooms."

"All young men think they are going to die young. It is a disease of youth. I felt the same way when I was your age. But I predict a long life for you. Small men do not put as much stress on their system as big men. Amadeo, could you and your charming mother dine with us? Next week?"

"We will be honored, Baron."

"Then I will have the necessary introductions for you."

The dinner was pleasant. Baron Grimm and Madame d'Epinay spoke German, so Mamma would feel at home, and assured her that her son would make a brilliant reputation in Paris, once he became acclimated and better known.

And although Madame d'Epinay was delicate now and seldom went out, she found two sunny, spacious rooms for them on the rue Gros Chenet that faced the street. Mamma agreed that they were much nicer than their previous lodging, although the rooms were chilly even with a fire, but she made the best of it for Wolfgang's sake. Their new address was close to Baron Grimm and the theaters and the nobility, and she liked the clean street, the healthy air, and her landlord who spoke German. He was often her only company, for Wolfgang was so busy establishing himself that she rarely saw him.

Grimm's first letter of introduction was to the Duchess de Chabot. It was one of the great houses in France and one of the few, Wolfgang was told, that could afford a maître de chapelle of his quality. He left the Baron's letter and a week later he was invited to call on the Duchess.

To create the best impression he came at the precise moment he had been invited. But on his arrival he was ushered into a vast, drafty chamber which had no fire and the wait was interminable. By the time the Duchess appeared Wolfgang was as cold as ice and she said, "I must entertain my company first. Then I will hear you play."

The plain, stout, thirty-year-old Duchess de Chabot sat down without another word and started to draw, in the company of four gentlemen who had just entered and who made a circle around her. No one paid any attention to Wolfgang. None of the gentlemen were introduced to him, yet it was assumed that he would stay. The windows and doors were opened and now, not only were his hands as cold as ice, but so were his feet and body, and his head began to ache. There was absolute silence as the Duchess drew.

Everyone had to watch her, and Wolfgang felt that he was the only sane person in the room. This went on for an hour. He thought, if it were not for Baron Grimm, he would have left a long time ago. Just as he could no longer endure the cold, his headache, and the tediousness, she looked up from her drawing and said, "You can play now, if you like."

While he was even more frozen than before, it was such a relief to do something, he ran to the pianoforte. It was a wretched instrument, but what annoyed Wolfgang the most was that all the time he played, the Duchess pursued her drawing without a moment's cessation, the gentlemen attentive only to her, and he was playing to the walls, chairs, and tables.

Suddenly this was too much and he rose to go. The Duchess looked up. She had been listening after all, he thought with satisfaction. She said, "Would you play your Fischer variations? I hear they are amusing."

"I would prefer another day when it would be warmer."

But she pulled him back to the pianoforte and ordered her courtiers to follow her example while she sat beside him and listened intently.

He forgot the cold, his headache, and despite the miserable pianoforte, played as he was accustomed to play when he was in good humor.

She said, "I see you got your hands warm."

He was shocked that she gave him nothing.

Wolfgang told Grimm, "Put me at the best clavier in Europe, but with an audience who do not care, and I lose all pleasure in playing."

"You are too touchy, Amadeo, it is foolish to be offended by the Duchess. She could have played cards while you performed."

Grimm sent him to the Duke de Guines, a close friend of Marie Antoinette and a power at court, and one of the most musical noblemen in Paris. Grimm assured Wolfgang that the Duke played the flute splendidly, that his daughter was a fine harpist, that this was a marvelous opportunity. But Wolfgang was suspicious now, and he called on the Duke skeptically.

The Duke de Guines greeted him pleasantly and without any of the patronization he expected. The elegant nobleman was smooth-skinned, which was rare in a Paris where most of the nobles used rouge heavily, and he wore his fine clothes without ostentation. At his daughter's age he had studied music with Rameau. And Wolfgang's mood mellowed.

The Duke's daughter was a pretty young woman, but too buxom, decided Wolfgang, and not nearly as attractive as Aloysia, yet the same age, which poignantly reminded him of Aloysia. Mademoiselle wanted to learn to compose. The Duke engaged him at once, and he wrote the good news to Papa: "For nobility, they are musical. The

Duke plays the flute very well, and she is excellent on the harp. He knows all about me, and if he were not so much in love with his daughter, he could become a strong supporter. But he is most interested in making a composer out of her, although I am not sure she has any ideas. I am to give her two hours of instruction in composition daily, for which I will be paid liberally, that is three louis d'or for twelve lessons. I am also going to write a concerto for flute and harp for them, although neither is an instrument I like, but it should please the Duke, who is kind and generous, unlike many of the French."

At the fourth lesson in composition the Duke said, when he saw Wolfgang look perplexed, "It is not my intention to make a great composer of Mademoiselle. It will be enough if she can compose for her instrument."

Wolfgang replied, "She knows the rules of composition."

The Duke said, "I am sure that she has ideas. It is only her modesty and her lack of confidence in herself that prevents them from appearing."

But that was the difficulty: *she had no ideas!* Yet how could he tell her father, who worshiped her, *She has no thoughts, nothing comes, I have tried her in every possible way, and nothing happens, her head is empty.*

The Duke asked, "What is the difficulty, Mozart?"

"Perhaps she just does not know how to begin," said Wolfgang. He composed the first bar, and asked her to continue, and she did that. Encouraged, he asked her now to start something herself.

There was much cogitation but nothing came. Instead, she was exhausted.

The Duke was irritated and Wolfgang said hurriedly, "What a stupid fellow I am. I have just begun a minuet, and I cannot finish the first part of it. Mademoiselle, would you have the goodness to finish it for me?" He handed her the four bars of the minuet he had composed already.

She was distrustful of her ability, but after much labor she created several bars which were musical and in keeping with what he had done.

He rejoiced that they had achieved something at last, and he said, "Now you have only to complete the melody. Continue as you have just done, and you will have your own composition." He turned to the Duke, who was pleased with her progress. "Tomorrow, sir, we will see her success."

The next day there was nothing. Mademoiselle was in tears.

Wolfgang came to dread these lessons in composition, for no matter what he tried, she did not improve. She remembered everything he told her; she knew all the rules of composition; she continued to play the harp beautifully; but she was unable to express a single original idea.

Finally he focused on the concerto for flute and harp he was composing for them. He wrote it simply, and balanced both solo instruments, so each performer would have just the right amount of virtuoso playing.

The Duke was delighted with this composition and told Wolfgang, "We must play it for the Queen. There will be great festivities when her child is born, and music will be in demand. This concerto could be fitting."

But after twelve lessons there was no pay. This troubled Wolfgang, and he wrote Papa for advice, and Papa answered immediately. "Patience, my dear son, you must keep in the Duke's favor, no matter how long you have to wait for your louis d'or. I have read about him often and that he has great power at court. So his daughter has no ability in composition! Do you think every one has a genius like yours? Her talent will come by degrees; she has a good memory. Eh bien! Let her steal, or, more politely, appropriate. I am sure that once Monsieur le Duc hears something composed by his daughter, he will be beside himself with pleasure, and become a passionate supporter of yours."

While Wolfgang practiced patience, the Duke and his daughter left Paris for their château in the country without a word to him.

This rudeness upset him even more than the Duchess. Grimm wanted to know why the lessons had ceased and he said, "I gave her twelve, and I have not received a sou."

"You will. But the Duke likes to take his time in such matters. Amadeo, you must not be bourgeois. In Paris one never shows annoyance about anything or people will take advantage of that. You must always maintain appearances. Your father was correct to advise patience."

"How did you know?" Had his letters been read here, as in Salzburg?

"Your father has been writing me. He worries about a young man living in licentious Paris, but I assured him that your morals are beyond reproach."

Wolfgang thought wryly, he knew as well as Grimm that there was more sensuality in Paris than any other city in Europe, and that he had not availed himself of this only because of Aloysia. But he said, desiring to sound worldly, "I have seen too many young men here who have the French disease to wish to risk it. Even when I was a child, I heard it said in Italy that syphilis was the greatest gift the French had brought them."

"I wouldn't say that in public, Amadeo."

"Isn't that why so many noblemen wear masks and heavy rouge, to hide the disfigurement of their venereal disease?"

"You should be as careful with your opinions as you are with your morals. It would have been useful if your father had come. He knows what to say."

"Have I offended the Duke?"

"I wouldn't put it that way. But couldn't you have made him believe that his daughter had composed something, even if it was yours?"

"As I told you. . ."

Grimm interrupted, "It is the Duke who needs convincing. However, he will be back. For the Queen's accouchement, if for nothing else. Then you can present him with the concerto, and he might play it as he promised."

"He has it."

"Without paying for it? Amadeo, how could you be so foolish?"

"Sir, he asked for the concerto."

"You must compose something for Le Gros. He pays for what he uses."

Fat, cheerful Jean Le Gros, opera composer and director of the Concert Spirituel, liked Wolfgang on sight and invited him to his house for lunch, where he became a regular visitor and met many musicians and several old friends. Wendling and Raaff, who were frequent guests, greeted him with such affection he was pleased and he told Mamma, "They are honest fellows, good musicians, and they send you their best regards." Wolfgang's mood also improved when Le Gros asked him to compose four choruses, and a duet for a *Miserere*, although he would have preferred something more exciting.

As he told Mamma, "It is not my own work. It is by Kapellmeister Holzbauer, but since he is in Mannheim and I am in Paris, and since Le Gros feels that Holzbauer's choruses are poor and weak and he wants them splendid and strong, I am to build them so for his orchestra."

Mamma, lying in bed, nodded her head.

"But it is a start. And I am to be paid. Papa should be pleased."

Mamma did not speak.

"What is wrong, Mamma dear? Don't you feel well?"

She did not know how to reply. The chill she had caught on the journey from Mannheim had not left her. But Wolfgang was so involved with the struggle to succeed, she could not add another burden. She forced a smile and said, "Don't worry. I am just tired. You must not keep Le Gros waiting. You said he is considering another commission for you."

He nodded, but as he rode in a sedan chair to Le Gros to avoid the mud and filth underfoot, premonitions about Mamma fluttered about him like a flock of buzzards. He had wanted to call a doctor, but she had refused to see a French doctor. Papa, hearing of her poor health, had written an urgent plea for her to be bled, but she had put that off too. Yet her cough had grown worse, and often he heard her crying out in her sleep, or moaning, as if in pain. He hated to leave her alone. "Yet the fact is," she said, when he apologized for that, "you have to earn sous for food and lodging," and she was right.

"A *sinfonia concertante* for flute, oboe, horn, and bassoon?" Wolfgang repeated Le Gros' request, wishing that the conductor had suggested a different kind of work to compose, one which was more to his own taste.

"Oui! Oui! Wendling says you write enchantingly for the flute."

"He is a virtuoso on the instrument. If anyone is."

Le Gros was excited. "He will be one of the soloists. He and Ramm and Punto and Ritter, the four most brilliant virtuosos in Paris."

Noverre, the renowned dancer and ballet master, who had met Wolfgang on the Grand Tour and at Le Gros' dinner table, said, "If Monsieur Mozart could compose music for my ballet, *Les Petits Riens,* it would be very kind. And it might lead to an opera scrittura, if the ballet music pleases."

Noverre means, thought Wolfgang, if the Queen approves, but to say that would be tactless. Noverre, the teacher of Marie Antoinette, was the director of the ballet at the Opera, her personal choice, and Noverre also had said that he had great influence with the director of the Paris opera. He asked, "Monsieur Noverre, how soon do you need the music?"

"As soon as possible. It is an emergency."

Wolfgang went to work with total immersion. None of the music he was composing filled him with enthusiasm, but he was too much the composer to do anything but his best. Whatever the awkwardness of the instruments or of the form, the music itself must be graceful and pleasing. Ideas came swiftly and with them lovely melodies, and, as always, trusting his fastidious taste, he put the compositions in the mood and tempo of the Paris salon and within several weeks delivered them to Le Gros and Noverre.

Yet the performance of the *Miserere* was almost more than he could endure. He whispered to Wendling, who seemed sympathetic, "The singing is atrocious. I can't understand a word. It is this awful French language. How wretched it is! German is divine by comparison. And the singers – although it is a shame to call them that, for they don't sing – they shriek and howl with all their might through their throat and nose."

"And Le Gros left out two of your choruses. Your two best."

Wolfgang said bitterly, "It doesn't matter, Wendling, hardly anyone knows I wrote the choruses, they are still attributed to Holzbauer."

A few days later, when it came time to rehearse the *sinfonia concertante*, the music had not been copied although Le Gros had urged him to complete it as swiftly as possible and had had the score for four days.

Wendling said, "Le Gros, the score must be engraved. I have seen it and it is lovely."

"Oui! Oui!" exclaimed Le Gros. "He is a prodigy."

"It must be copied immediately, for I have to leave Paris soon."

Le Gros shrugged and said, "By tomorrow, Wendling, if possible."

The next day Wendling and Wolfgang called on Le Gros to get the engraved *sinfonia concertante* and Le Gros said, "I forgot about it."

"Forgot about it?" Wendling looked incredulous.

"And now I have lost the score. I cannot find it anywhere."

Wolfgang, who had been searching through a pile of scores on Le Gros' desk while the conductor was occupied with an irate Wendling, discovered the *sinfonia concertante* under an overture by Piccinni. But if he mentioned this, he would make an enemy for life. He left it where it was.

Le Gros said, "Someone must have misplaced it."

But Wendling shouted, "It is a dirty trick, a French trick. You are nothing better than a whore, Le Gros. You and all you musicians at the Academie Royale de Musique. You French composers are so terrified of Herr Mozart's music, you are afraid to play it, or if you do, not as he composed it, so he won't expose what second-rate composers you all are."

"Oh, no, Monsieur, I was just about to ask him for a symphony."

"A symphony?" Wolfgang didn't want to sound interested, but he was.

"Don't let him trick you again," said Wendling. "Don't write a note, unless he pays you in advance."

"I will! Right now!" Le Gros handed Wolfgang two louis d'or.

"What about the choruses? And the *sinfonia concertante?*" demanded Wendling. "Herr Mozart is too trusting, but I am not."

"I will send his fee in the mail."

"No." Wendling was obdurate. "If Herr Mozart doesn't receive it, you will say it was lost. He must have this money now."

Le Gros slowly and reluctantly gave Wolfgang two more louis d'or, one for each of the compositions already completed, and said, "I am desolate about the loss of your *sinfonia* but the symphony should please."

Wolfgang was puzzled why Le Gros had requested another work, when he had intrigued against the *sinfonia concertante,* but Wendling said, "A symphony won't make the impression the other piece would have. The French adore music that shows virtuosity, and Le Gros doesn't want to offend you totally, just in case you do become the rage here."

The music composed for Noverre was a new disappointment. The ballet master did not give him a sou for the full-length overture and the thirteen dance pieces and only Noverre's name appeared on the program. Yet Wolfgang did not complain, for the ballet master promised to get him an opera scrittura, when a libretto was found.

Then hearing that the Duke de Guines had returned to Paris, although there had been no word from him, Wolfgang called on the Duke, who greeted him coldly and said, "Mademoiselle is no longer interested in lessons. She is getting married soon."

"Your Excellency, what about the lessons I have given her already?"

"What about them, Mozart?" The Duke was angry.

Wolfgang could not speak. To beg for money was too humiliating. As he turned to go the Duke said, "My housekeeper will pay you."

She gave him three louis d'or, and when he said, "What about my concerto?" she replied, "It is a mediocre piece, and you hardly helped Mademoiselle at all."

His impulse was to throw the three louis d'or in her face, but he needed the money desperately. Mamma had become quite sick. He hurried home for now he had money to pay a doctor, or, at least, to have her bled.

FORTY-EIGHT

Mamma still did not want a doctor. Wolfgang said, "You cannot use the excuse that we cannot afford one now," and she answered, "I don't trust French doctors." Although she felt worse, despite the warm weather which had come with June, she felt that Leopold's remedies which had cured them in the past, would cure her again. But when she did not improve the next few days, she consented to be bled. This seemed to help. She was able to get out of bed, and Raaff, who visited her regularly, took her to the Luxembourg Gardens which she enjoyed, although she was very tired afterwards. And Wolfgang was hopeful that she could attend the performance of the symphony he had composed for Le Gros.

The day of the concert he was disappointed when she said, "I don't quite feel up to going out, although I feel much better since I was bled. Don't write Papa that I had a bad spell. It will only worry him unnecessarily."

"I won't tell him if you see a doctor the next time you feel badly."

She hesitated, but seeing his determination and anxiety, she nodded.

"Papa will be relieved that you have been bled. He believes in it."

"Don't you, Wolfgang?"

He shrugged. "If it helps, I believe in it. Papa will be amused about Voltaire. Listen to what I have written." He read:

"*That godless rogue, Voltaire, died on May 30, like a dirty dog.*"

"Why do you dislike him so? You are friendly with other impious men. Schachtner, Wendling, Grimm. And they have been kind to you."

"Colloredo admires him. Voltaire's picture is on his wall."

"But they say that Voltaire died in the arms of the church. Wolfgang, if anything happens to me, you will have all the rites performed, please!"

"Mamma, nothing is going to happen to you."

They were joined by Raaff, who agreed with Wolfgang that Mamma was looking much better since she had been bled, and added, "When your son's symphony is a great success, you will forget all your complaints."

Wolfgang said, "I haven't much hope for it. The French are uncomfortable with my music. They do not know what to do with it."

Mamma said proudly, "But this new symphony in D Major is written with such authority, despite it being the first you have composed in years."

Raaff said, "I am sure this new symphony will please."

Wolfgang said scornfully, "Considering French taste, it does not matter. Or what they think. I care very little whether they like it or not. But I began it in the Parisian style, with their precious premier coup d'archet, vigorous and in unison, as if that were a great trick — what a joke!"

Yet as he sat in the Salle des Suisses of the palace of the Tuileries and waited for his first symphony in four years to be performed, he was nervous in spite of his contempt for French music. Had he neglected the symphonic form too long? Had it been a mistake to use the Parisian style?

As the first movement started, he thought the orchestra could be better. But the attack was good; the French were accustomed to strong openings.

No one seemed to notice that the first violin was off and he rose, to rush into the orchestra and correct him, and Raaff restrained him, whispering, "Good God, Mozart, such a gesture could cost your life, no one in their right mind risks that for a symphony," and gradually his anger subsided as the first violin caught up with those it was supposed to lead.

There was loud, spontaneous applause for a passage in the middle of the first movement, but he was not surprised, he had written it to please.

The slow, serious second movement shone with tenderness and grace, and was received without any enthusiasm by the audience.

But at the first forte of the vigorous third movement, the audience clapped, and shouted "Bravissimo!" and this continued to the end.

Le Gros, who wore the King's monogram, told Wolfgang, "This is the finest symphony that has been composed for us," but he did not give him the rest of his fee, introducing him instead to Piccinni.

Grimm and Madame d'Epinay congratulated him also, and Piccinni said, "We met before, Signor Mozart. In Italy, when you were a child."

Wolfgang was depressed. The first number on the program had

been an operatic overture by Piccinni, and it was the same old ding-dong-dung, he thought wryly, yet Piccinni was the favorite of Paris. He wondered what was more ruinous: Piccinni's music or Marie Antoinette's extravagances. But Grimm was watching him intently, so he bowed to Piccinni and said politely, "I am happy to make your acquaintance again, Maestro."

"Your symphony was interesting. Are you going to compose an opera here?"

"It has been suggested. Do you think I should accept?"

"Who can tell, Signore!" Piccinni's hands went up in an unexpected gesture of despair. "I did not come to Paris to compete with anyone, least of all, with Chevalier Gluck, whose music I admire, but now we are supposed to be bitter enemies. Yet our music is so different, as yours is from mine."

"As long as one's music is popular, nothing else seems to matter."

Piccinni flushed, as if this could be an insult.

Wolfgang hurried to say, for Grimm seemed displeased, "Signor Piccinni, I am sure your operas deserve all the praise they have received."

Grimm smiled benevolently as Piccinni, said, "You are generous, Signore."

"Not at all, Maestro. You understand your job, as I understand mine."

As Wolfgang turned to go, Madame d'Epinay asked, "How is Fräu Mozart? We heard she has been ill. If we can be of any aid, please call on us."

"Thank you, but she is better today." He bowed to everyone and left.

Mamma was worse when he arrived home. This time he was really alarmed. He informed her that his symphony had been acclaimed, and she didn't hear him. Wasn't she listening? He hummed a few passages of the symphony and she pointed to her stomach and whispered, "It hurts so, Wolfgang."

He ran to the apothecary and bought Papa's favorite medication, the anti-spasmodic powder that they always used at home for digestive ailments, but she got sicker. Her diarrhea became incessant. She was so drawn he was terrified. She pointed to the drug he had gotten from the apothecary and whispered, "There is nothing in that bottle that will keep me alive."

"Can I get you a doctor?" But she did not hear him. He had to shout to make himself heard.

Then she nodded, she would endure even that if it would ease her racking pain, and speaking with difficulty, very weak, she mumbled, "A German doctor, please, Wolferl, if possible," and became feverish and delirious.

Raaff, who had stopped in to say goodbye, he was leaving for Mannheim tomorrow, was shocked by her condition and said that he would stay with her until Wolfgang returned with a doctor.

When Madame d'Epinay heard that Fräu Mozart had taken a turn for the worse, she sent Wolfgang to Grimm's personal physician, an elderly German who had settled in Paris with the Baron. Rudolf von Koller was a professor of anatomy and an expert at dissection.

By the time Wolfgang returned with Doctor von Koller, Mamma was a little better. Raaff was singing the melody of the symphony to her, and she had come out of her delirium, she could hear him, and it seemed to please and distract her. She was relieved that the doctor was German; she could understand him and trust the remedies he prescribed.

Doctor von Koller looked seventy, but despite his age, he was energetic. He observed Mamma's labored breathing, uneven pulse, and strained bowel movements, and she said it was her stomach that hurt, that seemed inflamed, and he replied, "It is this cursed French food and water." He gave her a rhubarb powder in wine. "But no water, under any circumstances," although she yearned for it, for the powder and wine made her more thirsty.

Wolfgang drew the doctor aside and said, "What is her illness, sir?"

"Well, it is an indisposition rather than a malady."

Which meant, thought Wolfgang, it is upsetting but did not carry the terrifying implications a malady would have. "Then it is not a contagion?"

"Oh, no! It is not consumption, her lungs are not congested. It is not smallpox or scarlet fever. It is not a chill."

"But she complains constantly of the cold. Although it is June."

"As I said, it is an indisposition." The stout, red-faced doctor adjusted his carefully powdered wig and said, "If the pain does not ease in the next few days, call me. But remember, no water."

A little later Raaff said his farewell, kissing Mamma on the forehead and assuring her that he would see her when he returned to Paris in the autumn, and as Wolfgang walked him to the door, Raaff asked him, "Do you want me to give any message to Aloysia?"

"How much I would like to see her?" Wolfgang laughed bitterly. "What good would that do? I have written her and Fridolin, giving them advice. I even suggested they come to Paris, but so far, they seem reluctant."

"Do you blame them? After the way you have been treated?"

"She should succeed. She is beautiful, and she sings very well."

"Yes, she might succeed, as someone's mistress."

"Please!" Wolfgang could not endure such a thought.

"You surprise me. You know how young, attractive women, who are not of the nobility, succeed."

"But I love her!"

"That is why I don't want you to be hurt."

"Could anything hurt me more than Paris and their lack of taste?"

"Indeed, yes. But at your age indifference can be a disaster. Is there anything you wish me to convey to Aloysia?"

"Teach her. Please, Herr Raaff. It will improve her immeasurably."

"Not without a fee. I never give my services away. It is an attitude you should assume. You will get more respect, not less."

"I will pay you. I will send you the money for her."

"With your mother's illness? How could you?"

"I won't deprive her. But once she is better. . ."

"That will make me very happy. Her color is good, and the doctor should help her." Raaff handed Wolfgang several louis d'or and said, "I will tell Aloysia that you are flourishing. Ambitious young women like such news. And I will aid her, if I can."

Before Wolfgang could enjoy Raaff's kindness, Mamma became delirious and pleaded for water, which he could not give her because the doctor had forbidden it. Then she fell into a coma and lay as if dead. Wolfgang called the doctor, who looked at her now as he would a cadaver and said abruptly, "I doubt that she will last the night. You must be sure she makes her confession."

Wolfgang found a German priest and his presence aroused her, and she was able to confess, to receive the sacrament and extreme unction. This seemed to ease her, and after the priest was gone, she said, "I must be up and about. How much was the doctor's bill?"

"It doesn't matter, Mamma dear. Can you hear me now?"

"Of course I can. I heard the priest. Did you see Dr. Franklin?"

"No. Grimm was against it."

"The Baron does seem changed. Not that I think there is anything to the American taking lightning out of the sky. In Mannheim, they say his experiments attracted storms. Wolferl, it is much better to allow nature to take its course than to force it. You know that God can find anybody He wants to find, and no lightning rod can save them. Don't leave me alone!"

She didn't want to die alone. She was more afraid of that than anything else. Leopold should not have allowed her to come. It was so cold in the room, although the fire was going and Wolferl said it was June outside. She must be growing worse. Did Wolferl know how feeble she felt? In her delirium she saw the graveyard of St. Peter's, where she wanted to be buried. It was her favorite church in Salzburg, with its catacombs in the cliffs of the Monchsberg and she cried out, "Bury me there!"

"Where, Mamma?" sobbed Wolfgang.

She did not hear him. In her mind she was in the graveyard of St. Peter's, sitting on a grave, reading the inscription on the tombstone: *Here lies Anna Maria Walburga Pertl Mozart*, but she hadn't used those names for years. What were they laughing at: Wolferl at six knew more about music than any of them. If she could only say farewell. Leopold would never forgive Wolferl. But it was Paris that had murdered her. And so many other things. Faces clustered around her, they were around her grave, it was a good funeral, she thought with satisfaction, the devil could not cheat her of that even if he was everywhere. Only the faces were so difficult to recognize. Was God punishing her? She had loved her family so. She tried to pray but she was too weak. The words which formed on her lips had no sound. Yet there was a voice within her, crying out: My son sings with the voice of heaven, lift your head and you will hear him. Now she heard the concerto he had composed for Mademoiselle Jeunehomme; she loved the lyrical, singing slow second movement – it was, as Leopold said, "incomparable" – but she had never told Wolferl, and she must before it was too late. Then Mamma was certain she was dying, for she could not even hear Wolferl's music and blackness engulfed her.

For seven days and nights Wolfgang sat by Mamma's side as she lay in a coma. He ate virtually nothing. He took only an occasional sip of wine. He felt he would lose his sanity. He had no hope now, yet he could not leave her. When he lay down, it was by her side, in his bed which he had moved next to her in case she needed him. But she did not stir. Yet she was alive; he could tell from her faint breathing. No one would ever know what a dreadful time this was, he thought. Many times he wept at his impotence. Mamma was dying before his eyes and he could not do a thing to save her. Doctor von Koller stopped in twice, and was surprised that she was still alive, and said there was nothing to be done. His opportunities for new commissions vanished with Mamma's illness, yet it did not matter. In the desolate silence there was only her self and his self. He longed to compose something for her, a song would do, just a few golden notes, it would be his way of saying, "I love you," but he could not sing. He could only sit and wait and weep until he did not even have the strength for that, and his beloved music became a faithless mistress that had betrayed him too.

Then on the evening of July 3, a week after Mamma had received the last rites, she was seized with convulsions. Yet she sought to speak amid her anguish. Wolfgang heard her muttering, "Wolferl ...Leopold...Nannerl..." She tried to raise her head, as if to listen for a treasured melody, and she didn't have the strength. He pressed her hand and spoke to her, but she did not answer. He lifted her head to help her speak, and it fell back limp and suddenly he was stricken with terror. Crying, he kissed her over and over but there was no response. He put her hand mirror to her lips, which she had carried proudly throughout Europe, and there was nothing.

He knelt on the cold stone floor and weeping, prayed for her salvation, asking God for His compassion, to be a loving God, to think of Him in this instant as anything else was inconceivable – and whispered, "Dear God, let your angels lead our sweet mother into your eternal love."

When he stopped weeping, he did what Papa would have done in such a situation. Although it was two in the morning, he wrote two letters to prepare him for the awful news. The first was to the Abbé Bullinger:

"My Dear Friend   *For You Alone*   July 3

"Mourn with me on this, the most wretched and melancholy day of my life. I write at two o'clock in the morning to inform you that my mother – my dearest mother – is no more! God has called her to Himself. At twenty-one minutes past ten, she departed, no one being present but myself. I saw clearly that nothing could save her, and resigned myself to the will of God: He gave, and He took away.

"At present I cannot write you the details of her illness, but it is my belief that she was destined to die, that it was the will of God. Let me now beg you to prepare my poor father by gentle degrees for the sad tidings. I am writing him by the same post, but I am telling him no more than that she is very ill, and I now await his answer, by which I shall be guided. May God support and strengthen him. Oh, my dear friend, if you only knew what had to be endured! Only God has made it possible to face this great loss!

"Please, therefore, good friend, support my father. Say what you can to him, in order that when he learns the worst he may not feel too bitterly. I commend my sister to you also from the bottom of my heart. Call on both of them soon, but say no word of the death, only prepare them. You can do this whatever way you wish, but please, in such way, that I will not have a new misfortune to face. Comfort my dear father and my dear sister, and pray send me a speedy answer. Adieu. Your much obliged and grateful servant. Wolfgang Amadeus Mozart."

Then he wrote to Papa, which was even more difficult:

"The reasons I have left your letter of the 11th of June so long unanswered is that I have very unpleasant and sad news to communicate. My dear mother is very ill, and I do not know what to expect. So I have resigned myself to the will of God, and I hope that you and my dear sister will do the same. I find consolation in this reflection, after praying to God as earnestly as I am able for my

333

dear mother's life and health. If she should recover, I will bless His divine mercy. If she should not, I will accept His will and be thankful that she is in His arms. Meanwhile, a priest has performed all the necessary rites and her soul is at peace.

"I will not go into detail about her illness, except it seems to be an inflammation of the stomach, and thus, not a contagion. So you do not have to worry about me. I am as well as can be expected in such a sad circumstance, and my prayers are that my beloved father and sister are in good health in spite of my melancholy news, and will take care of themselves for my sake. I send you a hundred kisses and embraces and wish we were together with all my heart. Your obedient and loving son."

One friend attended Mamma's funeral the next day, François Heina. This French-horn player was also a friend of Papa's from the previous Paris visits, and his wife, a music publisher, had issued the *Violin School* in French. Heina had gotten into the habit of dropping in during Mamma's illness to bring Wolfgang food and wine.

The small, spry, middle-aged musician told Wolfgang, "You must have your dear mother interred at once, or as a foreigner, she will be buried in the charnel house with the paupers, thrown into an unknown grave, bodies piled on bodies in a communal grave, no better than a garbage heap."

Wolfgang shuddered at the thought of such a burial. To be thrown into the ground without identity would be the final humiliation. How could the earth be that inhospitable! He could not permit Mamma to be so degraded.

"And if she is buried in the church of St. Eustache, her grave will not be robbed, as it is often elsewhere in Paris, mostly by medical students."

So Wolfgang allowed Heina to arrange her funeral. But his blood ran cold as Mamma was placed in a small coffin. Either she had shrunk, he thought, or he had seen her as larger than she was, and it occurred to him that he would need only a small coffin also.

He told Heina to hire a carriage and a funeral cart, although he had to borrow louis d'or from Grimm to pay for that. The Baron apologized for not being able to attend Mamma's funeral, saying that Madame d'Epinay was indisposed and required his attention. Wolfgang shrugged and pretended that it did not matter, but it did, very much. In Salzburg, and even in Vienna, he reflected bitterly, there would be many friends in attendance.

He stared at the massive front of the church of Saint Eustache and counted the ten Grecian pillars to keep from crying, but that did not lull his torment. A little, ragged child urinated on the street while the coffin was carried in to the church. The garbage around it smelled as if it had been here since his previous visits to Paris years ago, and he saw a yellow stain on the wall of the church where many others had urinated also.

Inside, he saw that Rameau was buried here, which made him feel a little better about his choice of a cemetery. He noticed a grand tomb and read the gilt inscription above it: *"Jean Baptiste Colbert, Controller General of the Finances."* Wolfgang thought, this nobleman must have raised much money for Louis XIV, and the grandeur of the tomb filled him with melancholy. He was startled by another burial inscription: *"François de Chevett, Lieutenant General of the Armies of the King, 1695-1769."* He had played for this grand seigneur.

The few people within the church ignored the funeral; it was obviously too small to be of any consequence. Everything about Saint-Eustache chilled Wolfgang, the stone floor, the stone walls, the scanty light, and it was a relief to move into the graveyard and into the sunlight.

The priest, who was performing the last services, asked Wolfgang, "Are you Madame Mozart's closest relative?"

"Yes. Her son. Her only son."

"Monsieur, would you sign the church register, please?"

Wolfgang stared at the day's page to verify that it was correct:

On July 4, 1778, Anna Maria Pertl Mozart, aged 57 years, wife of Leopold Mozart, *maître de chapelle* at Salzburg, who died yesterday at rue Gros Chenet, has been interred in the cemetery in the presence of Wolfgang Amedée Mozart, her son, and of François Heina, a friend.

He signed it simply: "Mozart."

Heina added his name and Wolfgang prayed that God would embrace Mamma's soul. But as the last blessing was mumbled in French, and her body was placed into the earth with strangers, God seemed such a long way off.

FORTY-NINE

Leopold was sitting in the Tanzmeister-Saal of their house on the Hannibalplatz while writing to Anna Maria and Wolfgang, for this stately and beautiful music room was a fond reminder of them, when his son's letter about her critical illness arrived. He had just finished saying: "My Dearest Wife: Not to be wanting on your name day, I am writing you secure in the knowledge that this letter will reach you before then, and thus, that I can wish you all manner of happiness and pray to Almighty God that He will preserve you for many years, not only in health, but in as much contentment as is possible in this changeable and difficult world, and that, with His help, we will find ourselves together again, for this is what I find hardest to endure – *the separation from you* – *to be at such a distance* – *and to live at such a distance*! In other respects we are well, Thank God! We kiss you and Wolfgang a thousand times, and beg you to take the utmost care of your precious health. . ."

He halted to read Wolfgang's letter, and then he could not go on. There was such an air of resignation in it, so unlike his son, he had a sudden feeling of terror that Anna Maria was gone already. But God could not be so cruel, he told himself, it would be enough to make a skeptic of the most pious man. He called Nannerl to see what she thought and as she read her brother's letter she burst into tears.

He said, "What are we to think? Either she is dead, or she must be better, for this letter is dated the 3rd, and it is now the 13th."

Nannerl cried out, "Wolfgang called a priest! We must have lost her!"

"Yes, he takes too many pains to comfort us. We would not be this solemn unless he has lost all hope or the event has forced him to it."

Leopold and Nannerl were sitting silent and stupefied, in the deepest melancholy, when Bullinger entered. Leopold handed him

336

Wolfgang's letter without saying a word, and after Bullinger read it the stout, gray-haired priest looked sad and shocked and asked, "What do you think, Leopold?"

"I think Anna Maria is dead."

Bullinger said gravely, "I fear the same thing. Wolfgang would not be so serious unless he had good reason to be."

And as the priest sought to console Leopold, saying, "You must be brave, you must be prepared for anything," Leopold was sure what was behind this and he said desolately, "I not only believe that she is dead by now, but that she was on the very day this letter was written. Isn't that so, Bullinger?" His voice was firm, but inside he was stricken with anguish.

Blood drained from the priest's florid face and the silence that answered him had a deathly stillness. Then, what he had surmised, he knew.

Bullinger put his arms around him and Nannerl and the three of them wept.

The next day Leopold finished the letter he had started to Anna Maria, addressing the rest of it to Wolfgang. He left in the congratulations on her name-day, as if that would keep her alive. But he said he knew of the letter to Bullinger, and ordered Wolfgang to write him all the details of her illness and death. He tried not to wallow in self-pity, but he told his son what a grievous loss they had suffered. Yet he could not allow anyone to outdo him in self-control and certainly not his son whom he had spent a lifetime guiding, and her sacrifice must have some worth, it was the only way he could make sense out of her death. He wrote also, *"Do not be anxious on my account, I shall bear my sorrow like a man. Remember what a loving mother you had, now you will be able to appreciate her love and care."* He ended with the advice that Wolfgang concentrate on obtaining an opera scrittura, that this was more sensible than depending on Le Gros, Noverre, or even the Duke de Guines, although he was interested in knowing what had happened with them – his son had not mentioned a word about them.

Leopold wrote Grimm, too, thanking him for his kindness to Anna Maria and Wolfgang and asked him what he thought of Wolfgang's prospects in Paris.

Yet within himself Leopold kept asking how her death could have been averted, and the idea of Anna Maria lying alone amid strangers struck him as the saddest thing of all and was very painful to bear. Suddenly he had a feeling he must get his son home before Paris destroyed him, too, even as he hoped that Grimm would send him reassuring news about Wolfgang's career.

337

Many people called on the Mozarts the following week to express their condolences. Leopold was touched by their expressions of sympathy, but he sensed that the Countess Lützow had come for other reasons, too.

Although he thought her musical taste erratic and often undependable, she was one of the most important people in Salzburg, for as Colloredo's niece she wielded great power. He received her in the Tanzmeister-Saal.

She knew the concert hall well; she had taken many music lessons there; yet she could tell that Leopold felt this was a special occasion.

After they talked about Anna Maria's wonderful cheerfulness and what a loss her death was, she asked, "What is Wolfgang going to do now?"

"What should he do, Countess? He is a great success in Paris."

"But I heard rumors. . ."

"That his new symphony has been acclaimed at Louis XVI's own concert, the Concert Spirituel," he interrupted testily, positively. "And Noverre, Marie Antoinette's favorite, commissioned ballet numbers from Wolfgang, and the Duke de Guines, confidant and adviser to both the King and Queen, believes so in Wolfgang's genius, he has become his patron and pupil."

"But you have been always such a closely knit family. It doesn't seem natural for Wolfgang to be away from his folks."

"That is what my dear wife said. And now he is all alone." Tears came to his eyes despite his effort to be calm.

"Music is in a terrible state here. Fischetti has left for good, and Lolli is dying. The court Kapelle is very shorthanded."

"I know. I have been working like three men lately."

"His Grace appreciates that. And that is why he thinks you need help."

Leopold doubted that Colloredo was really concerned but he said, "What about Michael Haydn? He is a competent musician, when he. . ."

"Does not drink. Which is most of the time. It has put him in disfavor with His Grace. And now that Brunetti has an illegitimate child that everyone knows about, his appointment as Kapellmeister would cause a scandal."

He felt this was a decoy to get him to talk about his son, and was silent.

"And we need an organist desperately since Adlgasser's death."

"So our Prince wants an organist who is also a good performer on the clavier and a conductor. And which is almost impossible to find."

"So, as you can see, Herr Mozart, we are in an awkward position."

Indeed, Leopold thought slyly, but he said, "I have not the honor of knowing anyone who could fulfill His Grace's needs."

Suddenly she found it hard to suggest what she had come to suggest.

"Moreover, I would never venture to recommend anybody to His Grace, for it would be exceedingly difficult to find one who would suit him."

"Bravo! What a pity you are not a great minister of state!"

"Don't you want me to speak candidly?" He became silent again.

"Oh, of course, Herr Mozart. That is why I want your advice."

"Your Highness flatters me."

"Not in the least. You have a knowledge of music that no one else in Salzburg has. You have been to London, Paris, to virtually every musical city in Europe. You know who is qualified and who is not."

"Who would you suggest, Countess?"

"Wolfgang has been an object of admiration wherever he has performed."

"Except in Salzburg."

"Even in Salzburg!"

"Is that why my son was dismissed?"

"He resigned, Herr Mozart."

"His Grace gave us a different impression."

"His Grace was preoccupied with other matters then. Bavaria, Austria, Prussia, the possibility of invasion. He was distressed to hear about your wife. He sends his condolences."

"Is he still angry at Wolfgang?"

"He was never really angry. Irritated perhaps, but nothing else."

"But he still prefers foreigners to good, solid German musicians."

"Not any more. Herr Mozart, if you could write your son?"

"About what, Your Highness?"

"Well, the post of cathedral organist for one thing."

"I cannot. My son would ridicule such a proposal. Why the salary alone would cause him to turn it down."

"How much would he require?"

"He expects to earn a thousand gulden this year in Paris at least."

"Adlgasser only received three hundred."

"But you want more than an organist. You want a clavier player, a conductor, and a composer, and you would be getting the best there is."

"Without question. Yet a thousand gulden? It is a great deal."

"That is why I think it is foolish to pursue this matter further. I appreciate your interest, Countess, I know that your chief concern, like mine, is for the betterment of music in Salzburg. But I must also consider my son's future, and unless there are other guarantees, such as regular leaves of absence to write operas, we are wasting each other's time."

"There is much to be taken into consideration, but perhaps some adjustments can be made."

Leopold felt like Machiavelli in the way he had led the Countess Lützow to reveal Colloredo's wishes, and he was proud of his handling of the situation. Yet as he sat down to write Wolfgang his account of the offer – for offer it was, whatever the Countess said – he knew that his son would be harder to persuade. So he stressed: "I am not writing you this with the idea of persuading you, my dear Wolfgang, to return to Salzburg, for I do not place the slightest reliance on the Archbishop's word. Yet if anything should come of this, after what I said, they must propose the most favorable conditions. Then if Paris should prove disappointing, and one must be prepared for such contingencies, you would be treated here far better than you were before."

Engrossed in this maneuver, he was distracted from the pain of Anna Maria's death and this was what she would have wanted, he assured himself.

His plan seemed even more sensible a few days later when he got a bitter letter from Wolfgang about further difficulties in Paris: "My Dearest Papa: By now you know the sad and fatal news about Mamma and I will not dwell on these dreadful circumstances any longer.

"I have been offered the post of organist at Versailles, at 2,000 livres a year, but I would have to live six months at court and the other six in Paris. Moreover, this money, which amounts to 915 gulden, which would be worth something in Germany, is nothing in Paris, money goes so quickly here, and thus it would be foolish to accept this offer. Then, everyone tells me that to enter the King's service is to be forgotten in Paris. And to be an organist only – never!

"For instance, you advise me to visit a great deal, in order to make new acquaintances, or to revive the old ones, but that is impossible. Distances are too great and the streets are too muddy to go on foot; the filth underfoot is indescribable, to take a coach or even a sedan-chair costs four or five livres, and at Versailles they are far more expensive. Then it is all in vain, for people merely pay you compliments and then it is over. They ask me to come on this or that day – I play, and they say, 'Oh! c'est un prodige, c'est inconcevable, c'est étonnant! and 'adieu!'

"And even if I were willing to endure this, there are other difficulties. At least if I were in a place where people had ears to hear, hearts to feel, and some perception and taste, I should laugh over all these things, but really, as regards music, I am living among beasts. Le Gros owes me money, Noverre never gave me a sou for my dances and altered them until they became miserable French

340

pieces, and the Duke de Guines was insulting in his dismissal of me."

"As for obtaining a scrittura for an opera, it is my dearest wish too, but for a grand opera, not an opera *buffa*. And you could rely upon me, I would strain every nerve to do honor to the name of Mozart, and I would have no fear as to the result. But no impresario will pay attention to anything here unless it is by Gluck or Piccinni. Here in Paris it is more important to give dinners to three-fourths of Paris, and I neither care to do this or can afford it. Then the old libretti that are offered me have not been adapted to modern taste, and the new are good for nothing, but worst of all is the French taste, which becomes worse daily.

"I am so sad and depressed these days, that sometimes I wish I were dead. I endure Paris only out of love for you, but I shall thank God if I leave this place with my healthy natural taste.

"And Baron Grimm, who I thought was my good friend, who gave me a room in his house after my dear mother's passing, although it was Madame d'Epinay's idea, has changed. Not only did he discourage my taking the appointment at Versailles – ever since he lent me louis d'or to pay for Mamma's illness and funeral, he is a different man. He keeps telling me what I should have done. He makes me feel that only when I follow his advice, I am doing the right thing. If it were not for Madame d'Epinay's kindness and consideration, I would not remain here."

As Leopold was trying to digest Wolfgang's distress, there was an even more pessimistic letter from Baron Grimm about his son's prospects: "My Dear Herr Mozart: You asked me about your son's chances in Paris. I hesitated to answer you, but since you insisted the facts are these.

"Your son is too trusting, too good-natured, too generous, and too little concerned with the ways that one must use to succeed. Here, to make your fortune, you must be crafty, enterprising, audacious. I wish he had half his talent and twice as much cleverness, and then I would not worry about him.

"For there are only two ways here that he can make a living. The first is to give clavier lessons, but one cannot obtain pupils without much activity and being somewhat of a charlatan, and I doubt that he is strong enough for this occupation, for it is tiring to run to the four corners of Paris and to exhaust oneself in explanations. Then this occupation does not please him, for it keeps him from composing, which is what he prefers to anything else. Your son wants to give all of himself to composing, except that in this country the great public knows nothing about music. Everything depends on the composer's name, and his is little known here. At the immediate moment the public is absurdly divided between Gluck and Piccinni, and there is no interest in anyone else. So it is almost impossible for your son to succeed as a composer when everyone is preoccupied with this rivalry. You see, mon cher maître, that in a country where so many mediocre and even dreadful musicians have made great fortunes, I very much fear that your son will not even pay his own way.

"I have given you the truth candidly, not to upset you, but so that we may decide on the best course. There is no question in my mind but that his chances in Paris are nil."

FIFTY

The suggestion that Wolfgang could return to Colloredo's service if he wanted to made him ill. Yet he knew from the tone of his father's letter, whatever Papa pretended, his father wanted him to return very much.

He replied by writing Bullinger, believing that if he convinced the priest, the latter would convince Papa. He objected to going back to Salzburg by listing a catechism of evils: a gossipy small town that looked down upon musicians, and musicians that looked down upon themselves; no theater, no opera, not one good singer on the staff of Colloredo, and the female singers the weakest of a bad lot; an orchestra that was rich in what was useless, but poor in what was necessary; a court teeming with malice and intrigue; and most importantly a ruler who was a tyrant, who preferred the worst Italian musician to the best German, who would not allow him to accept an opera scrittura, and who was personally insulting.

This letter posted, he wrote Aloysia and her father. He had been corresponding with them regularly, and again he invited them to Paris, where he was sure he could arrange private concerts for her and work for her father. He begged her to reply quickly, swearing that her letters were the only thing that brought happiness to his sorrowful heart.

Then since Papa insisted on knowing the details of Mamma's illness and death – as if Papa had to pass judgment – Wolfgang gave him a step-by-step narrative of what had happened, although he did it reluctantly, for the reliving of it caused him to weep and he could hardly go on.

Hardest of all was the sending of her belongings home as Papa had ordered. He tried to pack them neatly as she would have wished: her clothes, her ring, her watch, and the rest of her jewelry, but it was painful, and the tears in his eyes made it difficult to see clearly.

He could not be as efficient as his father, and he wished that his father did not expect him to be. Yet he kept thinking like Papa. To ease his melancholy he included in Mamma's belongings the French publication of the *Violin School*, preludes he had composed for Nannerl, and a copy of the symphony he had written for Le Gros. It was assumed that since Le Gros had bought the symphony, it was his property and that the Frenchman was the only one who had the score. But because Le Gros had paid Wolfgang only half of the fee, Wolfgang had sat up all night copying the score from memory. The French thought they would outwit him, but he would show them. He remembered his symphony note by note. And the new compositions should make Papa and Nannerl feel better — such presents always had.

His melancholy ceased only when he began to create again. Madame d'Epinay had lent him one of her rooms and her harpsichord, but he did not think she was very generous, for it was her sick room. There was not even a closet, just a bed — the harpsichord had been moved into it — and a portable medicine cabinet. Yet he sought to make the best of it as he composed. He was determined to create as Papa had advised in his last letter. "If you have lost all your pupils because of Mamma's illness and death, compose something new. Then, even if you have to sell it for less than what it is worth, it will make you better known and keep you from borrowing.

"But be sure these pieces are brief, easy, and popular. Remember, Bach wrote nothing but trifles, yet he was the most successful composer in London. What is slight can still be great, if it is written in a natural, flowing, easy style, and at the same time is soundly constructed. Such compositions are more difficult to compose than all those harmonic progressions, which most people cannot understand, or works which possess pleasing melodies, but which are difficult to perform. Did Bach lessen himself by such work? Not in the least. Sound composition, good construction, this separates the master from the mediocre, even in trifles!"

But even as Wolfgang started to compose a simple sonata that any competent performer could play, and which should please quickly, he kept thinking of Mamma, and the music became the saddest he had written. He wondered: How did one grow old? How did one die without complaint? He smiled bitterly, deciding there was no answer, yet there was a consolation in creating and expressing his emotions. He had just finished the first draft of this sonata in A minor and was playing it over for revisions when Grimm and Madame d'Epinay entered. They must have something important to discuss, he thought, to bring them puffing to the top floor.

Grimm said, "The sonata is quite loud. It woke us up."

Wolfgang realized with a start that it was midnight, that he had been playing without any awareness of the time. He apologized.

She said, "We are sorry to disturb you, but I don't feel well."

Grimm didn't look sorry but displeased. He examined the new sonata.

Wolfgang asked out of politeness. "What do you think of it, sir?"

Grimm said sarcastically, "It is so full of despair no one will buy it."

"I tried to please." He thought it was the best sonata he had written.

She said, "The Baron is concerned that it will not suit French taste."

"I will make the rest of the sonatas more popular."

Grimm remarked to Madame d'Epinay as if Wolfgang had not spoken, "Perhaps our young friend should return to the Salzburg service."

Wolfgang blurted out, "But you invited me here!"

"It was your father's idea. He left me no choice but to be agreeable. Now you have failed. It is evident, isn't it."

Wolfgang looked to Madame d'Epinay for help, but she was silent.

"What am I to write your father? He keeps asking me what are you going to do. I haven't answered him yet, but from simple politeness I must soon."

Grimm's gout must be worse, thought Wolfgang, his tone had sharpened so. Yet Madame d'Epinay was wearing her favorite red satin gown and holding her precious red Chinese fan and he wondered if he had really awakened them.

"If you don't wish to return to Salzburg, I am sure that as a German, you will be more successful in Munich and Mannheim than you have been here."

"Sir, you act as if I were seven, which was my age when you first met me."

"You are as impractical as a child."

"Because I trusted Le Gros, the Duke, Noverre. They are all Frenchmen."

"I do not see the relevance."

"The French are asses, for they can do nothing in music for themselves. Every opera here has been composed by a foreigner, Gluck, Piccinni, Bach."

"But not by Mozart."

"I am fortunate. French is a language invented by the devil. It is dreadful for music. And the French sing just as poorly. I cannot bear listening to a Frenchwoman singing Italian arias. I can overlook her singing French trash, but not when she ruins fine music. It is horrible."

"Are you finished?"

"I will thank God if I escape from Paris with my taste unspoiled."

Grimm said, "Your symphony is French."

"So much the worse for it. The audiences are cattle. I have six sonatas to compose for sale. When I am paid for these and get the rest of my money from Le Gros and the Duke, I will pay you the ten louis d'or I owe you."

"It is fifteen louis d'or. Or will be when I have to pay for your departure. You will get nothing here for your music any more. Your position is well known in Paris. No one wants your music now."

So it was the money! Wolfgang said, "I can leave at once if you wish."

"Oh, there is no rush. I simply wanted you to be aware of the realities of your position."

"Thank you, Baron. As soon as I can pay you back with the money from the sonatas, I will make other plans. I will go where I am appreciated."

The three of them bowed politely, as if they were part of a stately ritual, and bid each other a good night's sleep.

But Wolfgang did not sleep. Unable to bear the dreadful, oppressive mood that had fallen upon him, he took an air by Nicholas Dezede which he loved and wrote nine variations on it, and called it *Ah, vous dirai-je, Maman*. This set of variations was so gentle it would not awaken the most restless sleeper but was a soothing lullaby. He had no intention of selling this composition. It was for himself, no one else.

None of his six sonatas sold. Le Gros asked him to write a new second movement for his symphony, saying that would make it more popular, and he complied, but he didn't get the rest of his fee. He tried to see the Duke de Guines and could not even see the housekeeper. When Papa wrote him that Lolli had died and Colloredo had agreed to all the conditions he had requested through Bullinger, except for a few unessentials, he knew he was supposed to accept, although he still did not wish to return to Salzburg.

But the situation should be better than before, as his father said:

"Thanks to my diplomacy and perseverance I have succeeded. I am to get Lolli's salary of five hundred gulden for performing his duties as the Deputy-Kapellmeister and you will receive five hundred gulden, too, for being Konzertmeister, cathedral organist, and helping me.

"The Archbishop has agreed also that you can travel to Italy every other year to compose an opera, or wherever you desire,

Mannheim, Vienna, or Munich. He has apologized for being unable at this time to appoint you Kapellmeister, but says that you should have the post eventually.

"Everyone in Salzburg, but especially the Countess Lützow, whose influence with Colloredo has become great, are deeply pleased that you will be returning, and she acts as if it is her victory.

"But no one is more eager than your loving father and sister. I know it must have been our dearest mother's wish that we be reunited as soon as possible. Without you, I doubt I will live much longer, but once I feel you in my arms I will have the strength to go on and so will Nannerl.

"You must realize, too, that the longer you stay with Grimm, who obviously resents the cost, the more we will owe him. Thus, you must leave quickly, before we owe him more than we can ever repay. As it is, the four hundred gulden I borrowed in Salzburg to pay for your journey is now seven hundred, and you wouldn't want me to be thrown into a debtor's grave, which could be my fate, if you don't return."

Wolfgang questioned Colloredo's sudden benevolence and Papa assured him that His Grace had changed, that he was tired of being cheated by Italian musicians and now was enthusiastic in his praise of Wolfgang's ability.

"What about Karl Arco?" wrote Wolfgang. "I won't return if he has anything to say about music."

Papa replied that Wolfgang would be independent in all matters, and said there would be a post for Fräulein Aloysia in Salzburg if she was interested, although he had heard that she was being hired by Karl Theodor for the German opera in Munich at six hundred gulden a year.

The departure from Paris was different than Wolfgang expected. He planned to leave by a fast, comfortable private coach which took six days to reach Strassburg, the first major stop on the way to Salzburg.

Instead, Grimm maneuvered so that Wolfgang had to leave a week before he intended to, and while the six sonatas he had just composed were still being copied, and then Grimm placed him in a slow, uncomfortable public diligence on the excuse that it was the fastest conveyance available.

The trip to Strassburg lasted twelve disagreeable days. Furious, he realized Grimm had put him in the cheapest coach, which was also the slowest, to save money. Grimm had paid the fare to Strassburg, but while the Baron had saved his own money, Wolfgang had to pay far more for rooms, for he had to spend twice as many nights in the costly inns on the road.

He could not sleep while riding, and each day he was awakened at three in the morning, so as to get an early start because of the slow horses. Then the seats in the mail coach were as hard as stone. By the time they reached Strassburg, he was not sure he would bring his behind home intact. The only thing that had made the journey endurable was the knowledge that it was bringing him closer to Aloysia.

FIFTY-ONE

Strassburg was a new delay. Despite Wolfgang's eagerness to see Aloysia, he allowed himself to be persuaded to stay there for three weeks to give three concerts. That earned him only seven louis d'or, much less than the concerts cost him, and he felt he was playing just for his own pleasure. He pretended not to care, but he was hurt by this poor reception.

By now, more than a month after he had left Paris, Papa was writing him to come straight home, warning him that the appointment would not be open much longer, but he went instead to Mannheim. Although the Webers had moved to Munich with Karl Theodor, he was hopeful that something would turn up in Mannheim that would save him from having to return to Salzburg. He decided to propose to Aloysia, as soon as he found work in Mannheim.

Cannabich was in Munich with the court, but Madame Cannabich welcomed Wolfgang affectionately and insisted that he reside with her.

Wolfgang was convinced that Mannheim loved him as much as he loved it, and he wrote his father of many possible projects that were blossoming in this congenial atmosphere. But when none of them materialized, yet Wolfgang still delayed his return, Papa wrote: "Your many plans bewilder me. If you suggest another project to me, I shall go crazy or die of confusion. All the way to Paris you conceived a multitude of plans, and since you have left Paris you have informed me of a dozen more ways that you will make your fortune, yet now, none have come to pass, and all that is left is an increasing burden of debt.

"You must end your gay dreams and cease making a liar out of me, or you will also ruin your father and sister who have sacrificed so much for you. I have prayed often after your dear mother's unnecessary death that you would not want on your conscience the death of your father, too. But you know that if your mother had returned to Salzburg from Mannheim instead of going on to Paris with you, she would not have died."

It took Wolfgang a long time to answer his father. Then he was brief, he did not allude to the criticism, but said he was leaving for Munich to see Fräulein Aloysia and that he would be home soon after. But it had been Papa's idea that Mamma accompany him, not his. He did not feel guilty; there was nothing to atone. And while he was deeply hurt, he tried to keep his reply affectionate, but he kept thinking: Papa blames me, yet Papa says he loves me, but I do not blame him because I do love him. He prayed that they could face each other without any more reproaches but a dark shadow had fallen upon him. Yet he must present himself to Aloysia as a conqueror. That he would have hurt Mamma in any way – it was unbelievable!

He arrived in Munich on Christmas Day, and called immediately on the Webers. They were living in a house near the theater and ducal residence of the Elector, and he noticed it was a great improvement in their situation. The house was large and looked like it belonged to a wealthy burgher.

Fridolin Weber opened the door and when he saw that it was Wolfgang, instead of looking pleased as Wolfgang expected, he recoiled and blurted out, "We heard that your mother had a contagious disease."

"Nonsense. She had an inflammation of the stomach. How is Aloysia?"

"Fine. You heard about her good fortune, of course."

"Of course. I am delighted. I knew she would succeed quickly."

"Your instruction was helpful." But Weber didn't ask Wolfgang to enter.

Constanze came to the door, hoping the visitor was Herr Mozart, and seeing him standing there, said, "Father, why don't you invite him in?"

When Weber didn't move, she took Wolfgang by the hand and led him into the parlor. He saw that she had matured, but he was so absorbed in Aloysia he noticed nothing else, not even her interest in him.

Constanze was disappointed by his indifference, but she called Aloysia.

Cäcilia Weber came first, however, and only when she was sure he was without a trace of anything contagious, did she allow Aloysia to enter.

Then Wolfgang was alone with his beloved and he did not know what to say. His heart beat rapidly; he had set such high hopes on her response to him, and she stood cool and distant. This was intolerable and he said passionately, "Aloysia, Paris was so lonely without you."

"That was too bad."

"I have been living only for the day I could see you again."

"Really?"

He cried out, "I would do anything to make you happy!"

"You are serious, Herr Mozart?" She seemed interested now.

"I have never been more serious. Aloysia, dear, will you marry me?"

"What did you say?" She did look surprised.

"Marry me. Now. I have a good appointment in Salzburg, and I can obtain one for you, too, as good as you have here in Munich."

This funny little man wanted to marry her. She smiled to herself.

He leaned toward her, to embrace her and to confirm their love, and she raised her hands in repulsion and backed away from him.

"Or if you don't like Salzburg, I will get an appointment here."

"There is no place for you here. You will be flattered, but you will not be hired, as you were not hired anywhere else. With all your grand dreams."

"You are teasing me. To see if I am sincere."

"Not in the least. I think it is about time someone told you the truth."

"What about the arias I composed for you? That you were happy to sing?"

"You are a competent composer, and you understand the female voice."

"But not the female heart?"

She stared at him and thought, I never flirted with him, it was his own need, nothing else. Her mother had said be nice to Herr Mozart, as a child prodigy he had been pampered by women and he was used to it, and he could be useful, he knew many important people, but he was no longer a charming child, a sensation, a miracle of nature, but a short, frail, insignificant young man and a failure wherever he had gone. Even dressed in the Paris fashion, in a red waistcoat and black buttons he was neither attractive nor romantic, and it was no wonder that the Elector didn't want him.

Her mother interrupted them. "My daughter does not have much time, Herr Mozart. She is due soon at the Residenztheater to rehearse for the Elector, a carriage is being sent for her, and she can't keep him waiting."

He had heard rumors that she had been appointed to the Elector's musical court because she was to be his next mistress, but he hadn't believed it. Now however, he wondered. The Elector had so many mistresses one more or less wouldn't matter to him. But he said, "Your daughter is fortunate to have friends in high places. I won't keep her much longer."

"Please. It will be appreciated." Cäcilia Weber retired.

He couldn't give up. Aloysia's lovely face had a sudden little blush which could be affection despite what she had said. Again he went to embrace her and she pushed him away. He stood as paralyzed. He could never touch anyone who didn't want him. And he couldn't make a spectacle of himself. But he had to say, "What about all our letters?"

"I never encouraged you."

That was true, he realized now, but he had been blind.

"You simply took some things for granted. Because you had to."

He longed to weep, thinking he had far too sensitive a heart, it left him without defense against the calculating, but he couldn't give her the satisfaction. Instead, with a gesture of disdain, he sat down at the pianoforte and sang, "I leave without regret such a fickle woman", and walked out.

But he was broken-hearted. To ease his pain he invited Bäsle to join him in Munich and to accompany him to Salzburg. In this letter he poured out his rejected feelings, saying the most intimate things, flirting cynically and erotically. It relieved him somewhat, but it did not lessen the loss of Aloysia. The gayer he was with Bäsle, the more he missed Aloysia.

This false gaiety vanished when he stood before the house on the Hannibalplatz several weeks later. Papa's letters had softened, once Papa had become certain that Wolfgang was really returning to Salzburg, but an undercurrent of criticism had remained. He had brought Bäsle with him to ease the anticipated blows but that did not lessen his apprehension.

Then he was knocking on the door of his own home. Nothing seemed changed. He still felt that returning to Salzburg, he was committing the greatest folly in the world, but he had missed his family so. There was no answer for a minute. Wolfgang was feeling cut off, when he saw Papa and Nannerl's faces at the window. But it seemed so long before they came downstairs.

A clever person like Wolfgang shouldn't take things so seriously, thought Bäsle, but he did, even as he pretended to be frivolous with her.

Now Wolfgang and Papa were face to face. Nannerl looked startled to see Bäsle, then smiled, as if, at least, it wasn't Fräulein Weber.

Suddenly Papa was trembling uncontrollably and Wolfgang knew with a moment of great relief, that it was still as it always had been between him and Papa. They were in each other's arms then, laughing and crying, surrendering to happiness and sadness, but somehow, never saying a word, as if that would profane this reconciliation.

PART SEVEN

===

The Prodigal Returns

FIFTY-TWO

Countess Lützow was pleased with Wolfgang's company and told him that since his return from Paris he had become the best dancer in Salzburg, and he was no longer flattered. Her wish to have him as a partner, even at the court balls, was considered a great honor, but now she seemed as old as Madame d'Epinay, but without the latter's wit and worldliness.

Countess Lodron wanted her daughters to resume studying the pianoforte with Wolfgang, and he did not feel it was the favor that she did. He longed to refuse, but he could not. A request from the Countess Lodron, as from the Countess Lützow, was the same as a command. And, as Papa said, her money would lessen his debts. But teaching her daughters was a chore.

And while his official title was first Konzertmeister and court organist, he felt no better than a valet de chambre to Colloredo. At their first meeting the Archbishop had been polite and had expressed his regrets over Frau Mozart's sad passing, but gradually their relationship became as it had been. Wolfgang was expected to play the organ every Sunday in the cathedral and wherever else Colloredo wished. He had to teach all the keyboard instruments to any member of Colloredo's musical establishment who needed such instruction. He also had to rehearse and conduct the Kapelle, but he refused to play the violin as he had in the past.

What saved his sanity was his compositions. At the end of eighteen months he could not keep track of all of them, but that didn't worry him, for his father had recorded what he had composed. Wolfgang was surprised however, by the amount of work he had done as Papa listed: "Three symphonies, one serenade, one divertimento, one pianoforte concerto for four hands, a *sinfonia concertante* for violin and viola, but no sonatas for the pianoforte or for the violin."

"I wrote six of each while I was away."

"They were so fine, you should have written more."

"Colloredo prefers religious music."

"You haven't been lazy there." Papa didn't think that Wolfgang had been in his profane music either, but his son had to be goaded or he would procrastinate. "Your sacred music has been plentiful, hymns, offertories, church sonatas, a Missa solemnis, and two splendid Masses and Vespers."

"Yet Colloredo makes me feel that all this work is minor compared to his own importance, particularly to the services he conducts."

"He cannot accept you as an equal. It is against his instincts."

"Some of the music I have composed here is as good as any I have done."

"And you have been paid for it."

"But I wrote the concerto in E Flat for Nannerl and me, and Lodron acted as if it were for her. She insisted on having her daughters give it the first public performance and they could not play it as one, as I intended. They ruined my lovely second movement."

"Lodron helped you get your post back. It is the least she expected."

"And the accompaniment! I wrote it for an orchestra with the Mannheim sound, majestic and sonorous, and our musicians went in all directions."

"They will play better when you and Nannerl are at the pianofortes."

"They will never play better. My *sinfonia concertante*, which you said had great depth and maturity, which you liked so much, was butchered, and it was played by the finest soloists in Salzburg, Brunetti and Haydn. I know Brunetti's playing has become erratic with age, but Haydn should know better. In the past he used to stay sober when he played music he liked. Is he so disgusted with Salzburg he can't even play the viola any more?"

"When you are in Munich, you will have your friends play it properly."

"But Colloredo said that the *sinfonia concertante*, possibly the finest music I have written, was too heavy and long. Yet he declared that my divertimento in D, which should please the simplest mind, was too sweet."

"You know his taste."

"But I have to satisfy it! My Coronation Mass is the best mass I have written, for a voice like Manzuoli's, and they give me an ass braying."

"You must have it performed in Vienna."

"A hundred years from now? When it won't make any difference to me."

"It would make a difference," Papa said solemnly.

"By that time who knows what the taste will be. I think, of all the pieces I have composed this last year and a half, I like best my *Vesperae solemnes de confessore,* despite its pompous title, and His Highness informed your humble servant that it was too dramatic, too operatic, as if that were a mortal sin and I should be sent to purgatory for committing it."

"Wolfgang, he wasn't that critical! You exaggerate!"

"Count Arco, who I had been told would not interfere in music if I returned, took special pains to inform me that His Grace said I wrote the soprano solo for an operatic prima donna, not for a church service."

"Didn't you?" Didn't you write it for an Aloysia Weber, Papa wanted to say, but didn't, deciding that it was better to leave that unsaid.

"I wrote it for the best kind of human voice," Wolfgang said, almost defiantly, "as I should write all my vocal compositions."

"And it is enchanting. But perhaps too personal for Colloredo."

"Too beautiful for our asses' ears. Have you heard anything further from Munich about the opera scrittura?"

"News should be forthcoming any day."

"I swear, Papa, I don't know how much longer I can stand Salzburg."

"I have stood it for over forty years and I am still sane."

But I am different, Wolfgang said to himself. Papa likes to teach, but I don't. Papa is a natural teacher, and I have no patience for it. Papa has given up composing, and I feel I am just starting. There is so much to say, the more I study music the more I hear. If I could have only ten years of peace and contentment, I could compose so much. Particularly for the stage. Papa is correct in implying that I wrote the soprano solo in the Vespers for an operatic prima donna but if I admit that, Papa will scold me for taking liberties with Colloredo's music. So I called it a *Laudate Dominum,* but it does not lessen my love for that aria, for aria it is, whatever it is styled. I must obtain a good scrittura soon, or I will go mad. Just as I am learning how to write for the human voice, I have to contend with these inhuman Salzburgian vocal chords. I have tried to be concerned about our debts and I am unhappy that we still owe so much, but it is far more difficult to live without fine music. Almost everything musical in Salzburg is involved with death.

One Sunday after the services in the cathedral Wolfgang, unable to bear Colloredo being congratulated when it had been his music that had excelled, excused himself from the throng that gathered around the Archbishop and strode over to nearby St. Peter's where Mamma had wanted to be buried. It was the oldest church in Salzburg, and its graveyard was against and under the Monschberg. But there was no privacy in the cemetery, there were so many mourners, so he climbed up the winding stone passage which led to the catacombs in the rocks of the Monchsberg. Here the first Christians in Salzburg, many of them martyred, had been buried and it was considered the holiest sanctuary there.

It was a warm, sunny September afternoon in 1780, and while over two years had passed since Mamma's death he missed her very much suddenly. He yearned to say a benediction for her here, which she would have liked, but the atmosphere had become oppressive. The stone corridor, which never felt the sun, was icy cold and the stairs were rough, unhewn, and all he could hear was the ghostly echo of his own footsteps. He had to grab the slits in the walls to keep from falling as he sought to climb upwards. Walking had become difficult, exhausting, and terrifying.

He was grateful when he reached a small stone balcony which was in the open air. Suddenly to be in the sun, in the air and the light was a great blessing. He stared at the mountains that curved around Salzburg, and even more than before, they made him feel like a prisoner. Perched out on the cliff of the Monchsberg, he was almost as high as the twin spires of the cathedral, and all he could think of was the mountain walls that were always there, that were always closing in, that were always about to fall on his head at any moment, yet there were houses under these cliffs and they had been there for hundreds of years. And above him and ahead of him was the Fortress Hohensalzburg, ever dominating the town.

As he started toward the ground, many yards away, he heard footsteps coming from behind him. He called, "Who is it?" But there was no reply.

Yet the footsteps continued and sounded far heavier than normal ones. He wondered if the devil coming after a man sounded like this, or if there was a devil. If there was, this was certainly the kind of place to find him in. At ground level the footsteps ceased, but the chill in his bones added to his hatred of cemeteries and spurred his desire to flee Salzburg.

A few minutes later, walking on the pavement of a very narrow street by a back way to the cathedral to avoid meeting anyone – he had left a score in the organ loft and he wanted to retrieve it before it was lost – he saw Karl Arco approaching. The pavement was just wide enough for one person, he could put out his hands and touch the opposite walls. He was struck with a single thought: Which one of them would have to go into the street?

He compromised. At a doorway which extended in, Wolfgang stepped within it as if he were looking for this address and was about to enter.

The chief steward continued to walk straight ahead without getting off the pavement, while Wolfgang, wedged into the doorway, felt ashamed.

And afterwards he had a dreadful feeling of humiliation.

FIFTY-THREE

The scrittura from the Elector of Bavaria to compose an Italian grand opera for the Munich carnival of January, 1781, was like a trumpet call from the Lord. Colloredo did not dare veto this commission, for Karl Theodor was too powerful a neighbor to risk offending, and so Wolfgang was allowed six weeks' leave of absence to complete this assignment.

He was elated. He assured Papa, "This opera will bring glory to us."

"You will have many problems," Papa warned.

"But Cannabich's orchestra is the best there is. I am sure he will hire singers to match it. I can probably thank him for getting the opera."

"He will use the singers the Elector prefers. Who knows what motives will be involved. Economy. Friendship. Politics. You must be wary."

"After my experiences? I will be!" But he was still happy, seeing this as the great opportunity to be free of Salzburg, declaring, "I am determined that *Idomeneo* will achieve such approval that many rulers will clamor for my services. I intend to make it heroic and powerful."

Karl Theodor, since he was using Colloredo's composer, as a diplomatic gesture had chosen a libretto by the latter's court chaplain, Giambattista Varesco. *Idomeneo* was an ancient Trojan legend which the poet had taken from several previous plays on the subject. And Wolfgang doubted that the court chaplain had improved on it. Much of Varesco's writing was stilted and declamatory. Yet the story, with revisions, could be exciting. The drama had possibilities for noble and eloquent music that no other subject had provided so far. The next few days, as the tone of the score evolved, Wolfgang wrote out the following, which he considered playable:

"Idomeneo, King of Crete, after the conquest of Troy, sends home the captive princess, Ilia, the daughter of Priam. Then he follows in

360

another ship. He is within sight of Crete when a thunderous storm at sea threatens him with shipwreck. The storm is so purposeful he believes it is caused by Neptune himself. To appease the sea god's wrath, Idomeneo promises to sacrifice the first living creature he meets on shore. The storm ceases and Idomeneo realizes that he is a hostage to the sea god.

"The first life Idomeneo meets ashore is his son, Idamante, who has come to welcome him home. The King, unable to face the consequences of his vow, decides to send his son away. On the advice of his confidant, Arbace, the King arranges for Idamante to escort Electra, Queen of Argos, back to her native land. This had another advantage, for while Idamante is pledged to wed Electra, his son and Ilia have fallen in love.

"Neptune is infuriated by Idomeneo's trick. At the moment of the son's departure he sends a new storm to halt Idamante's ship and a sea monster to lay waste to Crete. Idamante cannot stop the storm, which keeps him on shore, but he does slay the monster. Then Neptune's High Priest reveals Idomeneo's promise. Idamante accepts his father's obligation, but as he prepares to be sacrificed Ilia offers herself in his place. This appeases Neptune, and through a subterranean voice he commands Idomeneo to abdicate in favor of Idamante and to permit the lovers to wed. This is done, although the spurned Electra is furious, but she cannot halt them."

By the time Wolfgang prepared to leave for Munich he had composed some music, but relations with Varesco were difficult. Yet to use the libretto as it stood was to be crippled. He said to Papa, "I have to tell the court chaplain what has to be altered before his stupidities ruin my score."

"Wait until you are in Munich. Then it will be impossible for Varesco to prevent your corrections."

Wolfgang arrived in Munich a week early. He was eager to start the production of *Idomeneo*, and after he paid his respects to Karl Theodor, who was cordial, he met with Cannabich, who as the Elector's Kapellmeister, had chosen the singers and would direct the production.

Cannabich announced, "Idomeneo will be sung by Raaff."

"Isn't he too old? Oh, I love him dearly. He was devoted to my mother in Paris, he couldn't have been a better friend, but he is sixty-six."

"He is Idomeneo's age." Cannabich surveyed the stage where Raaff was to sing. "And he is the best German singer of Italian opera we have. He is famous in both countries. He will add prestige to your music."

"And he is the Elector's favorite."

"I wouldn't say that to them. They would be offended."

"Can the old man really hold up for such an arduous role?"

"If you don't make his arias too long, or too difficult."

"Then he is such a poor actor. He performs like a statue."

"He still sings skillfully, when the music is not too demanding. And you would not have obtained this opera if he hadn't used his influence."

"I'm sure it was you whose recommendation mattered the most."

"Oh, I suggested you, too, but it was Raaff who was the most eloquent."

"It isn't that I don't want the old man, but I feel that my whole future depends on *Idomeneo*, and my father feels the same way."

"I wouldn't worry. I'm sure you can write music he can sing."

I can write music that anybody can sing, thought Wolfgang, but that was not why he was composing this opera. Then he remembered what *he had to ask* Cannabich. Ever since the scrittura had been signed, he had imagined being approached by Aloysia, and her plea that she be given a role in *his* opera. And just when she expected to be refused, he would be generous and say yes. She would be so surprised and so much in his debt, who knew what still might happen. He kept telling himself that he was no longer in love with her, but he could not be indifferent to her. It would be a great joke – his becoming her patron. It had become one of his cherished dreams.

While he had been reflecting Raaff and Wendling had entered the theater.

Cannabich said, "Raaff, Wolfgang is delighted that you are Idomeneo."

Wolfgang cried, "I am honored!"

Raaff's stern features lightened and he asked, "I am not too old?"

Wolfgang shrugged and said, "You are mature, like Idomeneo."

"The boy is becoming a diplomat," Wendling laughed. "He will go far."

Wolfgang said, "Herr Kapellmeister, I would appreciate one favor."

"If it is possible." Cannabich did not look pleased.

"I want to recommend a singer for the role of Ilia who has great merit . . ."

Wendling interrupted, "She is no longer in Munich. The Webers moved to Vienna when she was engaged for the German opera there."

Raaff said, "I would have given her lessons, but she preferred Vogler."

Wendling said, "And Fridolin died a month after they reached Vienna."

Wolfgang said sadly, "He was a nice man. I'm sorry to hear such news."

Wendling said, "Too nice for his wife. Cäcilia Weber is a vulture.

But her daughter is her equal. The moment it looked as if Aloysia would have to support her family, she married and moved out."

Wolfgang was stunned.

"She married Joseph Lange, court actor and painter," said Wendling.

Had he been mad? Had she been an illusion? Papa had chided him for having "gay dreams" about Aloysia, but if he had had gay, sweet dreams about her it had been only to make his life endurable. Even now Papa felt he did not realize the tragedy of Mamma's death, but had Papa ever heard anything sadder than the second movement of his *sinfonia Concertante*!

Wendling said, "Lange is a widower, with two children. But he is employed by the German opera and he may be responsible for her post there."

"Is he a good actor?"

"He is a better painter. But you are fortunate to be free of her. Anyone who married her would become a cuckold, and of course, if she were discovered, she would simply say, 'Basta, accidents happen.' "

"Was she the Elector's mistress, Wendling?"

"It's time we talked about something else," said Raaff.

"But was she?" As if in the knowing it would be better, but how?

"Who knows," said Cannabich.

"Anyway," said Wendling, "whatever we told you, assuming we knew, which we don't, you would think what you want to think. You are well out of the Weber family. Now, I hear, her mother is suing Lange, saying that in return for marrying her daughter, he promised to help the family."

Cannabich said, "Dorothea, Wendling's wife, is singing Ilia. And her sister-in-law, Elizabeth, is singing Electra. Do you mind?"

"They sing very well. I wrote several arias for Dorothea."

"I promise you," said Wendling, "they will do whatever you want."

But it was Raaff who mattered, thought Wolfgang, and the elderly tenor was making no promises. He asked, "Who is the castrato?"

Cannabich, who seldom showed emotion, frowned. "Signor Del Prato. I am sorry to say that he has had no stage experience."

"Then how could you have cast him?" Wolfgang blurted out.

"He is the Elector's castrato. We have to use him."

Raaff said, "Don't be downcast, Wolfgang. Del Prato is young, your age, and he will be an attractive Idamante. And I will help him with his vocal production and stage technique. The voice itself is not bad."

No wonder the tenor had been so kind, Wolfgang thought sarcastically when rehearsals began, the castrato's faults made Raaff's less obvious.

There was only one remedy, as Papa had said, his music must make up for their deficiencies. The women were fine and gave him very little

363

to alter, but he was constantly revising to suit the limitations of Raaff and Del Prato. And the libretto remained a problem. It had scenes that were still unplayable, yet when he asked Varesco, through Papa in Salzburg, to revise them, the court chaplain said that Mozart was spoiling his masterpiece and refused. Wolfgang was forced to make the changes himself, for Cannabich, determined to avoid controversy, left everything in his hands.

Then Raaff complained that his arias were too difficult, when it was Raaff's voice that could no longer sustain notes of any length. His music had to be rewritten to allow him to show off his low register.

Del Prato was so awkward on stage that Wolfgang had to teach him his role as if he were a child. The castrato didn't know how to act; his high notes were trying. Yet actually, reflected Wolfgang, Raaff was right, the voice itself was not bad, but the castrato had no feeling, no shading, no method at all.

After several weeks of rehearsing the singers the situation grew worse. Varesco threatened to sue Wolfgang if he made any more changes without his consent; Raaff was insistent that his arias must be gentle and pleasing, although the role of Idomeneo was dramatic, not lyrical; while Del Prato, who was supposed to be romantic, was so girlish it was pathetic.

And there was a new anxiety. Maria Theresa was dying and the company was afraid that her death would halt the opera. Papa sent Wolfgang his black mourning suit, and begged him not to be dejected if her death cancelled *Idomeneo*, at least there would be one benefit, her son and successor, Joseph II, would be more musical and would offer more opportunities.

Maria Theresa's death brought a day of mourning in Munich, but while the Archbishop closed all entertainments in Salzburg for three months in honor of her reign, the Elector insisted that *Idomeneo* must go on.

At last, Wolfgang thought wryly, people would stop thinking of him as the child who had sat on her lap. It was said she had been a benevolent monarch but he wondered: the Poles didn't think so, or the Bavarians. She had been considered musical, but while she had praised him as a child she had given him nothing as an adult and showed no taste for his music.

What upset him was the knowledge that his leave of absence was due to expire soon. He could not return to Salzburg, not yet, and he wrote this to Papa who replied, "Don't worry. Just say nothing, do nothing, and if anyone raises the question here, I will say, that, as we understood it, you were given six weeks' leave to stay in Munich after completing the composing, for no one in their right mind could expect an opera of this magnitude to be composed, copied, and rehearsed and performed in six weeks."

Wolfgang was not certain he could compose at all. The constant arguments exhausted him. He could not keep up with the incessant revisions. They were destroying his music, not enhancing it. A month after rehearsals had begun he was still composing in his head, but now he could not write it down. It was futile. Whatever he wrote, someone wanted it altered. Many of the arias were unfinished because of the continual adjustments to the singers' demands, yet Cannabich told the company that Karl Theodor would be attending a rehearsal soon and that they must be superb; a poor rehearsal could still cause cancellation of the opera – and that the Elector would judge by the arias of Raaff, his favorite.

Later that evening Wolfgang sat by his candles and music paper but there was nothing in his mind but confusion and distress. Even in the worst circumstances he could usually compose, but tonight it was as if he were sick and the vessel that held his life was close to breaking. He had composed so much he had been told that he was facile, prolific, as if that were a sin; they should know how hard he worked. Music was his liberation and the revisions had become a dreadful bondage. He wanted so much to be free, not under the compulsion to satisfy the common taste. It was intolerable to be a prisoner of the deaf, the unhearing, the second-rate. Write to please? Please who? Raaff? Del Prato? Cannabich? Karl Theodor? Himself? He was meditating this when Raaff entered.

He was startled. They had had a violent argument just a few hours ago when the tenor had refused to sing his part in a quartet that Wolfgang considered the musical peak of *Idomeneo*. Did Raaff expect an apology? Yet sometimes he could love the old man for his dignity and style.

Raaff said, "I hope I haven't disturbed you, Mozart."

Wolfgang said ironically, "Does it matter?"

"We need your music."

"I thought the opera needed only singers."

Raaff's craggy face unbent into a small smile and he said, "You are sensitive, like all composers. Are you still thinking of our quarrel?"

"Aren't you, Herr Raaff?"

"If I remembered every quarrel I have had during the rehearsal of an opera, my memory would have room for nothing else."

"So to what do I owe this honor?"

"The aria you wrote where I meet Idamante for the first time."

"What is wrong with that?" He had written it lyrically as Raaff had wished and because that fitted. "Is it too high?"

"No. It is written with heart. As if you knew just how a father feels seeing his beloved son, whom he has not expected to see again, face to face."

Wolfgang, puzzled rather than flattered, asked, "Then why are you here?"

"We can't allow *Idomeneo* to be cancelled because of a few differences of opinion. I love this aria so much I sing it to myself constantly."

"Yet you are always demanding changes."

"I am used to altering my parts to suit my voice. But this aria should stay as it is composed. I can't find a note that does not fit my voice."

"What about the quartet?"

"You must realize it is a different kind of music that I usually sing."

"Is that why you came?"

"Is that why you didn't want me? Oh, I know."

"I never said I didn't want you."

"But that I was too old, which is the same thing. You couldn't expect me to be indulgent after that. But write music like this, and I will sing it."

"If it suits the opera."

"And not my voice?"

Wolfgang said quietly and simply, "Just as the words must be servant to the music, the libretto to the score, so the singer must be, also. Otherwise, the opera has no life and would be better in a museum."

"That is why it would be a disaster if you did not complete *Idomeneo*."

"The world would go on," said Wolfgang. But he was not sure he would.

"It goes beyond that." Raaff's voice had an intensity Wolfgang had never heard before. "I have sung the music of every opera composer of our time, but never have I met music of such beauty and grandeur. I wish I could have performed your opera twenty, thirty years ago, but now I have to do with what I have. And you, too, Mozart, must be content for the moment. It is the penalty of being both too young and too old."

For a moment Wolfgang thought Raaff was going to swear a Blutbruderschaft, the pledge of the German knights who made a small wound in their arms and rubbed each other's blood into the wound. Then suddenly, Raaff was the stern old warrior of the operatic wars who had revealed too much.

But at the door Raaff did ask, "You will be at rehearsal tomorrow?"

"Didn't you expect me?"

"You've written nothing for some time now."

"I have taken great pains to serve you well in your arias, but as far as the trios and quartets are concerned, the composer must have a free hand."

Raaff bowed formally and said, "I will listen to you, if you listen to me."

366

Within a week Wolfgang had composed as much as he had in the previous month. And as his authority grew, for now he had the support of Raaff, the most powerful member of the company, so did his genius for invention, and he cut for brevity and credibility without bothering to consult Varesco.

By the time Karl Theodor heard a rehearsal – which had been put off by Cannabich, Wolfgang realized, until *Idomeneo* was fit to be heard – even Del Prato was singing believably and Raaff had moments of genuine quality and the orchestra, which had the best music, performed superbly.

The Elector, who had been listening incognito in a chamber next to the rehearsal hall, although everyone in the company had been warned to do their best, entered after the first act and shouted, "Bravo!" He nodded approval and said he was not sure he could remain much longer, but he wanted to hear the thunderstorm at the start of Act III, and Raaff's aria to his son.

They pleased him very much. He ordered the rehearsal halted and indicated that Wolfgang could approach him and kiss his hand.

Then Karl Theodor said, "Herr Mozart, the opera is charming and cannot fail to do you honor. It is eloquent, noble music. Who would ever believe that such great things could be hidden in so small a head."

The Residenztheater, with its elaborate orchestra and galleries, was as fine an opera house as Leopold had ever seen. Yet while Nannerl marveled at the rococo magnificence of the interior, he was worried about the opera.

Then as the melodic strains of the overture began he sat in mute wonder. The music was stirring and grand as his son had promised. Wolfgang was using the resources of the brilliant orchestra to the fullest. The male singers could be better, particularly Del Prato and Raaff, but Raaff's low tones were still pleasing and most of his music was within his reach.

At the end the applause was tremendous. Karl Theodor congratulated the company and said to Wolfgang, "I knew everything would go well. Raaff was right to recommend you. Your music suited his voice beautifully. We must have several more performances in his honor."

Six more performances were arranged by Cannabich because of Karl Theodor's suggestion, but when Raaff's voice gave out after the second they were reduced to three and the last became a farewell concert by the tenor.

What mattered the most to Wolfgang was what Papa said. He commented, "Your arias for the women were the best in the opera."

"They had the best voices."

"Electra's arias, in particular, were beautiful yet dramatic."

"I could write for her as I wanted to. Elizabeth and Dorothea Wendling had voices I could trust."

FIFTY-FOUR

======

The Munich visit came to a sudden end when the Archbishop discovered that his court organist had extended his six weeks' leave of
absence to four months, without his permission. He ordered his musician to report to him at once in Vienna, where he had gone with his
court to see his ill father, Prince Rudolf Colloredo, an Imperial Vice-
Chancellor.

Wolfgang obeyed willingly, although he disliked the tone of the summons. He had lingered in Munich, finding one excuse after another to
avoid going back to Salzburg. He had been happy in the friendship of
the Wendlings, Cannabichs, and Raaff, who now that they had survived *Idomeneo*, were better friends than ever. But he had been disappointed that Karl Theodor, despite his praise of the opera, had not
asked him to join his musical court.

He arrived at Vienna on March 16, 1781, after traveling from
Munich as fast as he could, and he paused at the outskirts of the city
to absorb it whole. He stood on a hill of the Wienerwald and as he saw
St. Stephen's and the Karlskirche, he felt he was home. He told himself that he was more Viennese than Salzburgian; that nativity was an
emotion, a belonging, not a birthplace. The appearance of the city
filled him with affection. He remembered his initial view of Vienna
and how he had fallen in love with it at first sight, and now he loved
it more than ever.

Hurriedly, as if to make up for all the years lost and to recapture
what he had loved, he had his coachman leave him off outside the
Hofburg.

Then he strode down the crowded Kohlmarkt. It was a mild, clear
day, and there were many aristocrats in carriages. At the foot of the
Kohlmarkt he turned into the Graben, which was even busier, and now
he saw many burghers and artisans. He halted in the square of St.

Stephen's to admire the tall, single Gothic spire, and then started toward the Singerstrasse, where Colloredo had ordered him to appear. Now his steps slackened, as if, once he reached the Archbishop's presence, the idyll was over.

Seven Singerstrasse, which was near St. Stephen's, had a huge military cross on the front door and above it the Imperial Crown, with a pair of Hapsburg lions and a cross at the peak of the Crown that looked as much like crossed swords as a cross could. He realized, with a start of recognition, that this was the House of the Teutonic Knights and that Colloredo was staying here because his uncle, Count Karl Colloredo, was Commander of the Austrian district of the Order.

He asked to see the Archbishop, since his orders had been to report to him at once, but he was ushered in to Karl Arco, who said that His Grace was busy but that Mozart would be seen soon. But Arco did not move to notify the Archbishop until Wolfgang asked him to, and then did so reluctantly.

It was several hours before Wolfgang was admitted to the Archbishop's presence. Colloredo, who had been writing letters, did not greet him but asked coldly, "What do you want, Mozart?"

"You requested my appearance, sir?"

"Oh, yes." Colloredo didn't dismiss Arco or the two valets who were attending him as Wolfgang felt he should. "You overstayed your leave."

"Sir, it took six weeks alone to compose the opera, and almost six weeks more to rehearse and produce it."

"You were granted six weeks' leave, no more, no less."

"Your Grace, what about your agreement that I could travel when I had a scrittura to compose an opera?"

"Agreement? I do not make bargains with my servants."

"It was specified by Countess Lützow."

"The Countess speaks only for herself. Count Arco tells me that you are earning more than any other organist ever has, five hundred gulden."

"Four hundred and fifty gulden, sir."

"More than you deserve, with all your absences."

"One absence, Your Grace."

"It amounts to more when you are away so long. I am giving a concert for the Russian Ambassador tomorrow, and if I hadn't ordered you to appear, you would still be in Munich, playing for your own pleasure."

"I am to play for Prince Dmitri Galitsin, sir?"

"Why, Mozart?" Colloredo was surprised by his servant's interest.

"He is a friend of mine."

"I can imagine! Brunetti will tell you of the program that has been arranged, and the chief steward will assign you to your quarters."

Wolfgang wanted to reply, although the Archbishop had dismissed him, but Arco took him by the arm and led him outside, whispering,

"He is angry enough at you. One more affront and he won't allow you to perform."

Wolfgang expected to live in a room of his own choice, away from the confining atmosphere of the Deutsches Ordenshaus, but Arco said he could not so long as he was in the service of the Archbishop. He was forced to reside in a tiny room that was dark, musty, and cold, and at the table the chief steward placed Wolfgang with the valets, cooks, confectioner, and Brunetti, and when he was ordered to sit below the valets, who were at the head of the table, he realized this was punishment.

Now, he thought, he really was in Salzburg. He was quite offended.

During dinner there was much silly, coarse joking, and he didn't say a word. But when talk turned to the illness of the Archbishop's father, he asked, "Brunetti, what is wrong with the Vice-Chancellor?"

"The old man has bowel cramps."

"You're jesting. That's a child's complaint."

"Not at all. These grand lords eat too much, you know that." Brunetti felt safe with Mozart, who disliked Colloredo too much to repeat anything.

"Is that why the Archbishop is so grouchy?"

"He has bowel troubles, too. His diarrhea is worse. Yet they feed us this slop."

"What about the music for Prince Galitsin? What is to be played?"

"We have a chamber orchestra. Bonno, the Emperor's Kapellmeister, is conducting, in honor of the Russian Ambassador. But my piece hasn't been decided on. It is up to me. What do you suggest, Signor Maestro?"

Wolfgang knew that Brunetti was being sarcastic, but this could be a great opportunity nonetheless. "Who else is attending?"

"Count Pálffy, Countess Thun, Prince Cobenzl, a lot of mucky-mucks."

And old friends and supporters. "We could perform my *Sinfonia Concertante* in E Flat, the one you and Haydn played in Salzburg."

"The somber one! And Colloredo didn't like it!"

"The violin solo will show off your talents. It should bring you many gulden. Colloredo won't give you any, you know that."

"That's true," sighed Brunetti. "But who will play the viola?"

"I will."

"You can't. You haven't played it for years."

"I will manage. At least, I won't be drunk like Michael Haydn."

Nor be as good as I am, Brunetti thought smugly. By comparison, I will be another Tartini or Nardini. "Perhaps, it is possible."

Vanity, it almost always worked. "But I do have one favor to ask."

"What is it?"

"Play the music as it was written."

"I always do."

"But a little more than usual. Please?"

Brunetti shrugged. It did not cost him anything to promise. As Wolfgang stood up to leave, he said, "Meet me here tomorrow evening at seven and we will go together to Prince Galitsin's."

"Why?" Wolfgang said irritably. "I know where it is."

"Angerbauer, the Archbishop's chief valet, has to let us in."

I will let myself in, thought Wolfgang, but he nodded to avoid arguing.

The following evening Wolfgang went to Prince Galitsin's alone, and as he reached the top of the stairs, there stood Angerbauer, ready to tell the Ambassador's footman to conduct him in. But Wolfgang ignored the valet and the footman and went straight through the apartments to the music room and directly to Prince Dmitri and paid his respects to him, and then remained standing and conversing. The Russian Ambassador was pleased to see him again and said, "We are honored that you will be performing, Signor Cavaliere. Is it one of your new compositions?"

"New in Vienna, Your Excellency. I composed it in Salzburg."

Count Pálffy and Countess Thun joined them and greeted Wolfgang warmly.

She was a lovely, charming woman, he thought, as she said, "Prince Galitsin, we are fortunate that Herr Mozart has come to Vienna at last."

Count Pálffy, however, was indignant that Archbishop Colloredo had not told him that Wolfgang Amadeus Mozart was in Vienna. He grumbled, "He sends me Brunetti, his second-rate violinist, to perform at one of my musicals, when you are here. Is he trying to keep you just for himself?"

"I just arrived."

"So I heard. From Munich and your triumph with *Idomeneo*. There is much talk about your opera in Vienna. I must introduce you to Gottlieb Stephanie, who has a libretto that needs a good score."

"Is he a good librettist, sir?" He wanted no more amateurs like Varesco.

"Herr Mozart, he is Inspector of the German Opera in Vienna!"

Giuseppe Bonno, the Emperor's elderly Kapellmeister and an old friend, conducted the *Sinfonia Concertante* in E Flat as Wolfgang had composed it, as a symphony with two solo instruments, violin and viola, and led his chamber orchestra with taste and skill.

Wolfgang had not admitted to anyone, not even to Papa or to himself, for that would have been too painful, that many of his personal feelings had been woven into this work, but now he realized how large a portion of his own emotion had gone into this composition. He had written the opening movement *Allegro maestoso* so that it would be majestic and dignified as well as lively. And suddenly he was hearing it performed for the first time as he had written it, and he was greatly moved. As the long orchestral introduction was played with symphonic eloquence, yet always sang, he realized that he had been deeply stricken by Mamma's death, that part of him would never get over it, yet life had to be balanced, as were the two soloists and the orchestra. They said he was a young man, but sometimes he felt like such an old composer. He could weep from all that had happened to him the past few years. But music must never be maudlin. That was such poor taste.

He listened intently as he waited for the solo passages to begin, and he was pleased that his music was always in command in spite of the fierce intensity underlying the score. Who said he was only a *galant* composer; he would match the strength of this music against anyone. Then he smiled to himself as Bonno continued to conduct impeccably. There were two times when he truly heard his compositions: when he created them and when they were played correctly. As the first movement approached the entrance of the soloists he thought with a satisfaction that was not to be measured, that in these passages at least, he had achieved what he had imagined. By the time the solo instruments entered he knew this was a performance of which he could be proud. Brunetti, stimulated by Bonno's integrated accompaniment, played with a skill and clarity the violinist had not shown for years, while the viola replied as if they were having an intimate and loving conversation.

The second movement was so personal Wolfgang did not look at anyone as he played. He had placed the *Andante* in C Minor to express his sorrow. The sadness of the strings was almost too much to endure, yet when the music was most solemn it still sang. He had never heard Brunetti perform better, and he was gratified with his own playing. Everything was secondary to the eloquence of the elegiac main theme. There were tears in his eyes although he did not cry. No one must know what this movement meant to him. It was enough that he had said this much. But some of those who had suffered would understand.

The third movement was more like the music that was expected of him. It flowed spiritedly and gracefully, a rondo to be played *presto*, with all the instruments having their moments as virtuosi. Yet the solidity remained under the musical sheen. With all the detail, there was not any neglect of the main theme. And each instrument was part of the whole.

The Countess Thun marveled. The Mozart she was hearing was a far different Mozart than she had heard years ago. The *Sinfonia Concertante* in E Flat was a revelation and a surprise, profound and often mournful. The second movement made her want to weep although she seldom cried. It was as if Wolfgang had brought to this music an awareness of the essential tragedy of existence, and a fatalism she had not heard before. Deep emotion had gone into this. She saw that Pálffy was stirred too, as were several of the others, but Colloredo looked bored.

She felt he would have left during the second movement if Prince Dmitri had not been so interested. An enthusiastic circle gathered about Wolfgang to congratulate him on the beauty of the music and the performances. Everyone of importance, reflected the Countess, but the Colloredos who sat in a tiny knot, surrounded by their servants.

She joined the group as an excited Brunetti, overwhelmed by the praise his own performance was receiving, exclaimed, "Mozart, for someone who doesn't like the violin, you certainly wrote superb music for it." Then realizing what he had said, he added, "Especially the way I played it."

"Beautifully," said Wolfgang, "with a noble, unforced tone."

"You didn't think I had it in me, did you?"

"I wrote several violin concertos for you. Remember, Brunetti?"

"That was years ago. You know," he cried, as if making a marvelous discovery, "this *sinfonia concertante* is really another violin concerto."

"And symphony," said Bonno. "Its themes were truly symphonic."

"Because you conducted them with clarity, proportion, and feeling."

"Wolfgang, I conducted them as you composed them. It was the least I could do for such grand, masterly music."

Count Pálffy said, "Signor Mozart, you must play for me."

"I would be honored, sir, but I cannot without His Grace's permission."

"He won't refuse me," declared Count Pálffy. "I must introduce you to Stephanie. He can get his work done. He is a producer as well as an Inspector of our German opera, and he is a favorite of the Emperor's."

"Sir, do you think I could play for the Emperor?"

"It could be arranged," said the Countess Thun. "I will be having a musical evening at my house which he has promised to attend."

"I wouldn't want to impose," said Wolfgang, when it was his dearest wish to play for Joseph II, for a plan was evolving in his mind. Bonno was seventy-one and thus would be retiring soon, and although Salieri and Starzer were next in rank, there could be a place for him. "But my music might please him. It did years ago. And I would be deeply honored."

"We would be the ones who would be honored," said the Countess Thun. "Will this require permission of His Grace, too?"

"Unless it comes from the Emperor. I don't think he would refuse him."

Bonno said, "I don't wish to add to your problems, Maestro, but the Vienna Society of Musicians are giving a concert for the benefit of the widows and children of musicians, and we would be honored if you could play several of your compositions. It is to be given in several weeks, and the Emperor has promised to attend."

This could be the most rewarding invitation of all, but again Wolfgang had to reply, "I must get permission from His Grace."

"Let us all ask," said Prince Philipp Cobenzl, standing quietly in the rear. "For, I, too, have a request of the Maestro. My cousin, Countess von Rumbeck, would be honored to be your first pupil in Vienna."

Much as Wolfgang disliked teaching, this was not a request to refuse. The forty-year-old Philipp Cobenzl was youthfully handsome, with a delicate, tapering face; he had excellent taste; and he was one of the most influential noblemen in the realm, a special favorite of the Emperor.

There was a moment of silence as the others reflected on what Prince Cobenzl had suggested, and then it was agreed: they must ask Archbishop Colloredo, who was still sitting between his father and his uncle.

Before anyone could utter a word, however, Colloredo stated, "Mozart, you never play the viola any more in Salzburg."

Wolfgang longed to say, Because it isn't worth it, with your poor orchestra, but he said, "This was a special occasion."

"Is this why you choose this tedious *Sinfonia Concertante?*"

"Sir, I thought the guests liked it." Wolfgang tried to be reserved, but he glowed with satisfaction. He was excited by the respect and affection the guests had shown him. Colloredo must be jealous to be so openly critical. "Your Grace, didn't you care for it?"

"You know my opinion of this piece. You heard that in Salzburg."

Countess Thun said, "I am surprised, Your Grace, that you feel this way. I thought this music was as beautiful and moving as any I have ever heard."

Prince Rudolf Colloredo, the Archbishop's father, who, Wolfgang reflected, must have overeaten an enormous amount to have become so fat and gouty, and who had been listening with growing impatience, said condescendingly, "Mozart, you played for me when you were a child."

"Your Excellency, I played for many connoisseurs at that time."

"Oh, I am not musical," Prince Rudolf said proudly. "But I had been told that it was your first visit and that you were only six."

"That was true, sir."

"You were very much the fashion then. Even with the Empress."

Wolfgang said quickly, "I am a better musician now, sir."

"But not a wunderkind," Prince Rudolf declared with a sudden pedantic rudeness. He did not hold with this modern fashion that was becoming common among the aristocracy of treating musicians as almost equals. They were servants, and all the politeness in the world didn't alter that fact. He had warned his son, "Music is a whore, used to seduce the heart when the mind knows better. " He indulged his son's wish for an elaborate musical establishment only because it was useful politically, but in his eyes Mozart's music was the worst kind of a whore, for it deliberately set out to entice you. He growled, "A man fights with a sword, not with notes!"

Count Pálffy asked, "May Mozart perform at my palace next Saturday?"

Colloredo said, "He has to play for me that evening."

"I could alter the date."

"I wouldn't bother. My court organist owes me certain obligations."

What angered Wolfgang the most was when Colloredo refused to allow him to play for the Countess Thun or for Giuseppe Bonno, for this meant he would not be able to perform for the Emperor. Was Colloredo so jealous?

Colloredo stood up so that he towered over his musician, so that they would realize his organist's littleness. But he sensed that they did not agree with him, not even Prince Dmitri, and he said to himself scornfully, they are fools, they are benevolent to Mozart because it is fashionable, but let it come to supporting him and they will all turn tail and run. He would have dismissed him long ago, except that the organist was the only musician in his court that Vienna liked. But since he was paying him, he was entitled to his products, but no one else, for while the others might give him a few gulden he bore the real burden. It was galling to be outshone by a vagabond, a servant, who if not for his beneficence, would not know where his next meal was coming from.

Cobenzl asked, "Is Herr Mozart's time completely occupied, Your Grace?"

"Yes. I have a number of concerts planned for Vienna."

"When?"

"Not all the evenings have been decided on, but they will be soon."

"Evenings?"

"Of course! You wouldn't want to attend a concert in the afternoon!"

"Indeed, not. Then Herr Mozart should be free to give lessons."

"Prince Cobenzl, I don't understand." Colloredo was puzzled.

"My cousin, Countess von Rumbeck, would like to study with him. In the afternoon. With your permission?"

Colloredo felt tricked and he was furious, but to say no to Cobenzl would be regarded as an affront to the Crown. He said, "I am honored to put the services of my court at your disposal," and he felt better as he realized the lessons could not last, for they would be leaving Vienna soon.

Cobenzl turned to Wolfgang, "Are you willing, Maestro?"

"I would be delighted, sir."

Prince Dmitri said, "Please accept my gratitude, too, Maestro. It was a joy to hear you again, and I hope I have that pleasure in the future."

Colloredo signaled to his servants that he was departing, and when Wolfgang did not follow, intending to finish his chat with his friends, Colloredo motioned to his chief steward to correct this assumption. As Prince Cobenzl said, "Herr Mozart, I will be privileged if you could be my guest at my villa in the Wienerwald," Karl Arco took Wolfgang by the arm, and before Wolfgang could accept this invitation he had to leave with the rest of the Archbishop's entourage.

FIFTY-FIVE

The Emperor, at the suggestion of Cobenzl, said he would enjoy hearing Mozart play at the concert for the widows. When Colloredo was told, he replied that out of respect for Joseph his court organist could appear. But he was irate at the way his servant had gone over his head.

Wolfgang was angry, too, even as Colloredo's change of mind elated him. He felt this was a demonstration of support by the Imperial court, but the belated permission, given just several days before the concert, added to his problems, for he had been asked to compose pieces for the occasion.

Brunetti, who was to perform also, said that was impossible.

Brunetti *was impossible*, thought Wolfgang, nothing in composition was impossible if he set his mind to it. He said, "I will have three new pieces for the concert. A rondo for you, a pianoforte sonata for me, and a sonata for myself with accompaniment for your violin."

"When will you compose them? You have only two days."

"I can put them together in time." Brunetti was an ass to worry.

But the night before the concert Brunetti came to his room quite upset. "I have the rondo, but what about the accompaniment for the violin?"

"I will compose that later."

"Later? It is almost eleven now!"

"Then I will compose it between eleven and twelve, and in order that it be ready, I will write out only the violin part for you, and I will retain my own part in my head. Don't worry, I will remember every note. It will go well, and you will get many gulden for your performance."

To Brunetti's amazement, although his accompaniment was written out, Mozart played his part without a note written down, yet perfectly.

378

And Mozart was right: the Emperor sent him a gift of twenty gulden. But it was Mozart whom the audience loved. After he played his pianoforte sonata the applause would not stop and he had to encore, and then extemporize.

At the finish the Emperor stood up and shouted "Bravo!" and wanted to speak to him. Joseph had not changed much, thought Wolfgang; he was still slim, boyish, looking much younger than his age, and now that his mother was dead and he was the sole ruler, more democratic, avoiding the formalities and addressing his subjects like equals.

He said, "Herr Mozart, you still play with such a delicacy of touch. We must hear more of your music. You have been away from Vienna too long."

"Your Majesty, I am honored that you wanted to hear me perform."

"Of course. I have always enjoyed your music."

But before Wolfgang could speak of the future Joseph was called away.

The next week Countess Thun gave a concert that Joseph attended, but this time Colloredo said his organist could not play, and arranged a concert of his own for that night. Wolfgang was asked to play by Count Pálffy again and the same thing occurred. And the Archbishop refused to allow him to give a public concert, although there was a great demand. Wolfgang was corresponding with Papa, expressing his dissatisfaction with Colloredo and his reluctance to return to Salzburg, while his father was advising him to conciliate Colloredo, to do nothing rash, but the inability to give a public concert was the bitterest blow of all. Very upset, he wrote Papa:

"I am sorry my difficulties with the Mufti have made you ill. I would do anything to preserve you in health and happiness, and I am aware of what you have contributed to my life, but it is getting harder to stay with our Arch-booby. Whatever I want to do for myself, he forbids. Whenever I have a chance to earn some money, he stops me.

"What you say concerning his vanity in possessing me may be true but what is the use to me? One does not live by this. And then with what distinction does he treat me? I have dined four times with Countess Thun, and I go there almost every day; I have been the guest of Prince Cobenzl; but our Mufti still forces me to eat with his valets and cooks.

"All my dear Vienna friends agree that my chief aim should be to favorably impress the Emperor. He applauded my symphony that Bonno conducted – the orchestra had one hundred and eighty members and played magnificently. What I could do with such an orchestra! But in Salzburg a chamber orchestra of twelve is too much for my simplest divertimento.

"And even without the Emperor's support, I could prosper here. Vienna is a land of clavier players. I could easily earn a hundred gulden with a public concert – if only the Arch-booby would allow it. But for all the extra work I have done for him, I have received nothing. What makes me so desperate is that at a concert at Countess Thun's, which Joseph attended, all the soloists got fifty gulden. What an opportunity was lost!

"Dearest Papa, I cannot go on this way much longer. Either I must surrender my honest ambition to low servitude, or assert my honor as a musician. You know of the many insults I have taken, but even putting that aside, I have the most valuable connections a musician can wish for in Vienna. I am treated with great distinction by families of the first rank, and they will pay me in the bargain. Should I sacrifice all this for four hundred and fifty gulden? And eventually die of mortification?

"There are so many prospects in Vienna. Count Pálffy has introduced me to Stephanie, Inspector of the German opera and a favorite of the Emperor's, and I played him some of *Idomeneo* and he was much impressed.

"Stephanie says that if I stay in Vienna he will be honored to work with me. He will show me his libretto as soon as I decide what to do.

"Prince Cobenzl has gotten me a fine paying pupil in his cousin, Countess von Rumbeck, who pays me six gulden for twelve lessons – three times what you earn for teaching in Salzburg – and he has promised to get me more, if I stay. And I need only two pupils to support myself.

"Believe me, I know now that next to health money is most important, and Vienna is where I can make it. Do not worry if I leave the Mufti. If he should try to punish you, you and my beloved sister can come here and I will support all of us. I kiss your hands a hundred times and embrace my sister with all my heart and remain your loving and obedient son."

While Wolfgang tried to decide what to do, he asked Countess Thun what she thought of his prospects in Vienna. She was so musical, he thought, relaxing in the lovely and spacious music room of her palace. He was uncertain, apprehensive despite the optimistic tone of his letter.

She asked, "When you were in Paris did you see Marie Antoinette?"

"No."

"Did you try?"

"Not directly. But friends in her court orchestra approached her."

"What did she say?"

"She said nothing. She acted as if she didn't remember me. My friends repeated, 'Monsieur Mozart is in Paris and would be honored to play for you,' and she said, 'Gluck is my maestro. When we play music, we play Gluck.' "

"That is true here, too, Wolfgang. Gluck is Joseph's favorite also."

"He was kind and gracious when he heard me."

"When it doesn't cost him anything. That is typical of the Hapsburgs."

"You think I am foolish to count on him?"

"You must not depend on any one person. Yes, even me. But especially the Emperor. You must realize that even with the best of intentions there will be times that he will be too busy with other affairs."

"So?" he asked quizzically. "Do I return to Salzburg?"

"You have to decide that. Wolfgang, did you like Versailles?"

"Most of the ladies were whores or mistresses. And the gentlemen were dedicated to hunting, snuff boxes, and cuckolding their friends."

"You think they are much different here!"

"Then I should be cynical about Vienna, too?"

It was more than that, she thought. Wolfgang had such a need to care, to love, that sometimes it made him seem childish and naive, when actually, he was as shrewd and discerning as anyone about human nature. But without this caring, this loving he could not compose the way he wanted to, no matter how he sought to be worldly. He was lost without love. It was his faith, his strength. He could be caustic, even cruel about poor music and musicians, his ear and taste were too keenly developed to permit anything else, but he had been born into a world of love and caring and it had become as essential to him as food and water. Thus, his affectionate nature left him vulnerable, and to the callous he was not clever enough, not practical. She said, "I am concerned about your honor."

"My honor?" He laughed, almost bitterly, but when she looked hurt, he added, "I am a composer and I must protect that."

"And I want to protect it, too. I really do, Wolfgang. That is why I am trying to warn you of some of the hazards you will face."

In this instant he loved her. But that was impossible, she had three daughters she loved, she was twelve years older than he was and while it was far less of a difference than when he had been a child, he still dreamt of falling in love with someone young and pretty. Her pert, sharp features had become lined with age, although she was still attractive, and one of the most fashionable and elegant women in Vienna. He wondered if the woman he married would be so wise, so charming. But one did not marry for wisdom, he reflected, but soon, Dear God, soon! He was so tired of chastity, of being alone, of waiting for the right person, as if there ever was truly a right person. He had enough of being pure, of being a virgin in a world which was not.

She said, "You will find fulfillment, Wolfgang."

381

"I wonder." It was very difficult to be around attractive women constantly and remain platonic. For once, music was no relief.

"But remember, although your music may be sacred the world is profane."

FIFTY-SIX

A week later a footman informed Wolfgang that the Archbishop wanted him to leave for Salzburg the next morning. Horror-struck by this and shaken by the suddenness, he asked for an audience with Colloredo. It was granted reluctantly, and after he waited several hours the Archbishop gave him five minutes. Colloredo didn't ask him why he couldn't leave but stated, "No one can stay in the Deutsches Ordenshaus after this week."

"I can't leave Vienna, sir. At least, not for a week."

"I ordered you to depart tomorrow."

"Your Grace, I have several appointments I have to keep. I must bid farewell to my good friends, Prince Cobenzl and the Countess Thun."

"You can't abuse my uncle's hospitality any longer. You have been here too long as it is and he needs the Deutsches Ordenshaus for his own people."

"Then I will find new quarters, sir."

Colloredo was in no mood to argue. He snapped, "I will expect you to depart for Salzburg in a week. That should give you enough time to take care of your affairs. Now clear out, you cannot live here any longer."

"Thank you, sir."

"You try my patience. I don't know how much longer it will last."

Wolfgang had just returned to his room and was trying to decide where to go when Angerbauer, the chief valet, handed him a note, saying, "A young, attractive woman, with very pretty dark eyes and a fine figure, gave it to me, but not until I promised to deliver it in person."

For a moment Wolfgang thought it was a love letter, but from whom? As he eagerly opened it, he saw that it was from Frau Weber.

Then Constanze must have delivered it; she fitted Angerbauer's description. He read:

"Dear Herr Mozart: I hope you will forgive my taking the liberty of writing you, but I wondered if you knew of Fridolin's death. He was very fond of you, and his last words were that if Herr Mozart had been listened to, Aloysia would not have thrown herself away on an actor. Fridolin also said that I must give you his copies of your Mannheim compositions, instead of selling them, although, as you know, we are not rich. He said with his dying breath that only a musician of your genius should have them. Fridolin cared very much for your good opinion, as we all do, and he never forgave himself for being so brief with you the last time we saw you, but he was already failing and he didn't want you to be subject to his illness. And I was afraid to write you, for fear that Aloysia had poisoned your mind against us.

"Constanze, who insisted on taking this letter to you in person so as to be sure you would get it, has talked often about how wonderful you were to us. At the time of your dear mother's fatal illness Constanze went every day to the Capuchin church to pray for her soul. I didn't tell you then only because you were so concerned with Aloysia, who would never have thought of doing that, you would have been deeply hurt. But now that you see through her, as we do, some things can be told.

"We heard that you are in Vienna to play for the Emperor and Prince Galitsin, and you must be very busy with your good and great friends. But if you would enjoy a good, home-cooked German dinner, we would be honored to have you as our guest. Constanze has become an excellent cook, and your stomach, which you liked to joke about, will be in safe hands.

"We live within walking distance, at 11 Am Peter, which is in the Peterplatz, and since Aloysia betrayed us, I have been forced to take in roomers to provide for my three helpless girls, although my oldest is beginning to obtain singing engagements. But we want no more favors from you, except the privilege of your company.

"It will be sufficient if you answer in person. Cäcilia Weber"

The letter was providential, he thought. He went to the Webers immediately and he felt at home almost at once. Frau Weber said it was obviously the place to stay until he got settled or returned to Salzburg, and he agreed with her. He moved in the same day.

"Temporarily," he assured her. But he enjoyed being part of a family. From the moment he sat down to dinner, one of the girls was waiting on him, offering to run his errands, to mend his clothes, and Constanze, who was the most attentive, had become physically pleasing. And he liked the location. The Peterplatz was secluded from the adjoining Graben, and yet was very close, connected by a narrow lane, the Jungferngassel.

The Webers had the second floor and Frau Weber gave him the two best rooms. He wondered whether Wendling had been right about her, saying that she was lying and deceitful, for she seemed to have a better heart than she had been given credit for. She said he could eat with her family whenever he wanted to, but only when he felt it was necessary for himself. The rent was small, and it was understood he could move out whenever he wanted to.

"If I return to Salzburg," he told her. "But that will only be to please my father."

One remark of Cäcilia Weber troubled him. They had just finished dinner and she was halfway through a bottle of Rhenish wine, when she blurted out proudly, "In the Weber house, Monsieur, there is no problem of the French disease." Constanze blushed; Sophie, the youngest, looked puzzled, and Josepha dropped a dish, as if the clatter would erase her mother's remark. "Oh, don't worry," Frau Weber added, "I keep an eye on my girls. Would you like more wine, Herr Mozart?"

"No, thank you, Frau Weber."

Suddenly she excused herself and he was alone with the three girls.

He had little time to enjoy that, there was so much to do in Vienna the next few days. Artaria and Company, a new music publisher, wanted to see six sonatas for pianoforte and violin with the thought of selling them if they liked them; there were many people to visit; and now that he had moved Colloredo demanded that he wait every morning in his antechamber to find out what was required of him. Wolfgang did this for three days, but when the Archbishop did not appear and whole mornings were wasted in waiting, he stopped. Whereupon, he was ordered to present himself before Colloredo the day after he had ceased waiting.

At this audience the Archbishop began by reproaching him for failing to appear, and he retorted, "Sir, I was not hired on such terms, but I have always appeared punctually whenever you requested it or needed me."

"I need you now, I am sorry to say."

"I am your obedient servant, sir."

"Hm? At any event, I have a package for you to take back to Salzburg."

"I beg your pardon, sir . . ."

"Arco has arranged for your departure on the diligence tomorrow, so the package will arrive in Salzburg promptly."

"Your Grace, I can't! I am in the middle of negotiating for the sale of my music in Vienna, I have money to collect."

"When can you leave?"

"In a few days, sir. Saturday, I hope."

Colloredo looked so angry that Wolfgang thought he would explode, but all he said was, "I will expect you to depart on Saturday."

When Wolfgang did not go on Saturday, he was called before Colloredo, who asked sarcastically, "Well, Mozart, *when are you going?*"

"Sir, I planned to leave yesterday, but all the seats were taken."

"That's a lie. You had no intention of going."

"But I did, Your Grace."

"Is that why you didn't even pick up the package from the chief valet?"

"Sir . . ." Wolfgang was silent. It was true he had put off going, but Colloredo wouldn't understand. If he had lied, he had been forced to.

"Or even inform Angerbauer that you wouldn't appear!"

"Your Grace, I am not a Kammerfourier or a valet."

"But just a fiddler."

"I am no longer a fiddler, sir. I returned as first Konzertmeister."

"Before, you were nothing but a fiddler and incidentally a Konzertmeister."

"I am sorry if I displease Your Grace."

"Are you really, Mozart?"

Their eyes met and Wolfgang thought, Colloredo is trying to glare me down. Colloredo's eyes were scornful, his long nose and chin pointed at him like a sword, and Wolfgang stared back defiantly.

"When are you going?"

"As I said, sir, when I complete my affairs. Since you haven't paid me for all the extra work I have done, I must collect where I can."

"Do not presume. I do not suffer persons of your degree. If you do not leave at once, I will have your pay stopped."

"All the more reason I have to stay, sir. I will need the money."

At this Colloredo exploded. "You are the most slovenly lackey in my service! No one has served me as poorly as you have. You are a ragabond, a conceited fool! I have endured your insolence too long as it is."

"Sir, you are not satisfied with me?"

"You dare to threaten me, you lying scoundrel!"

Wolfgang tried to answer calmly, although he was growing angry and his impulse was to shout back. "I am trying to speak the truth, sir."

"Be careful, or I will have nothing to do with such a miserable liar!"

"Nor I with you!"

"To think that I pay you five hundred gulden!"

"Four hundred and fifty!"

"If you can't serve me properly, get out!"

Wolfgang bowed and said, "It will be my pleasure."

"I said, 'Get out!' I will have nothing more to do with you!"

386

"This is final?"

Colloredo didn't reply, too furious to speak.

Wolfgang said, with sudden decisiveness, "So be it. I will give you my resignation in writing tomorrow."

"Scoundrel! Lackey! Liar! You will fail in Vienna as you failed in Salzburg. Arco, Arco, show the villain out!"

But Wolfgang, feeling triumphant, was gone before Arco could answer. Afterwards however, he was shaken by what he had done. In Salzburg many subjects of the Archbishop had been thrown into the dungeon of the Fortress Hohensalzburg for much less, and suddenly he was afraid of what could happen to Papa. Had he been too hasty? But how could Colloredo have said he failed in Salzburg? Colloredo had sounded so revengeful, he wondered whether his animosity would destroy him in Vienna. He had to return to his rooms and lie down, he was so feverish and trembling. He spent the next twenty-four hours in bed but he could not sleep.

Then, the next morning, instead of going to the Deutsches Ordenshaus to beg for mercy as would be expected, he summoned all his courage and wrote Papa a detailed account of what had happened. In many ways it was more difficult to face Papa than the Archbishop, but there was no turning back. He said quietly but firmly that he had resigned and that he was making this official by writing a letter to this effect, which he would submit to the Archbishop through Count Arco. He added that if Colloredo did anything spiteful, like dismissing Papa, Papa and Nannerl should come to Vienna and he would take care of them.

He was sure that his father would object bitterly to his act and that his sister would weep, that he would be told he had gone too far, but he felt he had not gone far enough. Papa was the one person he wanted to obey, yet he had to live his own life, and Papa, with all his love, did not always understand his needs. When he sent this letter he felt better, it was the most important decision he had taken on his own, and now he was proud of himself. The need to assert his independence had become as vital as anything that had ever happened to him.

He wrote his letter of resignation as he composed his musical scores, precisely, every word having to be in the right place, with emotion.

FIFTY-SEVEN

===

"I am resigning from the Archbishop's service."

Wolfgang's declaration filled Leopold with despair. He read it over, but that did not alter the impact of the words. And the beauty, grace, and spaciousness of the Tanzmeister-Saal, where he was sitting, where he wrote his correspondence, increased his bitterness, for it had failed of its essential purpose, it had not kept his son in Salzburg.

Finding no solace in the Dancing Master's hall, he walked down to the nearby river, and stood on its banks where he could view the city best. Salzburg was beautiful today. May had come with a profusion of color. Everything was bathed in sunshine, the many church towers which were part baroque and part Turkish, the high Italian roofs of the houses along the Salzach, the old fortress hovering over the city like a living presence. With all his travels, it was one of the most attractive towns he had ever seen. But it was no use telling that to his son; Wolfgang wasn't interested in any place where the music failed to fit his needs.

He wished he could curse like Brunetti, or care less, but the idea of his son living in Vienna without him was like seeing the end of his life before him: a few more years to exist; an unwed daughter, who, if she ever found a husband, would have to take second-best; his own career finished; and only God knew what would happen to Wolfgang.

Yet in spite of his feeling of hopelessness, when he was unable to formulate an answer to Wolfgang that satisfied him, he asked his oldest and dearest friends to see him. It had to be at Hagenauer's, for the latter was ailing, and Schachtner and Bullinger could meet him there. But how could he tell them all the things that were in his heart?

He had to pause at the familiar door to wipe away the tears from his eyes. But that did not halt the memories. Nine Getreidegasse was unchanged. As he climbed the stone stairs to the first floor he almost wept. But he was an old man now, he told himself, sixty-one, and his friends would think him senile. At Hagenauer's door that helped him regain control of himself. His emotion was close to the surface however, and he embraced his friends with a fervor he seldom displayed.

Schachtner was surprised, Hagenauer was pleased, and Bullinger wanted to know what was wrong.

"Why?" exclaimed Leopold. "Has Wolfgang written you secretly again?"

"No. But there is something wrong, isn't there, Leopold?"

He told them that Wolfgang had had a terrible fight with Colloredo and had decided to leave the Archbishop's service.

Schachtner thought, What hurts Leopold the most is that his son is indicating that he doesn't need him. Leopold was so proud of his influence on Wolfgang, that he was a friend as well as a father. And both roles were collapsing. Schachtner, who had not ventured from the safety of Salzburg, although his tongue had been the freest, hesitated. How could he advise, when he had not followed his own advice? And Leopold looked so old. His sharp features had lost their strength and had become soft and shrunken.

Leopold asked Bullinger with intense feeling, "Did Wolfgang ever speak to you about Anna Maria wanting to be buried in Petersfriedhof?"

"What good would that do now?"

"A family should be together."

Schachtner said, "Wolfgang is behaving as you brought him up."

"I brought him up to be obedient, responsible, and prudent."

"And to dislike Salzburg. Every chance you got, you took him elsewhere."

"That was to help him. To make him a better musician."

"You made him into such a good musician, he is discontented with anything less than the best. Or do you want him to become like Haydn, a drunk because he hates Salzburg, or a slob like Brunetti?"

Leopold's face hardened and for an instant he was the forceful Leopold, prepared to defy the world for Wolfgang. Then he thought, it was true that his son was amazingly clever about some things, but in others he was often incurably innocent. "Wolfgang could have a precarious time in Vienna."

Bullinger asked, "Has he been happy here?"

"Who is really ever happy? Anywhere?"

"Wolfgang could be. It is his nature. But not in Salzburg. He kept saying to me, 'Who will ever remember a court organist in Salzburg?' And you know how he dislikes the organ now. Yet he loved it as a child."

"But I still owe money!"

Bullinger said, "That is not relevant and I haven't asked you."

Hagenauer said, "Neither have I."

389

"Grimm has. He keeps writing me, although I have paid back most of it."

"The Baron is a pimp," said the priest. "He sells his services to whoever pays the most. And he treated Wolfgang badly and you know that."

"Bullinger is right," said Hagenauer. "But it is hard to see the bird fly from the nest. I think being a parent is the most difficult task of all. You wish the best for your children, you want them to avoid your mistakes, yet to make you proud. Above all, you wish for them the best of all possible worlds, even as you know that is impossible."

"And if you are afraid of what the Archbishop will do," said Bullinger, "I don't think he will do anything."

They agreed with Wolfgang's behavior, thought Leopold. But he wondered if his son had lied, whether it had been all Colloredo's fault, and were the prospects in Vienna as good as Wolfgang claimed?

As he walked home Salzburg appeared even more attractive than before. By the time Leopold reached the Hannibalplatz he was hurrying in his need to convey this to Wolfgang. He wrote him extolling the virtues of Salzburg and warning him about the perils of Vienna. He ordered his son to withdraw his resignation. He said that to quit now would be foolish, wasteful, and dishonorable, and he was sharply critical of his son.

But after this letter was on its way and nothing could be withdrawn or altered, Leopold was remorseful. He sensed he had been harsher than was necessary. The more he thought about it, the more he wondered if he hadn't widened the gap between them instead of narrowing it. He felt separated by a distance so great it could not be measured, and wretched.

To ease this feeling he found himself writing to Anna Maria:

"Dearest Wife: I feel like a child's balloon that has been pricked with a pin and I will burst if I do not talk to you. Except in my case it has been many vengeful pins. Dearest Wife, only you would know how foolish it was of our son to write me as if I am no longer a father to him. Just as foolish as it would be – although you are no longer with us, for us to think you are no longer a wife and mother to us. Through eternity I will be a father to our children and a husband to you, and a friend to all of you.

"Dear Anna Maria, it is true that many times since your departure from us, I have felt like an angry dog, even a frightened dog, and the more frightened I become the louder I bark and perhaps sometimes I bark in helplessness at our son, but sometimes he must have earned it. I have always thought, Dear Wife, that you and I would grow old together. Didn't you?

"What could have been God's intention to suddenly make it otherwise? Man has such vanity to ask such a question. Never mind, I know you understand. But you do know, if no one else does, how I always thought I was carrying out God's wishes for entrusting me with such a gifted son. And now this son says I am not like a father to him. Then perhaps God is also saying I am not like a son to Him. Have I lost my way? I must have lost my way since our son is a kind and affectionate being. This is a fact I must admit despite his accusation of me. He has a fine emotional nature, which is part of his equipment as a composer. Without his special talent for feeling, he would only be half of what he is. Only half, Anna Maria!

"As I grow older, as our son grows older, as Nannerl grows older, only you remain the same. And naturally I realize I have less time to carry out God's wishes and make sure that Wolfgang will reach his zenith while I am still here. When anything happens that seems to threaten this goal I feel as though I am losing my mind. I do not have the same control over myself. The same patience. Young people cannot understand that. When he resigns from his post at our court, my judgment is a condemnation of his action. It is the only sure thing in his rootless life. Can you blame me, Anna Maria? Would you have agreed with me, when we have so little money and so many debts? I try to imagine myself in Wolfgang's place, not as his father, and I must admit I would not have had the courage to do such a foolish thing. I would have to hold on to the one certainty my genius has guaranteed for me, my post at court. Even when I try to forget debts, I cannot – knowing this life too well, knowing what fools and pigs our son has to be a servant to.

"Do I forgive him for hurting me? That would be easy. But I could never forgive him for hurting himself and that is what he is doing.

"Dear Wife, as I said, I thought we would grow old together and you would have seen to it that my impatience and fears did not drive me so.

"If I could mail this letter to you and be sure of a quick post and a quick reply! May God remember me to you. May God forgive me for feeling so lost. That is why man must have so much faith because he feels so lost since the moment of his birth. Always your husband. Mozart"

Leopold put this letter with his favorite keepsake of Wolfgang's, his son's first composition, which Wolfgang had written very straight despite its being on unlined paper, as if his son had known from the start what he had wanted to write. It had been a relief to write out his innermost feelings and doubts, and now Leopold felt better.

As he waited for Wolfgang's reply with apprehension and hope, Count Georg Arco – Karl Arco's father and still chief chamberlain although virtually retired – informed him that Wolfgang had submitted his resignation in writing to his son. And that his son had refused to accept it, until he had Leopold's consent, since it had been Leopold who had arranged Wolfgang's present appointment as court organist and first Konzertmeister. Whereupon Leopold quickly wrote Karl Arco that he did not condone Wolfgang's behavior, although he was sure there was much merit to his son's point of view. He added that at this moment he refused to consent to Wolfgang's resignation.

FIFTY-EIGHT

Wolfgang presented his letter of resignation as soon as he finished it. He was afraid as he entered the Deutsches Ordenshaus, unsure of what Colloredo might do to him, but he could not wait. And the valets regarded him with respect and ushered him into Count Arco, who was using the antechamber to the Archbishop's apartments to conduct his business.

The chief steward glared at him angrily but Wolfgang was not to be put off by anyone's disapproval. As he prepared to speak he noticed that Arco's bony, angular face was harder than ever, that his small, beady eyes glittered like a reptile's, and that there were sharp lines in his cheeks and forehead although Arco was not yet forty. The antechamber was a large, square room with a huge white porcelain stove and an ornate chandelier and could have been part of the Residenz. Wolfgang took a last look at it, determined never to come here again, and said, "I have a letter of resignation, and I would appreciate if you would give it to His Grace. And here are my traveling expenses, which consist of fifteen gulden, forty kreutzer for the diligence, and two gulden for food."

Arco refused to take it, saying, "You cannot resign without the consent of your father. That is your duty."

Wolfgang said sharply, "I know my duty to my father as well as you do."

"Well then, if he agrees to it, you may request your dismissal."

"And if he doesn't?"

"You may also request it."

"And then?"

"We will see."

"What a distinction!"

"Mozart, you are the one who wants to quit, not me."

"And if I withdraw my resignation?"

Arco smiled sardonically and said, "You will return to Salzburg."

"After what has occurred between me and the Archbishop?"

"Under the proper circumstances you could be forgiven."

"If I apologize? Crawl?"

"I have always told you that you were too emotional."

Wolfgang said proudly, "You need the Archbishop, but I do not. When will you present my letter of resignation to him?"

"I told you! When your father agrees to it!" Arco motioned to a valet to show Mozart out. "I will inform you when I hear from your father."

There was one consolation. Arco's attitude indicated that Papa had little to fear from Colloredo, although some apprehension remained.

Wolfgang heard from Papa first. But he could not take this letter to Arco. Papa's severity was a shock. He had not expected complete approval, but for Papa to order him to withdraw his resignation, to say that this present difficulty with Colloredo was largely his own fault, was almost more than he could stand. There was nothing of the Papa he loved and trusted in this caustic letter. Their connection had become strained, agonized, and everything seemed to exacerbate that further.

He wondered whether he should answer Papa, it seemed so futile, but love and habit prevailed, and he did. He could not quarrel with Papa, it was against his nature, but he did defend his behavior as rationally as he could. And he said that Papa must give his permission and blessing, since his departure from the Archbishop's service was inevitable, and Papa's regard and respect were very dear to him.

The waiting for further word from Papa and Arco became one of the most trying times of his life. He could not even visit good friends such as the Countess Thun or Prince Cobenzl. This struggle was between him and Colloredo and he could not involve anyone else. This was a testing of will and he had to win this himself. What worried him the most was that he could not compose. Until he was officially free of Colloredo, he could not create, and he found himself in a period of impotence.

His sustenance became the Webers. Frau Weber agreed with his decision to stay in Vienna, and Constanze, who was lively and carefree, gave him a kind of relaxed happiness he had had only with Bäsle. But he was proper with her, determined that no one would be able to gossip about them.

After keeping Wolfgang waiting weeks, Arco ordered him to appear at once in the antechamber of the Deutsches Ordenshaus. Wolfgang had submitted two more memoranda of resignation in the interim, hoping that their formal tone would be more acceptable, but they had been ignored.

An angry Wolfgang wanted to disregard Arco's summons, but Arco had added that he had a letter from Papa, so Wolfgang obeyed his order.

And Arco, who was as impatient as he was, said without any preamble, "Your father does not give you permission to resign."

"May I see his letter?"

Arco handed it to him triumphantly.

"He wrote this weeks ago. Why did you keep me waiting?"

"Does it matter?"

"It matters very much to me. To keep me dangling on a whim!"

Arco said mockingly, "The answer is the same. Today, or last month."

"Will you please submit my resignation to the Archbishop?"

"Without your father's permission?"

Wolfgang wavered; it would be the first time he was publicly disobeying Papa. But to do anything else was to betray his music. "Yes, please."

"Not without your father's approval. His Grace would not consider it."

"Does he dare regard me as his prisoner? I am not in Salzburg now!"

"He considers you insolent and vain."

"I treat him as he treats me."

"Don't you realize that all of us have to endure unpleasant things?"

Arco seemed almost friendly, then Wolfgang decided that the chief steward had not given his resignation to Colloredo because he was afraid of the latter's wrath. But he was not. Not any more. He said, "I will present one more petition, and if it is not accepted, I shall consider the matter at an end. And I will submit it through von Kleinmayr, Colloredo's secretary, for he, at least, is not a coward and a toady."

Six days later, when Wolfgang heard that the Archbishop was leaving Vienna the following day, he hurried to 7 Singerstrasse to submit his final petition. But von Kleinmayr wouldn't accept it, saying that this was the chief steward's responsibility. The thought of appealing to Arco again was revolting, but he decided to try just once more.

Arco didn't want to see him, and only agreed to do so when Wolfgang said he wouldn't budge from the antechamber until the chief steward appeared.

By now the giving of a letter of resignation to the Archbishop had become a matter of honor to Wolfgang. He had become possessed with the idea that he must show Colloredo that no one could dictate to him, that he had not been discharged but that he had quit.

Arco was very angry at Mozart. Whenever the Archbishop traveled, it was a distraught time, for everything had to be in perfect order or he would castigate his chief steward, yet the Archbishop himself was disorganized, untidy, apt to change his mind on the slightest impulse. And Arco was nervous, for he was in the middle of arranging the trip back to Salzburg, and he was anxious to see His Grace off, before the latter postponed it again, as His Grace had done several times already. He knew that Colloredo preferred Vienna to Salzburg, but no one was supposed to know this. And he was tired of the musician and his pleas. The Archbishop, without saying so, had indicated that Mozart's resignation should be ignored, so that he would come crawling back. Arco had sought to follow his master's wish, but it had become difficult, for Mozart had become more defiant rather than less. Yet Colloredo, much as he disliked the musician personally, didn't want anyone to think that he could be bested by a mere servant. Arco had sensed this from the start, although the Archbishop was too proud to put this into words. He could understand how Colloredo felt. Just because Mozart had been treated kindly by his sister in Paris years ago, and during the informality of childhood had played with the Arcos, was no reason for the musician to regard himself as an equal. It was about time someone put him in his place. And now Mozart stood at the entrance to the Archbishop's apartments as if to burst into them. This was heresy.

Arco said brusquely, "Be brief. I only have a minute."

"I have tried to resign five times, yet nothing I have presented has been given to the Archbishop. Why?"

"You know why. Now go."

"Where? I am no longer in the Archbishop's service."

"To hell, for all I care. His Grace is right. You are a scoundrel."

Wolfgang flushed, but he did not retreat. He declared, "If you will not submit my resignation to the Archbishop, I will do so myself."

"You have forgotten your manners in Vienna. No one is admitted to His Worship's presence without his permission."

Wolfgang paused. He could give in, and for the rest of his life feel humiliated, or he could battle for his rights and face the consequences. And even as he debated this in his mind, he knew he could no longer be humble and supplicating, he had had enough of that in Salzburg. Vienna was full of talk about how the Americans had defeated the British, although the French were taking the credit, and Joseph II was saying he believed in enlightenment. Perhaps a new order was not so far off. He said, "Tell His Grace that I will not move until he sees me."

"I will call the palace guard."

"You wouldn't dare."

"Footman, call the guard."

Wolfgang exclaimed, "You give me no choice! Here is my petition!"

He stuffed it into Arco's hand before the latter realized what was happening. "Present it to His Grace with my compliments."

Arco threw the petition back in his face, shouting, "Fool! Rogue!" And as Wolfgang bent to pick it up, Arco pushed him out of the door and at the top of the stairs gave him a vicious, deliberate kick on the behind.

The door slammed shut after Wolfgang and he landed in a heap at the bottom of the stairs. Never had he felt so insulted. He stood outside of 7 Singerstrasse, almost at the breaking point with rage, longing to go back and duel Arco, to beat him with his walking stick, to kick him in the rear as he had been kicked, but on a public street where many could witness it.

He was still furious as he wrote Papa a bitter account of what had happened. There was only one good consequence of Arco's foul deed, he said, it marked the end of Salzburg. But he was angry enough to run a sword through Arco's heart. The Archbishop must have put his steward up to this. He wondered if Colloredo hated him one hundredth as much as he hated Colloredo. Then he realized that if he did not empty himself of this hatred, it would poison him. He enclosed twenty gulden – although he had promised to send thirty – to prove that he was succeeding in Vienna.

Then he finished the letter, signing it *Your loving and most obedient son,*" for Frau Weber was having a pianoforte moved into his living room.

Constanze said, "My mother knew you were lonesome without one."

"How much did it cost?" He could have kissed Constanze in his delight.

"We will worry about that," she said. "It is not a Stein, but it is a good instrument. Try it, Herr Mozart?"

"Wolfgang? Remember, Constanze, my name is Wolfgang?"

She looked shy, but she nodded and asked him to play.

He did, composing as he went on, as if there was not a moment to be lost, and when he finished he suddenly jumped to his feet and kissed her. And although Constanze blushed and hesitated as a decent girl should, she responded with passion and he was elated.

When Leopold received the news of Arco's insult, this time, knowing he could not change Wolfgang's decision, he told Nannerl, "Your brother had a terrible fight with Arco. As he says, it is the end of Salzburg for him."

"He is not coming back?" cried Nannerl, as if she didn't believe Papa.

"Never."

"Are you sure? What will we do with all these rooms?"

397

"He is never coming back," repeated Leopold. "He has moved in with the Webers, and that, if nothing else, will keep him in Vienna."

"I didn't think he would really leave, despite all his threats."

"He sent me twenty gulden. He promised to send thirty, but already he is not earning as much as he expected. He thinks this will appease me."

Nannerl sobbed, "I will miss him."

"Vienna is not so far."

"But when will I go?" Then suddenly, she could not forgive Wolfgang, for Papa, as happened so often, was paying no attention to her own needs but was starting to write her brother. "What are you doing?"

"I am giving him my permission and blessing."

"But you say that he has resigned already."

"I know. But, at least, he will understand that I cannot support Colloredo after what Arco did."

"Well," she blurted out, "Whatever you pretend, I cannot forgive Wolfgang. You did so much for him, and yet he did not listen to you."

But Leopold was far away. Sitting at his desk, for once unable to find what to say, he was in a dream of what his life had been. Schachtner had been right, he had succeeded so well that Wolfgang had left Salzburg forever. He had been so dissatisfied it had rubbed off on his son. But he was still here. And half of his family was gone. Had he really succeeded? Or failed.

"Anna Maria . . ." he whispered.

Nannerl had her arms around him, consoling, loving.

"My little girl," he cried. "My little, little girl."

PART EIGHT

Constanze

FIFTY-NINE

=====

It was several weeks before Wolfgang felt truly free. But when there were no reprisals from Colloredo and Papa sent him his permission to quit, and Cobenzl invited him to his summer residence outside of Vienna, the wounds that Colloredo and Arco had inflicted began to heal. He sat at the pianoforte and said to himself: I have saved my honor. No one would tell him any more what to compose or when. It was a great victory.

He was working on the sonatas for pianoforte and violin that he was writing for the music publishers, when Constanze interrupted him. Usually he disliked being broken into while composing, but today he was pleased.

She said, "I cooked dumplings and I thought you might like some."

"Yes, if you will be my guest next Sunday for a carriage ride."

"But you are supposed to be at Prince Cobenzl's then!"

"I will come a day later. He won't mind."

"Such an important nobleman! He could help your career."

"I said Cobenzl wouldn't mind. Don't you want to go?"

"Unescorted? I'm not sure it is proper. I'll have to ask my mother."

Didn't Constanze trust him? He was not a libertine! He was hurt, and then he told himself that he shouldn't be, she was only eighteen.

"Are you going to have dinner with us, Wolfgang?"

"Are you going riding with me, Constanze?"

She went to ask her mother's permission, and returned a few minutes later with it, on one condition, that he bring her home before nightfall.

He agreed reluctantly to this stipulation, not liking what this implied, and while he accepted her invitation to dinner, he was quiet, almost sad.

But he could not stay somber or irritated, she looked so well for their engagement and Sunday was such a lovely day. There was a cheerful-

400

ness in everything: in the gentle July sunshine, the strollers in their best clothes, the fine carriage he had hired, the sharing this with Constanze.

The ten gulden he had not sent Papa as he had promised, that he had put aside for an emergency, had gone to pay for the carriage. He had only a few gulden left, but he was not worried. He would be at Prince Cobenzl's for three weeks, which would save money, and there were many prospects.

Constanze loved the opulence of the carriage and that they were going to the Prater. She said, "It is where the nobility drives, isn't it?"

"Yes. But that isn't why we are going there"

"Why are we, Wolfgang?"

"It is the nicest drive in Vienna." And the most romantic, he felt.

In these grand surroundings, thought Constanze, he didn't seem small and inconspicuous as Aloysia had sneered. He had a fair skin that she envied, a large, impressive head, and a high, wide forehead. Yet with his irregular features, cheeks that puffed out, and an uneven nose, he was not good-looking. Except when he was excited. As now, she noticed, the instant the wheels of the carriage started he was exuberant and happy.

He exclaimed, "I love traveling, the sound of wheels in motion, their tempo. But this is something I haven't told anyone else, Constanze."

"Do you use it in your music?"

"Not literally. But it stimulates me, and adds to my desire to compose. I guess it is because I did so much traveling as a child."

"Did you like traveling then?"

"Very much, when I thought about it. Most of the time, it just seemed the natural way to live, and I was too busy." They were at the Prater now and he showed her the magnificent thoroughfare, which was lined on each side with giant chestnut trees, and said, "Isn't Vienna exciting?"

"I haven't seen much of the city. I rarely get out of the Peterplatz."

"We must change that. I must show you the Danube, and Grinzing."

"People will talk."

"They will anyway, if we are together. What are you afraid of?"

She didn't like the criticism in his voice and she didn't reply. Then she wanted to look rather than talk, she was so excited by the aristocratic carriages. She remembered that the Emperor drove in the Prater sometimes, to show that he was democratic and shared his subjects' pleasures. She felt jealous as Wolfgang smiled warmly to a handsome middle-aged woman who was passing in a spacious blue carriage. "Who is that?" she asked abruptly.

"The Countess Thun. A dear friend."

"But she is so old!"

"Thirty-seven? That is just right for many men."

She said suddenly, "Do you have to go to Prince Cobenzl's tomorrow?"

"I thought you approved. You gave that as a reason for not seeing me."

"That was last week."

"But I am going there as much to rest and compose as anything else."

"Why don't you compose in our house? That is why my mother rented the pianoforte for you."

"It was very kind, but I can't refuse Cobenzl." It was important that he have the six sonatas for violin and pianoforte finished for Artaria, for the music publishers really seemed interested, and he needed the money. And it would be easier to compose at Cobenzl's country estate.

"I will miss you," she blurted out.

"I will be back by the end of July."

"Do you think Artaria will like your music?" She sounded very concerned.

"Will you?"

"Wolfgang, do you have to ask!"

"I will have a present for you when I return."

"A bracelet? Lace? Ribbons?"

He changed the subject. "Did you know the Prater used to be the royal hunting grounds, until Joseph opened it to the public? When I played with Marie Antoinette, she assumed I had a private hunting park as she did."

"Did you know her that well?" she asked with awe.

"I was a toy, to be played with as she played with the other toys."

"But did you really perform for the Kings of France and England?"

He laughed. "Yes. But it was not of as much importance as some people said. Neither of them were really musical or had much taste."

Her hand tightened in his and at a part of the Prater where there was no one, she met his effort to kiss her halfway. Then afterwards she said, "We mustn't do that again. We will give people a bad impression."

It was a little after dark when they returned to the Peterplatz. Frau Weber looked skeptical as Wolfgang explained that the Prater had been so crowded it had delayed their return.

She said, "I know, Herr Mozart, that you won't make a fool of an honest girl, but people will talk if you are indiscreet."

He turned quite red and replied with passion, "No one treasures Constanze's honor more than I do, or is more determined to preserve it."

"I hope so. Or I will have to chaperone you myself."

Constanze grimaced at that, and when her mother was not looking, she slipped a note under his door which said: "Remember, Wolfgang, I will expect a present when you return. A very nice one."

Wolfgang felt at home at Reisenberg, the summer residence of Prince Cobenzl. It had a splendid view and magnificent surroundings. Reisenberg was a spur of the Kahlenberg which overlooked Vienna from the East, and was close to the Leopoldsberg where the siege of the city by the Turks had been broken almost a hundred years ago. It was an hour away from Vienna and on a clear day the city could be seen in the distance.

And Cobenzl did everything he could to make Wolfgang comfortable. He took his letters into town to mail, provided him with a music room and a Stein pianoforte, bought him manuscript paper and pen and ink, and said it was an honor to be of service to Wolfgang's art. He was also deeply interested in Wolfgang's meeting with Stephanie in August. One afternoon over coffee and pastry, while Wolfgang was taking a rest from composing, he asked, "Excluding the fact that Stephanie can get his libretto produced, wouldn't you be wiser to seek a better librettist?"

"Who do you suggest?" said Wolfgang. Cobenzl had taste and influence.

"The best. Shakespeare or Molière. Molière would be ideal for *opera buffa*, and think of Hamlet or Othello as an *opera seria*."

"Their poetry would be too much for the music."

"Not your music."

"Thank you, Cobenzl, but librettos should be written for the music, not the music adapted to the poetry. If Shakespeare or Molière were alive today, and we could work together, that would be a different matter. But who could I depend on to alter their poetry to fit my music?"

"Have you ever thought of trying yourself, Wolfgang?"

"Occasionally. But I am not a librettist, although some say I have a gift for words. I am a composer, and I must compose for the voice."

"And for the idea."

"No, for the drama. And that is the problem. In opera the poetry must always be the obedient servant of the music. Nothing else is possible."

"Gluck would not agree with you."

"Do you come out of his operas remembering the words or the music?"

"The music, naturally. But it would be an interesting marriage."

"Or miscarriage."

"Mozart and Molière. Or Mozart and Shakespeare. I don't agree."

"Sir, I am honored by your feeling. I admire both poets, particularly Molière. But Molière is not here, while, at least, when the

403

librettist is alive, I can get him to arrange his libretto to suit the music."

"Do you really expect to get this from Stephanie or anyone else?"

"I expect the best, and anticipate the worst."

He returned to his work with determination. He had two sonatas still to compose, but he missed Constanze so. She was not beautiful like Aloysia; she was not witty like the Countess Thun; she was not intellectual like Cobenzl; and yet the Sunday in the Prater had been one of the happier days of his life. Gradually that became the theme of his first sonata. Ideas that had been in his head for many days flowered like an epitaph to the lovely day they had spent together. Her slim compact form became a living presence in the music. His loneliness vanished as this sonata developed with a simplicity and a sweetness that he saw as characteristic of her.

The final sonata was composed in a different mood. He wrote it so that it would be poignant and intense, and yet the music danced and was as melodic as he could make it. And he constructed it as if the pianoforte and the violin were part of a concerto. Yet he kept them inseparable, so neither was able to do without the other. He hoped that Constanze would like these two sonatas as much as he did.

He returned to Vienna sooner than he had planned in his eagerness to give her these sonatas and to enjoy her pleasure. But no one expected him. He entered 11 Am Peter unannounced, and as he approached the living room he heard Frau Weber screaming, "Constanze, I told you not to cook all the dumplings today!"

"But it is easier to do them all at once," answered Constanze.

"And more expensive. How many times do I have to tell you that we have no money? But you are so wasteful. Like your father."

Constanze was terrified into repentance but that didn't halt Frau Weber.

She shouted, "And no one has cleaned the house!"

"I can't do it alone."

"Did you expect me to do it? After all I have done for you?"

Constanze didn't reply and Wolfgang coughed to make his presence known.

Frau Weber, catching hold of herself, smiled and said, "I'm sorry you had to hear a family quarrel, but you know how families are."

He didn't agree. His own family had never quarreled like this.

"I wanted to save some of the dumplings for you, Herr Mozart."

"Thank you."

"But you are back earlier than you said you would be."

Frau Weber sounded hurt, thought Wolfgang, as if he had betrayed her.

"I shouldn't have lost my temper, but it is so difficult to bring up three orphans. Sometimes I think they will be the death of me."

Constanze asked, "Did you have a nice time, Wolfgang?"

"It was restful, pleasant. And I was able to find a present for you."

"A present!" Constanze was animated now.

"Two sonatas I composed at Cobenzl's."

He handed them to her but she accepted them reluctantly, looking disappointed, and then her mother told her to give them back, saying, "We appreciate your generosity, Herr Mozart, but she cannot take them."

"But I had planned to dedicate them to her."

"A great honor, no doubt, but it would cause a scandal if a young, unmarried girl took them, for it would indicate romantic feelings on the part of the donor."

"What do you think, Constanze?" asked Wolfgang. "Do you want them?"

"As my mother said, I am honored, but . . ."

"Constanze is a child," said Frau Weber, "and I am her guide. Herr Mozart, you should dedicate these sonatas where they will do you more good."

Maybe he should move out, thought Wolfgang, as Papa had suggested.

SIXTY

====

Gottlieb Stephanie greeted Wolfgang warmly. He said, "I am honored by your presence in my rooms, Herr Mozart."

"I am the one who is honored," Wolfgang replied, but suddenly he was suspicious of Stephanie. He recalled that the forty-year-old Inspector of the German Opera was also a playwright, stage manager, producer, and actor, and, he had been warned, an adventurer like Affligio. Yet Stephanie was not good-looking like Afflgio; his thick lips, blunt chin, broad nose gave him a coarse appearance. But he did have the reputation of being well read, a glib conversationalist, and a librettist who could get his work produced.

And Wolfgang liked his rooms. They were on the Michaelplatz, close to the palaces, churches, and rulers. The windows opened on a cool, spacious courtyard, and the rooms were splendidly furnished. Yet when he asked what an apartment such as this cost, Stephanie said apologetically, "Five hundred gulden. Far too much. But what can a man in my position do."

It was more than Wolfgang had earned in a year in Salzburg and he wondered if such an extravagant man could be trusted, yet Stephanie was saying, "I assure you, if I support your music, it will be performed."

"What about *Idomeneo*? You said it has a beautiful score."

"It is noble music. It is the reason I thought you could collaborate with me. But it is too serious for Vienna, if it is done in German. And you do want your first opera in Vienna to be in German, don't you?"

His first opera in Vienna had been when he was twelve. But he did not remind Stephanie of this, saying instead, "What is your alternative?"

"A libretto about an abduction from a seraglio." Stephanie added, "Turkish subjects are very popular in Vienna these days. The Viennese love to see Turks upon the stage, as long as they are villains."

Stephanie was right, Wolfgang had to admit to himself, but not wanting to give him too many advantages or to appear too eager, he said, "How do you know that your libretto will lend itself to a Singspiel?"

"The story of how Belmonte, a Spanish nobleman, rescues his beloved, Constanze, from a Turkish seraglio is touching and romantic."

Wolfgang knew he should not be affected by such a coincidence, but he was. There had been moments when he had imagined himself rescuing Constanze from her mother's clutches, although what he would have done then he was not sure. He asked, "How does the drama develop?"

"The action occurs in the palace of Pasha Selim, who holds captive in his seraglio the beautiful Constanze, her maid Blonde, and Belmonte's servant, Pedrillo. Pedrillo works as a gardener under the supervision of Osmin, the Pasha's cruel overseer. When Pedrillo sees Belmonte searching for Constanze, he introduces him to the Pasha as an architect eager to enter the Pasha's employ. Selim accepts Belmonte's services, and Belmonte and Pedrillo abduct Constanze and Blonde from the seraglio, and . . ."

Wolfgang interrupted, "That last scene could be dramatic and moving."

"It is. For, before they get far, they are caught by Osmin and taken to Selim, who discovers that Belmonte is the son of his worst enemy."

Wolfgang didn't look impressed, but questioning.

"Then Pasha Selim generously frees the four captives and they are able to marry, for Blonde and Pedrillo are in love, too."

There was a dead silence.

"Don't you like it, Mozart?"

Well, he thought, it was not Molière. He asked, "What is the title?"

"Belmonte and Constanze."

"Herr Stephanie, isn't there a work by that name by Bretzner?"

"Herr Mozart, dramas about Turks are very popular in Vienna. But this libretto is charming and picturesque, and should have great appeal."

"The title should be changed," Wolfgang said thoughtfully.

"Changed?" Stephanie was indignant.

"Yes. It doesn't tell an audience what the tale is about. If you want it to attract attention because it has a Turkish background, the title should suggest that. Such as *The Abduction from the Seraglio*."

Stephanie didn't like to admit it, but it was a better title. Yet he said sarcastically, "I don't know what I would do without you."

"You would find another composer."

But the librettist didn't use this opportunity to withdraw, thinking Mozart was highly regarded by important people and he was a skillful composer, although too daring sometimes. He said, "If the score could be completed quickly, I could have the opera welcome the heir to the Russian throne, Grand Duke Paul, when he visits Vienna in September."

"That is a very short time. It is the first of August now."

"Prince Galitsin assured me that the Grand Duke is his friend, and that the libretto will satisfy him. Don't you think your music will?"

"I can have it ready in time. But who will sing it?"

"Cavalieri or Lange will sing Constanze."

"Aloysia Lange?"

"If Cavalieri isn't free. Cavalieri has the better voice and is far more experienced, but Lange could do if necessary. Or don't you think so?"

As the librettist stated, reflected Wolfgang, Cavalieri was an acclaimed prima donna while Aloysia was an understudy by comparison, yet part of him still yearned for Aloysia. He asked, "Who else will sing?"

"Belmonte will be sung by Adamberger, Osmin by Fischer."

Fischer had a fine voice and so did Adamberger, and both were excellent actors. But if the libretto was mediocre and Stephanie refused to revise, there would be more heartaches as there had been with Varesco. And he had vowed never to endure that again. He did not answer.

"When are you going to make up your mind, Mozart? I can't wait forever! If you are not interested, I will submit my libretto to Gluck or Salieri."

"Suppose the libretto needs revising, as almost all librettos do?"

Stephanie said, "Just as the music has to be adjusted to the voices, the poetry has to be fitted to the music."

"Then you will revise when it is necessary?"

Stephanie looked angry but he said. "I give my word. It is as vital to me as it is to you that this *Singspiel* is a success."

Wolfgang said, smiling for the first time, "I will be honored to work with you, Herr Stephanie, if you are of the same mind."

Stephanie shrugged, and declared, "It will depend on the music."

"Naturally. When can I have the libretto?"

"Now." As Stephanie handed it to Wolfgang, he added, "You must start work at once, if we are to have it ready for the Grand Duke's visit next month."

Wolfgang rushed back to his room, and sat down at his desk to read the libretto. He was deep in thought when Constanze invited him to dinner. He said he was too busy, and she volunteered to bring the food to his room.

"What about your mother? Won't she be offended?"

"My mother?" Constanze made a face. "She is visiting Aloysia."

"I thought they weren't speaking."

"When it suits them. But now they need each other. Aloysia heard that you are going to compose an opera for the German theater, and she wants my mother to persuade you to use her. Would you, Wolfgang?"

"What do you want me to do?"

"After the way she treated you – No!"

Constanze was so angry he could have embraced her.

"I would never forgive anyone who treated me like that."

He grinned and said, "I would enjoy anything you cooked for me."

But the capon, although it smelled delectable and was steaming hot when she placed it beside him, as if it were a peace offering, remained untouched as he studied the libretto. Much of it was static, undramatic, obvious, and yet there was such a cascade of notes within him that even as he was critical of many of the situations he was composing music for them.

He did not leave his desk that night. When the candles burnt down he created in the dark. Whatever the difficulties of the text, he was possessed with a desire to write music that would express the abduction. And he liked the sound of the title in German – *Die Entführung aus dem Serail* – it was more appropriate than the usual Italian ones. He assured himself that it was a good omen that the heroine was named Constanze, and that the romantic scenes lent themselves to the kind of lyrical arias he yearned to write.

Constanze knocked on his door to make his bed and tidy up his room, and she was astonished that he had not slept and hurt that he had not eaten at all. But at this moment he loved her for being considerate and for being named Constanze; he loved her for being young and appealing; he loved *Die Entführung aus dem Serail* as a title, although Stephanie had not yet agreed.

She said, "I will bring your breakfast, but only if you eat it," and he promised to eat all of it, and she looked happy until he asked, "What happened with Aloysia?" She scowled and said, "They are friends again. It is useful." She left abruptly to get his breakfast.

By the time he wrote Papa to tell him what had happened, and for his approval, he was convinced he should do Stephanie's libretto. He stressed: "You will see for yourself, dearest father, that the story is worth doing, for while it requires altering and some of the poetry is weak, the Turkish locale should be popular, for it is the fashion here. And the text has brought many melodies to my head, and if a libretto can do this, it is an effective libretto. I have composed an aria for Cavalieri and for Adamberger, and an overture, with a Turkish theme, that is different from anything I have yet done. What used to take me ten days to compose, I do now in two. The instant the music is engraved and I have a revised libretto, I will send them to you. As you know, I would do anything in the world to please you, and if you should like the music, it will make me very happy. Your ever obedient and loving son, Wolfgang Amadé Mozart."

He hoped this would heal the breach between him and Papa.

Life had grown dreary in Salzburg for Leopold. Yet, he reflected, little had changed. Colloredo had said nothing about Wolfgang since his return from Vienna, as if his ignoring of Wolfgang showed his indifference. Karl Arco had avoided him, and he was still acting Kapellmeister, while Haydn and Brunetti filled his son's shoes where they could. But he was even more preoccupied with Wolfgang, for he knew now that a Mozart would never be the official Kappellmeister in Salzburg, and that the interesting things were happening to his son in Vienna.

Wolfgang's letter about the new opera made Leopold feel more like his former self. He felt that his son was not really satisfied with the story, but wanted no objections, and so had said it was a good libretto. And he could understand why. If this opera was performed for the Grand Duke Paul, it would be the most important musical attraction in Vienna. Yet it might also require intrigue and flattery, where Wolfgang so often failed.

And other fears nagged him. Friends, who had just come back from Vienna, had told him that there was much gossip about his son living in the same house with three unmarried girls. These tales had been cruel and caustic, and Leopold felt that much of this was spite, that their friends had never forgiven Wolfgang for leaving Salzburg, yet some of it sounded true. He was very upset by Albert von Mölk saying, "Frau Weber seems determined to get Wolfgang involved with one of her girls, for she has allowed him to be seen with Constanze Weber unescorted."

So, although he was pleased about the opera, he found himself writing:

"I think it is encouraging that you are being considered for the Seraglio opera, but you must not spend this money before you have it. And until you receive the hundred ducats you have been promised, and the Emperor is shouting, 'Bravo!' you must trust no one, and certainly not Stephanie, who is in this obviously for his own advantage.

"You cannot take any chances now. You inform me that you have only one pupil, and that with just one pupil, *you can barely make both ends meet*. Thus, it would be very foolish for you to saddle yourself with obligations when you may be on the verge of a career in Vienna.

"I agree that the Turkish story could be popular today, but, if it is like most librettos, it will need many revisions before it will be worthy of your music, and that is another reason why you must not involve yourself with new responsibilities. Should the *Singspiel* fall through, and there are many obstacles in your way, you will be in worse difficulties.

"Yet I am confident that should the proper changes be made, you will write a score of which you can be proud. *Idomeneo* had many dramatic

My advice is to accept the libretto, but to be wary of the librettist, for he has a reputation for plagiarizing. Yet, as you said, he also understands the stage and his plays are popular. So, whatever you think of him privately, always be civil to him but also distant.

"Above all else, you must always remember that I am convinced that you can do whatever is necessary in music. And that I always place your best interests beyond anything that happens to me.

"What troubles me is your impulsiveness and good heartedness, which is so quick to like those who cater to you, especially if a pretty smile accompanies that. I am worried about your living with the Webers. I have heard much gossip about you and the daughters. Some say that you are even going to wed one of them. At this crucial point in your career you must avoid even the appearance of that. It could ruin your career, to say nothing of your present plans for the Seraglio story. You know how concerned I am about the welfare of your soul, problems, yet you gave your music a nobility I had not heard before. and you cannot be such a blockhead as not to know what people will say about a young, marriageable man living in the same house with three unwed girls. I know young men are apt to err, especially with Viennese women and I do not expect you to be without sin, but Frau Weber is a cunning person and not to be trusted. Unless you are a scoundrel and interested only in entertaining yourself with her girls.

"All this gossip has made me quite ill. If you really mean what you wrote — *'that you will do anything to please me'* — you will move out of the Webers' at once! I cannot believe that you are such a fool that you could consider anything else under the circumstances. Your dear mother, who sacrificed so much for you, must be turning in her grave at the thought of such gossip about her son. For her sake, and mine, you must find more suitable quarters. Always your loving and devoted father."

But once again, after Leopold sent this letter, he was stricken with remorse. He had no feeling that Wolfgang would obey him. He wondered how much more there was to lose.

Wolfgang was wounded by his father's accusations and lack of trust, yet some of his advice seemed sensible. While he deliberated about what he should do, he was visited by Wendling, who was in Vienna for a few days.

His old friend said, "Why don't you sleep with her first and find out whether she is worth marrying?" and when he replied indignantly, "What do you mean?" Wendling regarded him indulgently and said, "Don't be a child! Why else would you be living there?" and added, "They are even talking about you and the Webers in Munich. You know the reputation the old lady has. She married off Aloysia to Lange.

The only reason she was angry at Aloysia was because she felt Lange should have paid more for her."

Wolfgang had not known this, and suddenly he felt threatened. He decided, that under the circumstances, it would be wise to move.

He did not tell the Webers until he found a room nearby on the Am Graben. He could not move far away. And only when his things were in his new quarters and it was too late to change his mind or to be persuaded, he announced at the dinner table what he had done.

Constanze looked on the verge of tears, Josepha and Sophie seemed unhappy, too, and he assured them that he was not far away, and that he would be dropping in occasionally.

But to his surprise Frau Weber stated, "You are doing the right thing, Herr Mozart. There has been too much talk, as it is, about you and my daughter. This way you will silence the gossipers."

"Fine." He rose to go, appearing confident and feeling very lonely.

At the door Constanze took his hand and said, "You will visit us for dinner sometimes. It will make me happy, Wolfgang."

"Of course." In a sudden impulse he added, "I will continue to get my mail here, since everyone knows that I have been living here."

SIXTY-ONE

———

Wolfgang didn't like his new room, which was dark and small and dirty, while Constanze had kept his rooms clean and tidy, and there were other comforts at the Webers that he missed. He went to the Webers every chance he got, on the excuse that he had to pick up his mail; he didn't admit, even to himself, that he missed Constanze very much, that he had come to treasure her cheerfulness. But as he plunged deeper into the composing of *Die Entführung*, as he polished his sonatas for Artaria, and there were new commissions with the coming of Autumn and the return of the nobility to Vienna, he had no spare time, and his visits to the Webers became infrequent. He was sure he had silenced the gossip, for Papa wrote him approvingly and focused on musical matters, like old times, and made suggestions about the libretto and the music, which Wolfgang liked and found helpful and stimulating.

When he finished the first act Stephanie arranged for the principals to assemble at the Burgtheater to see if the music fitted their voices.

Wolfgang had been composing at a feverish pace, and he was pale and listless as he approached the singers sitting on the bare stage. He felt let down, empty. He had worked so hard and now they would start picking apart his creation. He knew how his music should be sung, but did they?

He had met all the singers at one time or another, but he acknowledged the introductions as if it were a first meeting. As Papa had said, it was better to be formal, distant.

Caterina Cavalieri was a robust woman already, although she was only about the same age as Wolfgang, but she could be a fine Constanze, he thought. Belmonte, Valentin Adamberger, was in his late thirties, the age Raaff should have been, reflected Wolfgang, and should be satisfactory. He bowed to Karl Fischer, the bass who was to sing Osmin, and one of the most admired singers in Germany.

Fischer was several years younger than the tenor, but looked much older, with a heavy, strong face, which should make Osmin an effective and villainous contrast to Belmonte.

Wolfgang had been so intent on these principals, he had not noticed Aloysia, sitting almost in darkness.

Stephanie said, "As I told you, Madame Lange is understudying Madame Cavalieri. Gluck may be having an opera done at the same time, and Madame Cavalieri may be needed for that."

Gluck, naturally, would get preference, Wolfgang thought bitterly. His eyes met Aloysia. She was still beautiful, but there was a hardness about her that had not been there before. He bowed even more formally to her and said, "Should we begin, Herr Stephanie?"

Adamberger sang his opening aria with a tenderness and taste that pleased Wolfgang. Cavalieri performed her first aria with considerable bravura, but her tone was not as pure as Wolfgang desired, and he sensed he would have to adjust his music to her throat. It was Fischer's voice that excited him. Here was singing, which in its own way, rivaled Manzuoli's. The knowledge that Fischer had only one short song in the present text horrified Wolfgang, and he knew this must be remedied.

Then it was Aloysia's turn to sing. As she began sweetly, remembering what Wolfgang preferred and determined to impress him, he could not be indifferent. Her voice was not as powerful as Cavalieri's, but she sang with great expression. She had remembered what he had taught her and she had studied very hard. And she was singing with much warmth. Yet there was still a hardness in her that was not Constanze.

Stephanie thanked the singers, the impresario now, and said, "This gives you an idea of what *The Abduction from the Seraglio* will be like."

Adamberger said, "I thought it was called *Belmonte and Constanze*."

"I've changed it," said Stephanie. "*Die Entführung aus dem Serail* is a much better title. It tells the audience what the story is about."

Wolfgang started to protest Stephanie's taking credit for his idea, but didn't, deciding there were more vital matters to fight about.

"However," said Stephanie, "I do have one piece of bad news."

"The opera has been canceled!" Wolfgang exclaimed.

"Oh, no!" Stephanie said confidently. "Only postponed. Grand Duke Paul's visit has been put back until November, and thus, so has the opera."

Wolfgang sighed with relief. And in a way it was better, for many revisions had to be made, especially for Fischer, and now there was time.

Stephanie dismissed the singers, but stressed, "Study your roles. The opera will definitely go on. I assure you, on my honor."

Fischer lingered to talk to Stephanie, and Aloysia approached

Wolfgang as Adamberger and Cavalieri left and said, "You look well."

He felt he looked awful but he said, "What do you want?"

"I just thought it was so nice that we have met again"

"And you are married now."

She shrugged. "Many people are married. Don't I get a farewell kiss?"

"For the role?"

"Oh, for old times sake. Unless I have become ugly now."

"I don't know you that well." He was turning away when Joseph Lange entered. The actor, a tall, good-looking man, scowled at Wolfgang and appeared suspicious immediately and Wolfgang wanted to laugh. Instead, after Aloysia introduced them, he excused himself, saying he had business to discuss with Herr Stephanie, for Fischer had gone.

The moment the Langes left, Stephanie said, "Why don't you make a cuckold out of him, I'm sure she would be willing now."

Wolfgang didn't answer.

"Do you want her for the lead? She would be satisfactory, and grateful."

"Cavalieri has as good a voice, and is the better actress. Stephanie, what worries me is Fischer."

Stephanie knew what Wolfgang meant, for Fischer had just told him that he would not do Osmin unless there was something worth singing, but the librettist looked puzzled by what the composer was saying.

"Osmin has virtually nothing to sing, yet Fischer has a great voice and he could make Osmin a magnificent scoundrel, comic yet dangerous."

"It will mean a great deal of work."

"I have already composed a grand aria for him."

"When? You didn't tell me anything about it."

"When Fischer was singing his own short song. I have most of it in my head. But the libretto needs more than just changing and enlarging Osmin. Some of the situations are awkward, some of the poetry is unsingable."

"Mozart, what you want is impossible."

"Then I can't go on. I can't write music for a story I don't believe."

Stephanie's impulse was to allow him to quit, there were many other competent composers in Vienna, but the music was too lovely to give up, he had no defense against such melodies. And it was the music that the audience applauded, not the libretto. He said, "There is some merit to what you say about Osmin, and I am sure we can adjust other things, if you are willing to adjust the music."

They spent the rest of the day working on the proposed changes.

But as Wolfgang was leaving, Stephanie said, "I must caution you.

We must not seem good friends. I want it to appear that I am doing this *Singspiel* because the Emperor wishes it for the Grand Duke Paul. I don't want anyone to say that I favor you because of friendship."

Other musicians had warned Wolfgang that Stephanie was not to be trusted, but he was not sure. The next few weeks the librettist made some of the changes he had suggested, yet others seemed to baffle him. Rehearsals were going well musically and he was saturated with the score and in his enthusiasm for it, he had to discuss it with the one person whose musical judgment meant more to him than anyone else. He wrote Papa:

"My Turkish opera has been postponed until November because the Grand Noise now will not be arriving until then. But perhaps it is for the best, for so many alterations are still necessary, and this will give us more time and I will be able to compose with more care.

"Our greatest alterations are in the character of Osmin. Since Fischer possesses an admirable bass voice – although the Archbishop told me that he sang too low for a bass – it will be desirable that we turn his voice to account, especially as he is a great favorite here. In the original libretto, Osmin has but one single little song and nothing more to sing but in the terzetto and the finale. Now however, he will have another aria in the first act, and one in the second act.

"I gave Fischer's first new aria quite complete to Stephanie, having written the music before he knew anything about it. And it should produce a good effect, a comical turn being given to the rage of Osmin through the use of Turkish music. In the execution of this aria, Fischer will also be able to show off his beautiful low tones, yet too, in the quick notes, the audience will be able to feel his anger increasing. And then just as the aria appears to be ending, there comes the *allegro assai* which is in another time and key, and which, just then, should produce an excellent effect. For as a man in such a towering passion outsteps all the boundaries of order and moderation, and wholly loses himself in his excess of feeling, so also must the music.

"As, however, the passions, whether violent or otherwise, must never be expressed to a point of causing disgust – and music, even in the most terrible situations, must never offend the ear, but must always remain music and delight the listener – I have not chosen for the *allegro assai* the key in which the aria is written, but one related to it, A Minor.

"And Belmonte's aria in A Major, *O wie angstlich, o wie feurig*, expresses his throbbing heart by two violins playing octaves. This aria is the favorite of everyone who has heard it, and is written to fit Adamberger's voice. One feels his trembling, his irresolution, and the heaving of his swelling bosom by a crescendo. And one hears the whispers and the sighs by the first violins *con sordini* and a flute in unison.

"The chorus of the Janissaries is brief and jovial, and just fit for the Viennese.

"But I have had to alter Constanze's voice somewhat to Cavalieri's throat, and I have tried to express *Trennung war mein banges loos,* as much as the style of an Italian bravura aria will permit. However, it does cause me to wonder what our German poets are thinking of, for even if they do not understand the theater or opera, still, they should not have their people sound as if they were speaking to a herd of swine.

"The overture is short, and changes from forte to piano continually; at the forte the Turkish music always accompanies, and in this manner it modulates through the keys. I don't think anyone will sleep through it, even though they had not slept at all the night before.

"Yet I am growing anxious, for all this music has been ready for three weeks, yet I cannot proceed a step further, as most of the story could determine the fate of the music, and he said that he would decide is being altered at my request, and Stephanie says he is very busy with other work and is doing our opera slower than I like. You are quite right in your criticism of the libretto, but he has not badly conceived the character of Osmin. I am also aware that the verses are not as good as they should be, but luckily enough of them fit my musical ideas so that the total should please. By now I think Stephanie realizes that in opera the poetry must always be the obedient servant of the music.

"That is why Italian comic operas invariably please, despite their miserable librettos. The music is supreme, and everything else is secondary to it. Thus, so much more must an opera please when the plot is well constructed and the words written wholly for the music, and not for the satisfaction of a miserable rhyme, which in an opera only does mischief. Librettists who write in rhyme should go to the dogs. Yet I would be delighted to be united with a true poet, one who understands our music theater. I know very well what words are best for my music. But since we do not live in utopia, I have to work with what we have.

I am happy that you are feeling better, and that you like what you have seen of the score. Your ever loving and obedient son, W. A. Mozart."

Artaria accepted the six sonatas, although they said they must be altered in what they called "the too original places." They also asked whom he wanted them dedicated to, which was the custom, and which could determine the fate of the music, and he said that he would decide by the time the sonatas were published in December.

While he worked on the opera and the sonatas, he was asked to compose a serenade. He could not refuse this commission, for the patron, Frau Therese, was the sister-in-law of court painter, Joseph Hickel, who wanted to play the serenade for his friend, von Strack, Joseph's chief chamberlain.

Since both men were favorites of the Emperor, Wolfgang saw this as another chance to impress him with his music. He wrote the serenade with great care despite the shortness of time. He put it in E Flat and scored it for two clarinets, two horns, and two bassoons. And while this was regarded as incidental music, light, cheerful, to be played outdoors as well as indoors, in a garden as well as within a chamber, Wolfgang gave the instruments vivid melodies and graceful tempos as if they were having a festive conversation with each other. And since it was to be played by friends, he made it as much a joy to play as to hear.

In addition to being performed for Frau Therese and von Strack and Joseph Hickel on her name day; two weeks later, on Wolfgang's name day, while he was finishing an aria for Fischer just before going to bed, the musicians who had performed this piece before, serenaded him with it from his courtyard. Wolfgang had written this music to be practical, but he could not resist this act of good fellowship. Deeply touched, he insisted that the musicians be his guests at a tavern on the Kohlmarkt. By the time the evening ended it had cost him more than the serenade had earned him.

But long after the musicians were gone and he lay in bed and watched the dawn appear, he kept hearing the music. That gave him such happiness. It seemed inconceivable that things could go wrong in Vienna.

He was disappointed that the performance for Joseph Hickel and von Strack brought no request to play for the Emperor.

He was almost penniless, for he had not received one kreutzer for *Die Entführung* or the sonatas, when Prince Cobenzl said, "I have a new pupil for you, Josepha Auernhammer, the daughter of the economic counsellor. He has performed valuable services for Vienna, and I would appreciate if you could teach her. With your instruction she could become a concert pianist. And she will pay you the same fee my cousin does."

"Thank you," said Wolfgang. This was opportune, but he wondered when he would have time to rest, he had so much to do now.

Josepha wanted to take four lessons a week and her father, who doted on her, was willing to pay Wolfgang whatever he asked. She was very fat and she practiced with such energy that her sweating caused her to stink and he could hardly sit beside her, yet she insisted on cuddling close to him every chance she got and wore so little that her fleshiness was even more evident. But she had become his best-paying pupil, and his chief support, and her infatuated father was eager to have her perform and promised to invite everyone of importance in Vienna and to pay him generously. When Wolfgang accepted the proposal for a concert it increased his fees, but as he was at Josepha's house daily, it increased his discomfort. The contrast between the fat, sweaty Josepha and the slim, attractive Constanze heightened until the more he was revolted by the former the more he craved the latter.

Die Entführung was in full rehearsal and scheduled to be performed for Grand Duke Paul in less than a month now, and there was so much yet to be done on the score. And Wolfgang still was not satisfied with the text, for some of Stephanie's changes were worse than the original situations, but Osmin's role had been improved and the principals were singing excellently. Then, two weeks before November 25, the date of the opening, Stephanie asked Wolfgang to wait after the company left.

Wolfgang was in high spirits. It had been the best rehearsal so far and the music was starting to sound as he had conceived it, but Stephanie looked gloomy. Was he angry about all the changes he had suggested?

Stephanie got to the point at once. "The court has decided that *Die Entführung* is too frivolous for Grand Duke Paul. Gluck's *Alceste* is to be done instead, at the theater of the Schönbrunn palace, in Italian."

"In Italian? After the trouble we went to creating a German opera?"

"Grand Duke Paul says that German is virtually unsingable."

"But I have made it singable. And what about all the Emperor's talk of establishing a German opera?"

"Joseph does not want to offend our Russian guest. He may become our ally. But our abduction opera will be done. Another time."

"What about the singers? Won't this be a great blow to them?"

"Several will sing in *Alceste*. The others . . ." Stephanie shrugged.

"What is the real reason?"

"I told you, Mozart."

"You told me what you were supposed to tell me. But why Gluck instead of Mozart?"

Stephanie hesitated, not certain he should reveal the truth, but then, wanting to keep the friendship of the composer and still determined to get *Die Entführung* produced, for it could help his career, he said, "The Emperor said, 'I know what Gluck can do, I do not know what Mozart can do.'"

SIXTY-TWO

Frau Weber refused to allow Constanze to accept Wolfgang's invitation to attend the concert at the Auernhammers'. She said, "People will assume that you have serious intentions, Herr Mozart. And you don't, do you?"

They stood in the Weber living room and Constanze was agitated. How could her mother embarrass her so! She would drive him even further away.

Wolfgang didn't know what to say. If ever there was a time when it was difficult to be serious about anyone, it was now. There was so much to do in music, and so much uncertainty, and he was not sure how he liked Constanze. But to see her looking so sad was disturbing. He said rapidly, "I am fond of Constanze, she has been friendly and obliging."

"That's just it," said Frau Weber, "some people think too obliging."

"That's not true!" But Constanze looked even more unhappy, and he hurried to add, "but I do like her. There's no harm in that, is there?"

"If everyone was as understanding as we are, no," said Frau Weber. "But I don't want to be the innocent cause of any misfortune to you."

"Constanze is no misfortune!" declared Wolfgang, and then he halted abruptly. He had almost committed himself, and he mustn't.

"She is still a child. I think you should stop coming here. Unless – "

"Unless – what?"

"You are a man of the world. You know the proper thing to do."

"Mother, how could you!" Constanze cried out. "Wolfgang has been nicer to me than anyone else, and you make him sound like a scoundrel."

"Herr Mozart doesn't think so. Do you, Herr Mozart?"

Wolfgang didn't know what to think. He had never seen Constanze so agitated, and he was very upset himself.

Frau Weber warned, "Don't say anything that you will regret later."

"I regret nothing that has happened between Constanze and myself."

"Bravo! Spoken like a gentleman!"

"Mother, he is a gentleman."

"I said he is. But who will support you when I am not here?"

"Wolfgang, please don't pay any attention to my mother. If you want to see me again, I hope you will. Whatever people say."

"My daughter forgets that she is not yet of age, and can do nothing without my consent or that of her guardian."

Wolfgang, afraid that one more word and he would commit himself irrevocably, fled from the house wondering if he would ever see her again.

He was grateful for the distraction of the Auernhammer concert. But while Josepha played with musical sensitivity and as he had taught her, he saw her as an overripe melon about to burst and splatter him with her emotion. At the end of the concert he was relieved that his friends crowded around him to congratulate him, and separated him from her quivering flesh and possessive intensity. Prince Cobenzl expressed his regrets over the postponement of *Die Entführung*; Count Pálffy assured Wolfgang that if Stephanie said the opera would be done, it would be; Countess Thun said that Fraulein Auernhammer had played with distinction and perhaps it would be appropriate if he dedicated his sonatas to her.

Wolfgang drew her aside to ask why.

Countess Thun pointed out, "Her father has helped many people here."

Wolfgang admitted, "And he has been generous with me."

"He would be even more so, under certain circumstances."

"Are you suggesting that I should be more attentive to Josepha?"

"You wouldn't have to worry about earning a living. And she is musical."

He felt betrayed, and he didn't answer.

She said, "I'm only trying to be practical, Wolfgang, and helpful."

"What about my nature? Should I be false to it?"

"Will Constanze satisfy it?"

"I am not seeing her any more."

Countess Thun regarded him skeptically.

"Don't you believe me?"

"That is not the question. But you are impulsive, good-hearted, and quick to defend the abused, especially if she seems to be a Cinderella."

"Would you believe me if I dedicated the sonatas to Josepha?"

"The Auernhammers would buy many copies."

Wolfgang felt better, until he announced this to Josepha and her father. They looked so triumphant he was embarrassed, but he could not withdraw the dedication, for Herr Auernhammer was announcing the news to his guests as if it were a gift from the Emperor.

He was relieved by the approach of Baron van Swieten. Gottfried had aged very little, and they embraced each other affectionately. Van Swieten, now president of the court commission on education and director of the court library, wanted Wolfgang to meet a good friend and musical connoisseur.

Baron Raimund Wetzlar von Plankenstern bowed as Van Swieten introduced him by his full title, and said, "The Baron is kind, but it is a new title, given my family by Maria Theresa, and so, a bit more pompous than most."

Wolfgang smiled, amused. He liked Wetzlar's appearance. Wetzlar was attractively youthful, with expressive and animated features.

Wetzlar said, "It was a joy to hear such lovely music. Herr Mozart, people are always talking about how birds sing, but truly, you outdo them."

Josepha said, "Wolfgang couldn't write bad music even if he tried."

"Yes, I could." The emotion and effort that went into his music was often immeasurable. "It is much easier to write bad music than good."

"If I may differ," said Wetzlar, "I wonder if it is, for you, Herr Mozart. Your ear and taste must protect you against that."

"It is nice of you to say so. Are you a musician, Baron Wetzlar?"

"No, regretfully. I have no ear at all."

"But taste," said van Swieten, "excellent taste."

Josepha asked Wolfgang to dance, and this angered him. He loved to dance, but he preferred to choose his partner. There was no pleasure moving about the floor with Josepha. Her flesh bounced against his with an irritating familiarity. He felt tied to her while her worshiping father watched them approvingly as if already his Papa-in-law.

Terrified where their relationship was leading, he excused himself suddenly, saying that he didn't feel well.

But he couldn't fall asleep that night. He was so lonely, so unhappy. He had remained chaste because he could not fondle someone he did not love. Yet he knew the ways of the world as well as any man, one did not have to be a Don Giovanni to understand the frailties of the flesh. He had had many opportunities, but the vulgarity of whores sickened him. And the French disease was widespread and he felt a responsibility to his music that made such a risk impossible. Yet he was in such a dilemma. He craved Constanze so: the more Josepha had pressed against him, the more he had yearned for Constanze. But he could not seduce an innocent girl, although she might be willing. He must forget her, he told himself, she was a romantic illusion, a plaything of his imagination, be sensible, be indifferent. He turned toward the wall but the doubts, the scruples, the apprehensions and the desires remained and drove him in opposite directions.

The next day he went to see Constanze. He knocked on her door, not sure what he would do if her mother answered, and when it was Constanze, as if she had expected him, he was relieved. Yet he stood mutely and she cried out, "Wolfgang, what are we going to do? My mother says you can't come here any more." Constanze fell into his arms, weeping. "She is keeping me a prisoner here. It is as bad as that Seraglio you are writing about."

Up to now, with all his feeling, it hadn't occurred to him that there was anything to do. He asked, "Where is your mother?"

"Out. But she will be back soon. She went to console Aloysia, who is distraught because of the postponement of the Seraglio opera."

"I never promised Aloysia anything. She is merely an understudy."

"Do you still love her?"

"I . . ." Was that true, whatever he pretended. Then he remembered a basic rule of his life: he could not love anyone who did not love him. He declared suddenly, "I love you."

"Oh, Wolfgang!" She embraced him passionately and stopped crying. "Then we can get married. I can't stand my mother much longer."

"But we are not even engaged."

"It is because I love you that I don't want you to do anything wrong."

"We must think out a few things."

"Don't you want to marry me?"

"I didn't say that."

"You haven't even proposed," she said, almost petulantly. "What are you waiting for, Wolfgang? To ask your father?"

For a moment he was furious. Then she was saying he must leave, her mother would be returning any instant and must not find him here, and that was more than he could take. He blurted out, "Will you marry me?"

Her tone softened at once. "Dear Mozart, I will be honored."

"I will speak to your mother, when it is opportune."

"Do you have to?"

"You are a minor. To do it any other way would cause a scandal. Be patient, let me make the proper plans, and I will keep in touch with you, somehow. But don't say anything to anyone until I tell you. Promise?"

Constanze promised, and he assured her that they would be married as soon as it was practical.

SIXTY-THREE

=====

Wolfgang wrote Papa of his love for Constanze and of his wish to wed her, and waited for Papa's permission and blessing. He wanted him to be the first to know, and he spoke in detail of his need to marry and of his ability to provide for the future. Then before anything else could be done about Constanze, the Emperor asked him to compete in a clavier contest with Muzio Clementi at the Hofburg Palace on Christmas Eve for the entertainment of the Grand Duke Paul of Russia and his Grand Duchess.

He prepared carefully, practicing many hours for the contest, and for the performance borrowed the best pianoforte in Vienna, Countess Thun's Stein. She also lent him her winter carriage, although he lived within walking distance of the Hofburg, and he was grateful for her foresight, for Christmas Eve was snowy and blustery and her closed carriage kept his fingers warm and pliant and his fine clothes immaculate. He was still angry over the Emperor's substitution of Gluck's *Alceste* for *Die Entführung* and he was determined to show him *what Mozart could do.*

Everything he wore this evening was chosen with an eye to elegance and fashion, for Joseph, despite his talk of austerity, liked attractive people about him. Wolfgang was especially proud of his blue waistcoat which matched his eyes, and its silk damask lining that was as soft as Constanze's skin. It was the most extravagant article of clothing he had ever bought, and he was glad now that he had been able to give Josepha many lessons, for they had made this possible. He also wore white silk stockings, silver buckles, but no ruffles on his sleeves as did most men of fashion, for they could interfere with his playing.

He approached the Hofburg by way of the Kohlmarkt and the Michaelplatz, and passing Stephanie's apartment, he wondered if the librettist would be at the palace. He had not seen Stephanie for two weeks, and he was beginning to think that *Die Entführung* had been postponed permanently.

His mood improved as he neared the Leopold wing where the Emperor's apartments were. It was one of the four gigantic wings of the Hofburg that were on the Burgplatz and which formed a great oblong square – probably the largest courtyard in the world, he thought – and tonight, the gray stone walls of the palace, coated with new snow, shone with a silver grandeur. There were other closed carriages at the entrance, which was the Emperor's own, with the royal Hapsburg emblems of the cross, the crown, and the imperial eagle over the huge wrought-iron door.

Von Strack was waiting to greet him and to escort him to the music room, and Wolfgang took that as a sign of the Emperor's favor.

He was gratified that he had given so much attention to his toilet, for the chamberlain was wearing a waistcoat of precisely the same quality as his, and white silk stockings and silver buckles. Nothing that would outshine the Emperor, yet nothing that would offend him. And since von Strack reflected Joseph's taste, Wolfgang was pleased with his own.

Von Strack was a lean, taut man, with sharp features, and Wolfgang was surprised that von Strack, who could be genial, was quiet now.

He noticed that most of the rooms von Strack led him through on the way to the music salon had the same motif: white walls with panels of a deep red brocade and gilt trimmings. He liked their spaciousness and high ceilings and windows, the parquet floors, massive chandeliers, and white porcelain stoves that were fantastic in their beauty and variety and were like baroque sculpture. Yet with all the grandeur, there was much austerity, and he did not find this palace as beautiful or unique as Schönbrunn. But Joseph preferred the Hofburg, to assert his independence of his mother, who had favored the country palace.

At the doorway of the music salon von Strack halted abruptly and said, "Herr Mozart, I trust you are prepared to play your very best."

"I always am."

"I know. But this is a very special occasion. The Emperor is wagering our Russian visitors that no Italian can outdo a German on the clavier, and he will be displeased if you are surpassed."

"You are aware of my abilities, Herr von Strack."

"That is why you have been invited. But Clementi is a great virtuoso. And our Russian visitors would enjoy seeing us uncomfortable."

"Herr von Strack, I would be honored to serve the Emperor in whatever capacity he wishes." But the chamberlain didn't rise to this bait, and didn't give any indication of Joseph's feelings about employing him.

At the music salon Wolfgang felt as if he were approaching a jury, not an audience. He would perform as naturally as breathing, but this trial didn't depend on taste, it depended on emotion. His spirits rose as he saw Prince Cobenzl, Count Pálffy, Baron van Swieten, and Baron

Wetzlar. And he liked the quality of the music salon. It was spacious enough to carry the sound correctly. The upholstered chairs were comfortable, and no one should become restless too soon. And the huge porcelain stove should keep both the audience and the pianists warm.

The Emperor entered suddenly with the Grand Duke and the Grand Duchess, through high white doors which were cleverly hidden in the wood paneling.

The dark, heavy Grand Duke Paul was sullen, as if he didn't want to be here, and Wolfgang recalled the gossip that he had become somber, a Hamlet, because, upon the death of his father, Peter III, his mother, Catherine, had refused to allow him to become co-ruler with her as Maria Theresa had done with Joseph, but had made herself sole ruler of Russia.

But the attractive Grand Duchess was animated and stood close to the Emperor, who was very attentive. And Joseph said to his Russian guests as Wolfgang was presented to them, "Mozart is a great talent, a genius."

The Grand Duchess exclaimed, "I hear that Clement, is better!"

"We will hear," the Emperor said jovially, "and then decide."

Muzio Clementi, standing in the rear waiting to be recognized, saw a little man bowing with such grace to the Emperor and in such an elegant attire he assumed that this was a gentleman-in-waiting, and he was astonished, a minute later, to discover that it was Mozart.

Wolfgang was taken aback by Clementi's good looks and thought, this gave his rival an immediate advantage and the Italian, only a few years older than himself, was young enough to eliminate the asset of precocity.

However, both musicians, when they were introduced to each other, were full of civilities and compliments until the Emperor, bored by their politeness, stated, "It is time we began. Her Excellency, the Grand Duchess, is wagering on Clementi, while I am supporting Mozart."

The Grand Duchess said, "Would you like to increase the wager, Joseph?"

"I would be delighted."

They doubled, then tripled their wager, although the nature and the amount of the bet was not disclosed, and Wolfgang saw that the Emperor had grown intense, as if his victory had become a matter of honor to him.

There was not a clavier player in the world that Wolfgang felt second to, but he was sorry that such stress was being placed on this contest. He was relieved to see that Countess Thun's Stein had arrived safely, while Clementi was to play on the palace pianoforte.

The Emperor commanded Clementi to start, since he was their guest.

Three keys stuck but Clementi was gracious and said, "It is nothing," and went on with great technical dexterity and aplomb, and to cover these mishaps played his sonata *presto* and *prestissimo*, although this was much faster than the written tempo of the piece, Wolfgang observed critically.

Before the applause had died away the Emperor cried to Wolfgang, "Fire away!" as if calling him to battle.

But at the Stein there was nothing but the music and the instrument. He was playing one of his own sonatas, and it became a pianoforte performance new to Clementi. Although he had heard much praise about Mozart as a performer as well as a composer, this was playing different than he had ever heard or expected. Mozart played without any mannerisms, gestures, or flourishes, yet the ease and grace of his hands was astonishing. And he played with a precision and clarity that gave the music a magical purity. There was not one note that was calculated or perfunctory. Each was treated with the same care and spontaneity. Here was a unique performing musician, thought Clementi, one who commanded such mastery of the music and the pianoforte and of himself, they became one and the same thing. It was playing to remember for a lifetime.

Yet by the time they started their last number, Clementi – with all his admiration of Mozart – was forcing himself even more to excel his competitor. They were improvising now, and Clementi was completely the virtuoso. The more Mozart had performed with spirit, grace, ease, and an extraordinary control, the more Clementi played with brilliance, with a flashing technique, bravura-style, and with a rapidity of speed and an elaborate ornamentation that was spectacular in its execution.

The applause was very loud and Wolfgang saw the Emperor frowning, for this approach was so different from his own, and even the Grand Duke Paul had stayed awake while the Grand Duchess looked triumphant.

But he could not deviate from his own style. He made no effort to compete with Clementi in speed or brilliance or power of execution, but played the precise shading and tempo with an enunciation that was flawless. When he played *pianissimo* his music sang as softly as was possible, and when he played *forte* he articulated with the greatest care. And there was his enormous evocation of feeling. As he improvised he imagined Constanze listening intently, and Papa and Mamma and Nannerl, and the melodies became radiant moments in his hands. The music soared and he had a sense of physical delight. He felt in a state of grace.

He played with such expressiveness, with such impeccable taste, yet his touch was so light, reflected Joseph, he made Clementi sound like a hammersmith. It was as if he had been born from this instrument, and everything flowed from his imagination and hand. Joseph remembered how his father had called the child Mozart a "Kleinen Hexenmeister" – "a small wizard," he whispered to the Grand Duchess who was listening with rapt attention, and she nodded, and motioned for him not to disturb the playing.

She was thinking, just when his music and his performance seemed simple, a sensuous richness rose from a depth of feeling that touched her to the heart and gave her a realization of emotions within herself that she had not known existed. She had liked Joseph's flirting because she could not endure her husband, but it was love she needed, not frivolity, and suddenly she moved away from Joseph and leaned toward the music to hear it better.

The Grand Duke Paul was listening intently, too, for the darker passages expressed his own inner agitation, and he wished he had an outlet for his passion as Mozart did.

Wolfgang was aware that a great silence had fallen on the audience and when he finished there was an audible sigh as if they had been holding their breath.

He realized that he had pleased, for the Emperor exclaimed, "Mozart won!" and the Grand Duchess agreed and the Grand Duke Paul said suddenly, as if speech were an effort but this had to be said, "My good friend, Prince Dmitri, spoke highly of your prowess, but I thought he exaggerated. Herr Mozart, my country would be honored by your presence."

Joseph said, his competitive instinct aroused, "We would be sorry to lose you, Herr Mozart, to Russia or to anyone else."

"Your Majesty, my own country will always have first claim on me."

He waited for the Emperor to say I won't let you go, but Joseph merely smiled and said, "I am delighted the performance was so entertaining."

"I hoped you would be pleased, Your Majesty."

"Indeed! You convinced our visitors that we have clavier players in Vienna that are the best in the world."

"Vienna is a clavierland. I am always at your service, sir."

Everyone had moved away to allow Wolfgang a minute of privacy with the Emperor and Joseph said, "I hear that you are getting married." And when Wolfgang looked stunned that the Emperor knew, he laughed and added, "Herr Mozart, the news is all over Vienna. Didn't you know?"

"Oh, yes," said Wolfgang, wondering whom he could trust.

"Wouldn't you want your sovereign to know?"

"Of course, Your Majesty. I am honored by your interest."

"You know I have the welfare of all my subjects at heart."

"You are gracious, sir."

428

"That was why I was surprised when I heard who you were marrying."

"Don't you approve, Your Majesty?"

"It is useful for a musician to marry a rich wife. As Gluck did. And Salieri. It permits them to be more productive."

And so you won't have to help me, Wolfgang thought sarcastically, but he said, "I hope to gain enough by my genius to support the woman I love." Then, as he saw Joseph smiling cynically, he declared, "Your Majesty, I would not know what to do with a rich wife – she would expect my undivided attention and cause me to neglect my compositions."

"You must never do that." Joseph's tone grew serious. "I am sorry your Seraglio opera had to be put off. Adamberger and Fischer praised your score highly to me, and implored me to have it done."

"How do you feel, sir?"

"I am curious, naturally. We will try to find a place for it."

"And for me, sir, I hope, in your Kapelle."

Joseph said sternly, "You must be patient. You are a very young man."

"Your Majesty, I will be twenty-six soon."

"And Gluck was not appointed Kapellmeister for the court opera by my mother until he was forty. Von Strack will reward you for tonight's concert." The Emperor walked away abruptly.

A moment later Clementi was congratulating Wolfgang, declaring, "Never have I heard such a noble, melodious style of performance," and the Italian virtuoso was thinking that he must acquire some of Mozart's style.

Wolfgang bowed and replied, "Thank you. I found your performance interesting, too. You are an excellent cembalo player, with considerable power in your execution, and a brilliant right hand." But Wolfgang said to himself: *And without a kreutzer's worth of taste or feeling, a good technician, but essentially only a mechanic, nothing more. Clementi's best passages were his thirds, which I did when I was five.*

Two things that followed did impress Wolfgang. As he was about to leave von Strack informed him that he would receive fifty ducats for his playing, with the compliments of the Emperor, which was half of what Colloredo had paid him for all of last year – and now, perhaps, he could afford to marry.

And Baron Wetzlar said to him, "I am grateful van Swieten introduced you to me. Herr Mozart, you are one of the world's great natural resources."

If this were true no one should object to his marrying Constanze, not even Papa.

SIXTY-FOUR

===

Give his permission? His blessing? How could Wolfgang expect such a quixotic gesture? Several days had passed since Leopold had received the letter announcing his son's wish to wed Constanze, and he still could not accept the idea. He sat at his desk studying Wolfgang's words in the hope of finding a way to answer him without alienating him further, but as he reread the following he found no solution. His son had stressed:

"I would have told you of my true feelings before, but I did not want you to find fault. But since what you think and feel about me is very important, I prefer that you hear from my own mouth what has come to be vital to me. Most beloved father, please listen carefully. Yes, you may have guessed it by now – I am in love and I want to marry. And in the hope that you will understand, these are my reasons.

"Nature speaks in me as urgently as it does in any man, in fact, more insistently than in most men. Yet I cannot appease nature as do most men. I care too much for God, and I have too much regard for what the world would say, and too much honor to seduce an honest girl. And too much loathing of the French disease, and too much respect for my health to satisfy my nature with whores. Thus, I give you my word that I have never touched any woman in this way. But it has been difficult, Papa, to remain chaste. My senses were stirred at an early age. Even as a child, when I played in Paris, London, and Vienna, many lovely, elegant ladies thanked me for my music by kissing and fondling me. But always you said I must wait. I must respect my virtue as I respect my music.

"Yet how much longer must I wait? I will be twenty-six soon, and, as you know, I am not an ordinary twenty-six. I have lived in an adult world almost all my life; sometimes, with all that has happened to me, I feel that I have lived several lifetimes by now. So I cannot make light of my nature, or disregard it much longer.

"Even so, I am aware that this reason, however potent, does not justify love or marriage. But my temperament and the way you brought me up does make a wife essential to me. From childhood you and Mamma raised me to prefer a quiet domestic home life to one of dissipation. That is what will enrich me, not one woman after another, *à la* Don Giovanni. I, who all my life, never had to look after my own possessions, clothes, linen, find nothing more indispensable to me than a wife. As it is now, circumstances frequently force me to spend wastefully because I do not have the time to attend to such matters. But I am sure that with a wife I will be able to arrange my affairs far more sensibly and carefully than I am doing alone. For then, I would have an orderly life. In my judgment, a single man is just half alive. This is a situation I have given considerable thought to and I do not intend to change my mind.

"But who is it that I love? That I want to marry? Yes, it is one of the Webers. Please, dear Papa, do not be shocked, do not reproach me and say that you told me so. I am in love with Constanze, the middle one.

"The others, ah, I agree with you – never in one family have I seen such variations in character. The mother is loud, indolent, selfish, and not to be trusted. Aloysia is always looking out for her own advantage, and will play the coquette with anyone if it will serve her purpose. Sophie, the youngest, is too naïve to know what is happening around her; she is simply a silly, easy-going child. She needs God's protection, or she will be quickly seduced. The oldest daughter, Josepha, has a fine voice, and with the proper teaching she could sing like an angel, but she is even lazier than her mother, and vain and ambitious.

"Constanze, however, is the sweetest, cleverest, nicest girl, the one jewel in the lot. She takes care of everything, and yet they insist that she does nothing right. Oh, what a martyr her family has made of her.

"But I want you to see her as she is. She is not ugly, yet she is certainly not beautiful. Her entire beauty is in her dark eyes and attractive figure. She is not witty, or worldly, but she is sensible enough to fulfill her duties as a wife and mother. And she is very thrifty. She has had to dress cheaply, for whatever the mother has managed to do for her children has been done for the others. Yet like every girl of spirit, she would like to dress cleanly and neatly, but not like a lady of fashion. She is good with a needle and can make most of her own clothes; she does her own hair every day, and very prettily; she is a fine cook and knows how to keep house, and is the only one who has made any effort to keep 11 Am Peter tidy, for she has such a kind heart.

"And I love her and she loves me. So how could I find a better wife!

"I would also like you to know, Dear Father, that I did not lie to you. When I quit the Grand Mufti's servitude, I was not in love with

431

her, but it grew from her tenderness and consideration while I resided in her house.

"And I am almost sure that I will have an assured income. I have three good pupils, and all of musical Vienna is available to me.

"So please, my dearest and most beloved father, I implore your *permission* to rescue my unhappy beloved, and your *blessing* will make us very happy. I have revealed the deepest recesses of my heart to you and I hope you will respect it and treat it with all the compassion at your command. I remain your always loving and obedient son, W. A. Mozart."

But, thought Leopold, how could he support what he did not believe in? Yet still unsure what to do, he asked Nannerl's advice. This was something he seldom did, but a woman's judgement might be best at such a time, before a hasty word shattered his relationship with his son into irreparable bits.

Nannerl was pleased that Papa was consulting her for a change and she tried to sound very wise. "Do not oppose him openly – that will make him stubborn. But why don't you suggest that the Webers should give a dowry. If someone wanted to marry me, you would be asked for one."

Leopold smiled suddenly. "The Webers would never be able to give one."

"So, say that you have no objection to Constanze Weber, that from his description, which you accept, she must be a fine person. But that it is the custom for the bride's family to furnish a dowry, and until that is done – regretfully, you will have to defer your permission."

Leopold put that in writing.

Then Nannerl said, wondering whether her brother really understood women, "Doesn't he realize that the Webers are out to trap him?"

"A young man in love always thinks it is his charm."

Wolfgang returned home from his contest with Clementi to find a frantic message from Constanze, saying that her mother was sending her away unless he could give satisfactory assurances to her guardian. And the next day, as he prepared to visit her, there was an answer from Papa. It was moderate and affectionate as he had hoped, but it didn't give Papa's permission and blessing. Papa said that would have to be withheld until the Webers gave a dowry as a sign of their good faith.

It was a distraught Wolfgang who arrived at the Webers. He prayed that he had come in time. Yet to ask for a dowry? Where would they get that?

Frau Weber answered the door as if she expected him.

Had she written the message, he wondered, to lure him here?

Frau Weber declared, "You have behaved irresponsibly, Mozart."

"Where is Constanze?"

"In safe hands. With her guardian."

"Because of the letter you wrote me?"

"Constanze wrote it. But I found out. She can't keep anything from me. Mozart, do you really want to marry her?"

"You know I want to . No matter what you do."

"Her guardian, Herr Thorwart, will decide that. He is inside, waiting to talk to you."

"Is that why you had Constanze bring me here?"

"I told you, she wrote the note of her own accord, but Herr Thorwart, hearing the rumors about you and my daughter, decided to put a halt to your compromising her. But if you are afraid to talk to him . . ."

Wolfgang stepped inside. He knew Johann Thorwart, tall, thin, in his forties, who was noted for his skill in advancing himself, it was his one talent. Stephanie had warned him to be nice to Thorwart, that he had influence; van Swieten had said he was an Affligio, not to be trusted; Wetzlar had told him that Thorwart had come from an even more humble background than his own. Son of a tavern attendant, Thorwart had begun as a house servant and a hairdresser, but after marrying a rich doctor's daughter, had risen rapidly. Now, through guile, he had become the business manager and treasurer of the National Theater. It was said that wherever a kreutzer could be made Thorwart would be found.

As they stood face to face, Thorwart declared, "You could ruin the poor girl. You have no assured income. You will jilt her."

Wolfgang didn't reply, but turned to Constanze, who was weeping, and asked her, "Did you write the note I received last night?"

She nodded, whispering, "I haven't slept for days. Ever since you asked me to marry you. My mother says it was simply an excuse to entice me."

"Do you think so, Constanze?"

"They won't let me think! They keep questioning me. They want to know what you did, what you said. And had you dishonored me."

"What did you answer?"

"Wolfgang, I told them the truth. You are a gentleman. Then they said they would send me away if you visited me again unless . . ."

Thorwart cut in, "We cannot allow you to associate with Constanze unless you sign a written agreement to marry her within three years."

"What about a dowry?" Wolfgang asked.

Thorwart exclaimed, "But she is the injured party! You have damaged her reputation. No one will marry her now!"

"I will," Wolfgang said proudly.

"But first you want a dowry."

"It is the custom."

"You are the one who should furnish the money. You have made it impossible for her to marry anyone else. Isn't that so, Frau Weber?"

"Oh, I am sure that Herr Mozart is an honorable man."

"We will see," Thorwart said sternly. "The days that he tampers with an innocent girl's reputation are over. I cannot allow him to have anything more to do with this poor girl unless, in addition to signing a written agreement to marry her within three years, he promises that if he changes his mind, he will give her three hundred gulden a year."

Constanze broke down then, sobbing with a sadness that shook Wolfgang violently, and he thought: how absurd! Nothing was easier for him to sign. He had no intention of deserting her; he couldn't bear that idea. Were they such fools to think that a piece of paper mattered.

Yet, after he wrote down what Thorwart dictated, he read it aloud: *"I promise to wed Constanze Weber inside of three years, and if, for any reason, I should not, I will give her three hundred gulden a year."*

The guardian said, "You must swear on a Bible."

"A *biblia pauperum*, a pauper's Bible," Wolfgang said sarcastically.

"This is no joking matter," Thorwart said harshly. "The world has no respect for poverty. But I know you can afford to take care of this girl. The fifty ducats you are getting from the Emperor comes through my hands."

Wolfgang said positively, "My signature is good enough."

Thorwart was furious until Frau Weber said, "Herr Mozart has been a good friend. I am sure we can trust him. At least, in this."

Thorwart said, "It goes against my judgment, but if you insist."

Wolfgang signed it as he would one of his compositions, distinctly.

But as soon as the guardian left, Constanze wanted to see the document. Her mother handed it to her reluctantly and Constanze said to Wolfgang, "I require no written pledge from you. Your word is good enough for me." Before her mother could halt her, she tore the agreement into shreds.

Whatever of Wolfgang's shabby feeling that had remained was gone now. Constanze was an angel. He loved her more than ever now.

Frau Weber mumbled, "You gave your word, Herr Mozart."

"I intend to keep it. But our marriage must be arranged properly. I want my father and sister to attend the wedding and that will take some time to plan. And we will have to find a suitable place to live."

"You could live here," said Frau Weber. "The board would be moderate."

"Not here!" he declared quickly. "And if you send Constanze away from Vienna, I will follow her, wherever you send her."

Frau Weber said, "Now that you have given your word to wed my daughter and to provide for her properly, we can be friends again."

To show her faith in him, she allowed him to say goodbye to Constanze alone.

Constanze was contrite about having asked him to come here.

"You had to," said Wolfgang. "You had no choice." He could not accuse her of duplicity, not after the way she had torn up the agreement.

"But we won't wait too long? Please, Dear Mozart!"

"No longer than is necessary. We will marry as soon as I get my father's permission and blessing. It is the least I owe him."

SIXTY-FIVE

He wrote Papa what had happened with Thorwart, with Constanze as the heroine and himself as the hero, and Leopold was irate at the guardian and Frau Weber and thought they should be punished for heaping such indignities on his son. Leopold also felt this proved that he was right to withhold his permission and blessing for Wolfgang to marry Constanze.

When his son asked for it again, he repeated what he had written before, that it was the absence of a dowry that troubled him, not so much the money itself, but the lack of faith that indicated, and that now, even more than before, in view of what had happened, until there was a dowry he could not say Yes. He added that it was gracious of Wolfgang to invite him to the opening of *Die Entführung*, which had been rescheduled for July, but at his age the long, arduous journey from Salzburg to Vienna would be too much for his precarious health. This decision hurt Leopold, for he had hoped to hear his son's new opera, but if he attended that he would also have to attend the wedding and he couldn't do that.

With *Die Entführung* back in favor, Wolfgang decided that it would be appropriate to marry Constanze in conjunction with the opening of the opera.

"It will be two elopements," he told her happily, "and perhaps in July, when the weather is better, Papa will change his mind and come to the opera and the wedding." He could not discuss the dowry again with anyone, not even his father, and he hoped that ended the matter, and when the proper time came Papa would give his consent, as his father should.

Constanze was not as optimistic as Wolfgang that his father would give in or come to the wedding, but she did not argue with him. She was grateful that her mother had not put any new obstacles in their path.

The opera was to be performed for Joseph after all, for since Wolfgang had defeated Clementi, he had become curious about it. And Thorwart, who got a percentage of each seat sold at the Burg-theater, was nice to Wolfgang, not wanting anything to interfere with his profits.

Wolfgang, with the coming of spring, became very busy. He had four pupils now, and they occupied all of his mornings. His circle of influential friends had widened and he was in constant demand to play at dinner parties, and he could not turn any of them down, for each invitation was a potential patron. Then he was invited to perform at the first of a series of twelve public concerts in the Augarten, one of the great popular parks in Vienna. Since this had the patronage of the Emperor and was also supported by van Swieten, Countess Thun, and many other prominent patrons, he had to accept, although the first concert was only a modest success.

By the beginning of June the only time he had to see Constanze was late in the evening. And between all these activities he had to work on his opera. Often he composed till one or two in the morning and was so exhausted he could not fall asleep. Yet he had to start each day at seven, for it was the only time his hairdresser could come, and by eight he was fully dressed, and then he tried to compose until ten, before his lessons.

But what tired him most were Frau Weber's bitterly sarcastic remarks.

One night in the middle of June while he and Constanze were sitting in her parlor, discussing where they should live after they married, Frau Weber blurted out, "Mozart, why don't you live with your father? He is the only one you listen to!"

"Mother, that isn't nice!" exclaimed Constanze.

"But it is nice for your marriage to be put off and off, always on the excuse that he needs his father's permission. If he has to wait for that, he will never get married."

Wolfgang said firmly, "It is true I want his permission. But I will marry Constanze, whether I get it or not. In July, as I promised."

"I don't believe a word you say. I ought to put the police on you."

Constanze stood up. "Mother, if you say another word . . .!"

"You will do what?"

"I will leave."

"Bravo! And where will you go? To Herr Mozart's? Unmarried? It will destroy what little reputation you have left."

"I will find a place."

"You don't even know how to catch a man – how do you expect to manage anything else!"

437

"Are you aware of what you are saying? Mother, have you been drinking?"

"What if I have. It is the truth. You wouldn't even have him sitting here now if it wasn't for me."

"How can you say that?" Constanze was so agitated, she was trembling.

"I could say much more if you didn't keep interrupting me."

"Frau Weber," said Wolfgang, "that isn't fair."

"I didn't ask your opinion. As long as my daughter is under my roof I will say to her what I please. Remember, she is still not of age."

The next day Wolfgang arranged for Constanze to stay with the Baroness von Waldstätten, on the excuse that the Baroness was ill and needed Constanze to attend her for a few weeks. Constanze moved when her mother was out, and left a note explaining the circumstances. And since the Baroness was a titled lady, Frau Weber was afraid to provoke her even as she grumbled•that Mozart was abducting her daughter and if Constanze wasn't returned soon she really would go to the police.

Wolfgang was pleased with his stratagem. The Baroness attached great importance to her reputation for being one of the most enlightened women in Vienna. Separated from her husband, a rich Austrian dignitary, she was proud that she could maintain an eminent salon without his help. At her musicals she was often the star attraction. She was a fine pianist and had an insatiable love of music. She was also incurably romantic, as if, because it had been denied her, she sought it for everyone else.

Constanze loved her spacious house in the Leopoldstadt, the suburb between the Danube canal and the Danube river, and which was too far from the *Peterplatz* for her mother to reach on foot, and her mother never took a carriage unless someone else paid for it. But she did wonder if the Baroness, whose chief occupation was pleasure, was interested in Wolfgang. Her Ladyship was a plump thirty-eight, but still attractive, and her mother had said, "A bourgeois man like Mozart is always flattered by the interest of a Baroness. I wouldn't trust him a moment with her."

Yet the Baroness said, "My house is at your convenience, Constanze. It will be a pleasure to outwit your mother."

Wolfgang had hurried off to a rehearsal of *Die Entführung*, and Constanze replied, "But won't people talk about my being here?" The Baroness von Waldstätten's reputation was not above suspicion.

"They will, anyhow. If you stopped people from talking, you would take away their entertainment. They would be bored to death." And she adored playing the matchmaker, the accomplice; it

438

gave her the feeling that she, too, had a role in *The Abduction*. "But now, we must plan your marriage."

"Wolfgang insists he has to wait until he gets permission from his father. And I doubt his father will ever condescend to that."

"It is of the utmost importance to him and you must cater to him."

"I have. I sent his sister gifts, wrote her affectionately, but while I get polite answers, I get nothing else. Sometimes I think my mother is right when she says he uses this as an excuse to put off our marriage."

"She isn't right. She is a shrew, a virago, and not to be trusted."

"Not even by her own daughter?"

"Is that why you are here?"

But Constanze still wondered if Wolfgang really intended to marry her.

The opening of *Die Entführung* was only three weeks away now and Wolfgang, who had his heart set on marrying Constanze the day of the opening, wrote Papa, telling himself it was the last time he would ask permission. "Dear, good father: I must now beseech you, by everything we treasure between us, to give me your consent to marry my beloved Constanze. As it is, I am deeply disappointed that you cannot attend my wedding or opera, but I cannot wait much longer. An immediate marriage is essential for the sake of my honor, and for the sake of hers, too. And the more I wait, the more I become restless, confused, distracted, my heart and head in such a sad condition it is almost impossible for me to compose with any clarity or feeling. That frightens me, for, as you know so well, I have been able to compose under any circumstances. So, dearest father, consent and bless us. For it would hurt me grievously to wed without your permission, but time is growing short, and what is inevitable cannot be postponed many more weeks. Your devoted and obedient son. W. A. Mozart."

A week passed before there was a reply and then Papa said that Wolfgang must not be impatient, that time took care of everything, and that he had a most important commission for him. Sigmund Haffner, the son of the former burgomaster of Salzburg – who at the time of his death in 1772 had been the richest merchant in the town – desired a symphony to celebrate his becoming a member of the Austrian nobility. Since Haffner had been a generous patron in the past, Papa urged Wolfgang to get the piece done for the ennoblement ceremony on July 29.

Wolfgang accepted the commission, to please his father and because he needed the money, and promised to have it done in time, now less than a month away, although he did not know when he could compose the symphony, there was so much yet to be done on the opera.

Rehearsals went on all day and most of the night and what free time he had he used for corrections that never seemed to end. He was still worried about the libretto, it was still too static and obvious to suit him.

He was concerned also about the role of the Pasha. Stephanie refused to cast a singer, saying there was no one available who could convey the nobility of the part vocally, except Fischer, and they couldn't take Fischer away from Osmin. "Or would you want a castrato, Mozart?"

"For Pasha Selim? It would be unbelievable."

Stephanie smiled to himself, thinking that he would show the composer, who was so critical, that the Pasha would be an expression of his skill and the dramatic personification of the story. But he said, just in case *Die Entführung* was a success and he needed Mozart again, "At any event, it is too late to cast a singer and to compose music for the role. And we cannot allow anything to jeopardize our opera."

So Wolfgang reluctantly accepted the fact that there would be no arias for the Pasha and tried to find time to work on the Haffner symphony, and he could only do that if he stayed up all night. He had just found what he wished to say, when he received another urgent request.

Baroness von Waldstätten desired a serenade for her name day, less than a week off and only a few days before the opening of the opera. She said she would appreciate if Wolfgang would whip up something light, but good, since connoisseurs would be attending her musical. She apologized for the shortness of time, and added that she would be eternally grateful if he could do this for her – and to please use wind instruments, for everyone was still talking about the serenade in E Flat he had composed last year.

Hurriedly as that serenade had been created, this one had to be shaped even more hastily. Yet he could not turn her down. This was what she expected as her reward for sheltering Constanze. The sleepless nights he had been giving to the composing of the Haffner symphony were devoted now to the piece for the Baroness. He could hardly keep his eyes open and only his ability to compose whatever the difficulties kept him going.

Since the serenade in E Flat had been for six instruments, and he needed variety for his own sake, he placed this one in C Minor and scored it for eight wind instruments. It was supposed to be entertainment music for a happy social occasion, but as he composed he was pervaded with melancholy.

440

His exhaustion made him somber, and the realization that Papa and Nannerl were not coming to his wedding or to his opera added to his bitterness. This seeped into the serenade, and as his concentration intensified because of the way he had to work, so did the music.

Hearing it at the Baroness' concert, he thought no one could tell he had created it in such a great hurry, it sounded so carefully wrought.

Constanze said, noticing that his eyes were puffy and that he was shockingly pale, "You don't look well. Have you been worrying about us?"

"No more than usual. What day is this?" He had lost track.

"You have been working too hard. I haven't seen you once this week."

"Do you like the serenade?"

"Nice. But awfully heavy, isn't it, for a party?"

"It is what you want to make it." He was tired of analysis, although he was glad that at one point in the music, with all of its seriousness, he had written a love duet between two of the instruments.

Constanze said sadly, "We won't be able to have our wedding with the opening of *Die Entführung*," and tears came into her eyes, for he was not listening. Wolfgang was hearing the theme of the first movement of his Haffner music, grand and imposing as befitted the ennoblement, yet *Allegro con spirito*, which, he decided, should produce an excellent effect.

SIXTY-SIX

═══

Completion of this movement was halted by the opening of *The Abduction from the Seraglio* several days later. Wolfgang was surprised by the excitement at the Burgtheater. His spirits rose when the Emperor came promptly at 6.30 p.m., the scheduled start of the opera, and all the seats were filled to witness his arrival. But as the conductor entered the pit and there were boos amid the applause his heart sank. He sat in van Swieten's box, between the Baron and Countess Thun, with Constanze behind them with Baroness von Waldstätten and Wetzlar, and he longed to shout back.

Van Swieten said, "Don't be upset. It's nothing. Just a few envious composers and their friends. Joseph should like your music very much."

That was the trouble, he thought, staring at the Emperor nodding graciously to his subjects from the royal box. His future in Vienna could depend on one man's taste and he hated that. Yet if Joseph truly cared for the opera the rumors that were circulating in Vienna and Salzburg that he was entering his service could come true. Then there would be no worries about supporting Constanze; he could devote more time to composing; and it would be a slap in Colloredo's face. But he was so weary. He had worked so hard. He had put so much of his own emotion into this music. He had waited so patiently for Papa's permission and his absence hurt deeply.

Papa should be at his side now, congratulating him on getting his opera done. They had been tied together by a bond that was even stronger than blood. How could his father risk that for anything? Was he really jealous of Constanze? He would have given much for a loving family embrace.

The Emperor raised his hand for quiet, and the opera began.

The overture was a symphonic movement in itself, van Swieten reflected, richly orchestrated and finely structured and it led eloquently into the opening aria. And Belmonte, singing of his heart-felt search for his beloved Constanze, was poetic and moving. Osmin's music was superb too, but of a very different kind, and van Swieten understood now why Wolfgang had taken such care with it, Osmin had become such a real, amusing rascal.

How could they hiss any more? Wolfgang wondered. Osmin's second aria was dramatic and powerful, yet not violent, but pleasing and musical. And the acceleration in Osmin's music, to express his passion, was a fine effect, yet there were hisses at the end of this aria. As if by an organized cabal, he decided, probably supported by Gluck or Salieri.

But when Belmonte sang one of his favorite arias, *O wie angstlich, o wie feurig,* Constanze whispered to him, "It is lovely, Wolfgang."

He hoped so. He had composed this aria to express his love for her. Yet the chorus of the Janissaries, which was Turkish and martial, and simple, was applauded much more loudly, and he remembered that Stephanie had told him that the Viennese preferred noisy music, the noisier the better.

He was furious when the closing *terzetto* of the first act, which he had constructed with great care so as to bring forth bravos at this finale, was spoiled by Fischer, who went off and took the other two singers with him. He wanted to rush backstage and warn Fischer not to dare allow this to occur again, or he would stop the perform-ance on the spot, until Fischer was properly rehearsed. He was in such a rage van Swieten had to restrain him. Fischer, who had the best voice, had failed him. Had the bass been bribed? Many con-gratulated him on a fine first act, and he wasn't listening.

Wolfgang didn't feel better until Blonde's aria which opened the second act. Her voice conveyed the grace and delicacy of the music as he had composed it and he sang with her to himself. And Osmin made no mistakes in his duet with Blonde which followed.

The sad aria he had written for Constanze in which she expressed her grief over the absence of Belmonte brought tears to his eyes. Cavalieri sang with such tenderness he was glad he had chosen her over Aloysia.

Constanze sighed, relieved. No one was coughing now, or hissing.

Mozart was so profligate with his music, Stephanie reflected, standing in the wings to keep a tight hold on the production. Barely had Cavalieri finished singing an aria of great poignancy, when the composer gave her another, that in some ways, excelled the first. Mozart had questioned the juxtaposition of these two lengthy arias by the same singer, and had said that the second scene was not dramatic enough. But when he had refused to alter the story and had insisted this was the moment for Constanze to defy the Pasha in the most heroic way, the composer, putting aside his doubts, had responded with music of nobility and virtuosity.

As Cavalieri was singing now, it was as if Stephanie was hearing this aria, *Marten aller Arten,* for the first time. The librettist realized that this scene would have been more effective later, as Mozart had said, but as a display piece for a prima donna it was stunning and Cavalieri was taking full advantage of it. And the audience responded with such enthusiasm Stephanie felt very clever that he had employed Mozart.

But everywhere else Wolfgang's music was dramatic as well as melodic, van Swieten told himself. And how like Wolfgang to give his secondary characters songs as lovely as the principals. Blonde's aria *Welche Wonne* was delightful. Pedrillo's songs were admirable, too, and perfectly expressed his character. The duet where Pedrillo got Osmin drunk enchanted him, and he was fascinated by the skill of the quartet of Belmonte, Constanze, Pedrillo, and Blonde that concluded the second act.

Constanze was happy that the applause had increased enough to drown out the boos; Baroness von Waldstätten was chatting with Countess Thun, while Wetzlar was thinking if Mozart only had a librettist worthy of his music.

Wolfgang wished he could tell what the Emperor was thinking, but the latter was so impassive it was impossible to judge. Yet Joseph was attentive as the third act began and seemed to be listening carefully.

A deep hush had fallen upon the audience. Apparently they had become accustomed to the lyricism of the music, thought Wolfgang, and now wanted to hear more.

Belmonte's aria brought the Countess Thun back to the days of her youth. Waiting to be reunited with Constanze, his music sparkled with eager anticipation and reminded her of when she had loved her husband. But much as she had been moved by Belmonte's aria, she was overcome by what followed. Pedrillo sang a simple serenade that touched her as music rarely had.

Pedrillo's air, for Wolfgang could not think of it as an aria, it was so simply composed, was more than music to him. It was his life, his self. He had carved this melody with such love. This air would rescue him as he would rescue Constanze. Did she realize what he had wrought?

Constanze leaned forward, to be closer to him, and trembled as their hands touched. He wanted her so and he wanted to tell her this, and he prayed that his music conveyed what his words could not.

Constanze sighed, but Wolfgang couldn't tell what she was feeling.

Wetzlar, trying to listen only to the music, was bewildered. He still thought the libretto was dull, almost a nuisance, yet the score brought it to life. He was irritated by the Pasha's lack of music, but it whetted his wish to hear the others. By the end of the opera he found himself standing with most of the audience, shouting, "Bravo Mozart!"

There was a tremendous roar when Wolfgang appeared before the curtain with Cavalieri, Adamberger, and Fischer, and Wetzlar thought: He is a marked man, he is caught in the struggle between the flesh and the spirit, the pagan and the puritan, the sacred and the profane. But could he fight, could he scheme? Wolfgang's red lips were parted in his pale face as he smiled to acknowledge the applause, his eyes were bright as if they had never felt fatigue, yet he looked very small beside the towering Fischer.

Wolfgang had not forgotten or forgiven Fischer's mistakes in the first act. Before he could compliment the bass on how well he had sung the rest of the opera, he had to mention the errors, although Stephanie tried to stop him, and Fischer retorted, "The difficulty is, Herr Mozart writes music for perfect voices, which makes it almost impossible to sing."

"Not if you sing correctly," said Wolfgang. They were in the wings now.

Fischer shrugged, "I did my best."

"You could do better," said Wolfgang. "I will not allow the opera to be done again until we have a rehearsal for the singers."

Stephanie said, "We have already sold out our next two performances."

"Then we will have a rehearsal tomorrow afternoon, before the performance."

Adamberger asked, "Weren't you pleased, Maestro? The audience, once they became accustomed to the music, seemed to love it."

"You sang very well. Everybody did. But all of you could be better."

Von Strack approached Wolfgang, who had become passionate and stated, "Herr Mozart, the Emperor would like to speak to you."

At his box Joseph said, "The libretto doesn't seem original."

"It was probably taken from Bretzner, who took it from four others."

"And the music?"

"It is original. No two of my operas are the same. Sir, what did you think of *The Abduction from the Seraglio?*"

"Too original, too beautiful, too expressive for our ears. And with far too many notes."

"Just as many, Your Majesty, as are necessary."

Wolfgang was dismissed then, without another word.

445

SIXTY-SEVEN

—

It was with some bitterness that Wolfgang resumed work on the music for Haffner. He was gratified that the second performance of *Die Entführung* was even more successful than the first, the Burgtheater was crowded to the ceiling, the applause was far louder than the boos, the cast sang without error, many arias had to be encored, yet he could not forget Joseph's criticism. He was pleased that the audience loved his music, but it was the Emperor who gave the commissions and chose the operas.

As he paced up and down his small room on the Graben a week after the opening, struggling to finish the Haffner music, he gave the slow second movement the same lyrical intensity he had expressed in *Die Entführung*.

But it was difficult to concentrate. All that he had heard from Papa had been a cold letter warning him about the perils of marriage; Papa, for the first time in their relationship, had not congratulated him on the opening of his opera. Constanze, tearful whenever he saw her, said she couldn't wait much longer, and he couldn't wait much longer either.

He was still reflecting on this when young Sophie Weber stood at the doorway of his room and when she saw that he was in, she sighed with relief, although she was in a state of obvious agitation.

"What's wrong?" she asked. Sophie also looked frightened.

"My mother says she is going to have the police take Constanze home. She knows the Baroness isn't ill – the Baroness was seen at the opera. And she says she will have you arrested for abducting her daughter."

Wolfgang gazed at her in astonishment. Sophie was a child, only fifteen, and flighty and easily upset.

"I am not lying, Herr Mozart."

"Does your mother know that you are here?"

"No! She would never forgive me if she knew!"

But Fräu Weber kept a close watch on her daughters and Sophie never left her house without her permission. Yet he lived just around the corner of the Peterplatz and was easy to reach. He asked, "Then why did you come?"

"I don't want her to spoil Constanze's life, as she spoiled Aloysia's."

"But Aloysia was so independent-minded."

"Do you think she wanted to marry Lange? It was my mother's idea."

He was shaken, although he didn't want to be.

"I'd like to see one of us get free of her. But now she is talking of stopping you from marrying Constanze." As he hesitated, she added, "I can't stay away any longer. I've been away too long as it is. She is determined to send the police to bring Constanze home, and to arrest you for abducting her. She is waiting only for Thorwart to decide when."

"And she ordered you to tell me this."

"No, No! I said she doesn't know I'm here. And don't you tell her."

"But now that I know, how will she think I found out?"

"The maid could have talked. Or my mother might have told someone else. I wouldn't wait, Herr Mozart, she may have gone to the police already."

While Wolfgang still suspected that Fräu Weber was behind Sophie, to goad him into marrying, he couldn't take the chance. If Fräu Weber did what Sophie said, it would be a grave indignity and a scandal.

At the Baroness' home he was relieved to learn that nothing had happened so far. He asked her, "Are the police allowed to enter your home? In Salzburg, no commoner can touch the nobility, whatever the provocation."

Constanze was in tears and the Baroness answered gravely, "I cannot conceive of the police entering my home unless I called them. But think of how unpleasant this story sounds. It must be all over Vienna by now."

"Do you think it is a trap to force Constanze to return home?"

Constanze cried out, "How long are you going to wait for your father?"

Wolfgang said, "Baroness, what do you advise?"

"Once you are married, no one can say anything. But you will need Thorwart's permission. Since he is her guardian."

"I will see him at once. Today, if possible."

Wolfgang found Thorwart in the office of the Burgtheater.

Thorwart smiled to himself with satisfaction as he saw Mozart standing in front of him. How simple and sensible it had been to use the police as a threat! And innocent Sophie, purposely allowed to overhear that, had fallen for their ruse without ever realizing it. It was amusing.

Wolfgang said, resolved to attack and angry that Thorwart sat like an inquisitor, "When are you going to give Constanze permission to marry me?"

"You are joking!" He was supposed to ask the questions, not Mozart.

"Not at all. You and her mother have never said Constanze could marry me. It has always been whether I could marry her."

"What are you talking about?"

"You make it sound as if marriage is my decision, when it is yours."

Thorwart felt confused, and thus defensive, and so he tried to be even more unyielding. He declared, "At this moment I am drawing up a petition asking that you be arrested for injuring Constanze's character."

"Because I am marrying her?"

"What? When?"

"Whenever the date can be set. What day do you suggest?"

"I . . ." Thorwart paused, at a loss for words.

"Unless you have been leading me on and don't want me to marry her?"

"Oh, we do!" Thorwart caught hold of himself, fuming that Mozart had dared to put him at a disadvantage. "But we must have assurances."

"We went into that before. I had hoped to marry at once, tomorrow if possible, but you make it so difficult." Wolfgang turned to go.

"Just a moment, Mozart. Tomorrow is too soon, but in a week or two?"

"I must have a definite date. I cannot be kept dangling any longer."

"We kept you dangling?" Thorwart's long, angular jaw dropped.

Wolfgang said severely, "And don't take any liberties with me. You have tried to humiliate me long enough. When I am insulted, I expect satisfaction. Really, I cannot endure this stupidity much more."

Thorwart's mouth was open in a vacuous grin.

"Enough vicious slanders have been spread about me and Fräulein Weber."

"Why are you telling me?"

"Because you probably spread them. You, and her mother. I am

448

sick of the whole intrigue. And now when I want to set a date you won't. I address you seriously and you refuse to give me a straight answer."

"Will August 4 do? It is about two weeks away."

"Yes." For it would also allow Papa one more chance to support him, but he said, "That will give us time to make the proper arrangements."

"I will draw up the marriage contract."

"Immediately. I want no more delays." Then Wolfgang was gone.

That night he wrote Papa with all the clarity at his command:

"Beloved, dearest Father: I am surprised and disappointed that you did not see fit to congratulate me on the fine reception of my opera. Far from being just pleasing, it is such a sensation in Vienna that the public does not want to hear anything else, and it is scheduled for eight more performances.

"The Haffner music has become a symphony as you wished and I am putting it in D Major because it is a key you prefer. But I have been able only to finish the *Allegro* – which is enclosed – I have been so busy with my opera and a serenade for wind instruments which had to be composed in the greatest haste. I am working on the *Andante* and when I complete it, and two minuets and the last movement, I will send them to you. And if I have time I will write a march for it. If this music does not arrive for the ennoblement, use the old Haffner music, no one in Salzburg will know the difference.

"I am unhappy because you have not yet given your fatherly consent to my marriage. *I implore you, if you love me, please send your blessing and permission.* For we are marrying August 4, no matter what happens. The date has been set and I do not intend that it shall be changed. It would make me very sad to wed without word from you, but it is impossible to wait any longer. Your ever loving and faithful son. W. A. Mozart."

He prayed that Papa would respond promptly. He was not certain how much longer he could continue to believe in Papa's wisdom and love.

It was late July when this letter arrived in Salzburg. Leopold had been reading the complete score of *Die Entführung,* and it was, indeed, far more than pleasing. But the marriage announcement was like a blow between the eyes and he had to blink to keep the tears from showing. It made no difference what he said: *Wolfgang was doing what Wolfgang wanted to do.*

When he told Nannerl that Wolfgang was getting married, she wasn't surprised, but said sadly, "So we've lost him after all."

449

"Actually he's been lost to us ever since he left the Salzburg service."

"What are you going to do, Papa dear?"

"Does it matter?" he said with sudden bitterness.

"Of course. He wants your blessing more than anyone else's."

"Yet he does what he wishes, whatever I advise."

"Just the same, your consent would make Wolfgang happy."

The next week became very painful for Leopold as he tried to decide what to do. He stared at the mountains around Salzburg, that Wolfgang had resented so, and recalled how as a young man – Wolfgang's age – and just accepted into the Salzburg court orchestra as fourth violinist, and not yet married because he could not afford to, he had longed to carve LEOPOLD MOZART in bold, bright letters on the Unsterberg. Instead time had moved by inexorably and it was thirty-nine years that he had been in the Salzburg Kapelle and he had never become Kapellmeister, and if he would be remembered, it would be only because of his son. But would Wolfgang, with all his accomplishment, be remembered if he wed a Weber? Leopold assured himself that this was why he opposed the marriage, not for personal reasons.

Yet suddenly it was August 1 and he had not written his son and there was no further word from him, just the *Andante* of the Haffner symphony, and two minuets, but no last movement or march, or explanation, which was most unusual. Wolfgang always discussed his music with him.

To lose this would make life so empty. But as he wrote his consent he was sick at heart. He had always sought to be honest with his son and now he had to lie. He was about to bless what he didn't believe in. Suddenly he paused, unable to write at this moment, thinking of a cherished dream.

Ever since Anna Maria's death, Leopold had been secretly saving money to buy a family funeral plot in the Petersfriedhof in Salzburg. He had even dreamt of bringing her body back from Paris, although the cost would have been prohibitive. He wondered if she had spoken to Wolfgang about wanting to be buried in St. Peter's graveyard, the oldest in Salzburg; she had admired it so when alive. Many times he had visualized the four graves: Leopold, Anna Maria, Nannerl, and Wolfgang Mozart. A family should always stay together, Anna Maria had said. And now this dream was shattered, as were so many others. He had failed, the labor of his life was turning to ashes. He wept as he resumed writing Wolfgang and it was hard to keep his tears from blotting the page. Stricken, bereft, he felt like an old man.

And he had delayed his consent so long he was not sure his letter would arrive in time. God! He missed Mamma so!

The day of the wedding Wolfgang waited in his new rooms on the Hohe Brücke for Papa and Nannerl, telling himself that his father and sister would surprise him at the last moment – it was inconceivable that his family would not come to his marriage. How could they be so cruel! Yet there had been no word, not even an answer to his last letter.

And when the morning passed and there wasn't any sign of them and the hour of his marriage approached, he couldn't wait any longer. He took a last glance at his rooms and prayed that Constanze would like them. He felt so cut off without her. She had been living with her mother while preparing for the wedding, and he had rented these rooms temporarily so that they would not have to stay with Fräu Weber. He had bought linen, china, furniture, and a large matrimonial bed with the ducats he had received for *Die Entführung*. He wasn't sure she would care for his taste, although he had a keen sense of what women liked. These small, dark rooms, with their dank, musty smell – even in August – were not what he desired for raising a family, and he desired that very much.

He put on his white satin vest, his black waistcoat – he preferred brighter clothes, but they would not have been appropriate – and left.

He had not invited any of his Viennese friends because of the presence of Fräu Weber and the circumstances of his marriage. But since he had to have a best man, he had obtained a childhood friend from Salzburg, Herr Franz Gilowsky, Doctor of Medicine. Gilowsky was living in Vienna, an easy-going man of his own age, who would not embarrass him with questions or advice, but express approval, which he needed desperately.

As he walked toward St. Stephen's, where the wedding was to occur, he could not bear his loneliness. Without his family he felt like half a man. If Mamma were only here! Someone from his family should be with him on this day of days. Gradually he saw her elongated face, her high hair, her fair coloring. He had had such a chill, although it was a hot day, but now it was as if Mamma's hand was in his and they were walking to the wedding together and she was as excited as he was. She knew the Webers; she had met them in Mannheim, and they had gotten along well. Mamma would not desert him at such a vital moment.

With the feeling that she was by his side he felt better as he entered St. Stephen's, although he was nervous. He loved the great cathedral, which was the center of Vienna for him. And today it shone in the sun like a magnificent jewel and its superb south tower dominated the horizon. He was grateful that he was being married within its walls, which had given so many sanctuary. He told himself that this was a good omen.

But when he did not see Papa or Nannerl inside, his heart sank. Mamma had vanished, and he still felt so cut off, even when he saw Constanze. She stood between Fräu Weber and Sophie, dressed all in white and her face seemed just as pale. It was a small wedding, indeed, he thought somberly: Cäcilia and Sophie Weber, Thorwart, Franz Gilowsky, and Karl von Kronstorf, District Councillor for Lower Austria and witness for the bride.

Wolfgang and Gilowsky embraced each other, but everyone else was formal.

The guardian, who was a great one for documents, insisted that he read the marriage contract. It seemed satisfactory and Wolfgang noticed that on the seals of the document his was the only one without a coat of arms.

Then the priest was in front of them and as he and Constanze knelt side by side he sensed that she was as frightened as he was.

He thought, Will I be able to please her?

She thought, Can I trust him? Will I be able to hold him?

As they were married he whispered to her, to reassure himself as much as her, "We have the blessing of God, Stanzi. It is all we need."

She began to weep. He couldn't tell whether it was from happiness or sorrow or relief, and he felt so intensely he wept, too, and the priest, deeply moved by their emotion, appeared on the verge of tears. Then Fräu Weber kissed Constanze and wanted to kiss Wolfgang, as if everything was forgiven now that they were married, and he gave her his cheek, unable to bear the thought of her lips on his, and smelled wine on her breath.

The guardian congratulated him and said, "It was about time, Mozart," von Kronstorf assured him everything was in order, and Gilowsky gave him a friendly hug, kissed the bride, and told him that he was a lucky man.

That night the Baroness von Waldstätten gave a marriage feast for the Mozarts, surprising them with a performance of the serenade for wind instruments that he had just composed for her. Now he understood the reasons for the Baroness' haste and he was pleased. The music was suitable, had a fine effect, and he lost some of his nervousness.

But this returned as they entered their rooms. He showed Constanze the china, the linen, yet she seemed reserved, almost remote. Then Wolfgang brought forth his surprise: a ring of Mamma's that he wanted her to wear and a lovely handbag. "Open it, Stanzi, open it," he urged.

There were ten gold ducats in it.

"For you, Stanzi, to spend as you wish. You're free now, free. You will never have to ask anybody, especially not your mother, for anything."

It was the most money she had ever had. She stared at Wolfgang in astonishment and then as he put Mamma's ring on her finger, wishing it were Mamma's wedding ring, but Papa had kept that, she kissed him fervently and cried out, "Thank you, Wolfgang, I will never feel cheap any more."

Now he proudly showed her the spacious matrimonial bed he had bought, the papier-mâché screen which was there for her convenience – he wanted Constanze to feel like a Queen—and as he put his arms around her protectively, she clung to him passionately. Suddenly he realized that she desired him as much as he desired her. That she had been distant because she had not been sure whether he truly loved her.

Afterwards, he laughed with joy and said, "They called the marriage register the Copulationsbuch. It's amazing, how well we are suited to each other."

Papa's permission and blessing arrived the next day.

PART NINE

The Musicians

SIXTY-EIGHT

Two days later Gluck requested a special performance of *Die Entführung*. This was a great honor, for the Royal Kapellmeister was the most famous musician in the Empire and the Emperor's favorite. The one musical taste Maria Theresa, Joseph, and Marie Antoinette had had in common was Gluck.

And immediately after this performance he invited the Mozarts to his home to dine with him. Wolfgang, although he had been taught by Papa from childhood to be suspicious of Gluck, had a deep respect for his ability to compose for the human voice, and he was pleased that Constanze was included in the invitation. He accepted at once.

As they rode toward Gluck's house on the Michaelplatz, Wolfgang said, "It has been more difficult to meet Gluck than the Emperor. Stanzi, it is like a wedding present. He must want to support me now."

"But you told me that he has always stood in your way."

"That's what Papa said. When my first opera was blocked in Vienna, although Affligio stopped it, Papa felt Gluck was behind that. He forbade me to have anything to do with him when I was in Paris. He was right, everything was Gluck or Piccinni and I was ignored. Then *Die Entführung* was postponed and almost pushed off the boards because of his operas. And I am not in love with his intrigues and politics. Should we turn back?"

Their carriage was almost at the Michaelplatz. Wolfgang was in such high spirits ever since their first night together and he was eager to meet Gluck, whatever his doubts, she didn't have the heart to halt him. Yet she had to ask, "Do you think he stood in your way deliberately?"

"I don't know. But now, perhaps, we can find out."

"And you do like his music."

"Almost enough to forgive anything else."

456

"Then you've given yourself the answer."

She took his hand and he helped her out of the carriage as if she were the loveliest and most honored of all the great ladies in Vienna. He had to make an entrance to match the grandeur of this Kapell-meister's house.

And he adored Gluck's location. The mansion was across from the Burgtheater and close to the Hofburg – ideal for a court musician.

Wolfgang also had heard many stories about the lavish way Gluck lived, and as liveried footmen led them toward Gluck's presence he realized that they were true. The rooms glittered with fine Gobelin tapestries, sumptuous carpeting, crystal chandeliers, scrolled furniture, and gilt stucco. The drawing room where Gluck sat, his gouty foot propped up on a cushion, was as magnificent as some of the chambers at Schönbrunn. It reminded Wolfgang of what Papa had written him recently, pointing out that Gluck had wed so favorably that from the day Marianne Pergin, eldest daughter of a rich merchant-banker had become his wife, Gluck had acquired such a large dowry he had been delivered of all economic cares and had been free to compose only what he wanted to compose.

Christoph Willibald Gluck started to rise as he saw his guests standing before him, thinking *Mozart is so young!* Wolfgang bowed and said, recalling that his rival had received the Order of the Golden Spur from the Pope as he had, but Gluck had been forty-two while he had been just fourteen, "Please, it isn't necessary, Chevalier. We are the ones that are honored. I would like you to meet my wife, Constanze."

"Delighted, Mozart, delighted," Gluck said in a cracked, hoarse voice. "Please accept my congratulations. You are just married, I hear."

"Yes. There is no happier couple in the Empire!"

"You have been married how long? Three days?"

"Four, sir!"

Wolfgang's voice was so blissfully boyish Gluck was envious; he had not felt that way for many years. But he smiled and said, "My wife will join us soon. She allows no one to prepare my food except herself."

Gluck's reputation as a glutton was almost as great as his musical reputation, and just a year ago he had had a stroke, and his right arm hung limply. His face was that of an old man, with many pock-marks of smallpox, coarse in contour and expression. Yet he was known to be a clever conversationalist and one of the shrewdest intriguers in Europe.

Gluck said, "I am happy that you have been able to join our table. His Majesty was impressed with the way you outdid Clementi."

Wolfgang wondered what Gluck desired but he said, "Thank you, Chevalier. Your opinion is one of the few that matters to me."

"Yes, you've even paid me the compliment of imitating me, Mozart."

Wolfgang thought. Not imitating, but improving, but he bowed again and said softly, "One should learn wherever one can."

Before Gluck could reply, he was interrupted by his plump, elderly wife who invited them into the dining room. And although she was polite, her eyes never left her husband. Fräu Gluck made it clear that her husband was a great man, as if even the way he ate was profound and significant, when actually Gluck gorged himself with a voracity that made Wolfgang nervous and never said a word while he ate.

But after he had finished eating, as satisfied as Wolfgang had ever seen anyone at the dinner table, he said, after belching, "Mozart, I was fifty before I was acknowledged. Why are you in such a hurry?"

"Hurry? My first opera was produced when I was twelve."

"You were a prodigy," Gluck retorted testily, as if that were something that had to be endured but certainly not liked.

Constanze asked, "Chevalier, what did you think of *Die Entführung*?"

"Spirited. Melodic. A young man's opera."

"A young man's opera?" exclaimed Wolfgang. "It is my tenth opera!"

"And it is sentimental, youthful, romantic, and such magnanimity as the Pasha displays toward Belmonte I find difficult to believe."

Wolfgang was silent, although his impulse was to be vocal.

"However, your score gave the libretto a vitality and charm that the poetry did not really have. Much of your music touched the heart."

"Thank you. Your opera music was the first I felt and liked."

"And now?"

"Whenever I've been where your operas were being sung I've heard them. Anyone who cares for the human voice must listen to music such as yours."

"That is a gracious thing to say, Herr Mozart."

"Chevalier Gluck, you are a superb melodist."

"And where do you place yourself?"

"Between grace and beauty," said Wolfgang, putting himself between Fräu Gluck and Constanze, "and count myself the most fortunate of men."

"I've heard that you are not always so flattering."

"Gossip. I'm much more concerned with getting my work done. As it was, *Die Entführung* was almost pushed off the boards."

"There will come a time when your work will push others off. As

458

you feel I did to you. Oh, I know that your music was postponed because of *Alceste*. But there is no equality in music, as there isn't anywhere. One struggles for advantages and once in a while one is rewarded."

"It shouldn't have to be so. Merit should be able to make its own way."

"Is that why there is so much malice in musicians?"

"If a man has talent, he is envied. If he has genius, he is hated."

"Is that why you cannot praise Salieri?"

What was there to praise? thought Wolfgang, but he said, aware that Salieri was a protégé of Gluck's, "I am not the one who envies or hates. And how can I be accused of disliking a man I have never met?"

"You have heard his music."

"Many of his melodies are pretty." And in ten years' time, Wolfgang told himself, no one will take any notice of them.

"Would you like to meet him?"

Wolfgang hesitated: had that been the reason Gluck had invited him? And had heard *Die Entführung*? Did he really threaten his favorite?

Gluck said, his hoarse voice taking on feeling for the first time, "I am an old man, and I haven't much longer to live." And when Wolfgang said that wasn't so, Gluck added, "Oh, it's true. I had a stroke last year, I could have another at any time and I am approaching seventy. But you and Salieri are fortunate. You are both young, you have energy, you can afford to be generous. Both of you have many years ahead of you."

It was not what Wolfgang felt when he got overwhelmingly tired, which had been occurring with increasing frequency, but it was not something to reveal. He said, "Perhaps Salieri doesn't want to meet me."

"Oh, I'm sure he would be delighted," said Gluck. "You are the two most promising composers in Vienna. You should get acquainted."

"With an introduction such as yours, Chevalier, I will be honored."

"Then I will arrange it," said Gluck. "At your convenience." He closed his eyes suddenly to indicate that the evening was over.

But as Wolfgang was saying goodbye, Gluck mumbled, "You are not always kind to your singers, Mozart. Sometimes you expect too much from them."

Constanze was not sure the dinner had been a success. She felt that Wolfgang and Gluck had addressed each other like diplomats, politely but without affection. Yet Wolfgang was curious to meet Salieri, so she did not differ with him, not that he would have listened in such a matter.

Gluck sought to make that relaxing, inviting all of them for lunch.

As Antonio Salieri was introduced he bowed almost to the floor and exclaimed, "Herr Mozart, I have wanted to meet you for a long time!"

"I am honored," replied Wolfgang, and wished he could believe him.

Salieri said, "I have heard much of your music. It is interesting."

"So is yours," said Wolfgang, determined not to be outdone in civility. Salieri resembled Piccinni, a little man with an animated expression, fine dark eyes, and a magnificently large nose and mouth.

"My music owes everything to our Maestro, Chevalier Gluck."

Wolfgang's eyebrows rose at this extravagance but he didn't comment.

"He is the master of us all."

Salieri was so eager to be Gluck's disciple, it sickened Wolfgang. Now he realized what he disliked most about Salieri's music: the Italian imitated Gluck, and so, like all imitations, it would soon be forgotten.

"I wrote all my early music under the eye of his genius, and with his advice and inspiration, I hope to compose work that will approach his."

"A worthy objective," said Wolfgang, embarrassed by this adulation.

But Gluck adored it. When Salieri added, "*Alceste* was perfection, and *Orfeo ed Euridice* was heavenly," Gluck beamed and nodded agreement.

Wolfgang looked so uncomfortable, Constanze was relieved that Salieri changed the subject to that of money. She thought, Salieri was still obsequious, but Wolfgang shouldn't care, it was what Gluck expected.

Suddenly Wolfgang felt there was nothing to say. Gluck and Salieri were discussing their wealth with a vanity that disgusted him. He had rarely seen such a display of greed. The first chance he had to break in, he thanked Gluck for his hospitality and excused himself, saying that he had an audience later in the day with the chancellor, Prince Kaunitz.

Wolfgang had accepted both invitations for the same day so he could use the Prince's in the event he wished to cut short Gluck's. And while Kaunitz was not as close to Joseph as he had been to Maria Theresa, he was still the second most powerful man in the Empire.

Prince Kaunitz was cordial and said, "It is nice to see you back in Vienna, Herr Mozart. I admired your virtuosity as a child, and I wondered what it would come to. Your opera was pleasing and I enjoyed it."

But there was no talk of an Imperial appointment, and Gluck and Salieri remained first and second in the Emperor's musical household, while Bonno, even older than Gluck, continued to be the working Kapellmeister.

It was more satisfying to hear from Papa that the Haffner symphony had been liked in Salzburg, even though the last movement had arrived too late for the ennoblement ceremony. Papa wrote, "The *Allegro* and *Andante* were just what our new lord desired, the first movement nobly sonorous and the second moving and tender, and now you can use the final movement for yourself."

Papa seemed reconciled to his marriage and Wolfgang, eager to complete the reconciliation, immediately planned to visit Papa with Constanze, certain that once Papa knew her, he would love her, too.

In September, however, just after he informed Papa that he was arranging with his pupils – his main means of support – to do without him for a while so he could visit Salzburg, Count Orsini-Rosenberg, Director of the National Theater, told him that the Grand Duke Paul was returning to Vienna to hear *Die Entführung*. And that the Emperor hoped Herr Mozart would conduct the opera himself, in honor of the heir to the Russian throne, and to be sure the performance was up to Viennese standards.

So Wolfgang sent his apologies to Papa, and planned to go in November to celebrate Papa's name-day on the 15th. The performance for the Grand Duke was stirring; Wolfgang rehearsed the cast intensively, and conducted from the harpsichord with the freshness and excitement of an opening.

Other musical matters delayed their departure for Salzburg, but finally they prepared to leave on November 13. Their trunks were packed, they rose with the dawn to take the first coach and it was snowing so hard there was no trace of the sun. The air was bitterly cold and when Wolfgang went outside his face turned blue and he was quickly drenched and chilled.

At the coach station he was informed that the weather had become so bad coaches could hardly get through Vienna, and that the mail coach to Salzburg, in spite of its eight horses, had been unable to reach even the first stage and had had to turn back to Vienna. He was warned it was not a day to start a journey of over three hundred miles.

Then Constanze had a miserable headache and was nauseated.

"From the excitement and anxiety," he said, and added consolingly, "Don't be disappointed, Stanzi. We will go later in the year."

She was relieved. The thought of meeting Leopold terrified her. She knew *how he felt about her,* whatever Wolfgang said.

"It's a pity," said Wolfgang. "Papa will be disappointed, too."

"I feel awful," she said. "I had better lie down."

Alarmed, he assured her that he would be right back and ran to fetch Gilowsky. The doctor was annoyed when Wolfgang pulled him out of bed. Gilowsky had been up most of the night with a confinement; there was a foot of snow on the street, but Wolfgang was insistent.

After a brief examination of Constanze, Gilowsky emerged from the bedroom with a broad grin on his face and announced, "She is pregnant."

"Does Constanze know?"

"She does now."

"How is she? She was quite sick. And she is only twenty."

"A good age. She shouldn't have any trouble. The pains are normal. But I wouldn't take her to Salzburg with this weather and winter coming."

Constanze expected Wolfgang to criticize her for being so clumsy that she didn't know she was pregnant, but he was elated. He immediately wrote Papa the good news, expressed his regrets over this new postponement, but swore that they would visit Salzburg after Papa's grandchild was born, and promised Papa that they would name the baby after him.

He started to look for new quarters, for their present rooms were too small and dreary now, and Wetzlar offered them the third floor of his own house: a living room, bedroom, kitchen, and an anteroom where the maid could sleep. Wetzlar resided nearby and Wolfgang accepted at once.

He told Fräu Weber and she said, "You can't. Wetzlar is a Jew."

"How can he be? His family has been raised to the nobility."

"His family converted," she said critically, "just a few years ago. After his father made a fortune selling supplies to the Emperor's army."

"He is my friend. My good friend. And he has excellent taste."

"Even though he is a Jew?"

"What difference does that make!" Wolfgang said impatiently.

"Once a Jew, always a Jew."

"Once a man, always a man."

"I don't want my daughter living in a Jew's house."

"Give my regards to Sophie. We'll see you after the child is born."

But as Wolfgang expected, after they moved into Wetzlar's house, his mother-in-law visited them on the excuse that her daughter needed her. And when she met Baron Wetzlar, she regarded him as a tradesman, until Wolfgang reminded her that he was a good friend

of van Swieten, whereupon she discovered that he had good qualities
– for a Jew.

Wetzlar did everything within his power to make them comfortable. There was only one difficulty; he wasn't sure how long the Mozarts could have the third floor, for he would need it for his sister who was returning from Berlin in a few months. But until then, he said, it would be a privilege to have the Mozarts as guests. He refused to take any rent.

Wolfgang was too busy to worry about moving again. He was so happy he had to create all the time. He resented anything that took him away from composing. He taught just enough to pay his expenses; the third floor was cozy and they had a maid who took care of all the household chores.

He had vowed to write a Mass if his courtship of Constanze succeeded, and he felt he had made a covenant with God. Papa was enthusiastic about the Mass, which was rare these days, and said it would be appropriate if it could be performed in Salzburg when Wolfgang visited him next year, and Wolfgang agreed and worked on this Mass with great devotion.

One day in December, while he was trying to sing one of the soprano solos to himself, Constanze said, "Let me try it, Wolfgang."

Her voice lacked breath and technique, but it had a warm, melodic tone, and he was pleased with the musicality of her interpretation.

She explained, "My mother concentrated on Aloysia, while I had to do the housework, but my father taught all of us how to sing."

From then on, Wolfgang gave Constanze vocal lessons and composed one of the soprano solos in the Mass for her voice. He discovered that she had a lyrical, pleasing upper register, and he wrote music to display this, and he was sure this would cause his family to respect her.

He was giving all of his free time to the composing of the Mass, when Count Orsini-Rosenberg wanted to see him. The Director of the National Theater chose most of the operas that were done in Vienna. He hurried to the Burgtheater, sure this was a commission for another opera.

But Orsini-Rosenberg, who sat in his palatial office like an Emperor, said, "There is an ode to the British victory at Gibraltar by the Jesuit priest and poet, Denis, which a Hungarian lady, a dear friend of mine, would like set to music, to surprise Denis, who is also her friend."

"Your Excellency, I will be delighted." He was disappointed.

"I hear you plan to give a grand concert at the Burgtheater."

"I hope to, sir."

"Good. If the ode pleases, I will try to have the Emperor attend."

As Orsini-Rosenberg stood up to indicate that the audience was over, he added, "A new pianoforte concerto or two would be useful. His Majesty is still talking about the way you outplayed Clementi."

So Wolfgang set to work on the ode and two new pianoforte concertos. He could only give the Mass a few hours a week now, but he continued with Constanze's vocal lessons. It was difficult to compose music for the ode, its sentiments irritated him, and he turned to the creation of the concertos with relief. He sought to be pleasing and cheerful, for he intended to offer them at subscription for one ducat a concerto. And he composed a third as an encore. It was the ode that remained the problem.

After he completed the three pianoforte concertos he wrote Papa:

"I think you will like my new concertos. They are brilliant, pleasing to the ear and natural without being vapid, and are as smooth as oil. Here and there are passages which only connoisseurs will truly appreciate, but they are composed in such a manner that the ordinary listener should like them even if they don't know why.

"What is far more difficult is an ode by Denis which I have been asked to put to music. My patron thinks the ode is majestic, beautiful, but for my taste it is affected and bombastic. But what can one do? The golden mean, the balance of beauty and truth, is no longer felt or appreciated. To gain applause one must either write in such an obvious and commonplace style that even a coachman can sing it, or so unintelligently that it pleases because no one can understand it.

"I would like to write an Introduction to Music, but while I think I could get it published, I would not write it under my name, for my opinions would outrage the powers-to-be, and so, I hesitate.

"But my darling wife looks forward to the day when she can share the love you have given me in such abundance. Your devoted children. W: et C: Mozart."

Orsini-Rosenberg wanted to see him again. He entered the Count's office hesitantly, for the ode was unfinished. But before he could explain, the Count said, "Could you make a pianoforte arrangement of your opera? We have been getting requests for it from other theaters."

"Yes, sir, but what about the ode? It is not quite done. . ."

"The lady who was so devoted to Father Denis has expressed her devotion in another way. She entered a convent."

"What about the portion of the ode I have composed?"

"Send it to the good father. Or use it for yourself."

Wolfgang didn't reply, angry and upset.

"Of course, you are aware," said Orsini-Rosenberg, "you will not be paid for these opera performances elsewhere, or for the pianoforte arrangement. But it could lead to a commission for a new opera, Mozart."

Wolfgang had no heart for this new request, but there was no choice.

And when he gave Count Orsini-Rosenberg a pianoforte arrangement of *The Abduction from the Seraglio* within a week, the Director of the National Theater congratulated him on his speed and efficiency.

SIXTY-NINE

It was a relief to be involved in van Swieten's musicales. Every Sunday at noon there was a concert and a discussion of music in the Baron's official residence in the court library. The Baron had created a Society of Noblemen for the cultivation of classical music, and it was the one place in Vienna where connoisseurs and musicians were welcomed as equals.

One Sunday afternoon van Swieten drew Wolfgang aside and asked him to come into his study. There were other guests in the spacious but austere music room, Cobenzl, Pálffy, Wilhelmine Thun, von Waldstätten, Wetzlar, Kapellmeister Bonno, Salieri, Adamberger, Fischer, Constanze, Stephanie, yet van Swieten said, "Mozart, I have something I must show you first."

"Won't Salieri be offended if we leave?" asked Wolfgang. "Adamberger is about to sing an aria from one of Salieri's operas."

"Not if I do it. And we won't miss much." Van Swieten led Wolfgang into his study, where the walls were lined with books from the floor to the ceiling, and went to a wall safe and took out some scores as if they were precious jewels and said, "I brought these back from Berlin, where I acquired them when I was Ambassador. As you may know I studied composition and conducting with the Prussian Kapellmeister, Kirnberger."

"I know." Wolfgang had heard van Swieten conduct his own composition and he hoped fervently that his friend would not involve him.

"And I would like you to do me a favor."

Wolfgang waited apprehensively.

"Examine these scores. They are unknown in Vienna, and I wondered whether they would help me in my study of composition."

Nothing would help van Swieten, thought Wolfgang, but his

friend would be mortally offended if he said that. He asked, "Who are they by?"

"Handel and Sebastian Bach."

Wolfgang took the scores reluctantly. He had known Handel's music ever since his visit to England as a child, where Handel, dead just a few years, was the most honored and played composer, but he had preferred Christian Bach and he had known Sebastian Bach only as his favorite's father. And Christian Bach had just died, which was a great loss, and he wasn't interested in these old composers. But there was an insistence in van Swieten that wasn't to be denied, so Wolfgang said, "I'll read them during the week. I don't want Salieri to think that I'm ignoring his music."

"Read them now. You won't regret it. And Salieri can wait."

"But Constanze will worry if I am absent too long."

"I will see to it that she feels at home. Sit in my reading chair," which was an honor, "I think there is something here that you might like."

Hours later Wolfgang was still studying the music that van Swieten had brought back from Berlin. He had not cared much for the operas of Handel that he had heard; they had been too undramatic for his taste; but these fugues were another matter. They had a strength that was striking and moving, and an inner intensity that was vital and admirable.

But it was Sebastian Bach who delighted him. The old man's fugues – he could not think of him as young, Sebastian Bach had had so many children – astonished him with their craft and feeling. Wolfgang was deep in *The Art of the Fugue* and *The Well Tempered Clavier*, studying the separate parts of each, some sheets on his knees, some on the table, others on the arms of the chair and in his hands, when van Swieten returned with Constanze. He didn't hear them. He was listening to Sebastian Bach in his imagination. Both of these works had been written for *"learning,"* but *what learning*! Wolfgang cried to himself.

Van Swieten asked, "Do you like Sebastian Bach's music?"

"Like?" Wolfgang came back to the present almost unwillingly. "That is hardly the word. Here is something one can really learn from!"

Constanze said, "Salieri looked annoyed when you walked out."

"Salieri! Stanzi, there is no comparison between his music and what I have here. Van Swieten, what a treasure of good music you have here!"

"Would you care to play some of Sebastian Bach?"

"I would be honored. But what about the others?"

"Everyone is gone. You have been here for hours."

Constanze said, "I was worried, Wolfgang."

"Wait until you hear these fugues. They are magnificent."

Van Swieten said, "Fräu Mozart, I think you will like them."

Wolfgang said, "But I should learn them by heart before I play them."

Now Constanze was curious, Wolfgang was so excited. She begged him to play several fugues, despite his lack of practice. And after he did with a devotion he usually gave only to his own music, she cried out, "No wonder you love them. I could listen to nothing but fugues. Haven't you written any?"

"No – except what I improvised out of my head."

She scolded, "You've neglected the most beautiful and scientific part of music. You must write a fugue for me, as soon as possible."

"Is that an order, Stanzi, dear?"

"I'm serious. Dear Baron, tell him how fine they are. He will believe you. They were wonderful. And he played them perfectly."

"I was hardly perfect. But with a week of practice I will be better."

Constanze asked, "What were you doing these past hours?"

"Getting acquainted. One does not absorb a Sebastian Bach in a day. Baron, may I borrow Bach for a week? I would be eternally grateful."

"Do you think I can learn about composition from him and Handel?"

"Everyone can. Everyone who cares about music."

All that week Wolfgang practiced the music of Sebastian Bach. His fugues were as superbly constructed as any music he had ever heard; he had not known that the resources of the fugue could be so remarkable. The fugues that Padre Martini had taught him were trivial by comparison.

The following Sunday, when he played the fugues by Bach and Handel for the others, with a dignity and nobility that was eloquent, he discovered for them what he had discovered for himself.

The next few Sundays nothing was performed at van Swieten's but the music of Bach and Handel, while Constanze would not let Wolfgang alone until he wrote a fugue for her. He also arranged five fugues from *The Well Tempered Clavier*, wrote preludes for them which were very Mozartian, and presented them to van Swieten as an expression of his gratitude for having been introduced to Christian Bach's father.

Two fantasias that he composed after this meeting with Sebastian Bach had a gravity and a darker dramatic intensity than any music he had composed for the pianoforte. After he played them for Constanze and van Swieten, she liked them very much and said he must compose more music such as this, but the Baron warned him, when he spoke of including them in his grand concert at the Burgtheater, "Vienna is not ready for this music. The audience will admire your craft, but they will be disturbed by the difficulties. You must realize that while Vienna is familiar with the music of his sons, particularly Johann Christian and Philipp Emanuel, the father is unknown here. Not a note of the Lutheran Cantor's music has been performed publicly in Catholic Vienna."

"Can I depend on Rosenberg?" asked Wolfgang, putting aside his fantasias.

"Only Rosenberg can depend on Rosenberg. But it is better not to offend him. He does have the ear of the Emperor."

"Forgive me, but I thought you had more influence."

Van Swieten smiled wryly, "Many people have influence with Joseph, and none. He listens to me sometimes, or to Rosenberg, or Cobenzl, or Kaunitz, and often he listen to no one. And I am sure he would not listen to Sebastian Bach. Italian music is very much his preference."

"Should I go ahead with the concert at the Burgtheater?"

"Of course. Whether Joseph comes or not, everyone else will."

In the midst of Wolfgang's preparation for the concert he had to move, for Wetzlar needed their rooms for his sister. Wetzlar was apologetic, and when Wolfgang found a place on the Kohlmarkt, Wetzlar paid the cost of moving and the rent of these quarters, insisting that this was the least he could do until his dear friend found a decent apartment.

At the moment Wolfgang didn't have the time to look for new rooms, he was so busy arranging his program at the Burgtheater like an impresario.

He sat at his living room table which was also serving as a desk, and studied the score of his Haffner symphony, and wondered where to place it. He had asked Papa to return it to him, having decided to include it in his concert, since no one in Vienna had ever heard it, and thus it would be new music for them, and the symphony amazed him. He said to Constanze, "I have forgotten every note of it, but it should please. It is very effective music," he added, as if he were noticing this for the first time, and Aloysia entered and smiled sweetly.

He braced himself, but suddenly Aloysia was embracing Constanze and congratulating her on their marriage, and Constanze blushed, but looked pleased, although she had to say, "You don't mind?"

"Constanze, Joseph and I are very happy. Wolfgang, now that we are related, may I give you a sisterly kiss?"

Wolfgang shrugged and Constanze said, "You never asked before."

"You were never married before." Aloysia approached Wolfgang,

469

and he turned his cheek and she kissed him on the lips. There was an obvious effort to be passionate, but he did not feel any emotion.

He asked, "Aloysia, what do you want?" She was dressed beautifully.

"I could sing your music at the Burgtheater."

"That is up to Constanze."

Constanze thought angrily, Trust Aloysia to compete, but she said, "If Wolfgang would like you to sing his music, why should I object."

"I would sing it very well. I am sure my little sister knows that."

Aloysia was probably right, he thought, for as Cavalieri's understudy in *Die Entführung* she had sung Constanze with delicacy and taste. And she could add variety and interest to his program. When he said yes, she was so grateful it was absurd, yet gratifying.

The March 23 grand concert at the Burgtheater came to assume great importance for Wolfgang. He felt that if it were successful, he would be able to support himself with his composing and performing and could stop the tedious teaching. And the omens were good. All the seats were sold. The Emperor attended. The audience was the most distinguished in Vienna. At the end of the program the applause was deafening. Proud and optimistic, he wrote Papa an account of it a few days later:

"I am sure that you have heard about the success of my concert, for it is the talk of Vienna, and news of it must surely have reached Salzburg. The Emperor was there with his entire staff, and contrary to his habit, attended the whole concert, applauded me loudly, told me that he approved fully of my choice of numbers, encouraged me to give more such concerts in Vienna, and presented me with twenty-five ducats.

"And I really think you will like my choice of a program.

"The orchestra began with the Concertante in D Major, which I had composed in 1779. Then they played the Haffner symphony.

"Next I performed my D Major pianoforte concerto with a new rondo finale that I wrote for this occasion, then I did the third of my new subscription concertos, the one in C Major, and for encores, I performed variations on airs by Gluck and Paisiello, who were in the audience.

"For variety, Therese Teyber sang an aria from my last Milan opera, *Lucia Silla*. Aloysia Lange did an aria from my Munich opera, *Idomeneo*, and another rondo I just wrote. And Valentin Adamberger sang a scena I composed recently for him. Then, at the request of the Emperor, the finale of the Haffner symphony was repeated at the end of the program.

"I am playing at a concert of Therese Teyber's as a payment for her appearance at mine, and I have many other private engagements.

"I have been assured of a profit from this grand concert at the Burgtheater, for there was not an empty seat, and most of them were paid for – although there are many expenses, particularly the cost of the theater. And now I must close or I will miss the post. My beloved wife kisses you a hundred times and we embrace our dear sister with all our affection and are, as always, your devoted and obedient children. W: A: et C: Mozart."

Wolfgang knew he had not exaggerated the success of the concert, for von Strack and Orsini-Rosenberg congratulated him, too, which meant that the Emperor had been sincere; van Swieten said that his program had been wisely chosen; Paisiello thanked him for arranging his air so sweetly; and Gluck invited him and Constanze and the Langes to lunch as an expression of approval, and Salieri, who was also invited, was cordial.

But Thorwart's bookkeeping shocked him. He expected the orchestra to be costly, but he had been told that the receipts of the concert had amounted to 1600 gulden, yet by the time all the expenses were deducted, particularly the rent of the Burgtheater, there was nothing left for him.

When he complained, Thorwart said, "Rosenberg approved my figures."

Wolfgang tried to discuss this with the Director of the National Theaters, but before he could open his mouth the latter said, "I assured you that the Emperor would attend. I always keep my word. Now, if you will excuse me, the Emperor is waiting for my accounting."

"Does the Emperor know how much the concert earned and cost?"

"Certainly. It is his theater. Do you want to discuss the expenses with him?"

Wolfgang shuddered. Nothing would be more tactless. Whatever chance he had to enter the Emperor's service would be shattered irrevocably. Under these circumstances there was nothing more to do but bow politely, thank Orsini-Rosenberg for his support, and passively depart.

But it was ridiculous. Wherever he went in Vienna his concert was praised, and all he had to show for it was the ducats the Emperor had given him, and they had to be put aside for Constanze's confinement.

And several days after his meeting with Orsini-Rosenberg, while he was leaving his rooms to play for the Countess Thun, whose carriage was waiting for him, he was halted at the door of the carriage by a bailiff who said if he didn't pay the thirty gulden he owed his tailor he would be arrested.

What an embarrassment! He could not pay even part of that sum.

Attracted passionately by a handsome red coat with pearl buttons, he had told himself that it was just what he needed for the grand concert, genuine, beautiful, of excellent quality, and that it would impress everyone with his affluence, and he had bought it, although he could not pay for it at the time. But he had expected to do so from his earnings from the concert, or the subscription for his concertos, yet hardly anyone seemed to want to buy them and the sales had been very disappointing.

It didn't help to insist that he intended to pay this debt after his next concert; the bailiff replied, "If you do not pay this amount by tomorrow, we will bring an action against you! Or throw you in jail!"

He promised the bailiff he would have the money tomorrow, but as he rode toward the Countess Thun's concert he didn't know where to turn. He couldn't touch the money for Constanze's confinement; he couldn't ask the Countess Thun – his friendship with her was too precious to jeopardize. The thought of asking anyone to lend him money was repugnant, but the scandal that could occur if he failed to pay could be far worse.

He was distracted while playing, which was unusual, and the Baroness von Waldstätten asked, "Are you worried about Constanze?"

"It's an unexpected debt," he answered. "I would be delighted to write a new concerto, serenade, or symphony for you, whichever you prefer, if you could lend me thirty gulden, immediately."

The Baroness looked as uncomfortable as he did and said, "I don't need any music," and she avoided him the rest of the afternoon.

Wetzlar, seeing his distraught manner, asked, "What is wrong?" After Wolfgang told him, he handed Wolfgang fifty gulden, and when the latter protested that this was more than was necessary, Wetzlar said, "Who knows what is necessary? I have it now. I might not have it tomorrow."

Wolfgang embraced him to express his gratitude, and Wetzlar blushed and added, "I think I have found better rooms for you, on the first floor of a house on the Judenplatz, large, sunny, and cheerful," as if he were responsible for the Mozarts' present lack of comfort.

Wolfgang assured Wetzlar that he would repay his kindness as soon as he could, and swore never to fall into debt again.

That was difficult. It took weeks to pay Wetzlar back. His income remained irregular; sometimes pupils paid him, sometimes they did not, or missed lessons or left him. *Die Entführung* was to be done in Prague, Bonn, Frankfurt, Warsaw, Leipzig, and had fifteen performances in Vienna, with more scheduled, yet he would not get another kreutzer. Papa had criticized him for charging a ducat for his subscription concertos, saying it was too much, and Papa had been right, for the sales of this pianoforte music were still sparse. And most of his performances were for dear friends, and *how could he charge them for his playing?*

To ease his discontent with his economic situation – and he did like his new rooms on the Judenplatz, they were good for working and Constanze was happy in them – he began to compose a string quartet, a form he had not touched for a long while, as if, in this, the most advanced form of musical creation, he could assert his independence from material cares.

At the same time he studied the quartets of Joseph Haydn, which he had liked so much ten years ago, and new ones, the Russian quartets, that Haydn had dedicated to the Grand Duke Paul. They were the best Wolfgang had ever seen, and he traced them note by note to understand their construction. All four instruments were treated equally, and the themes were deeply embedded in the melodies with a unity and intensity that he loved.

As he finished his quartet in G Major he fell ill from worry over his financial straits, anxiety over Constanze's uncertain health, and from exhaustion. The entire month of May he was unable to compose a note, and the ducats he had put aside for her confinement were all he had.

Yet at van Swieten's in June, his first appearance there in a month, his friend wanted his help, asking his advice about a letter van Swieten had received from a music teacher in Bonn, Herr Neefe. Wolfgang read:

"Dear Baron, your reputation as a connoisseur having reached us in Bonn, I am begging your indulgence while I plead the case of a young pupil I am having the privilege of teaching. Both his grandfather and father were singers and this boy resembles Wolfgang Amadeus Mozart, who I hear, is a good friend of yours. At eight this boy played the violin well; at eleven he performed Sebastian Bach's *The Well Tempered Clavier* fluidly and feelingly. And now, at twelve, he has become a brilliant improviser on the pianoforte, and is composing sonatas for this instrument, which is his favorite. But this young genius, Ludwig van Beethoven, needs support to enable him to travel and study. If he progresses as he has begun, he is certain to become a second Wolfgang Amadeus Mozart, and I would deeply appreciate anything you could do to help him. And if he could become a pupil of your great friend, you would be doing a great favor to the art we are all devoted to, music. Your obedient servant. Christian Gottlieb Neefe."

"What do you think?" asked van Swieten.

Wolfgang knew what his friend wanted him to think, but he had too many pupils as it was. He said, "When it comes to child prodigies, many are called, but few are chosen."

"Would you be interested in teaching this young Beethoven?"

Wolfgang sighed. He had gotten out of bed to please van Swieten, who had been alarmed by his absences from the Sunday musicales. He said, "Who would pay for him in Vienna? Even if I was willing to teach this boy, who would keep him in food and board?"

"I don't know."

That was what Wolfgang expected, for while van Swieten could afford to support several Ludwig van Beethovens, his thrift was as well known as his interest in music. He said, "I am sure young Beethoven is a worthy pupil, like many others. If he comes to Vienna, I will be glad to hear him."

This child prodigy dropped out of Wolfgang's mind as the birth of his first child approached. His health was better now, and sitting by Constanze's side night after night, in case she needed him, he started a new string quartet to occupy himself during the lonesome hours.

Often, even while she slept she cried out in pain or trembled, and when she was awake she was depressed and withdrawn, ashamed of her unsightly appearance, although he was tender and affectionate. And despite his desire to have children her discomfort gave him moments of doubt.

He put his new string quartet in D Minor so that he could express gravity as well as grace. And even as he wrote the opening movement *Allegro moderato* to convey the balance and eloquence he found in Haydn's Russian quartets, he kept remembering the terrifying amount of infant mortality that existed in Vienna and a mood of fatalism prevailed.

Inevitably his mind turned to the person who had borne him, and he wondered if Mamma had suffered while carrying him as Constanze was now. He could accept Papa or Nannerl not being here, but he could not believe that Mamma would have been absent. Fräu Weber had offered to stay, but Constanze had said no, that this would upset her, although her mother was within call.

The second movement was melodic, as suited his *Andante*, but it was also full of melancholy and ghosts. Mamma must have slept as restlessly as Constanze, and she had given birth to seven children. Yet he had never heard her complain, although she had lost two boys and three girls. Now he realized why she had wished to be buried in St. Peter's in Salzburg: it had been where his dead brothers and sisters had been laid to rest.

Menuetto (Allegretto) was how he scored the third movement, and as he thought of the difficulties of birth, it was sorrow that dominated his music.

All his brothers and sisters had been alive at birth, Papa had told him, yet five of them had died within six days to six months. That must have been the cruelest blow of all, he thought, and as he prayed that it would not happen to him and Constanze he was overcome with emotion.

The next morning, when Constanze was cheerful for a change, he wrote Papa, "You must be our child's godfather, you cannot refuse this loving request" – for Papa had never referred to that when he had suggested it months ago – "and since you cannot be here, I will arrange for someone to be present in your name, for whether our child is *generis masculini* or *feminini*, we are going to call it Leopold or Leopoldine."

A week after he wrote Papa the labor pains began. Now Wolfgang sent for his mother-in-law. She had had four children; she would know what to do. Fräu Weber came at once and immediately called the midwife. She said a doctor wasn't necessary, in this matter he wouldn't know as much as a midwife, and so Wolfgang agreed, although his apprehensions remained.

Fräu Weber ordered him to stay out of the bedroom, saying that he would only be in the way and that his anxiety would upset Constanze.

He returned to his string quartet, working on the last movement, *Allegretto ma non troppo*, with the most intense concentration. Hearing her moans, he had to translate her pain and suffering into order and beauty, otherwise it would be unbearable. His chief resource was his kind of feeling. But as Constanze was tortured, so was he; as she cried, so did he; as she seemed pursued by the devil, it went into his music. And while the craft of four instruments playing as individuals and yet as one never faltered, and the construction of the quartet was impeccable, he was creating a new tonal world that touched on the agitation of birth, and its tragedies.

Suddenly Fräu Weber appeared, needing a basin and hot water, and stared at him a moment, sitting quietly and putting down one note after another with meticulous care, and exclaimed, "How can you be so callous? So detached?"

What else was there to do! He wanted to throw her criticism in her face, but it was not his nature. Instead, hoping that his child would be born as well constructed as his new string quartet but without its inner agitation, he asked, "How is Constanze?"

"The child will be arriving soon, if God is good and we are lucky." She rushed back to her daughter, the bedroom door bolted behind her.

Half of him studied the quartet to be certain he had not made any mistakes when she had scolded him, half of him waited.

Just as he thought this night would never end, his mother-in-law appeared in the doorway of the bedroom and proudly announced that it was a boy – she had had four girls – and that Constanze was a true Weber, her daughter had given birth to a perfect child.

475

After he saw his son and kissed Constanze, both of whom looked remarkably well, he thought, considering what they had gone through, his mother-in-law took charge of the household. She insisted on staying with Constanze until her daughter was fully recovered; she obtained a foster-nurse for the baby, who would also be a foster-mother, which seemed sensible to Wolfgang, since he was afraid to have Constanze nurse the child, because of the danger of milk fever.

The moment Baron Wetzlar heard of Constanze's safe delivery, he visited them and said, "I will be honored to be the boy's godfather."

Wolfgang hesitated, remembering his promise to Papa, but how could he refuse Wetzlar, the latter had been such a good and dear friend, and he could still call his son Leopold.

As he was trying to decide what to do, Wetzlar said, "Thank you, Wolfgang, now you have a little Raimund," and kissed the baby.

So the child was christened *Raimund Leopold Mozart*, and Wolfgang wrote Papa explaining why, and added, "But he is also called Leopold, and everyone tells me that he is a copy of me, which, I am sure, pleases you."

SEVENTY

===

When Wolfgang and Constanze felt that Raimund Leopold was safely in the care of a foster-mother in the Vienna suburb of Neustift, they departed for Salzburg. Both of them had doubts about the wisdom of leaving their infant with someone else, but Fräu Weber insisted that their month-old baby would not survive the journey but would flourish under the attention of a trained foster-mother who kept a home for infants. She convinced them by pointing out that it was the traditional way to raise infants, that she had done it with her own, and that she would keep an eye on him.

Approaching Salzburg, Constanze thought the country was beautiful, but she was sweating profusely. Wolfgang was lucky, she thought, he would feel at home, but the closer she came to his family the more apprehensive and uncomfortable she became. Suddenly they were through the mountains and jolting down the Linzerstrasse, and she saw the Fortress Hohensalzburg on top of the Monchsberg, dominating the city like an iron crown.

Fear appeared on Wolfgang's face and he cried out, "That is Colloredo's castle! He doesn't live there, but he could put me in its dungeon."

She was taken aback by this. She expected him to be happy; he had been talking about visiting his family ever since they had married.

Now he was expressing the same concern he had voiced in Vienna, exclaiming, "Colloredo could have me arrested! He has never officially dismissed me or accepted my resignation. You have no idea how vicious and vindictive this prince can be!"

"But your father assured you that it was safe to come, that Colloredo never refers to you, and has a new Kapellmeister, Lodovico Gatti."

"Papa wanted us to come. But Colloredo is malevolent, full of trickery, and it wouldn't be the first injustice he has done. And if I see Arco! Anyone who attacks a nobleman in Salzburg is punished with twenty-five lashes on the back, but I could run a sword through his heart."

Yet he was better off than she was, she told herself, he could express his fears, but she couldn't, she had to pretend to love two people whom she was sure resented her. It was no good to state this; Wolfgang assumed that once his family knew her, they would like her – it was one of the reasons they were visiting Salzburg – but she didn't believe him. She felt that his father couldn't like any woman who had taken Wolfgang away from him, and that his daughter inevitably followed his example.

As their coach halted in the Hannibalplatz and the large square was quiet, without any sign of Colloredo's authority, Wolfgang brightened and said, "The Grand Mufti must realize that I am too important to touch."

He took her hand to help her out, and as he noticed her sweaty palm, her nervousness, he added strongly, "Remember, do not belittle yourself. Remember always who you are." Once Papa knew her, he must love her.

Then the four of them were face to face. Wolfgang gazed at Papa with an eager yet anxious stare, but Constanze was surprised by his appearance.

She had expected a larger, more impressive looking man, but Leopold Mozart wasn't much bigger than Wolfgang. He must have shrunk, she thought, recalling the pictures she had seen of him, and he was an old man now. And Nannerl was plain – how could she put on any airs?

Wolfgang introduced them and waited for Papa and Nannerl to embrace and kiss him and Constanze. Instead, they stood at a distance, Papa saying that he felt fine, that his rheumatism was almost gone with this lovely July weather. He was putting up a gallant front, Wolfgang thought, but Papa looked gray around the mouth and couldn't keep his hands still, the way it was with people who were nervous or frightened.

His formality struck Wolfgang as silly and he embraced Papa, who stood like a stick for a moment, then trembled violently, as if in a convulsion, and despite his efforts to be distant tears trickled down his cheeks. Wolfgang kissed Nannerl then, put her hand in Constanze's and cried out, "Now you will really get acquainted! And become such good friends!"

Yet neither Papa nor Nannerl kissed Constanze as Wolfgang wished, and she couldn't make the first move. Nannerl had let go of her hand almost immediately and his father's face sharpened as he gazed at her.

His son had been right, Leopold observed, his wife was far from

478

being beautiful, although she was not ugly. Her dark eyes were pretty, and she had an attractive figure, but she hardly had the look of the martyr that Wolfgang had said, but the manner of an ordinary young German woman.

Wolfgang frowned however, when he didn't display any affection to his wife, so Leopold hurriedly said to her, "I'm glad you had a safe trip."

"Thank you, Herr Mozart."

"Papa, Constanze, Papa," stated Wolfgang.

But his father hadn't suggested that, and she said, as Leopold led them into the Tanzmeister-Saal, which was easier than talking, "You have lovely rooms, Herr Mozart. You must have chosen them with great care."

"Frugality, and many years of foresight and teaching."

"Wolfgang must have been inspired here."

"Hard work. Sweat. Discipline. Good teaching. And his own genius."

"Come, Papa," said Wolfgang, seeking to break the tension. "We have more important things to discuss. I brought a great amount of music I want you to see. Fugues, preludes, two fantasias, three concertos. . ."

"What about the Mass?" Papa interrupted.

"I had to put it aside when other matters interfered."

"Half-finished?" Papa asked critically.

"I will complete it here. Now that we are all together again."

"What about the infant? I'm surprised you let him out of your sight."

"Raimund Leopold is with a foster-mother."

"But an infant cannot be left like a composition, with a written receipt to signify its eventual safe return."

"Papa, you were the one who taught me that it is wrong for a mother to nurse her own child. I'm trying to follow your example."

"Your mother and I never left you or Nannerl alone. Not for an instant."

Constanze was silent. She missed her baby very much, but to admit that to her father-in-law would give him, already hostile, too great an advantage. And Wolfgang changed the subject by handing his father his new compositions.

It was something that Leopold could not ignore. He put on his spectacles to examine the fugues, while Nannerl picked up the fantasias.

Leopold studied the fugues with a rising admiration and a sinking heart. His son had fallen in love with Papa Bach and his own influence was gone.

Wolfgang said to Nannerl, who had just exclaimed that the fantasias were difficult and dark in tone, "Yes, but you must play them with your quiet, even touch, and your natural lightness and flexibility. If you play them rapidly or loudly, you will produce an ugly sound, like Clementi, who played everything *presto, prestissimo,* and *alla breve.*"

After Nannerl played, Wolfgang asked Constanze to sing.

Leopold was surprised at how musically Constanze sang. Her execution was excellent and her voice gave pleasure. As she finished Leopold said, "Bravo," Nannerl applauded, and Wolfgang felt that they were a family at last.

But that night, when Wolfgang desired to make love, Constanze refused. He was stunned. She had never refused him before. And they were so well suited to each other. She said, "I can't." She was embarrassed to be sleeping next door to his father, and afraid they would be overheard.

"Then we won't make any noise, or you'll sing and I'll applaud."

"Be serious, Wolfgang."

"I am. Have I told you in the last five minutes how much I love you."

"You are saying that to make me feel better about your father."

"I am saying that because it is true, true, true, true!"

"Sssh, you'll wake the whole house."

"They know we are married."

"That's just the trouble. I think your father put us next door to. . ."

"Please, Stanzi, this was my room before I married."

She lost her temper, while he begged her to reflect. There was no happiness in bed that night, for everytime he tried to embrace her, she talked about his family and it remained a barren evening.

The next morning Wolfgang asked Papa if they could move into the guest bedroom, that he knew it was smaller, less comfortable, but it would be cooler, and he preferred the coolness in the summer heat. Leopold started to remind his son that he had loved this room before he had been married, winter and summer, but Wolfgang looked so unhappy that Leopold said, "Whatever you wish," and was positive that Constanze was responsible.

Once Constanze felt out of sight and hearing she overwhelmed Wolfgang with her gratitude, and he was hopeful that they would become a bride and bridegroom again and that this could become a second honeymoon.

July 30 was Nannerl's birthday and Leopold used this occasion to invite some old friends to celebrate that and to meet his daughter-in-law.

As Constanze saw the simple, direct, happy way Bullinger,

Hagenauer, Schachtner and others embraced Wolfgang, she realized that these friends cared for him with a real and deep feeling. She was moved, too, by their warmth to her. She felt they were glad to meet her, that anyone Wolfgang chose, they chose; they made her feel at home.

Then Johann von Berchtold zu Sonnenburg entered and Leopold introduced him with pride. Sonnenburg looked about fifty, a pleasant-looking official in the minor nobility, but nothing unusual, thought Constanze. He was attentive to Nannerl, who was a different person from the instant he arrived. Wolfgang had told Constanze that this was Nannerl's thirty-second birthday, and she had assumed that his sister was destined to be a spinster, but now she was not sure. She felt Nannerl was in love with Sonnenburg and expected to marry him, and she wondered if Leopold would object to her marriage as he had to Wolfgang's and order her to wait. Her father-in-law looked truly happy for the first time since she had come to Salzburg.

A few days later, Wolfgang, hearing that Michael Haydn was ailing, visited him. Haydn was agitated, although he was glad to see Wolfgang.

He blurted out that while he was still recuperating from a serious illness, Colloredo, expecting guests soon, had ordered him to supply two duets for violin and viola, in case Colloredo wished to play for his visitors. "And I can't write a note. I'm not strong enough." He took some wine and added, "But I will be held responsible if I fail to furnish the music. And I can't afford to leave him, as you did. I haven't anything saved, and I am too ill and tired to start afresh."

"Are you sure the Grand Mufti is going to punish you?"

"Do *you* have to ask? You know he won't accept any excuses, once he makes up his mind. He has ordered my salary withheld until I furnish the duets. And I don't even have the money to pay my apothecary and doctor."

"When do you need them?"

"That's another problem. He wants them right away. He won't even give me time to get well. And you know how I can compose, when I am not ill."

Wolfgang nodded and said he would return soon.

Two days later he handed Michael Haydn two finished duets for violin and viola and hushing the latter's grateful, "They are lovely!" he said, "Put your name on them. The arch-booby won't know the difference."

After this music was played Colloredo ordered Haydn's salary restored and told Brunetti, "I never thought Haydn capable of composing such fine, melodic music. Instead of drinking beer, he should favor burgundy."

Brunetti repeated this to Haydn, and added, "But I thought the duets sounded like your brother's music."

From then on, Wolfgang concentrated on completing the Mass. Michael Haydn, to express his thanks, arranged for it to be performed at St. Peter's, where he was the organist, and Wolfgang thought this should please Papa, who had become unusually attached to this ancient church.

There were several letters from Fräu Weber, telling them that Raimund Leopold was fine, then in September she stopped writing. Wolfgang was worried, but Constanze wasn't. She said her mother hated to write, that she was surprised that her mother had written at all.

There were no encounters with Colloredo – it was as if they lived in different worlds, although they were residing within a mile of each other – but one day, as Wolfgang hurried into St. Peter's to rehearse his partially finished Mass, he came face to face with Arco at the entrance.

Arco's waistcoat was adorned with jewelry, his powdered wig was of the latest style, his shoe buckles were of silver, his red lips were rouged, but he became very pale when he saw Wolfgang.

Wolfgang's instinct was to shout, "Scoundrel!" and slap him.

But Arco was gone before he could say or do anything.

Wolfgang told Haydn of this meeting, and he replied, "Arco never refers to you, nor does Colloredo. I think they are ashamed of what happened."

"Was that discussed here?"

"After all, you were born here, you carried the name of Salzburg over most of Europe. Who would ever have heard of the city if not for you."

"What was said?"

"There were rumors that you and Arco fought. Some said you hit him, others that he cursed and kicked you. None of them were pleasant."

"At least they haven't bothered me now."

"They wouldn't dare. You are the Emperor's favorite."

Yes, he thought, except when it came to getting a Royal appointment and a regular salary, but he said, "Joseph has better taste than Colloredo."

"Have you ever thought of returning?"

"To a town so provincial it has half an orchestra, to an arch-booby who can't endure German musicians and who hates opera? There is an old Salzburg proverb, that he who comes to Salzburg in the first year becomes stupid, in the second year idiotic, and in the third a true Salzburgian."

On the 26th of October Wolfgang conducted his Mass in C Minor at St. Peter's with Constanze as one of the two soprano soloists. He had not been able to finish the score, but he felt enough had been completed to express his gratitude to God for his happiness with Constanze.

The audience was a friendly one. There was no one from Colloredo's court, but many old friends, most of whom had known him from childhood. Yet he had eyes only for Papa. He still hoped that the Mass would improve Papa's feelings toward Constanze. While Papa had been polite in the three months they had been here, Papa had also been cool and formal.

He noticed that Papa was listening intently, but he could not tell what his father was thinking.

And then Constanze's clear soprano rose in a lovely prayer and he was lifted with it. He was tired of the world's stress on the earning of money, on Colloredo and Arco; his music was expressing his exaltation in Creation, in the Supreme Creator, in the gift of life.

Schachtner marveled at the sublimity of the Mass. Schachtner, who had no religious convictions, understood now why faith had to be created by those who knew man's needs; that man had to have pure emotion such as Wolfgang's to survive, and Wolfgang was conveying that with a devoutness that was above any creed.

Leopold heard the Mass with mixed feelings. Much of the music struck him as being more symphonic and operatic than pious and spiritual, yet there were moments of overwhelming sweetness and sincerity. And his son had constructed this Mass with great skill. But there was nothing of himself in it, Leopold thought sadly. As he had detected in the fugues, his own influence had vanished. In some ways this was the worst loss of all, and he was somber and full of suffering. Yet the musician in Leopold was too strong to allow him to slight the music, and as Constanze sang again his instinct was to applaud her in spite of his antipathy toward her. He still doubted that she would ever have a big, operatic voice, but even in the difficult passages she sang with taste. Then suddenly he longed to laugh madly. It was absurd. His son regarded her as a goddess when, except for her voice, she was such an ordinary girl.

After the services everyone gathered around Wolfgang while he waited for Papa to speak, who said, almost reprovingly, "This is the first church music you have written since Salzburg."

"I haven't had any ecclesiastical appointments. Why should I?"

"I brought you up to be a good Catholic."

"I am. Constanze and I go to church regularly."

"This Mass was often more profane than sacred. Wasn't it, Nannerl?"

Nannerl, who felt depressed, for Sonnenburg had not attended as she had hoped, said, "Perhaps it is the Vienna fashion. The music was loud."

"Loud?" Wolfgang reddened and stared at his sister in amazement.

"It was the singing," Nannerl said.

"Constanze's?" exclaimed Wolfgang.

Nannerl hesitated. Wolfgang looked so stricken. And Constanze had sung better than she had expected. But she also felt spiteful, thinking it wasn't fair, someone like Constanze had a husband and she had to struggle to be courted. She said, "Oh, I'm sure she would be better if she had more training."

Leopold said, "My little girl is very musical, as you all know."

This was too much for Schachtner, who had liked the performance. "What's wrong with you, Leopold? Can't you say a kind word any more?"

Leopold thought, What do you know about the pain of losing what you love the most! But he said, "My intention simply is to be accurate and helpful."

Schachtner said, "You think Wolfgang still needs your help!"

Leopold said proudly, "He still asks my advice."

Schachtner retorted, "Because he is a better son than you are a father."

They glared at each other and Wolfgang, very distressed, cried out, "Please, I don't want to leave Salzburg with another fight on my hands."

There was no warmth in Papa or Nannerl when he and Constanze departed the next day. Papa did ask him about money, and he assured his father that everything was fine. "We have no difficulties, no difficulties at all."

Neither Papa nor Nannerl embraced or kissed Constanze goodbye, although she thanked them for their hospitality and invited them to visit Vienna as her guests. But she was unhappy over their coldness. They had shown her many fine gifts that Wolfgang had received during his tours, but had not offered her a single one. As the coach pulled away and Leopold and Nannerl managed to wave goodbye, she waved back and smiled, for Wolfgang's sake, but she had little hope of matters improving between her and his family.

However Wolfgang felt better, for Papa and Nannerl had embraced him and had promised to visit them in Vienna. He said, "Papa didn't intend to be so severe about the Mass, but he wants me to try harder. He told me that you sang well, with excellent method and feeling."

"Then why didn't he tell me?"

"It is not easy for him to admit he made a mistake. He said that what he really meant about sacred and profane music was that I used the most profane resources of my craft to compose my most sacred music."

"That's odd. Everybody else thought the Mass was magnificently devout. Schachtner said it made him get down on his knees and he is not a believer."

"Schachtner always has preferred profane music. And the others feel I might be saying goodbye to Salzburg."

"Are you?"

He shrugged. He had tried to say goodbye to Salzburg for years, but it hadn't been easy, however little patience he had with his birthplace. He took a long look at Salzburg, just in case it was the last time.

On the way home they stopped in Linz as the guests of Count Johann Thun, the father-in-law of Wilhelmine Thun. The Count insisted that they stay several weeks and his cordiality was pleasing after the coldness at the Hannibalplatz. Count Thun desired only one thing in return: a symphony.

Since Wolfgang didn't have a single one with him, yet he wanted to express his appreciation of the Count's hospitality, he started a new one.

His host needed it for a concert on November 4, which gave Wolfgang only four days to compose a symphony. He wrote Papa, between movements, "Scribbling with great speed, I hope to have something acceptable."

Constanze had come to take his amazing facility as a matter of course, but she was astonished by this Linz symphony in C. It was constructed adroitly, without a trace of haste, with fresh melodies, and a masterfully worked score. When she remarked about this, and that in four days he had conceived, written, rehearsed, and played this splendid symphony, he smiled and replied, "I haven't composed any symphonies for several years – perhaps it was developing in me all that time."

Wolfgang arrived in Vienna in a very good humor, for the new symphony had been received enthusiastically in Linz, and he was pleased that he had fulfilled his vow to God with his Mass. He and Constanze went to Fräu Weber's to fetch Raimund Leopold, and she burst into tears and wailed, "Raimund died of an intestinal cramp on August 19. I didn't write you because I was afraid it would spoil your trip."

485

SEVENTY-ONE

═

After such sad news Wolfgang vowed that he would never leave a child of his in anyone else's hands, while Constanze couldn't talk about Raimund Leopold without weeping. But Fräu Weber swore that the child would have died whether or not they had stayed in Vienna, intestinal cramps were so prevalent, even among the nobility. And Wolfgang couldn't find fault with her or with the foster-mother, for it was true that many infants had died from internal infections the past few months. When he recovered from his grief he saw only one solution: they must have another child.

The discovery some weeks later that Constanze was pregnant brought them happiness for the first time since they had returned home. Wolfgang celebrated by moving into better quarters in the Trattnerhof. This large building on the Graben had been built by Thomas von Trattner, who as a printer to the crown had become rich and had been ennobled.

Von Trattner was proud of his interest in the arts and fancied himself a painter and liked to dress in an artist's smock and a Rembrandt hat to prove that. His wife was one of Wolfgang's most devoted pupils and they were delighted to have the Mozarts as tenants.

Wolfgang arranged to use the first floor of the Trattnerhof for his concerts, and it was a great convenience. The next few months his popularity as a performer and as a composer soared. It was as if everything that had occurred before had gone into the creating of his reputation and his art. To attend his concerts and to applaud his playing and his new pianoforte concertos was the vogue now. The public's passion for him and for his music seemed insatiable.

By February, 1784, he was so busy creating new works he had to start a thematic catalogue of his compositions to keep track of them. As soon as he finished a work, he entered it by kind and key in his catalogue, with a few bars of the theme for further identification, and the date he had completed the work. He was so pleased with the clarity this gave his life, he began a regular account of his receipts and expenses. He put his receipts on a piece of paper, and he carried it with him and glanced at it often to remind him that he was earning more money than he ever had, and that soon he would be out of debt. He wrote his expenses in a book, and placed that in a secret place, where no one could read it, not even Stanzi.

In this burst of organization he also kept a record of all of his performances and a list of the subscribers to his concerts. This would show Papa, who had warned him that he could fail in Vienna – that he had made many enemies with his candor – that this wasn't so. He wrote Papa:

"I am enclosing a list of the one hundred and seventy-four subscribers to my concerts. If you can find a name that is important in Vienna that is missing, I will be surprised. I am now the fashion and anyone who does not subscribe to and attend my Wednesday concerts at the Trattnerhof is considered unenlightened. Some of the subscribers are old friends such as Thun, Pálffy, Wetzlar, Galitsin, van Swieten, and some are new such as von Born, Dietrichstein, Esterházy, Harrach, Hatzfeld, Heberstein, Lichnowsky, Mecklenburg, Oettingen, Paar, Pufendorf, Raab, Schwarzenberg, Sonnenfels, Starhemberg, Württemberg, and Zinzendorf.

"So you can see that those good friends of ours who told you that I have numerous enemies in Vienna are wrong. Oh, I grant you that Gluck is jealous and that Salieri could become dangerous under other circumstances, but neither of them would dare to slander me now, for the loftiest nobles of the Empire are pleased to call themselves my friend. And they are also paying for the privilege. The price of my first three concerts is six ducats, yet all of the seats have been subscribed in advance. I will also give two concerts at the Burgtheater, with the Emperor's approval.

"To give you an idea of how much in demand I am, here is the list of some of the concerts for which I have been engaged.

Thursday, February 26, at Galitsin's.
Monday, March 1, at Esterházy's.
Thursday, March 4, at Galitsin's.
Friday, March 5, at Esterházy's.
Monday, March 8, at Esterházy's.
Thursday, March 11, at Galitsin's.
Friday, March 12, at Esterházy's.
Monday, March 15, at Esterházy's.
Wednesday, March 17, my first concert in the Trattnerhof.
Thursday, March 18, at Galitsin's.
Friday, March 19, at Esterházy's.
Saturday, March 20, at pianist Richter's – as a special favor.

Sunday, March 21, my first concert at the Burgtheater.
Monday, March 22, at Esterházy's.
Wednesday, March 24, my second concert in the Trattnerhof.
Thursday, March 25, at Galitsin's.
Friday, March 26, at Esterházy's.
Saturday, March 27, at pianist Richter's – another favor.
Monday, March 29, at Esterházy's.
Wednesday, March 31, my third concert in the Trattnerhof.
Thursday, April 1, my second concert at the Burgtheater.
Saturday, April 3, at pianist Richter's – an encore concert.

"Do you think I have enough to do? At this rate, I think it will be difficult for me to get out of practice."

Every seat was sold at these concerts and Wolfgang earned many gulden. He was gratified, but Constanze was worried, for at the end of the third subscription concert he looked exhausted. She begged Wetzlar, whose opinion Wolfgang respected, to persuade him to drive himself less hard.

So Wetzlar, who felt the same way she did, said, as they walked to van Swieten's for the usual Sunday musical, "I don't know how you do it, Wolfgang. You never get to bed before midnight and you are up at six to prepare for the day ahead, you teach all morning and play all evening, and yet somehow, you continue to create one work after another. How many pianoforte concertos have you composed the last two months? Three?"

"Four. But that is no great trick. The difficult thing is to play them properly. Did you like them?"

"Very much. You have gained great honor with these grand concertos."

"They do make the performer sweat, but never so the audience knows."

"Aren't you giving the public too many concertos?"

"No. They are easily bored. I have to have at least one new work for each of my concerts. Otherwise, the audience will feel cheated."

"How can you survive such an arduous schedule?"

Wetzlar looked so concerned Wolfgang felt his friend deserved an explanation. He said, "I have also written two horn concertos for my Salzburg friend, Leutgeb, who speaks like an ass and plays like an angel. And more sonatas for the pianoforte, and I have begun another string quartet – it is a form that fascinates me – and arias for Aloysia Lange and Adamberger, who are after me all the time for music for their voices, they sing my arias at every opportunity. But perhaps you are right, Wetzlar. Perhaps I am writing too much music."

"That is not what I mean. Whatever you write, I want to hear. It is the drain on your energy that worries me. One of these days you will get another commission for an opera and you will be too tired to do it."

Wolfgang laughed. How could he be too tired for that!

"Have you any ideas for an opera?"

"Many. But the librettos that are offered me, or that I have come upon, are so poor that an infant could do as well. And I must write pieces that will earn money now."

"Like your quintet for oboe, horn, bassoon, clarinet, and pianoforte?"

"It received extraordinary applause, Wetzlar."

"And you played it for friends, and did not receive a single gulden."

"I do think it is the best I have yet written."

"It was lovely. I enjoyed it very much."

"Wasn't it performed beautifully?"

"I agree. But you looked very pale and drawn when you finished."

Wolfgang paused, thinking Wetzlar was right. Toward the end of the performance of the quintet, during which he had played the pianoforte, although the audience had been flattering, he had become very tired. He had had a sudden wish to stop playing, mere playing, and perhaps this was impossible, but this music gave him such longings to compose and do nothing else. But Vienna would consider that unreasonable. The Great Lords for whom he played so much these days declared that no one else could play Mozart like Mozart. He laughed wryly to himself. He used to think so, too. Wetzlar was discerning. There were days when with all the pleasure and adulation of the night before, he awoke so aching with fatigue he desired just to lie on his back and rest. But he could not tell him, or anyone else. He would be laughed at. He would be told that he was too young to have such feelings. He would be reminded that he was not yet thirty, that this was the prime of a man's existence, but there were moments he was so tired he felt like a hundred. Yet he could not halt. There was such a flood in him. He did not have the time to put down all the music he was hearing. He had a new pianoforte concerto in his mind and Wetzlar would say that he must write it down before he forgot it, but he would not forget it. Yet this concerto would not leave him alone until he put it down. That was what really disturbed him. He had to write out this music, even if he had to stay up all night. These days he felt there was no problem in music he could not solve.

Wetzlar said, "Your fertility astonishes me, Wolfgang. But I doubt that you, or anyone else, has the energy to match such an output."

"I will be able to rest one of these days. When I get an opera commission. Then I will concentrate just on that."

"You will never concentrate on just one composition. Even if you want to, something in yourself won't allow that."

"But I'm fortunate. Some people can't write a single note without complaining."

Later that Sunday, van Swieten asked Wolfgang to stay after everybody left. Van Swieten, who was struggling desperately to learn how to be a composer, who needed a year of the most painful labor to write a symphony, was startled by Wolfgang's speed and envious. He didn't discuss his own intense interest in composing, which was his reason for bringing up the subject, but said, "I have a friend whose son, about twelve, shows considerable musical ability."

"This Beethoven boy you discussed with me last year?"

"No, not him. This is another child prodigy."

"And this new prodigy, he wants to be a composer?"

"How did you know?" Van Swieten looked surprised.

"As young Beethoven's teacher wrote you, every youngster who shows a little musical talent hopes to become a second Wolfgang Amadeus Mozart."

"You don't think there will ever be another?"

"My dear friend, do you expect another Sebastian Bach or Joseph Haydn?"

"No."

"Then if one has to be a composer, he must be his own man."

"You studied everybody."

"And still do. But that doesn't make me a composer. You know that."

"What does? The boy said to me 'I should like very much to compose something. How am I to begin?' "

"Tell him to wait."

"You composed much earlier."

"But asked no one about it. If one has the spirit of a composer, one writes because one cannot help it."

"I must tell the father and his son more than that. Could you, at least, recommend a book or books? In addition to other composers?"

"Come, come, van Swieten," said Wolfgang, sensing that his friend was really speaking for himself. "All this is no use." He pointed to his ear, his head, and his heart, and added, "Here, here, and here is my school. If all is right there, then you may take your pen in hand without any delay."

When Wolfgang had copies of his four new pianoforte concertos he sent them to his father for his opinion, and asked him which one did Papa prefer.

Leopold replied that the concertos were excellent and that he liked them all, but expressed no preference. He did question whether his son should risk public displeasure with such difficult works. He said that as long as Wolfgang could play them, there would be no complaints, but once his music had to depend on other virtuosos, it could take too much time and effort to get accustomed to the difficulties. He warned his son that it was dangerous to destroy the old ways, however cleverly these innovations were disguised. Leopold was much more excited over the news that Nannerl was going to wed Herr zu Sonnenburg in August at St. Gilgen, where this widower with five children was the village magistrate. Mamma had been born in St. Gilgen, and Leopold said this was a good omen.

Wolfgang told Constanze, "St. Gilgen is a small village about fifty miles from Salzburg. I hope Nannerl will be happy there."

Attached to a widower with five children? Constanze thought critically, Couldn't his sister have married better? But she said, for he didn't like criticism of his family, "A wife should go where her husband lives."

"Perhaps. I am glad she is getting married. She has had other suitors, but this is the first one she has accepted."

Wolfgang wrote Nannerl an affectionate letter of congratulations, and told his father he should leave Colloredo and come stay with them.

Constanze was not for Leopold living with them, but she didn't voice her disapproval, certain that his father would reject such a proposal.

As she expected, Leopold did, saying that he couldn't give up his salary, that he couldn't depend on anyone else financially.

If Wolfgang was disappointed, he didn't show it. He said, "Papa always has to be independent. One can't change their habits at his age."

They were out of debt now, Wolfgang informed her proudly, and the next few months he purchased many things he had always desired. Constanze was worried about the increase in the cost of food and he insisted on buying the most expensive delicacies. He obtained waterproof cloth for his scores, of the finest quality. With the coming of summer he hired a carriage every Sunday and took her riding in the Prater. He bought her clothes that were better and more expensive than any she had known. A favorite purchase was a starling. While he was rehearsing the theme from a new pianoforte concerto the bird began to sing. Wolfgang was excited. The starling was virtually able to accompany his theme. He taught the bird how to follow this music and when it was able to whistle the rondo, he scored it for the starling's voice and under this passage wrote, "How pretty!"

SEVENTY-TWO

Wolfgang was deeply gratified when Constanze gave birth to a son in September without any difficulty. Von Trattner was honored to be the child's godfather and the infant was named Karl Thomas after him.

Soon afterward Wolfgang celebrated his new affluence by renting larger, more attractive rooms on the Grosse Schulerstrasse. He did this without consulting Constanze, so she would not try to stop him because of the cost.

But the instant the deposit was paid he insisted that she must see their new home. "It isn't far!" he exclaimed. "Just around the corner from St. Stephen's. It is a fine location, close to everything important in Vienna, and you will love it as I do." He led her past the great cathedral and added, "We are moving into a better neighborhood."

She did not agree. The Grosse Schulerstrasse was narrower and dirtier than where they had been living. She disliked the heavy cobblestones underfoot, and she thought that the paving was better on the Graben. The front door was heavy and hard to open. The entry was small, dark, and was lit poorly by a flickering lamp. Then there was a staircase five flights high and a little piece of sky above it, which as she looked up seemed only one yard wide and five yards long. Was this the sun and light he was praising? How could he be so carried away?

"Lean on me," he said, "if you get tired. There are ten steps," he explained, referring to the stairway to the first floor. "And then a stone cornice you can rest on. Three more steps, and only ten after that."

She knew his love of numbers, and how he had counted steps as a child, but actually, there were twenty-three steps to climb, however he counted them, and in her growing irritation that seemed much too many.

At the top he declared, "I rented the first floor because I know you don't like steps, particularly when you are pregnant."

She knew that if he had his way she would be pregnant again and soon, for he desired a large family. She thought the two bedrooms facing the Domgasse and Blutgasse appropriate but nothing to get excited about.

She asked, "What about the kitchen? The dining room?"

"They are combined." He showed her a small room with a stove and a floor of red stone. "Almost the same as Unsterberg marble, my favorite marble. Except it would have been too costly to bring it from Salzburg."

"Is this what you are so enthusiastic over?" she asked skeptically.

He grinned mischievously and led her into the drawing room.

It was beautiful, she realized, with its own elegance and charm.

"Now we can really entertain!" he cried. "Look at these windows. Aren't they handsome? I love high, grand windows!"

"But what does this cost?"

He waved aside her apprehensions and ushered her into the music room.

The walls were of white Italian marble, there was a magnificent marble arch over the entry, and a ceiling with some of the finest stucco work she had ever seen. It ornamented the ceiling with a lovely, voluptuous Venus in the center panel, and graceful, attractive nymphs and cupids around her.

"Wolfgang, what are we paying for these rooms?"

"Two hundred and forty gulden for six months."

She said fearfully, "That is four hundred and eighty gulden a year. More than you earned a whole year in Salzburg. In a few months we will be in debt again. We didn't have to move from the Trattnerhof. It was only one hundred and fifty gulden a year."

"I have earned two thousand gulden already this year. Do you like our new home?"

There was no use complaining, she thought, that wouldn't change Wolfgang. And perhaps he was right. More subscription concerts were being arranged for the coming winter, and every seat had been sold in advance.

Her affectionate hug gave him the feeling that he was irresistible and he said, "You'll see, Stanzi. We will be very happy here."

The music room was a proud one for Wolfgang and his affectionate nature responded to it with love. Long ago he had learned to compose under any conditions, but he had never lost his yearning for space, light, and comfort, and now that he possessed it, he wrote with a new contentment.

The four pianoforte concertos of the spring had been received with such acclaim, he started two more, working on them at the same time. For variety he also began two string quartets and several sonatas for the pianoforte.

He found other things he liked about his new home. When he came out of the doorway and strode through the Domplatz he was at St. Stephen's, which was just several minutes away. Yet if he went down the Blutgasse and after a short walk turned right, he was at the House of the Teutonic Knights where he had been kicked down the stairs. Now that seemed an infinity away. He also enjoyed watching the sun creep over his bedroom window in the late morning. He told the time by it, and he slept next to the window, the one favor he asked of Constanze, who thought him a trifle foolish about this. Once the sun was on his window he knew he had to get out of bed or he would not accomplish what he desired. With the increase in his income he had reduced the number of his pupils. He was sleeping later; he no longer felt exhausted; he had the energy of a young man again.

Constanze went down to the cellar to the common well to get water, for the maid had strict orders never to leave Karl Thomas alone, and when she passed the toilet for the house, which was a hole one stood over or sat over, and then washed down with water from the well, she lost some of her enthusiasm for their new home. This was the practice wherever they had lived, but somehow here, with their fine rooms, she felt it should be different. Others might joke about it, but at such moments she felt sorry for herself.

Today, as always in cold weather, when she finished washing her face and hands, she put her feet in the water so as not to waste it, but not her whole body. That was unthinkable – she would not wash her entire self until warm weather returned, many months from now, and they could go to the Danube. After she washed she doused herself with perfume and felt a little better, and when she met Wolfgang entering and he kissed her more like a lover than a husband she felt him growing large with passion.

He was quite excited. "Van Swieten is going to introduce me to Joseph Haydn. The Baron said Haydn wants to meet me. Me! Stanzi, I am so honored!" He grabbed her by the hand and danced around the drawing room.

Yet the Sunday that was to occur, Wolfgang entered van Swieten's with trepidation. Haydn might be another Gluck, or a Salieri, although he was a better composer; Haydn could be hostile, jealous; and Haydn was fifty-two, and might regard him as hardly more than a precocious boy. He could think of many reasons why they would not like each other.

Van Swieten introduced them as if they were two heads of state and announced that this afternoon was just for the three of them. The

Baron sounded so pompous Wolfgang wanted to laugh. But Haydn looked solemn, so he did, not wanting to offend him. He saw a man somewhat taller than himself, with a long face, a large nose, a prominent chin, skin heavily pockmarked from smallpox, thoughtful, deep brown eyes, and dressed neatly and properly in brown, with a simple white powdered wig.

Haydn noticed that Mozart's cheeks were puffy, that his nose and chin were more round than pointed, that he was a little man with a magnificent forehead and eyes that were alive with energy.

They stood in stillness and suddenly this was more than Wolfgang could bear and he blurted out, "Herr Haydn, I've wanted to meet you a long time."

"You have?" Haydn appeared surprised and said, "So have I."

They laughed, amused and wondering whether this was truly so.

Haydn added, "I want to thank you for what you did for my brother."

Wolfgang shrugged to indicate that it had been his pleasure.

"It was generous of you and the music was lovely. The Archbishop must be a fool indeed not to have known it was your music."

"There are all sorts of fools, Herr Haydn. The arch-booby is one of the obscene kind. Did the Baron tell you how happy I am to meet you? I have been admiring your music for a long time." But when Haydn didn't reply, he felt he was standing in a false intimacy.

Haydn didn't know what to say. He didn't trust most compliments; they usually confused him. Yet he had heard himself in Mozart's music, which was a genuine compliment, and he liked much of what he had heard.

Then van Swieten, who had not said anything since the introduction, stated pedantically, "I'm sure music will profit from this meeting."

"I don't know about music," said Haydn, "but if Herr Mozart could share some lunch, we could sit down and relax."

Wolfgang grinned boyishly and said, "A splendid idea. As my guest."

Van Swieten asked, "Don't you want to discuss composition?"

Wolfgang said ironically, "For my sins?"

Van Swieten said, "You love music, don't you?"

Haydn said, "Maybe that is why we shouldn't talk about it."

Wolfgang said, "Would you excuse us, Baron?"

Van Swieten felt that he was being robbed and he was resentful – listening to the two best composers he knew he would surely learn more about composition, but he couldn't admit that. Or sound ungracious. He said, "My housekeeper is gone, or you could dine here."

It was his excuse to save money, and Wolfgang and Haydn's eyes exchanged an unspoken understanding. They thanked van Swieten for bringing them together, and said they didn't want to impose on his kindness any further.

At a nearby coffee house Haydn spoke very little while eating, and Wolfgang ate sparingly, he was so interested in Haydn, and looked at him all the time. He was seeing beyond the physical man, and sensing the consciousness that had created the complete musician. There was a directness and naturalness in Haydn that was unusual, as if he knew how strong and durable he was without having to ponder about such matters.

When he finished eating he looked at Wolfgang for the first time since they had sat down and said, "You've eaten hardly anything, Herr Mozart."

"I am not hungry. But please, do not stop on my account."

Haydn smiled and said, "I have never lost my peasant's appetite."

Wolfgang was still too excited to eat, and as they heard a serenade in the street they were both attracted by the beauty of the singer's voice. With a simple mandolin he was singing a plaintive and touching song.

Haydn exclaimed with pleasure, "It's Pedrillo's air from *Die Entführung!*"

"You know the opera?"

"Yes. To write so expressively and yet so simply is an act of genius. It is an enchanting score. I would have given much to compose it."

"What about your string quartets? They are the best I have ever heard."

Now they were both embarrassed, afraid that they would not be believed.

Yet Wolfgang could not contain himself. After the singer finished and he sent out ten kreutzer with the waiter to reward him, he said, "Since I heard your Russian quartets, I have been composing a set of my own. I have finished three, and I would be deeply honored if you could hear them at my house. I could arrange it soon, perhaps even tomorrow."

But Haydn remembered that tomorrow he was supposed to be on his way back to his post at Eisenstadt and that lateness would not be tolerated. He explained that to Wolfgang, who was incredulous.

Wolfgang said, "I extended my leaves from the Archbishop. Oh, he would get angry, and threaten me, but he never really punished me. After all your years with Prince Esterházy, surely one day more or less..."

"No." Haydn halted him, affable but firm. "I cannot be late."

"Don't you mind such servitude?"

"What choice is there?" But Wolfgang was so disappointed, he added, "I will inform you when I visit Vienna again."

"You will keep your word?"

"I will keep it. I will be happy to hear your quartets."

As Wolfgang walked Haydn to his rooms and they saw St. Stephen's, Haydn said, "I was a choir boy there. And when my voice began to change, Reutter, the Imperial Kapellmeister, suggested they make a castrato out of me, that it was the only way I could have a musical career. But when my father learned about this, he rushed to Vienna from his home in Lower Austria, although it was a long, costly journey and he was hardly more than a peasant, and forbade it. So, instead of being a Manzuoli, I became a composer."

"And a dear friend, I hope!" Wolfgang cried out.

Haydn hesitated; he had been telling this experience to lighten the seriousness of their parting. But suddenly, when it came time to say good-bye, Wolfgang impulsively threw his arms around Haydn in an affectionate embrace, and Haydn, who generally was not demonstrative, was greatly touched, and responded with genuine emotion.

Friendship had come to be of major importance to Wolfgang and when he was invited to join the Freemasons he accepted with alacrity. He admired their devotion to the moral power of reason and nature, their regarding each member as a fraternal equal, nobleman and commoner alike, and their belief that God was a great and enlightened architect who had built a rational order which man must strive to perpetuate on earth.

Van Swieten, Cobenzl, Wetzlar, Pálffy, and many other friends belonged. The Emperor supported Freemasonry by allowing it to exist – as a counterweight against the church, whose influence he was seeking to diminish – although many of its members, such as Wolfgang, considered themselves good Catholics. Wolfgang wasn't impressed by van Swieten telling him that its members included Frederick the Prussian, Goethe, Voltaire, Franklin, Jefferson, George III. He did care about its feeling for brotherhood. After Colloredo, he couldn't accept the church's stress on sin and repentance. He still observed the rituals, but he saw vast differences between God and His worldly representatives. Admitted to the Beneficence Lodge as an apprentice, he was welcomed in all the lodges as a musical brother and quickly promoted to the second grade, journeyman.

Haydn kept his word. The next time he visited Vienna, he informed Wolfgang in advance, who invited him to a musical evening in his honor at the Grosse Schulerstrasse, and who sent a carriage to bring him there.

Wolfgang dressed like a courtier in deference to his distinguished guest, yet the only other guests were musicians to play and hear the quartets. He invited Haydn to play, but Haydn preferred to concentrate on listening.

Then there was nothing but the musicians playing and several listening, and Constanze sitting with the four-month-old Karl Thomas in her arms, which was Wolfgang's wish, and gradually the baby fell asleep without a whimper while Wolfgang seemed to sing to himself as he played.

No one said a word until the three quartets were finished and then Wolfgang turned to Haydn and asked, "What do you think, Maestro?" As Haydn did not answer, he felt panic. He was surprised at himself; he rarely allowed himself to care that much for what someone else thought. But if Haydn disliked these quartets it must be for a good reason.

First violinist Ebert said, "We should have rehearsed more."

Second violinist Pozzi said, "I got so lost in the music."

"No," said the cellist, Favart, "We weren't good enough."

"You are too humble, gentlemen," said Haydn. "Your performance was fine."

"Would you like some wine, Herr Haydn?" suggested Constanze.

"Thank you, Fräu Mozart, but the music was intoxicating enough."

"You liked them?" Wolfgang's eyes, which had been dull, lit up vividly.

"That is hardly the word. The quartets are very original, and owe very little to me." Haydn was thinking: who dared to say Mozart's music wasn't intense, compressed, dramatic! The structure might resemble his, but the harmonies were Mozartean. Then he grew disturbed. There were elements in Mozart's quartets that surpassed his own. For a moment he was envious, and then as the fatalism and force of the quartet in D Minor pervaded his heart and mind he was deeply moved and his eyes were wet, and he thought, Mozart wants to sit at my feet but I should sit at his! "I will feel privileged to hear the rest of your quartets when they are finished."

"Within a few weeks, I hope," said Wolfgang. "My father has accepted my invitation to be my guest in Vienna and he should arrive next month. I plan to have them ready for him then. Will you be here, Herr Haydn?"

"Yes. My master intends to spend the rest of the winter in the capital, so I shall remain, for he will require my services."

Karl Thomas had been awakened by the conversation and had begun to cry. At a signal from Constanze, the maid took the baby to his room.

Haydn stood up slowly and said, "The child is right. It is time for bed." He shook his head wonderingly, "Wolfgang, if it wasn't time to leave, I could sit and listen to your quartets all night."

"We would be delighted, and honored."

"So would I. You have such a nice home to hear music in. We even have a Venus and cupids in the audience." Haydn indicated the ornamented stucco ceiling. "And a gracious lady as hostess." Haydn, with a courtliness that surprised Wolfgang, bent and kissed Constanze's hand, and added, with unusual fervor, "You are to be congratulated, Wolfgang, on having such an attractive home and family."

SEVENTY-THREE

It was surprising and disconcerting. Leopold had not expected to be so emotional visiting Wolfgang, but he was. He stood in front of the house on the Grosse Schulerstrasse, having just stepped out of the coach, in a neighborhood he knew well, and he had to pause to collect his thoughts.

Nannerl had warned him that his life would be in peril if he traveled to Vienna in February, when the weather was at its worst, but he had known that if he hadn't gone now, he never would have gone. Each year he grew feebler, and Nannerl was expecting a child this summer and he wanted to be in Salzburg when this occurred. Yet, at this moment, his central concern was Wolfgang's career. His son had continued to write that it was moving favorably, but he had to see for himself. He must hide the cold he had caught on the journey, the rheumatic pains in his legs and back and stand as straight as his son. He swung the iron knocker vigorously and a minute later Wolfgang was at the door, spontaneously embracing him. As his luggage was carried upstairs, his son escorted him inside, saying, "You are lucky we are on the first floor, there are very few steps to climb."

He was grateful that after too many steps for his comfort, there was a little stone wall to rest on. He was out of breath, but the stone was cold and sent a chill through him. He rose quickly, and accepted his son's help, although he disliked the aged feeling that gave him.

Constanze greeted him pleasantly and insisted that he have lunch, and the hot coffee warmed him. She showed him Karl Thomas and he was delighted with the child's good humor and he didn't wish to be critical, but he found himself saying, "I hope the same mistakes won't be made with Karl Thomas."

Wolfgang said hurriedly, as Constanze flushed, "Papa, you must rest. We have a busy schedule, and we want you to enjoy every minute of it."

Leopold was awakened from his nap by the sound of billiard balls. To his astonishment his son was practicing billiards with great skill. When he remarked on the strangeness of this just before a concert – Wolfgang was to give the first of six Friday subscription concerts this evening – his son replied, "I bought the table to keep my fingers pliant. I have been composing so much lately my hands become cramped from holding a pen if I don't exercise them."

"Don't believe him," said Constanze, "he likes billiards for its own sake. Just as he loves dancing. Sometimes, I think he loves that even more than his music. He never gives me any rest when we are at a ball."

In this complaint she was closer to Leopold than she had ever been while flattering him. He said, "Wolfgang always loved dancing, even as a child."

But Wolfgang, after executing a brilliant shot at the billiards table with unusual dexterity, returned to his desk, saying, "I must finish copying the last movement, so the conductor can have something to guide him."

"You haven't copied the rondo and you expect to perform it properly?"

"Of course. I have the whole concerto in my head."

"That may be true for you, but what about the orchestra and the conductor? They will be seeing the score for the first time."

"The orchestra men are good sight readers. And we know each other."

Constanze said, "He hasn't even played the last movement for himself."

"I know how it will sound," Wolfgang said, almost testy. "Just be sure both of you listen carefully, without any preconceived judgments."

The Mehlgrube casino, where the concert was to be held, was full. Wolfgang explained to his father that this large, three-storey building had been given its name because of the flour stored in its cellar, but was used for any purpose that would make money. He assured an anxious Leopold, "The acoustics are excellent, I have played here before, and my entire subscription of one hundred and fifty is sold out. It is the same distinguished list I sent you last year, but a little smaller. I moved from the Trattnerhof so this could be more select, and because the rent is less. I expect to earn at least six hundred gulden from these concerts."

His father looked impressed as he hoped.

"Don't you think I've been a good business man?" Wolfgang asked eagerly.

501

"That depends on how much you save. Your rooms with that fancy ceiling and fine windows must cost a great deal."

"Only four hundred and eighty gulden a year, Papa."

"Only! I've never earned more than that in a year from Colloredo!"

Before he could reproach Wolfgang for being extravagant, his son was pointing out that Gluck, Salieri, and Bonno were in the audience.

"Not Haydn?" asked Leopold, disappointed.

"No. He is being admitted to the Concord Lodge tonight as an apprentice Mason, and he couldn't attend. You will meet him tomorrow evening. And become a Freemason yourself, I hope, before you leave."

"Perhaps." Their relationship was going too well to risk offending. And there was an excitement in the Mehlgrube that reminded Leopold of how much he had given up when he had stopped touring with Wolfgang.

"I expect this concerto in D Minor will provide some surprises."

It was far more than that, felt Leopold, as the orchestra opened with a power and somberness he had not heard in his son's concertos before. Yet when the pianoforte entered Wolfgang's hands were as graceful as ever, and it was as if he had played this music many times. It was the drive in the score that was disturbing. What manner of man had written such dramatic and tragic music! It was not his son. He did not know this man. But the passionate nature of the music was compelling. This persisted with an intensity that could not be denied. Wolfgang had gone far beyond what he had intended for him in composing. What would the audience think? This was so advanced. What would be the consequences? Where had these notes come from? Had Wolfgang suffered this much? Or did he know at thirty what it took most men twice that many years to comprehend? Even the slow movement of this concerto in D Minor was tragic, with all of its beauty and singing tone.

He sat in silent wonder as Wolfgang played the unpracticed rondo without a flaw, and thought, he should have continued to write the book that he had started to write about Wolfgang when the latter had been a child. But no one would have believed it. This concerto was for another century, and he had only a few years left to live, whatever his children said.

The next evening was devoted to the just completed set of six string quartets. Wolfgang invited the best musicians he knew to perform: Karl Ditters von Dittersdorf and Johann Baptist Vanhal and Joseph Haydn.

Leopold knew Dittersdorf and Vanhal by reputation. Dittersdorf was a fine composer and violinist, and a special favorite of the Emperor's. Vanhal was a less important composer, but the best cellist in Vienna.

As Wolfgang introduced his guests to his father, Haydn said, "Herr Mozart, your *Violin School* has been quite important to me. The violin is my instrument, and I found it a very sound book indeed."

Dittersdorf seconded these sentiments and then so did Vanhal.

This reminded Leopold that all compliments must be accepted warily, that the donor's true reasons must be determined before the worth of the praise could be evaluated and he sat back in his son's cherrywood chair and studied the three musicians. Haydn had the same nose, jaw, and eyes as his brother, but was homelier and more benign-looking. Dittersdorf dressed like a courtier and his attractive appearance was an obvious asset. Yet Vanhal, who had an odd face, with a wide brow, indented cheeks and a jaw that fell away, was also very popular in Vienna.

Dittersdorf and Vanhal declared that Herr Haydn must play with them.

Haydn didn't object this time as Wolfgang expected, but said he would be privileged to perform the quartets with them. They replied that he must play first violin, and when he agreed, Dittersdorf took the second violin part, Wolfgang the viola and Vanhal the cello.

Leopold thought, If there is such a thing as pure music this is it. The other composers played his son's quartets with a reverence he would have expected them to give only to their own music. And when they finished Wolfgang embraced them all warmly and gratefully.

Constanze served coffee and pastry and wine and Dittersdorf said suddenly, apparently uneasy at the quiet which still prevailed – and perhaps, thought Leopold, eager to provoke a little excitement with controversy, "The Emperor, recently, asked me what I thought of the respective abilities of Clementi and Mozart."

Haydn and Wolfgang didn't even pause in their eating, but Vanhal looked up from his wine and said, "I hope you were accurate, Dittersdorf."

"Indeed! Indeed! I said that in Clementi's playing there is just skill, but in Mozart's both skill and taste."

"Thank you," said Wolfgang, and went on eating, and so did Haydn.

"But Joseph does think you are a spendthrift with your musical ideas."

"The Emperor? Who ever said he had any knowledge of music?"

Leopold winced. No wonder Dittersdorf was more successful than Wolfgang with the Emperor. Dittersdorf would cater to Joseph's vanity where his son would disregard it. But before he could say anything, Haydn stopped eating and declared, "I wish I had some of Mozart's ideas."

"Oh, I told Joseph that Mozart is one of the greatest of original geniuses, that I have never known any composer who has such an amazing wealth of ideas. But I almost wish he were not so lavish in using them."

"Do I waste them?" Wolfgang asked, with a sardonic smile.

"In effect, yes," said Dittersdorf. "The hearer does not have time to catch his breath, for hardly has he grasped one lovely theme, when another, even more beautiful, destroys the first, and this goes on until it is impossible to remember any of these fine melodies."

Vanhal muttered, "I remember them. And wished I had used them."

Dittersdorf said, "Of course. I said that, too. But the Emperor complained that our friend's music for the stage has such a full accompaniment, it overwhelms his singers."

Haydn snapped angrily, "This is nonsense. Mozart is the finest musical talent I know. These quartets are magnificent."

Wolfgang said seriously, "But I learned how to compose quartets from you."

"And as I said before, you really owe very little to me." Haydn turned to Leopold, who had stayed out of this discussion with difficulty and declared, *"Herr Mozart, before God, and as an honest man, I must tell you that your son is the greatest composer I know in person and by name. He has taste, and a sensitivity to beauty that is incomparable, and the most thorough and profound knowledge of composition."*

Wolfgang bowed his head as if he had been blessed by God, and Leopold could hardly keep from crying – so all the work had not been in vain.

Then, as everybody rose to go, Haydn said to Leopold, "Herr Mozart, I truly wonder if there would have been a Wolfgang without a Leopold."

SEVENTY-FOUR

——

Twenty-four hours after what had become one of the great moments of Leopold's life, he heard his son play another new pianoforte concerto at the Burgtheater in the presence of the Emperor. He was amazed by how different it was from the previous concerto. Wolfgang had put it in F Major and it was as lyrical and melodic as the D Minor had been dramatic and somber. It was so loving Leopold cried. Then he caught hold of himself. He had been emotional ever since he had arrived in Vienna; he had been on the verge of tears several times; he, who prided himself on his self-control and cynicism. But he kept recalling what Haydn had said; it had been very gracious, and the thought that he would have missed that if he had remained in Salzburg made his blood run cold.

The music pulled him into the present. Wolfgang would wish to know what he thought, and he must be accurate. He was well placed in a good box, able to hear as he should. From the opening passages this music sang. This concerto was admirably written. It was more like the music he was accustomed to from his son. It followed his precepts to please, to flow like oil. How lovely its melodies were! The structure was perfect! There was not a note, not a passage, not a tempo he would have altered. But he must not be sentimental, he must not praise Wolfgang, or his son would sit back and be content when there was so much else for his son to compose. Yet he found himself swaying back and forth with the music.

The applause thundered through the Burgtheater and the Emperor took off his hat and waved it and shouted, "Bravo, Mozart!" and now the applause went on and on.

After the Emperor departed Wolfgang stood outside the Burg-theater and as many congratulated him, he wanted to know what Papa thought.

"What is there to think? You saw the audience's pleasure." He changed the subject. "How many concertos have you composed this past year?"

Wolfgang counted on his fingers. "One in E Flat, one in B Flat, in D, G, and B Flat again, in F – which you heard tonight – and one in D Minor, that you heard on the day you arrived."

"Seven? In one year?" Leopold was incredulous.

"I told you that Vienna was a clavierland. And I composed three others after I came here. That's ten pianoforte concertos, so far. But Papa, you never answered me when I asked you which ones you preferred."

"How could I? What is there to prefer?"

"You didn't care for them?"

"The Emperor did," Leopold said brusquely, to hide his own emotion. "That's enough. And you shouldn't be standing out here." It had started to snow heavily and the wind was howling. Wolfgang had played with such fervor he was perspiring profusely and his clothes were drenched with sweat, yet in the excitement he had come outside without his coat. "In this awful night air you could catch a severe chill. Where is your overcoat?"

"The Emperor decreed that no servant can enter the Burgtheater by the front entrance, so the man who had it had to wait outside. I presume he got tired and went home."

"With your coat?" Papa was appalled by such carelessness.

Wolfgang shrugged. He had more important matters on his mind.

"Here, use mine," said Wetzlar, who had joined them. When Wolfgang declined, Wetzlar insisted they join him in his carriage and not wait for theirs, which had been delayed by the snowstorm. As they rode toward Wolfgang's home, Wetzlar said to Leopold, "I hope you can get your son to work less hard, and to take care of himself. He won't tell you, but he has had attacks of rheumatic fever, and severe chills and cramps."

Leopold said sadly, as the weather grew worse, one of the harshest storms he had ever experienced, "He doesn't listen to me – anymore."

"Oh, yes I do, Papa. But I'm not sweating now, and I feel fine. Did you enjoy the concert? I thought the Emperor was rather *Entführung* in Germany and elsewhere, Joseph never thinks of me gracious."

"He seems to admire your playing very much."

"That is the trouble. He continues to regard me as a performer on the pianoforte rather than as a composer. When he does like what I compose, it is always instrumental. Despite the success of *Die* as an opera composer."

A few days later Fräu Weber invited Wolfgang, Constanze, and Leopold to lunch. Leopold learned about it, overhearing his son and daughter-in-law disagreeing about the invitation. They were in the kitchen, thinking he was in his bedroom, unaware that he had been unable to nap because of the cold and that he was approaching them to fetch more wood for the stove.

Constanze was saying, "I don't think we should accept. Your father has always been hostile to my family, and he isn't going to change now."

Wolfgang said, "He should see for himself. Your mother is not an ogre."

"But she is a schemer."

"So is Papa, sometimes." Wolfgang was amused at the idea of the meeting.

Leopold almost interrupted them then – his schemes had been only for Wolfgang's benefit, as Haydn had proved – but he retreated as if he had not heard anything. When his son told him they were to be the guests of Fräu Weber, he said, "I'm not up to that. How can you expect me to accept her hospitality after all the unpleasantness she caused you?"

Wolfgang laughed and said, "It turned out fine. Why should I hate her?"

Leopold didn't reply. Although Constanze had been a good hostess, he still had serious doubts whether she was sensible or provident enough for his son, and their relationship had remained polite and formal.

"Papa, if I don't have a grievance, why should you?"

"Fräu Weber knows I am the one who has been the most critical of her."

"And she will be honored if you accept her invitation."

"Do you really think so?"

"It will signify that you do approve of the marriage."

Was his son testing him? Leopold hesitated, but when he saw the imploring look in his son's eyes, he said, "If you want it, Wolfgang."

Constanze dressed fashionably and demanded that they take a carriage to her mother's, although the Am Peter was only a short walk away.

Leopold took a long time to get ready, but finally he couldn't put it off any longer, and as they climbed the steps to the Weber rooms he was nervous. He feared his pent-up years of anger would erupt in a volcanic burst and ruin the mellowness between him and his son. But he was surrounded by Wolfgang and Constanze, who held Karl Thomas. And he was curious about Fräu Weber and Aloysia Lange.

The rooms had been cleaned in a last-moment way, and Sophie Weber greeted them. Leopold thought her pleasant-looking but not pretty.

Then Wolfgang introduced him to Fräu Weber, who swept in like

507

a grand lady, her hair in a large, towering coiffure. As his son had said, she must have been stunning at one time, but now she was thick-waisted, stout, and her layer of cosmetics gave her wrinkled skin a florid complexion.

She declared, "How nice of you to come, Herr Leopold!"

He answered dryly, "I am sorry if I put you to any trouble."

"Where did you get such an idea. We are delighted that you could come. You are the guest of honor."

"Indeed!" His eyebrows went up skeptically.

"Do you like Vienna?"

He said curtly, "As long as it likes my son."

There was a heavy silence, but then, as if it were impossible for her to stop talking, she said, "Your son does you great credit in Vienna. He is the favorite of society, and of the Emperor, too."

But he still longed to attack her for being a poacher on his domain, and he retorted abruptly, "You didn't always feel that way."

"Oh, yes I did. I just didn't want our children to do anything they would regret later. It was a difficult situation."

"And you made it more difficult."

"How can you say that, Herr Leopold."

He could have said much more, but Wolfgang broke in. "Cäcilia, Karl Thomas looks like a Mozart, but the next one, I promise, will look like you."

Diverted, she responded proudly, "The Webers have always been an attractive family. And the baby will be, too."

Constanze asked, "Where is Aloysia?"

Her mother said piously, "Your dear sister is coming after lunch. She didn't want me to do any more cooking than necessary."

Constanze didn't believe her. Aloysia always had to make an entrance.

Lunch was unexpectedly sumptuous. Sophie served what her mother had prepared: roast pheasant set in cabbage and potatoes, with glacé fruit, pastry, and coffee. Everything was succulently flavored and Leopold had to admit that Fräu Weber was an excellent cook.

The Langes arrived in time for coffee, and Aloysia entered even more grandly than her mother. Her husband trailed her, and Leopold wondered what his son had seen in her. Aloysia might have been beautiful once, he thought, but now, although she was only in her mid-twenties, that was gone. Her face had hardened, and while she was still attractive, there was nothing charming about her appearance, but a weapon to be used, at its best a regular profile that was impressive, even at times handsome, and at its worst almost inhuman, like a hawk's, prepared to seize every advantage.

Leopold liked Joseph Lange. The actor had sensitive features, an excellent figure, and a resonant voice. And he disdained small talk.

While the women discussed Aloysia's new gown and Constanze disagreed with everything Aloysia said, and Wolfgang sat reflective and indifferent to Aloysia, Joseph Lange remarked, "Herr Leopold, your son's quartets are amazing. He uses the traditional forms, which shows that he has been splendidly trained, yet his harmonies are unique." Lange made his words sound as complimentary to Leopold as to Wolfgang, and sketched Leopold and quickly created an excellent likeness.

And Wolfgang still sat detached, as if Lange were speaking about someone else, until Aloysia announced she would like to sing his music. He became animated and as he sat at the pianoforte he played with feeling.

Everyone was attentive. Leopold was determined to be ruthless, but he realized now what his son had seen in her. Aloysia's voice had a beautiful tone, and she used it with taste and expression. But there were moments when she sang too carefully and coldly to please him. She glanced at Wolfgang as he accompanied her, but he looked back at her objectively, as if she were a vocal instrument and nothing more.

Leopold sensed that whatever his son had felt for Aloysia, it had come to an end. But he applauded her, saying, "Madame Lange, I can understand your success. You have a splendid voice and you use it well."

"I am honored by your good opinion, Herr Leopold," she answered, with a deep bow. "Your reputation has been known to me all my life."

"All your life?" He couldn't be that complacent.

"Yes," she said, with unexpected sincerity. "My father was musical to his fingertips and he taught me in the hope that the Webers would become as musical a family as the Mozarts. He admired the way you trained Wolfgang."

Startled, confused, Leopold blurted out, "Children grow up thinking the world owes them something. It doesn't. Except what they give to it."

"That's what my father said. He wanted the Webers to be as famous as the Mozarts. But singers do not become child prodigies."

Leopold asked thoughtfully, "You liked your father very much?"

"Very much. As Wolfgang feels about you. If he had lived. . ."

Fräu Weber stated, "Whatever I did, Herr Leopold, I did for my daughters' sake. To raise four girls in this cruel world is not easy. I am sure you have done some things you would have preferred not to do."

For a moment he almost liked her. Then he remembered her efforts to compromise Wolfgang and he realized he could never forgive her, however much he tried. And when he didn't reply she began to discuss music, as if she could not endure silence, only she didn't know what she was talking about.

Wolfgang, seeing Papa frowning, stood up suddenly. It had gone better than he had hoped, at least Papa was aware now that the Webers were human beings, and Cäcilia could talk too much. He interrupted her bluntly, "We have to leave. I have a concert tonight and we have to rest before it."

As they departed, Fräu Weber said, "Herr Leopold, we must have the pleasure of seeing you again," and Aloysia thanked him for listening to her, but he preferred Sophie, who had said very little, but had waited on all of them with a sweetness he had not seen in anyone else in her family.

The next few weeks passed at such a feverish pace Leopold wished they would end. The excitement, the activity was exhausting him. Wolfgang seemed determined to overwhelm him with his success. He wrote Nannerl:

"Your brother is playing so much it is a wonder he doesn't get ill. Yet he insists that he loves it, and no matter how busy he is, he claims he has one more concert to spare, one more concerto he can always compose.

"Since I have been here your brother's pianoforte has been carried many time to the theater, to the Mehlgrube, and to numerous noble patrons.

"And there is no doubt that he has become very popular – if it will only last! There is a great demand for his playing, and to a lesser extent, for his music, and he is welcome everywhere.

"I think, if he has no debts to pay, he might now be able to put two thousand gulden in the bank. The money certainly has been earned – at one concert alone in the Mehlgrube, he earned a profit of 559 gulden – and the housekeeping, as it concerns eating and drinking, is economical.

"But you know how careless your brother can be with money, and I fear that a thousand gulden at least will slip away through poor management. I do not say anything however, unless I am consulted, for he refuses to allow me to pay for a thing and since I cannot question what he spends on me, how can I question him elsewhere. Yet his easy way with money troubles me, and if he is not saving at such a favorable time I am not sure this felicity will last. Your brother senses my concern, for he assures me that when Gluck dies he will get an Imperial appointment, and he tells me that he keeps an exact record of his earnings and expenditures, but he hasn't shown them to me and I doubt that he will.

"My personal opinion is that as long as he remains so popular he will not have any difficulties, but should taste alter he is in a dangerous situation. But what I write you is between ourselves. God willing, perhaps your brother will remain the favorite of Vienna. I wish I could believe public taste was so faithful. His new concertos are fine."

Wolfgang begged Papa to stay as long as he liked, for good preferably.

Leopold said, "It is generous of you, but I must keep my independence."

"You will be as free as you wish. You will have the run of the house..."

Leopold halted him. "You have a huge performance schedule, much entertaining to do. I would only be in the way."

"You could advise me. As you used to do."

"You really think you would listen to me? And it wouldn't be fair to your wife. She might not say anything, but she would feel this wasn't her own home. And I want to be close to Nannerl when she has her baby."

But he did agree to become a Mason, for this had become dear to his son.

Wolfgang was pleased when his father was granted special dispensation by his Lodge and admitted as an apprentice, and several weeks later, at his request, was promoted to the second grade with Masonic ceremonies.

Leopold didn't feel as strongly about Freemasonry as Wolfgang did, but now his son treated him almost as if they were the same age.

Then Leopold, who had been given a six weeks' leave by Colloredo and extended it to fourteen, was notified by the Salzburg Exchequer that His Grace had ordered his pay stopped immediately unless he returned at once. So he prepared to go as soon as possible.

The day of departure was devoted to packing and as Leopold finished, Constanze sighed with relief. There had been moments when she had thought he would never go. It had been a tense time, but at least there had been no quarrels and very little criticism and he had taken a liking to Sophie, who had visited them several times.

Wolfgang had spent the entire morning helping Papa. Part of him was aware that Papa's presence was a strain and could hurt his marriage, with all the good will in the world, yet he didn't want Papa to go, he needed and loved him and why should anything interfere with that? Time should bring mutual understanding between Constanze and Papa. And that would give him such happiness. He said suddenly, "Don't go yet!"

Leopold said sadly, "I don't want to, but I must. It won't work if I stay. I will be an irritant, whatever we pretend."

Wolfgang heard the clatter of the coach coming for Papa, and there was nothing more to say. And parting must be quick, for all their sakes.

But with all of Leopold's resolve to be calm and reserved, he held his son's hand as Wolfgang helped him down the stairs. He felt victimized by age and time, and filled with a dread that he would never see his son again.

Wolfgang had the same presentiment; his father got so chilled walking down the steps. Papa's hand was like ice, like death.

Constanze had stayed upstairs to allow Wolfgang a last moment alone with his father, but he was shouting, "Aren't you going to say goodbye to Papa?"

There was an urgency in his voice that demanded to be obeyed, and she hurried downstairs, and then she didn't know what to say.

Leopold took her hand, but again, he couldn't display affection he didn't feel. He said, not knowing what else to talk about, "I have been meaning to ask you about your vocal lessons. You have a nice voice."

"I don't have time, what with taking care of Karl Thomas and Wolfgang."

"You have a maid."

"There is still so much to be done. Wolfgang is untidy and we do so much entertaining these days that it has become a full-time occupation."

And perhaps the real answer was that she was not truly musical, he thought, but had only a slight musicality and inclination.

Impulsively Wolfgang got into the coach with Papa and announced, "We will go as far as Purkersdorf with Papa. Come on, Constanze."

Purkersdorf was some miles outside of Vienna, and seemed impractical to Leopold and Constanze. But it was the only way Wolfgang could show Papa how he truly felt. Even then, it wasn't enough. As he lost sight of Papa's coach he had a terrible sense of loss. He realized now how his father must have felt when he and Mamma had left for Paris and vanished from view.

Leopold didn't look back. One must never look back, he told himself, no matter how little there was ahead. But above the sound of the coach wheels, he heard the opening passages of the D Minor pianoforte concerto, dominant, agitated, not as he had taught Wolfgang, yet with a feeling that spoke for himself, too. And Haydn's words. That was his son.

SEVENTY-FIVE

Now, having been saddened by the parting from Papa, Wolfgang had to respond by composing joyous music. The pianoforte concerto in C Major he completed soon afterward was as sparkling and jubilant as any score he had written. It came at a suitable time, for Orsini-Rosenberg arranged a gala concert at the Burgtheater in honor of the Emperor's support of music. Orsini-Rosenberg programmed compositions by Gluck, Salieri, Dittersdorf, Mozart, Haydn, and Vanhal, and invited them to attend.

The composers sat in a special box, except those who were to perform, and as Wolfgang waited backstage with Dittersdorf and Vanhal, while Haydn sat with Gluck and Salieri, he was gratified that many of his patrons were in the Burgtheater, although he saw supporters of the others, too. And it could be an argumentative audience, he sensed, however his music pleased.

Joseph sat in the royal box surrounded by attendants and he was amused by the excitement in the theater. The audience acted as if this was an affair of state, when actually, it was simply an exhibition of ego.

There were many more vital matters to be concerned about. Tales of his sister's extravagances on the throne of France were circulating through the courts of Europe, and he had been warned that she was very unpopular in France. Yet he, who was as enlightened as she was selfish, who had accomplished more reforms in the Empire in the five years since his mother's death than Maria Theresa had attempted in her lifetime, was being as bitterly opposed as if he were an invader. Maria Theresa was the *Great Queen* now, and the public longed for *"her good old days"*, although she had lost a sizable portion of the Empire. For every nobleman who shared his respect for Freemasonry, there were three who feared and hated it.

When he had freed the serfs, liberated the Jews, and taxed the

513

nobles and the clergy, he had been accused of being a traitor to his class. He had sought to have everybody educated, and he had been told this was a contradiction of human nature. The difficulty was, he thought wryly, his subjects wanted to have serfs to spit on if they wished, to hate Jews if they liked, to avoid taxes if they could, to give money to churches to make them luxurious even though there was poverty next door. His people didn't desire to be improved; they wanted to be entertained.

He signaled for the music to start, and then seemed to listen carefully. It was expected of him. He was known as a lover of music. It was the one place where he surpassed his mother in the public view. He wondered what he could do about Marie Antoinette.

After Aloysia Lange and Valentin Adamberger sang arias by Gluck and Salieri, who had preference as members of the Emperor's household, Wolfgang performed his new concerto in C Major.

As he played with all the grace and clarity at his command, Wolfgang felt this music was as expressive as any he had written. By the time he reached the second movement it had become one of the most emotional experiences of his life. If there was a Judgment Day, he hoped the Lord would listen to this.

The audience stirred restlessly during the slow movement, and in the last movement there was visiting from box to box. Wolfgang saw Joseph clap, but it seemed perfunctory to him, as if the Emperor were in another world, while there were boos amid the applause, which was just moderate.

The second part of the program featured a pianoforte concerto in D Major by Haydn that he had asked Wolfgang to play. Wolfgang was deeply honored by his friend's request, and he performed the concerto with the same devotion he gave his own. He found the music lovely and lyrical, as admirable and affirmative a concerto as he had ever played, and he was disappointed that the applause was polite rather than enthusiastic.

What excited Joseph was the final performance of the evening.

Regina Strinasacchi, an Italian violinist who had won a considerable reputation, had asked Wolfgang to write a sonata for her to play for the Emperor and he had complied. But in his desire to perfect his performance of Haydn's concerto, he had put off her piece. Then, at the last moment working day and night, he had composed it and had written out her part so she could study it, but had had no opportunity to place his own part on paper. Now, meeting her for the first time at the Burgtheater, they were executing the sonata without any rehearsal. And it went as smoothly as Wolfgang had conceived it. The music made him feel gleeful. He had discovered a new way to express what he wanted to say. It did not trouble him that none of his notes were written down. He had them all in his head.

And Signora Strinasacchi was a genuine violin virtuoso; her sensitive tone had a clarity and a persuasiveness that led to a sudden outburst of applause. Then Joseph, looking down on the stage, was startled to see that Mozart had no notes before him. He sent for him and demanded to see the score, and was astonished that it was only a blank piece of paper.

Joseph asked, "How did you play it?"

"Out of my head."

"But when did you rehearse it?"

"We didn't. I wrote it yesterday, sent the violin part to Signora Strinasacchi this morning so she could study it, and played it tonight."

"And it was so long!"

"Seventeen pages." When the Emperor looked shocked, Wolfgang added, "May it please Your Majesty, there was not a single note lost."

The other composers gathered to accept Joseph's congratulations: Gluck first, as befitted his rank, making a proud effort to keep his frail frame erect, saying in his cracked, coarse voice, "How kind of you to come, Your Majesty. Last winter I was so ill I didn't think I would have the pleasure of your attendance again." Salieri was next, bowing and declaring in Italian, which Joseph preferred, "I am greatly privileged that you allowed my music to appear on the same program as Signor Gluck's." Dittersdorf followed, then Vanhal, and Wolfgang, unable to allow Haydn, the best musician there, to be last, backed away so he was the last one presented.

Joseph couldn't resist asking, although he had no intention of punishing Haydn, "Why did you face Mozart and the orchestra?"

It was the custom that no one could sit with his back to the Emperor, but Haydn had leaned over his box to hear his concerto, disregarding everything else. He said, "It enabled me, sir, to have a more intimate awareness of the music, since this was the first time it was being played as I wrote it."

Salieri said, "I thought the concerto resembled his quartets."

"So!" Wolfgang became belligerent. "You don't like his quartets?"

"I didn't say that. But they are dry, without much melody."

"Believe me," shouted Wolfgang. "If the two of us were melted into one, we would still be a long way from amounting to Haydn!"

"I still wouldn't have written the concerto that way."

"Neither would I. You know why? Because neither you nor I would have been so inspired."

Salieri flushed angrily while Haydn looked pleased but embarrassed and Dittersdorf said, "Our colleague, Herr Mozart, has such a large heart suddenly, for fellow musicians. I didn't know he was so generous."

Wolfgang retorted, "I am generous when it is merited."

For a moment it appeared as if he were going to challenge

Dittersdorf, too, until Haydn said, addressing the Emperor, "Do not be angry, sir, we are not diplomats but we are devoted to Your Majesty's music."

Joseph nodded, and indicated to Orsini-Rosenberg that he invite Gluck, Salieri, and Dittersdorf to join them at the Hofburg for refreshments.

Wolfgang assured himself that he didn't care that he had been excluded.

He had found in Freemasonry the companionship he had always yearned for, and the next few months he devoted himself to their activities. He composed a Cantata in honor of the Society, *Davidde penitente,* which he put together from his C Minor mass and several new arias, and wrote Masonic Funeral Music in homage to the passing of two brother Freemasons, Count Franz Esterházy and Georg August, Duke of Mecklenburg-Strelitz.

The only personal thing that happened during this time that mattered as much was the birth of a son to Nannerl, who named him Leopold.

All through this period he had been revising his six quartets and writing a dedication. When that was finished, in Italian, for that was the language Haydn was most comfortable reading – for Haydn's first instruction in music and in reading had been by Nicolò Porpora, one of the most famed of Italian vocal teachers, whom Haydn, as a boy, had served as a valet – he invited Haydn to the Grosse Schulerstrasse and presented it to him. There was no one else present. Constanze was putting Karl Thomas to bed, the maid was in the kitchen, and Haydn read with growing wonder and awe:

"To my dear friend Haydn: A father who had decided to send his children out into the great world naturally wished to entrust them to the protection and guidance of a very celebrated Man, particularly when the latter fortunately happened to be at the same time his best friend. Here they are, most celebrated Man and my dearest friend, these six children of mine. They are, to be sure, the fruit of long and laborious effort, yet some friends have encouraged me to believe that these children of mine may not go unregarded, and this flatters me into the hope that some day these offspring will give me comfort. You yourself, dearest friend, expressed your approval of them during a previous visit to this capital. Your regard above all encourages me to place my children in your arms, and leads me to hope that they will not be altogether unworthy of your good will. May it please you to receive them kindly and to be their Father, Guide, and Friend! From this moment I relinquish to you all my rights in them, but beg you to view them indulgently whatever deficiencies that a father's partiality may have overlooked. And despite their failings, to continue in your noble and generous friendship to him who values it so dearly. I am, with all my heart, gracious and dear friend, your most sincere friend. W. A. Mozart."

Haydn, when he finished, looked so preoccupied Wolfgang was afraid that he had offended him somehow. He blurted out, "I hope you don't mind, Papa Joseph. I have worked very hard on these quartets. Harder than I have ever worked on anything. Months and months revising them. I have never sweated more over a piece of music. I didn't write them to please. They are from the heart, Papa Joseph!"

"How could you be so thoughtless!" cried Haydn.

"What?"

"To think that I would mind." Haydn bent over and kissed Wolfgang on both cheeks and then, overwrought by this passionate evocation of friendship, he muttered tearfully, "I don't deserve this, Wolfgang, I don't, but I will always treasure it," holding the dedication as he would a love letter.

PART TEN

===

The Operas

SEVENTY-SIX

===

"An Italian opera, sir? Is this what His Majesty desires?"

Orsini-Rosenberg looked intently at the little man standing before him in his office at the Burgtheater before replying, as if measuring this composer's capabilities, then said decisively, "Yes, Mozart, that is why I invited you here. The Emperor is eager to see a full season of Italian opera. Signor Salieri and Señor Martín y Soler are expected to have new works for the coming year, and with the addition of the excellent *basso buffa*, Benucci, an opera with a strong baritone role would be welcome."

"He has a fine voice. It would be an honor to write for him, sir."

"But it must be comic, an *opera buffa*. His Majesty wishes to have his beloved subjects amused. He believes the world is too serious, as it is."

Which means really, reflected Wolfgang, Joseph has a new reform in mind and wants to divert criticism by involving his subjects in make-believe. But he said, "Yes, yes, I agree, Your Excellency."

"You know Italian, of course."

"Of course. I toured Italy three times. I had had three operas produced there by the time I was seventeen. The Emperor's brothers, the Archdukes Leopold and Ferdinand, were kind enough to applaud my work."

"Oh, yes, I remember. Our first meeting was in Florence when you were a child prodigy. There was much talk about you."

More than there was now in some respects, thought Wolfgang, but he bowed and said, "Thank you, sir."

"I enjoyed your last concerto. It was cheerful and pleasing. It would be useful if what you submitted conveyed that tone."

Wolfgang turned this advice over and over the next few weeks as he read many librettos without finding one that satisfied him. He was told by van Swieten that the Emperor was receptive to a new *opera buffa*, that in this at least he could trust Orsini-Rosenberg, the last efforts of his favorites, Salieri and Soler, having failed. He was warned to hurry, however, for there were indications that the Emperor might change his mind.

He found several Goldoni plays he liked, as plays, but which he thought were wrong for opera. He re-read the comedies of Molière that Fridolin Weber had given him, which he had taken with him wherever he had gone.

While he liked the comedies as much as ever, none of them struck him as operatic except *Don Juan*, and he feared that Joseph, who was prudish, would consider it licentious and too somber for an *opera buffa*.

He told Wetzlar of his difficulties, for again his desire to compose an opera transcended everything else, although he was planning new concertos for this autumn of 1785, and Wetzlar handed him the French publication of Beaumarchais' comedy *La Folle Journée ou Le Mariage de Figaro*.

Wolfgang exclaimed, "But Schikaneder, our actor-producer friend, told me that the Emperor banned his production of this comedy."

Wetzlar smiled knowingly and said, "Is that why everybody is reading it? Look at it. Who knows? If you like it, perhaps something could be managed. Even if I have to finance it myself."

"A private production in Vienna? The Emperor would never allow that."

"London or Milan could be receptive."

Wolfgang's eyes gleamed. He had always treasured the triumphant way he had been received in England and Italy. But there were other problems. "Even if I like it, it still has to be altered to fit my music."

"You need a good librettist."

"I can't work with Varesco or Stephanie again. Not on a large opera."

"Wolfgang, I have an excellent librettist for you. Lorenzo Da Ponte."

"Da Ponte?" Wolfgang repeated critically. "An Italian. I have heard of him. He wrote the libretto of *Il Ricco d'un Giorno*, for Salieri. It failed. No wonder Da Ponte turns to me."

"He turns to you because he admires your music."

"And because Salieri said after the failure of that opera, he would prefer to cut off his fingers than put another line of Da Ponte's to music."

"All the more reason you should work together. You have a common enemy."

"From what I hear of *Figaro*'s candid criticism of the nobility, it

521

may take more cleverness to get this piece produced than to write it."

"Read it first. Please. Then decide."

"Why are you so interested in this Figaro piece?"

"You think because I have a title I don't have to bow or scrape. It would be a great joke if it was passed by the censor. As it was in France."

After Wolfgang read the play it was impossible to fall asleep. It was full of sardonic social comment and he understood now why Joseph had not allowed it in spite of his reputation for enlightenment. Yet the play was clever, amusing, and caustic, and it was clear why it was the talk of Vienna. The way Figaro constantly outwitted the arrogant Count touched Wolfgang's heart. The Count was an absolute ruler whom Figaro could outsmart only by his superior wits. It reminded him of his struggles with Colloredo, Arco, even Joseph and Maria Theresa. And it could lend itself to music.

He sat in the darkness of his music room so he would not disturb anyone, composing a song for Figaro, for Benucci's voice. He was fascinated by Figaro's sarcastic declamation of the pathetic lot of the soldier and the words *"Non piu andrai"* reverberated in his ears with a stirring martial melody, half gay, half bitter. He jumped to his feet. It could work!

Constanze stood behind him, holding a heavy robe, saying, "Wolfgang, put this on before you catch cold."

"I'm fine, Stanzi. I have the tune."

She was accustomed to his nocturnal labors and she lit a candle.

"That's not necessary. I have it in my head."

She yawned. He would be tired tomorrow, but he would not admit it, for he had a concert to play at noon at van Swieten's.

The next day when van Swieten asked him what he thought of the quartet his friend had just composed, he said, "Interesting," and added, "Baron, you are the court censor. Could you lift the ban on *Figaro?*"

"Impossible! His Majesty has expressed himself firmly on the subject. Why don't you do something classical? Like Gluck? That would be safe."

But now he desired to do *Figaro*. He stood, wondering how this could be accomplished, and Wetzlar said, "Wolfgang, I want to introduce you to a poet who deeply admires your music, Lorenzo Da Ponte."

Since Wetzlar had suggested Da Ponte as a possible librettist he had learned that the poet had been born a Venetian Jew, who had been baptized at fourteen when his father had become a Christian. Da Ponte, taking one of the few paths open to a clever but poor youth, had entered a theological seminary and had become a priest and a professor of rhetoric. Amid many amorous affairs he had written a group of poems on the subject: *"Is not man happier in the state of nature than in the social order?"* which had been critical of the privileged classes and its social institutions. This had caused a sensation. He had been tried by the rulers of Venice, who had banned his poems and dismissed him from the priesthood, and their opponents had acclaimed him as a true adventurer and poet. Wolfgang had expected a sly, furtive figure. Instead he saw a tall, lean gallant, a few years older than himself, with attractive features, a long, aquiline nose, dark hair, a large, strong chin, and the clothes of a dandy.

And Da Ponte seemed genuinely glad to meet him, saying warmly that he was honored. But when it came time to discuss *Figaro,* Da Ponte became secretive and said they should not discuss it here, in the house of the court censor. Da Ponte suggested a nearby coffee house. He was surprised by Wolfgang's enthusiasm for *Figaro.* "Oh, yes, I know the play," he said. "I know almost every play. But you have heard how the Emperor feels."

Wolfgang wasn't sure they understood each other. The librettist was assuming they would work together, but he hadn't said a word about that.

Da Ponte asked, "Maestro, do you really like the comedy that much?"

"I like it. How much? That depends on many things."

Da Ponte was silent.

"Even if the Emperor's permission was obtained, what assurance do I have that the libretto will be satisfactory, that it will suit my music?"

"What assurance do I have that you will not object to whatever I write?"

Wolfgang felt they were two diplomatic powers measuring each other. He asked, "Why do you want to work with me, Signor poeta?"

"You are the best composer in Vienna."

"And the only one available, now that Salieri refuses to work with you."

"I am still the Emperor's official court poeta, and at this moment I am writing a libretto for Martín y Soler, which will be produced soon."

Wolfgang tried to look indifferent – as Papa said, one must not appear too eager, or one would be at a disadvantage – but he was interested, for Martín y Soler, while no genius, was a composer of competence and taste.

"However, if you prefer Herr Stephanie?"

Wolfgang grimaced. He didn't want to go through that again.

"If I am the librettist, I will get the opera produced. Even *Figaro.*"

"How?" Wolfgang was interested despite his suspicions of Da Ponte.

The poet rose, put his cane behind his back, leaned on it theatrically, and declared, "It will be a comedy of intrigue worthy of Figaro himself."

"What about Orsini-Rosenberg? He has asked me for an opera himself."

"It is Joseph who counts, no matter what his Director claims. It will be a great achievement to persuade Joseph to allow a drama he has banned. I will write a few scenes, without the political references. I will make it a comedy of love and its intrigues. If you can compose some music, in the event Joseph wishes a sample of it, I am certain he will give his permission. My dear Mozart, wouldn't that be a triumph!"

Da Ponte was so eloquent and passionate Wolfgang nodded, intrigued more than convinced, for some of his doubts remained.

Several weeks later Da Ponte gave him the first act. For the most part, it was a translation of the French publication into Italian but with the social and political references excised. Yet there was wit and conciseness in what the poet had retained and it suggested *opera buffa*. Da Ponte had learned his trade well, thought Wolfgang; the Venetian might not be an original poet, but he was a competent craftsman. *Figaro's* first arias came quickly, for Wolfgang had Benucci in mind and the character appealed to him. The music for the women and the Count were more difficult.

Meanwhile, Da Ponte obtained an audience with the Emperor.

Joseph granted this readily. Amid the many problems of governing, Da Ponte was a relief. He didn't always trust his new court poet, but the Venetian never bored him as so many people did. Joseph was amused by his audacity. He still remembered the first time he had met the Venetian.

Da Ponte had approached him for the post of court poet on the recommendation of Salieri, and he had asked, "How many plays have you written, Signor Da Ponte?" and the poet had retorted, "None, sir, none." Laughing, he had said, "Excellent! Now we really have a virgin Muse!"

Da Ponte had bowed to acknowledge this bon mot and Joseph, pleased with his own witticism, had appointed him court poeta. And while his librettos had not been as witty as his conversation, he always had an excuse, usually an amusing one. But Joseph was surprised that Da Ponte desired to convert *Figaro* into an opera. He was proud of his enlightenment but he could not tolerate this scandalous criticism of royalty.

He said severely, "Signor poeta, I banned it for good reasons."

"For the best of reasons, sir. The play's approach is vulgar. But I'm removing all the references that could offend public decency or good taste."

"Isn't that the point of the play?"

"Sir, if I may say so, intrigue is. The intrigue of love, which, I am sure, you know as a master. And the music is lovely. By Mozart."

"Some of his pianoforte concertos are delightful, but he has only composed one opera, *Die Entführung*, and that is certainly not unusual."

"Without Your Majesty's kindness I would have written nothing here."

Joseph hesitated. He liked Da Ponte's appreciation.

"Sir, why not read the libretto and hear the score? With your exquisite taste, I will accept whatever you say. If you don't like it, I won't even try to have *Figaro* produced elsewhere, as has been requested."

"Elsewhere?" Joseph was annoyed.

"London and Milan have asked for it. But I prefer to see it done in Vienna. Sir, if you do not sponsor it, I will destroy what I have written."

"I will read what you have done."

The next day Wolfgang was ordered to appear at the Hofburg that night, and to bring his score. There was so little time he had to beg Aloysia and Adamberger to come with him, to sing what he had completed, although their voices were not as suitable for this music as he desired.

Joseph, who prided himself on his knowledge of music – he was a good sight-reader – insisted on scanning the score as he had the libretto. He had liked what he had read; all the unpleasant social and political comments had been cut out and it could be amusing. And what Adamberger and Lange sang sounded melodic if a little too German for his taste. He said, while Mozart and Da Ponte waited anxiously, "The Governor General of the Austrian Netherlands will be my guest in Febraury. There will be a fete for him in the Schönbrunn. I have a *Singspiel* in one act that needs a score. If you could compose it, Mozart, you would be compensated."

Wolfgang asked, "What is the libretto, Your Majesty?"

"*The Impresario*. By Stephanie."

Wolfgang wanted to refuse – he had had enough of Stephanie's work – but how could he ask for *Figaro* if he declined the Emperor's request? He said, to recover his presence of mind, "Who will sing it, sir?"

"Herr Adamberger and Madame Lange will be fine. Signor Salieri will be composing an opera for the same occasion, and if you are not interested in my request he will be."

Da Ponte was virtually shoving Wolfgang to his knees and Wolfgang kneeling humbly, said, "I will be honored to serve Your Majesty."

Then Da Ponte asked, "But sir, what about *Figaro*?"

"*The Impresario* will be presented in February. If it is satisfactory, you can arrange with Count Orsini-Rosenberg, the Director of the National and the Court Theaters, the date of the production of *Le Mariage de Figaro*."

"Begging your pardon, Your Majesty, *Le Nozze di Figaro*. We will make it an Italian *opera buffa* that will surpass all endeavors in this field."

"Signor poeta, when it comes to music we must not be emotional."

SEVENTY-SEVEN

The libretto of *The Impresario* was a simple tale of two prima donnas competing for the favor of an impresario, and only four arias and an overture were required. Wolfgang thought, Stephanie had given him just the outline of a one-act *Singspiel*, and he had to put flesh on the skeleton, there was nothing in the libretto to suggest vocal substance. So he focused on arias of lyrical brilliance and a strong and melodic overture, and this increased his desire to plunge back into the writing of *Figaro*. But he had to wait until the production of the *Singspiel*. It was foolish to continue the composing of the *opera buffa* until he was sure it would be produced.

He turned to other compositions. Concerts had diminished from the peak of the previous year, although he had some scheduled for Lent of 1786, and while he had earned almost three thousand gulden in the last year, there was nothing left. He didn't know where the money had gone and neither did Constanze, yet once again, there was the desperate need to earn money quickly. He had stopped recording his receipts and expenses; it had become a diversion, a worry, and he had to preserve his energy for vital things, such as composing, performing, and teaching, although he still disliked the last. But he continued to list every new composition in his thematic catalogue. The next two months he noted the following works:

"Song with Pianoforte – from *Das Veilchen* by Goethe
Sonata for Pianoforte and Violin in E Flat
Rondo for Pianoforte in D;
Scena and Rondo for Soprano – for Aloysia Lange
Duet and Aria for the private performance of *Idomeneo*
Concerto for Pianoforte in E Flat
Concerto for Pianoforte in A;
The Impresario – Singspiel."

When *The Impresario* was praised by the Emperor and his royal guests, Wolfgang was given fifty ducats by Thorwart – he learned that Salieri had been given one hundred for his opera – and informed that he would receive one hundred for *Le Nozze di Figaro* if it did not offend the Emperor.

Orsini-Rosenberg added that it would be scheduled for May 1.

That was less than three months away and there was so much to do, but Wolfgang nodded and said, "I am grateful, sir, for your support." He was surprised that as he left the Director did not smile back but frowned.

He mentioned this to Da Ponte, who replied knowingly, "Salieri heard that *Figaro* could be a success, and told Orsini-Rosenberg. They are jealous. Then you didn't give the Director anything, did you, Wolfgang?"

"No. What should I have given him?"

"It is customary for composers and librettists who have been honored with the royal favor to present the Director with a token of their appreciation. Ten ducats, when you have earned fifty. Or twenty, when you have been given a hundred. Or at the least dedicate work to him."

"But what has he done? For us?"

"It is what he could do. Against us."

"What do you advise?" Da Ponte was like Papa, clever at intrigue.

"As long as Joseph favors us, Orsini-Rosenberg is powerless. And even if we flatter him, or pay him, he will still prefer Salieri. But don't worry, I have the ear of the Emperor, I will take care of everything. Schikaneder tells me he has a child prodigy, Hummel, he wants you to hear."

Wolfgang grumbled, "Yes, and I haven't any time to spare."

"Are you going to listen to him play?"

"What choice have I? Schikaneder and Papa Hummel are friends."

But it wasn't Schikaneder who came with the eight-year-old Hans Hummel but the boy's father, who was the producer's musical director; Schikaneder sent word that he was too busy. Wolfgang was working intensely on *Figaro*; it was permitting him to do things in music he had desired for years, yet he greeted them in his drawing room and said, "My dear Hummel, it is good to see you. Sit down, and you, my young friend, find yourself a chair."

They did, both of them looking embarrassed.

"What brings you here?" Wolfgang asked, teasing a little.

Hummel said, "If you heard my son, perhaps you would teach him."

"But as you know, I dislike teaching. It takes up far too much of my time and breaks into my composing." Yet when he saw the disappointment in the boy's eyes, he added, "All right, go ahead, show me what you can do."

The boy sat down at the pianoforte and played the English Bach, while Wolfgang listened without expression. But as the child went on Wolfgang became attentive, and his eyes grew beautiful in their pleasure and excitement. He nudged the father gently to express his approval and nodded appreciatively. When the boy finished Bach, Wolfgang put one of his own compositions before him, a much more difficult piece, to judge his ability as a sight-reader. And now the youth's execution was even smoother, as if he had confidence, too, and Wolfgang suddenly whispered to his father, "You must leave the lad here with me. Something can be made of him."

"I don't understand, Maestro?"

Wolfgang hurried over to the boy, patted him warmly on the head, and whispered, "You performed splendidly. Play like this all the time and you will accomplish much." He took the child by the hand and sat him on the sofa with affection, then turned to his father, "It is agreed, then, I will teach the boy, but he must live with me so that I can keep an eye on him. He will have everything free, lessons, lodgings, food. You will not have to worry about anything. Agreed?"

Hummel's eyes filled with tears and he embraced Wolfgang, thinking what a dear man, and thanked him with an overflowing heart. He had a feeling that now Hans might even become a second Wolfgang Amadeus Mozart.

Soon afterward the boy moved into the Mozart household and was regarded as a son by Wolfgang. Constanze objected to this arrangement, pointing out that they were having a difficult time as it was without having an extra mouth to clothe and feed, but Wolfgang declared, "He could be a genius!"

"But you are upset about the number of pupils you have to teach now?"

"Unlike most of them, Hans should amount to something."

From his tone she realized she was protesting in vain, and from then on, she sought to make the best of this new situation. Hans was attractive, likable, and did everything Wolfgang asked, even imitating his style of performance, and displayed an abundant talent. Even as some resentment remained in her, she sensed that Hans had become more than a prodigy, he was a reliving of Wolfgang's own childhood and attachment to his own father.

One night, a few weeks after they had taken in the boy, they returned home from a party and as they entered the drawing room they found Hans stretched out on several chairs sound asleep. It was midnight, but Wolfgang didn't want to put him to bed. A new pianoforte sonata he had composed had just come back from the copyist, and he was eager to hear it.

"Stanzi, wake up Hans, but softly, so we don't startle him, and give him a glass of wine so he can play."

Wolfgang was surprised and disappointed that Hans, usually a fine sight-reader, read poorly and was distracted. Yet he could not scold him. It was late, he reflected, the child was tired. Then he saw why Hans was off. There was a hole in the cloth of the billiards table, obviously torn by a cue. For a moment Wolfgang was furious. His beloved billiards table damaged! And he had told the boy never to use it without his consent.

Then Hans wept, and Wolfgang, who could rarely resist tears, took him into his arms and said, "He doesn't know any better. Stanzi, do you think Papa is having the same difficulties with his new grandson?"

She shrugged and didn't reply. Leopold had taken in Nannerl's baby, and he seemed more interested in his grandson than his son, and she wondered whether this hurt Wolfgang. He never could criticize his father, no matter what happened, but he was writing much less to him.

Leopold was upset by his son's dwindling letters. He stood at a window of the Tanzmeister-Saal and was filled with nostalgia. His son, who used to write him often, didn't write for weeks now. He thought of his eight-month-old grandson, whose presence in his home gave him such pleasure, but the baby was far too young to be trained as he had Wolferl. There was no sign of the mail coach, it had been delayed by the weather, which happened often during the winter. There was only one release. He wrote to Nannerl, who had become a regular correspondent from her home in St. Gilgen:

"Young Leopold loves to hear me play. It halts his crying almost at once, and I have high hopes that he has the Mozart ear. God willing, may I have enough time to encourage him, but sometimes I feel so old I wonder if I am only sixty-six. I have not had one line from your brother in weeks, and there is virtually no one here any more with whom I can talk intelligently. I am sorry if I sound querulous, but most of my information about your brother comes from other sources.

"The Emperor has consented to Le Mariage de Figaro, and the last time I heard from your brother he blamed that for not writing, saying he needed all his free time for composing. I find Figaro a tedious piece, with much talk about intrigue, and much running about, which will have to be altered considerably to make an opera. However, I am sure the music will please. I only hope it is worth what it will cost your brother in energy, in arguments and aggravation. But they say this Da Ponte who is adapting the play is a clever man. He will need all his cleverness to please Joseph."

Music of Wolfgang's arrived the next day with a brief note explaining that he had been so busy composing, casting, and altering *Figaro* he had been unable to write. There were two new pianoforte concertos, a sonata for pianoforte and violin, and two arias from the new opera.

Leopold had been feeling bored and sorry for himself, but suddenly there was something to do. Figaro's aria was so sparkling that Leopold wanted to sing it himself, while the music of the Countess was tender in its evocation of love and brought tears to his eyes. Then his practical side asserted itself, and he wrote Wolfgang that his arias were fine, but difficult and would need superb voices and much rehearsing.

Wolfgang responded to Papa's advice at once, informing him that for the first time in his life he might have singers equal to his music.

He knew all the singers and he was pleased with the casting. Benucci was singing Figaro as he had hoped. Luisa Laschi, at whose concert he had played and whose voice he admired, was doing the Countess. Cherubino had been given to Dorotea Bussani, another soprano he liked, and her husband, Francesco, a fine actor-singer, was doing Bartolo and Antonio. The Count was being sung by Stefano Mandini, who could be effective, but a singer he had doubts about, for Mandini was a friend of Salieri's. The small but vital role of Marcellina was being done by Mandini's wife, Maria. Michael Kelly, also a good actor-singer, was playing Basilio and Don Curzo, and Susanna was being sung by his favorite vocalist in Vienna, Ann Storace.

Ann Storace and Michael Kelly were half of what Wolfgang called "the English colony". The other half was her twenty-two-year-old brother, Stephen Storace, and the twenty-year-old Thomas Attwood, promising young English composers, who were studying composition with Wolfgang.

When the rehearsals progressed favorably, Wolfgang coached the principals and worked on the score. Benucci's bass was aggressive and convincing, yet full and warm; his only weakness was an occasional weak high note and a tendency to posture; but Benucci was pleased with what Wolfgang gave him to sing as Figaro and obeyed him diligently.

Laschi's Countess was also what Wolfgang desired, but he was troubled by Mandini's Count. The baritone had the skill and strength to do the role, but he complained that he had no display arias and that he could not sing with heart when there was no heart in the Count.

Bussani's Cherubino and her husband's Bartolo were fine, and Wolfgang liked Kelly's acting. The Irish-English tenor's flair for comedy gave Wolfgang pleasure, and they became good friends.

It was Ann Storace who excited Wolfgang. Her father, an Italian musician living in London, had taught her and her brother, Stephen, while her English mother had given her a cultivated education. At twenty-one Ann possessed a soft, dark, graceful beauty, and had as musical a soprano as Wolfgang had known, which she used with an exquisite taste and warmth that even Aloysia had never quite achieved, and acted with spirit and sensibility. And she studied his music with such devotion he was touched. Ann was eager to be coached by him.

One day while he was having her practice the not-quite-finished aria she was singing to Cherubino, she halted suddenly. They were working at the Burgtheater, alone, and he was sure she was going to complain that although she was the heroine, this was her first solo aria in two acts and then it was not a display piece. Instead she said, "Cherubino must respond to what I sing. Otherwise, it will not be convincing. Do you mind?"

"Cherubino's acting will divert from your singing."

"But you always say the music must push the drama on."

"Yes, that's true." When you worked together steadily, he thought, it was easy to hate each other or . . . ! He wondered if Ann was playing a game. He sensed that she liked him; she was with him whenever she could be. And she was the first singer since Aloysia who had a strong physical attraction for him. Ann was such an artist! By now he had given up the idea, once intriguing, of making a singer out of Constanze. The desire wasn't in Stanzi, but Ann Storace could sing whatever he wrote. They could even discuss composition, which bored Constanze. Yet he was happy with Stanzi. He sought to appear remote and to control his emotions.

"Wolfgang, don't you feel well?" He had grown quite pale.

Why couldn't he love both women? He felt unexpectedly vulnerable.

"Would you like to lie down? I have a couch in my dressing room."

It was an invitation, he told himself, and then he wasn't certain. Yet it was common gossip that at opera rehearsals the composer indulged in love affairs with his prima donna supposedly to obtain realism. He allowed Ann to lead him to her dressing room and then he didn't know what to do. He did feel a little faint, he had been working very hard, and after he sat a moment he felt better. Her dressing room was charmingly feminine and intimate, with the score of *Die Entführung* on her table.

That surprised him. "Do you know it?" he asked.

"Very well. It is a remarkable score. I wish I could have sung Constanze. But *Figaro* will be even more beautiful when it is finished."

"You really think so?"

"Wolfgang, I have been singing opera since I was fourteen. I've sung Handel, Pergolesi, Gluck, Piccinni, Salieri, Paisiello, Martín y Soler, but never have I sung music that expresses the emotions as deeply as yours. Yet with all your lyricism, *Figaro* is the Italian of Italian *opera buffas*, light and gay when necessary, dramatic and passionate when that is needed."

He was silent. Her voice had grown fervent and her olive skin was flushed. Sitting close to him, Ann was no longer the woman of the world who had been wed at eighteen to a man twice her age and who had left him quickly because of his cruelty, but a girl who was wistful and yearning.

Ann wondered why Wolfgang hesitated. No one would know. Or care. Except perhaps his wife, and she was never at the theater and didn't seem interested in his opera. She glanced at him sitting near her, but not near enough, and thought, he is small in stature but his music is magnificent in its scope and feeling. And his art revealed that he knew a vast amount about women. Where had he learned it? Or was it his nature? His sensibility? He should be a marvelous lover, he wrote about love with such understanding and ecstasy. There was so much tenderness and sweetness in his music, she could not imagine Wolfgang hurting her as her husband had. Yet while the emotion in his arias was intense, it was never excessive or maudlin, but right. His melodies were pure yet sensuous, poignant yet pulsing with life, and they danced with the joy of existence. She was sure that to know his love was to have an experience deeper and more enriching than ordinary life could give. But as she put her hand on his, to bring him closer, he stood up.

He said, "You have been most gracious and I am grateful. But would you excuse me now, please? I have much work to do. On the opera, and on Susanna." Constanze had just told him that she was pregnant again, and he could not practice infidelity at such a time, however much he desired Ann.

She nodded, without saying a word.

He hurried home, wishing she weren't so attractive. He hoped she would not seek revenge by spoiling Susanna. Then he assured himself that Ann was too fine an artist to do this, and that the emotion which mounted in him when he was near her was simply admiration for her polished singing.

SEVENTY-EIGHT

At home Constanze was annoyed that Wolfgang was preoccupied. He was not even attentive in bed, where he was usually at his best. He said he was too tired to make love, which was not like him. She wondered if he was interested in another woman, there were many opportunities for an opera composer at the Burgtheater, but there was no proof. She complained that her pregnancy made her feel unwell and he kissed her.

But a few minutes later the familiar look of abstraction came into his eyes and he jumped out of bed and ran into the music room. When she asked him if he wanted a robe, he didn't hear her. He was sitting at his desk writing incessantly. She told herself that she would be glad when *Figaro* was over, and she prayed that it would be soon.

Da Ponte finished a whole draft of the text quickly, and as they became involved in each other's work Wolfgang's respect for him grew. The poeta was contributing little that was original, and his libretto remained an adaptation of the play, but he was a clever craftsman and he made the changes Wolfgang suggested. And Wolfgang was grateful for his singable words, his lyrical phrases, his good ear, his taste and humor, and his awareness that the poetry had to be the servant of the music.

There was little time for anything else but the production. These days Wolfgang saw more of the cast than he did of his family, yet Constanze tried not to quarrel or to feel jealous. Such resolves were not easy to keep, for Wolfgang's air of abstraction increased and often she speculated that there must be someone else, no opera should demand such devotion.

One night when he didn't come to bed at all – sitting all night in the music room and composing – she was alarmed and she said the

534

next morning, "You are going to ruin your health, working this way."

"I must. The Count's role needs more. Mandini isn't pleased with it."

"Will Mandini take care of you when you get sick?"

"Stanzi, it will be over soon. Then we will take a long vacation."

It would never be over, she thought, while he had breath.

Wolfgang was upset, overhearing Mandini telling his wife, "The Count is impossible to sing effectively, he is such a rogue! Doesn't Mozart know I must have sympathy! Salieri would never do this to me!"

Wolfgang backed into the wings so as not to be seen, while Mandini's wife replied, "Speak to him. Marcellina is a small role compared to some of the others, yet what he has given me to sing is as good as anybody else's."

"Bravo! Bravo! Should I be grateful for your good luck! He is too involved with Storace to consider me," Mandini said with an obscene leer.

"I have seen no evidence of anything," said his wife.

"Do you need evidence? She is a heroine. The prima donna."

"I think the Countess has the more beautiful arias."

"That is another thing. I can't compete with her if he gives her all the display pieces. He wants to damage my reputation."

But now, after much work, he had a new aria for Mandini, *Vedro, mentr'io sospiro*, that should equal any music in emotion. Yet after Mandini sang it, he said, "It is so serious it is more suited to tragedy."

Da Ponte said, "It would be even more tragic if someone else sang it."

The baritone shrugged.

"And now it is the longest solo aria in the entire opera."

"Basta, don't you think I can do it?"

"We do. That is why we wrote it. And it shows off your voice."

"Oh, I will sing it, Da Ponte. Only don't expect me to love it. As it is, there is too much love in this opera. And this aria is hard to sing."

Wolfgang was pleased. Mandini had sung *Vedro, mentr'io sospiro* splendidly and the aria gave the Count a passion he had lacked until now.

It was working with Ann that disturbed him. He tried to regard her with nonchalance and it intensified his feeling. She refused to be difficult, but was willing to do whatever he asked.

Now he was grateful that her music until the final act was with someone else, and he used that as an excuse to always rehearse her with another member of the cast. Yet when he reached her only truly

535

solo aria in the last act, *Dehi vieni,* he poured her sweetness into this music. And because he sought to express this with the utmost simplicity, it became one of the hardest arias he had ever composed, and he wrote it over and over before it suited her voice and what he desired to say.

Completing Cherubino's arias was a relief after the pain of composing for Ann. He gave himself up to the sheer delights of love and to pleasing himself. Cherubino was in love with love, as he had been and still was at times, and half of him was sympathetic and half of him was mocking.

But everything was written from the heart. And as he worked on the Countess' arias his emotion overflowed. He felt her predicament intensely: she loved a husband who lusted after virtually every attractive female within reach. In the play she had been superficial, but he deepened her character, giving her music of great pathos and poignancy. There was much of himself in her arias, yet he did not take sides. He dramatized her situation musically with all his affection and compassion and then let it speak for itself.

There was even more of himself in Figaro, but this music came easier. He felt fulfilled by Figaro's outwitting of the Count as he had outwitted Colloredo, and he enjoyed the creation of his music as much as any he had ever done.

Then, one day, while he was coaching Anna Gottlieb in the small role of Barbarina with the same devotion he gave to everyone else, she handed him a bouquet of flowers. He was taken aback. "What for?" he asked.

Anna Gottlieb blushed and whispered, "You are so kind, Maestro. Allowing me in your opera. I am very young, you know, sir."

Young, indeed! She was only twelve. But she was right for the role, he reflected. Anna came from theatrical parents; she was an excellent little actress, with precisely the kind of girlish voice Barbarina needed.

She said, "If you put them into water, Maestro, they will live."

Suddenly he realized she was in love with him. But this was impossible, she was just a child. Yet he couldn't ridicule it, as he knew most men would. There was something endearing about it, something that touched his heart. He answered, "I hope they will live a long time."

"Oh, they will, sir. I bought flowers that would, with the proper care."

Anna Gottlieb was the one member of the cast who was shorter than he was, and he bent over and kissed her on the brow.

536

Tears came into her eyes and she asked, "You are not dissatisfied with what I am doing, Maestro?"

"Not at all. You are very good. Just right."

"Not too young, sir."

"Not for Barbarina. And please, don't call me sir."

"Yes, sir."

Wolfgang returned to her song in the last act, where she entered searching for a lost pin, and added to it music of enchanting tenderness and plaintiveness, although Da Ponte said he was foolish to waste such an exquisite melody on a minor character. But when she sang it with sincerity and taste, Wolfgang felt rewarded, although he still regarded Anna Gottlieb as a child and endeavored to be fatherly whenever she was present.

A few days before the scheduled opening the first dress rehearsal of what Wolfgang and Da Ponte hoped was the final form of *Le Nozze di Figaro* was held. The entire libretto and score had been rewritten several times, but now everything appeared ready, except the overture, but Wolfgang assured Da Ponte there was nothing to be anxious about.

"I have it all in my head, from the first note to the last."

"Orsini-Rosenberg is watching," said Da Ponte, indicating the figure standing in the shadows at the rear of the Burgtheater.

"He should be pleased. Herr Director won't have to postpone this opera as he had to do with so many others."

"Are you satisfied, Mozart?"

"With the score, yes."

"What about the poetry?"

"Let us see how our cast can sing it, and then we can judge."

Da Ponte ignored the Director as the rehearsal began, and sat close to Wolfgang, who wore a crimson pelisse and gold-laced cocked hat to celebrate the occasion. Wolfgang seemed calm as he conducted, but when Benucci sang *"Non piu andrai, farfallone amoroso"* with great animation and vigor, Da Ponte heard Wolfgang, sotto voce, crying out, *"Bravo! Bravo! Benucci!"*

And when Benucci came to the vital passage, *"Cherubino, alla vittoria, alla gloria militar,"* which he shaped with extraordinary eloquence and brio, the effect was electric. As Benucci finished, all the performers on the stage and the entire orchestra, as if moved by one feeling of delight, shouted, *"Bravo! Bravo! Maestro! Viva, viva, grande Mozart!"* Da Ponte thought the orchestra would never stop applauding, beating the bows of their violins against their music desks. The first act finale brought the same acclamation, as did several of the other numbers, but now Wolfgang refused to halt unless the opera did. At the end the orchestra stood up and cheered and this time

Wolfgang took Da Ponte by the hand and led him on to the stage and insisted that Signor poeta share this applause.

They were about to leave the Burgtheater when they were informed that the Director wished to see them. It was a command, and as they entered Orsini-Rosenberg's office he didn't ask them to sit down, but looked at them sternly and declared, "Da Ponte, you put a ballet in *Figaro*."

"It is essential to the story, sir."

Wolfgang added, "You saw how the cast and orchestra liked it."

"They were moved by self-interest. I am sure you are aware that the Emperor has prohibited dancing in his theaters."

Da Ponte said, "I didn't know it related to opera."

"It relates to all his theaters. You will have to remove the dancing."

Wolfgang protested. "But sir, that will ruin *Figaro*!"

"That is your concern. Da Ponte, I want the text."

Da Ponte, apparently with great reluctance, handed him the libretto.

Orsini-Rosenberg, with a gesture of grandiose importance, tore out the pages that contained the ballet.

Wolfgang cried, "We cannot do *Figaro* without it!"

Orsini-Rosenberg laughed, "And you cannot do it with it!"

"That's not fair. There's not enough time to change the story."

The Director stated, "We will find another opera to take its place, Mozart." He stood up to indicate that the interview was over.

Wolfgang was furious. He paused outside the Burgtheater, ignoring the carriages rolling by, the pedestrians, and said this was unendurable, they must appeal to the Emperor, but Da Ponte disagreed.

"I have another plan. The Director is not the only one who can intrigue."

Da Ponte sounded so assured Wolfgang grew calmer, although he still couldn't understand how Orsini-Rosenberg could do this to them.

"It is easy. He has the last word, except for Joseph. Salieri must have warned him that *Figaro* could be a great success and drive his own work off the boards, and when he saw for himself this was true, he used the dancing as an excuse to stop us. But Joseph may not agree with him."

"It was Orsini-Rosenberg who originally asked for an *opera buffa*."

"In the event there would be no other. Or if we paid him as Salieri does. Do you want to try that?"

Wolfgang refused, disgusted with such a suggestion.

"Then we must give *Figaro* for the Emperor."

"Without the dancing?"

"Of course."

"But it won't make sense!"

"Precisely," Da Ponte said with a sly smile. "That's just the point."

Joseph accepted Da Ponte's invitation to attend a dress rehearsal when the latter said, "Your Majesty, we would very much like your opinion, just in case you think there is something that should be changed. We want to please you, above anything else."

Joseph was pleased with *Figaro* until it came time for the dancing, where pantomime was substituted. This irritated him; suddenly the story was incomprehensible, when everything hitherto had been clear and amusing and without any scandalous attacks on authority as he had feared. He ordered the rehearsal stopped and exclaimed, "Da Ponte, this doesn't fit the opera!"

Da Ponte shrugged and gave Joseph a libretto which contained the ballet.

Joseph asked, "Signor poeta, why isn't it in the opera?"

"Herr Director, Your Majesty, stated that dancing was prohibited."

"Prohibited!" The Emperor ordered Herr Director to appear at once.

Orsini-Rosenberg, who was in his office, came immediately.

But before he could utter a word, the Emperor said, "How dare you do this without consulting me?"

"Your Majesty, you said that dancing is forbidden."

"When it is vulgar and immoral. But here it is appropriate."

"Sire, what about *Figaro* itself? You banned the play."

"Because it offended public decency and taste. But this is charming."

"And the dancers in the Burgtheater, Your Majesty, will not please you."

"Then get some that will."

"But, sir, on such short notice, I . . ."

"It is the Imperial wish!" When the Director tried to find a new excuse, the Emperor said, "I will be very angry if *Figaro* is delayed any more. I am eager to see how it ends."

"Happily, Your Majesty," said Da Ponte. "If we are allowed."

"You are allowed. I will wait until the dancers arrive, for I intend to see the entire opera and form my own judgment on its value."

A dozen dancers arrived a few minutes later and while they were rehearsed Wolfgang entertained the Emperor with several encores. Joseph wanted to hear two of the Countess' arias again, *Porgi Amor*, which lamented the loss of her husband's love, and *Dovo sono*, where she sadly recalled the time when her husband still loved her. These arias touched Joseph. He had suffered from infidelity himself. His first wife had preferred his own sister to himself, although he had loved her deeply, and she had died early in their marriage without ever responding as he had desired.

He enjoyed the dancing; it relieved his melancholy and fitted the text. Joseph ordered *Le Nozze di Figaro* to open on May 1, as scheduled.

Two days later, just before the opening of the opera, Wolfgang wrote the overture. Weeks before, with meticulous exactness, he had worked out the score to the last detail, and now all he had to do was to put it into execution. He had waited to permit more time for rehearsals of the other music, but he was determined that the opening should express the mood of the opera. It must set the tone from the start. He didn't interweave the major themes into the overture as was done usually, but stressed mood and tempo, and wrote it as an instrumental aria with its own kind of uniqueness.

From the instant Wolfgang appeared on the conductor's stand, Joseph Haydn – who had made the long difficult trip from Esterházy to Vienna just to attend the opening of *Le Nozze di Figaro* – was glad that he had gone to such effort to be here. There was an assurance in the composer that was exciting. Wolfgang stood only five feet tall, but as he raised his hands for the music to begin, he towered over the orchestra and the harpsichord in front of him. And there wasn't a wrong note in the overture, thought Haydn. Wolfgang seemed to dance as he led the orchestra and the overture danced too, from the first passage setting the stage for a mood of gaiety.

Figaro's opening with Susanna carried on the tone of the overture and enchanted Haydn. By the end of the first act he had been led into a world brighter and with more feeling than any he had experienced musically. The cast was fine, except for Mandini's Count, which was uneven, as if Mandini couldn't decide how to sing the role. But Wolfgang's intensity illuminated the music, and he kept everything under control, using the orchestra to accompany, to lift, to express the singers, but never allowing it to dominate, even when he was at the harpsichord. At the end of the opera Haydn was sure it would be a success, there was so much beauty in the score, but at the curtain there were boos as well as bravos.

Many friends gathered around Wolfgang to congratulate him, van Swieten first, as befitted his position in Viennese musical society, Wetzlar, the Countess Thun, Count Pálffy, Count Cobenzl, but when he saw Haydn his eyes filled with tears and as he felt the warmth of Haydn's embrace, he knew, whatever anyone else said, he had accomplished what he had set out to do. But before he could

540

spend any time with Haydn and his other friends, Orsini-Rosenberg informed him coldly that the Emperor was waiting to see him.

Joseph received him and Da Ponte in the royal box and said, "Bravo! Signor poeta, it was entertaining. I hope you didn't mind the boos."

"Of course not, Your Majesty. The more jealous others are, the more worthy you know your own work to be."

"And you, Mozart, are you satisfied now that Italian is far more suitable for opera than German?"

Wolfgang hesitated. Why did Joseph have to appoint himself a critic, when his knowledge of music was superficial? Haydn was waving goodbye, having to leave for Esterházy, and he would have given much to be able to spend a few minutes with him. But as it was Joseph was irritated by the slowness of his reply. He said, "Your Majesty, I am satisfied that *Figaro* is worthy of your approval."

"Oh, it is a competent piece, but too frivolous to be remembered long."

Le Nozze di Figaro was put in the repertory of the National Italian Opera Company by Imperial decree, but as Joseph had predicted it did not hold the interest of the public. Viennese connoisseurs said the music was too German, that it lacked the bravura of Italian *buffa*. Instead of inflaming the passions, as they preferred, Mozart's music expressed them.

When Martín y Soler's new opera, *Una Cosa Rara*, opened in November and was the success of the season, Orsini-Rosenberg announced that *Le Nozze di Figaro* would be withdrawn from the repertory after its ninth performance in December. The public had fallen in love with a new dance in the new opera, a waltz. What made this music, taken from an Austrian peasant dance, so popular, was its irresistible sway and the theatrical manner it was done by the main characters in the opera. The waltz became the sensation of the moment, and with it *Una Cosa Rara*.

Da Ponte didn't share Wolfgang's distaste for its obvious text and score. This simple tale of how the Infante of Spain fell in love with a beautiful peasant girl and won her was so successful he could choose any composer he wished; even Salieri wanted him as a librettist again. For he had written the libretto, and now Mozart could see for himself that the poeta could be more important than the composer.

SEVENTY-NINE

It was difficult for Wolfgang to be cheerful these days, for the son who was born in October died four weeks later from suffocation.

He lay in bed on a cold, gray morning in November, the day after Johann Leopold had been buried, and he thought of his two dead children and what they might have been if they had lived. He had been up most of the night, troubled by his kidneys, yet the cure had been as unpleasant as the ailment. Each time he had run down to the toilet he had been frozen and he had returned aching all over, and he had lain in bed, unable to sleep, worrying that his hands would be afflicted.

But when Constanze awoke, he offered to get her breakfast. She should stay in bed, he suggested, the last six weeks, starting with her confinement, had been so painful for her that she needed more rest.

Instead, she sat up, fully clothed except for her shoes – the bedroom had been icy cold once they had put out the stove and Wolfgang liked a window to be open, he had a fear of suffocation – and she said sadly, "I won't be able to sleep – not with Johann Leopold lying in the ground."

"Three children born, two dead! What kind of an equation is that?"

"It's fate," and suddenly she began to weep.

He sought to console her. "We'll have another, and another, and. . ."

"They'll die like the others," she blurted out. "We shouldn't have any more children." When she saw his dismay, she added, "At least for a while. Until we can take better care of them."

He stared down the Blutgasse and thought of how it led to the Deutsches Hans, only several hundreds yards away, where he had been kicked down the stairs, and how he had expected the success of *Figaro* to wipe out that forever from his memory. Instead, there had been no more scritturas for an opera, and the subscription list for his concerts had vanished. The last two concerts he had given had been only half filled, and he had lost money. So he had composed just two pianoforte concertos, for that had been the extent of the demand for his playing. Did Constanze know they might have to move, that the rent was becoming more than they could afford? Unable to endure such pessimism, the idea of making love possessed him.

He lit the stove and hurried to undress her.

She backed away, repeating, "No more children, at least not now."

He halted as if struck by a whip.

He looked so stricken she quickly said, "Oh, there are other ways."

Afterwards, Wolfgang wasn't sure he liked the other ways.

At breakfast he brought up something else that was on his mind. He said, "Stanzi, I would like very much if you would invite Kelly, Attwood, and the Storaces for an evening."

"Why can't you, Wolfgang? You know them far better than I do."

"It would be nicer coming from the lady of the house."

"Because of Ann Storace. You think that will quiet the gossip?"

"There is nothing to gossip about. But I would like you to be friends."

Constanze said cynically, "Because we have you in common."

"Because they want us to go to England with them."

"Me, too?" Constanze was incredulous.

"Of course. Stanzi, do you think I would go without you!" His blue eyes gleamed, and his skin was red with excitement, and his fingers drummed on the kitchen table as if he were at the clavier. Then he danced her about their drawing room, holding her gently, yet with such affection and grace she allowed him to lead her to the desk where she wrote the invitations.

Constanze dressed grandly; Ann wore a simple gown. Constanze expected hostility from the prima donna, and Ann thanked her warmly for inviting her. They had met several times casually but briefly, but this was their first full evening together. Constanze knew Ann's brother better, for Stephen Storace and Thomas Attwood came to the house regularly to study composition with Wolfgang, while Wolfgang loved to play billiards with Michael Kelly, for he always defeated Kelly, who always praised his skill.

But Constanze marveled at Ann's graceful nonchalance. She felt compressed to indecency in her tight, low bodice, and gowned too smartly, yet Wolfgang approved. His admiration for her small, compact form was obvious as he led her to the table where the maid served them.

Later there was the inevitable game of billiards between Wolfgang and Kelly, and the inevitable victory for Wolfgang. Then Kelly, determined not to be outdone, mimicked Da Ponte. He did it cleverly; the more graceful the poeta tried to be, the more awkward and vain the poeta became.

Suddenly Attwood, as serious as Michael Kelly was gay, asked, "Maestro, have you given any further thought to England?"

"Much thought, Attwood. I hoped you could convince Constanze."

He said, "Fräu Mozart, the Maestro would be a huge success in London."

Like Vienna, she thought bitterly, but Wolfgang would be unhappy if she suggested that. She replied, "I will be honored to go wherever he goes."

"And we will be honored to have you and the Maestro with us," answered Attwood. "You will give our party great distinction."

But they were so young, Constanze told herself: Attwood and Ann Storace were only twenty-one; Stephen Storace was just twenty-three, Kelly twenty-five. That would cause them to disregard her fears. She felt much older than they, although she was only twenty-five herself. "How would you travel?"

Storace said, "By way of Salzburg, which should please both of you."

Wolfgang grinned with delight, but Constanze winced and said nothing.

"Then to Munich and Mannheim where the Maestro is very well known."

Wolfgang nodded, looking more and more pleased.

"And a stop in Paris. I wrote Le Gros that you might be with us, and he replied promptly, saying he would be privileged to arrange a concert."

"After the way he treated my husband!" exclaimed Constanze. "Wolfgang, how could you ever trust him again?"

"I don't trust him. But I don't have to hate him."

"Finally, on to London," continued Storace, "where your previous tour is still warmly remembered, where you are certain to be a great favorite."

Ann said, "They will adore your music. As we do."

"See, Stanzi," Wolfgang said, "this is a great opportunity."

She didn't want to be a scold, but someone had to be practical. "What about Karl Thomas? We can't take him on such a long journey."

"Papa can take care of him."

"Have you asked him yet?"

"No, but he is taking care of Nannerl's child. There is no reason why he shouldn't take care of ours."

She couldn't share his optimism, but the others acted as if the journey was a fait accompli, and discussed what music he should take with him.

Storace said, "You must play your C Minor pianoforte concerto in London. It is such profound music. Lofty, powerful. How anyone can say your music is just pretty after the C Minor is beyond my comprehension."

"But they do," Wolfgang said sadly. "Or when I do compose in a minor key, they accuse me of being cloudy, or having no heart or feeling."

"No heart!" cried Ann. "Your music is all heart!"

Attwood said, "For myself, I prefer your new concerto in C Major, which you played at your last recital, for it has so much genuine emotion. But to rank one above the other is idiocy. All your music stirs me. How many pianoforte concertos have you composed the last two years, Maestro?"

Wolfgang consulted his thematic catalogue, then announced with surprise, "Twelve since 1784." He added ruefully, "I forgot a few."

"Twelve in two years?" Attwood was incredulous.

"What is there to be astonished about? If music is in you, it comes out."

"But that much in such a short time?"

"Attwood, the number doesn't matter. No one cares whether you have composed twelve concertos or one. But they do want the music to please."

"Yet each concerto is finer than the previous one!"

Wolfgang said reprovingly, "I like all my children the same."

"Of course, Maestro!" exclaimed Storace. "But every time I think of the C Minor, I tell myself that I am an amateur composer by comparison."

"You are an opera composer, and a good one."

"Good perhaps, but not a Mozart."

"You think it is always so wonderful to be a Mozart."

There was a moment of shocked silence. Wolfgang walked over to the high double windows of the drawing room which looked out on the street. He had had such high hopes when he had moved in here. But he despised self-pity, especially in himself. And it wasn't fair to his guests. As he turned around he forced a smile, but Ann saw his white face and his enormous eyes.

She said, "You must come to London where you will be truly appreciated."

Storace added, "And bring your Hadyn quartets. He is known in England."

Wolfgang said, "I offered them for sale here, singly or by subscription, but they haven't sold at all. They do not please, they are too different."

"Too good for the Viennese," Ann stated with sudden passion. "You need a reliable manager. To handle your affairs."

Constanze stood up to indicate that the evening was over. Now she didn't wish to go to England. Storace was saying that Mozart's reputation would rank with Purcell and Handel in England, but she had a feeling of despair. She would never be able to compete with Ann there. It wasn't that the prima donna was that beautiful; she found the soprano pretty, but not unusually attractive; but Ann was so musical; Ann would give Wolfgang artistic understanding and sing his music, which always appealed to him. And she would never master English, while he could speak it fluently already.

Ann sensed Constanze's fears and was amused. Wolfgang's wife was such a hausfrau basically. Constanze must have considerable physical appeal for him, she thought, she couldn't discern any other evidence for his fidelity. Yet there must be other reasons, she thought, Wolfgang was too perceptive to be in love for that motive alone. She must proceed carefully. But once in London, singing for him, many things could occur.

The eyes of the two women met for a moment, but there was no communication between them, while Wolfgang stood fixed and still.

As Leopold read his son's request that he take care of Karl Thomas while Wolfgang and Constanze went to London with their English friends, he was sure there was more behind his son's impulse than the desire for a change. Wolfgang's letter seethed with emotion, and was passionate in his wish to take such a reckless step. Leopold had heard rumors that his son was involved with his Susanna, Wolfgang had spent so much time with her during rehearsals and that was expected. He wrote his answer as carefully as any music he had ever composed, and then, afraid that he had caused a breach between him and his son, he informed his daughter of what he had done:

"Wolfgang has asked me to undertake the care of his child, so that this coming spring he can tour Germany and then go on to England, where he seems eager to settle. His English friends, who are returning to their home, assure him that he will prosper in England, with subscription concerts and a scrittura for an opera. Madame Storace, in particular, appears to have made his mouth water and to have set the whole scheme in motion.

"And when he learned that little Leopold was living with me, he must have assumed I would have room for one more. He forgets that you reside nearby, in case my health, no longer reliable, should fail, but that England is many months away. So I have refused, as a friend and a father.

"Your brother and his wife must think they are very smart – they will journey in peace, when I traveled all over Europe with two small children. But they could die, or stay in England while I would be left with their child on my hands. It is true he offers to pay for the care of his son, even enough to hire a maid, but how do I know it will be forthcoming? I hear that his subscription concerts have fallen off to almost nothing, so I would have no surety that I would receive this money. And while *Figaro* has a lovely score and Wolfgang has surpassed himself in many ways, there is no assurance that the English will be any more enlightened than the Viennese, who prefer Salieri and Soler's tum-tum, which they can whistle.

"Thus, I have written him a fatherly letter, telling him that he will earn nothing by a journey to England, arriving in summer, which is the wrong season, and that he will need two thousand gulden to finance such a trip, which he certainly does not have now. So I have advised him, firmly but sensibly, to concentrate in a country like Austria, where, at least, he is at home in the language and is well known."

But while Leopold sounded positive in his letter, he wasn't sure within himself. Many nights he didn't sleep, or when he did, he had nightmares. Anna Maria appeared often, as if she were calling him or reproving him. Yet when he awoke he told himself he had been right to refuse his son; he was the only one in the family who knew how to arrange a tour. If his son failed in England, there would be no place to retreat to. He thought of the book he had meant to write, of the diary he should have kept, of the letters scattered over Europe. It was too late to do anything about his son's life. Some days he was so tired, he could hardly go on. But he had pride, too. He couldn't tell his children he felt death approaching. He wondered if he would ever see Anna Maria again. There had been a time when the Mozarts had been a single body. At least his children, he consoled himself, had known a Mamma and a Papa's love.

Wolfgang was packing for England when he received his father's reply. For once, he couldn't be forgiving. His pain and disappointment were severe. He felt that if he didn't go to England now, he never would. Yet he couldn't leave Karl Thomas with Fräu Weber, not when they would be away for such a long time. Perhaps his father was right. But even as he said this to Constanze, he didn't agree, he didn't feel obedient, and he was surprised that she did agree with Papa. His father mustn't feel well, he thought; it was the only excuse he could think of to justify Papa's refusal.

He had just finished telling the Storaces that he couldn't accompany them, feeling as depressed as he had for a long time, when he was invited to visit Prague to hear *Figaro*, where it had become a great success. And Count Johann Thun, Wilhelmine Thun's father-in-law and the head of this influential Austrian family, for whom

Wolfgang had composed his Linz symphony, invited the Mozarts to be his guests while in Prague.

The Bohemian capital was only a few days away. Without any further ado, Wolfgang arranged to leave his son with Fräu Weber and to take Constanze to Prague, for the vacation he had promised her for so long.

At the same time Hans Hummel left the household to tour Germany with his father as a Mozartean child prodigy.

And Wolfgang decided to bring Prague a present. A new symphony.

The creation of it expressed how Constanze felt, too. From the moment Wolfgang told her that they were going to Prague, she stopped worrying about Ann Storace, and she sought to make it possible for him to finish the symphony he wanted to give Prague. Many nights she lit the candles for him and filled the inkstand and bought him fresh pens and manuscript paper. Often she watched him bending over the paper, his eyes bulging, his cheeks puffed out, his attention riveted on the score. He didn't object to her presence, but preferred it. She marveled at his ability to compose no matter what was happening around him. But, as he explained, he did most of his composing in his head, when he was alone, when he walked.

Suddenly, this night in early January, 1787, he stood up to dance the passage he had just jotted down while she sat near him, sewing a button on his winter coat, for it would be even colder in Prague, which was to the north. Apparently he liked the tempo, for he sat down quickly.

Many hours drifted by. She didn't complain, content to be close to him. He composed without regard for the time. The candles burned down, the tallow dripped on his paper as he moved closer to capture the light, never thinking to change them, that would distract him. But he did like fresh, clean pens. He took pride in his meticulous handwriting. He could write perfectly straight without a line to guide him.

It was odd, she thought lovingly. As he worked feverishly to complete the last movement, before they left tomorrow for Prague, he sat with his wig half on, pulling at it in moments of emotion, his feet crossed, such tiny marks he made, and even after all the years together she marveled that from these jottings came such wondrous sounds. And she sensed that this music was something special. He was full of gratitude and sorrow, of passion and strength. Then his hand went up and down in time to the music he was hearing in his imagination. Such a decisive beat! His foot tapped on the floor. His eyes were shut and he was listening. He bowed his head a minute. And now he looked up with a slight smile, as if what he heard was good, and began to write again. She wondered if he would ever finish, and they were to leave early the next morning, but she couldn't prod him to go to bed, not tonight, and she knew now that if he wanted more childen she would do her best to give them to him, whatever the risk. His left hand had clenched into a fist and she longed to run over to him and say the passage is very good, it must be very good, but he knew that. Suddenly his fist opened and he moved both hands as if he were leading an orchestra, and he stood up again. She thought he was finished then, but he sat down abruptly and rubbed out what he had just composed and sighed. He had blotted several notes, which always annoyed him. She handed him a clean blotter and he took it without a word and worked on and on and just as she thought the composing would never end, he smiled at her and announced, "It's over."

"Properly?" she couldn't help asking. He looked so casual.

"Of course. I've said what I want to say."

"I hope Prague will like it."

"They will." He kissed her affectionately, filled with the sense of well-being that he felt only when he was truly satisfied with what he had created. "And so will you. My audience of one."

EIGHTY

===

The new work in D Major became his Prague symphony. Wolfgang was glad he had composed it with majestic and sonorous eloquence, for from the instant he set foot in Prague he felt this music fitted the grandeur and solidity of the city. Prague was full of magnificent baroque palaces and medieval churches, and he was fascinated by the sweep of the Moldau.

Count Thun, who had moved from Linz to Prague, welcomed them warmly and gave them rooms in his palace. There was so much space and comfort in their apartment Wolfgang and Constanze wanted to rest and enjoy it, but their host had many plans for his honored guests.

Le Nozze di Figaro had become such a sensation in Prague, everyone desired to meet Herr Mozart. The elderly, often gruff Count Thun, who prided himself on his musical taste, told Wolfgang, "It is the most interesting thing that has happened in Prague since I arrived here."

Wilhelmine Thun's father-in-law was so excited by the composer's presence, he arranged an immediate concert to celebrate his arrival.

Wolfgang and Constanze, who had arrived at noon, only had time to change and wash for lunch, for Count Thun was having his orchestra play for them right after that and he was eager to have Wolfgang hear them.

Count Thun's musicians tried hard, thought Wolfgang, and he was pleased that they played his music, but when they performed the Divertimento in D that he had composed a long time ago, they skipped four bars. This upset him and he was tempted to halt them and correct them. But Constanze, who sensed his mood, put a restraining hand on him, for Count Thun was gratified with his musicians. Yet he was certain they had omitted the bars, although he hadn't heard this music for years. His good humor was restored when they played

550

a serenade of his with every note in place and at the proper tempo.

At the Bretfeld ball that evening Wolfgang was the center of attention. Applause greeted his entrance. Many beautiful young women desired to dance with the celebrated composer and were eager to flirt with him, but Wolfgang, who loved to dance, refused to Constanze's surprise.

"I'm too tired," he sighed. "And too shy to flirt," he teased.

But he could hardly restrain himself when the orchestra played a waltz and then a quadrille arranged to the music of *Figaro*. And as an encore a soloist sang, *"Non piu andrai"*, and the applause was deafening.

A group gathered around Wolfgang, talking of nothing but *Figaro*. Count Thun introduced him to Signor Pasquale Bondini, the impresario of the National Theater of Prague who had produced *Figaro*, and who cried out, *"Figaro*, there is nothing like it in the world, Herr Mozart! It has saved our theater. And it was composed by a German, too. Fantastic!"

Wolfgang bowed, pleased yet a little amused.

"We will give a special performance of the opera if you will attend."

"I will be honored."

"Oh, no, Maestro, we are the ones who will be honored. And if you should be kind enough to like our performance, and could conduct one later, it would be the greatest honor of all."

Before Wolfgang could reply, Daniel Breicha, one of Bohemia's leading writers, and an actor and a doctor, handed him a poetic tribute he had written to Herr Mozart to celebrate the creation of *Le Nozze di Figaro*.

Wherever Wolfgang went in Prague, people spoke only about *Figaro*. Nothing else was performed, sung, whistled, or hummed but his opera. He learned that *Figaro* had run through the winter without interruption, and had rescued the National Theater from ruin, that it was arranged in every possible form, for the pianoforte, for wind instruments – as garden music, as violin quintets for chamber music, as German dances, as waltzes and quadrilles and contradances. The melodies of *Figaro* echoed in the streets and in the gardens. He sat in a beer garden and the blind harp player at the door, to gain an audience and a kreutzer, struck up *Non piu andrai*.

Yet when he gave the wandering harpist a gulden, he was told, "It is too much. Poor thing, the beggar won't appreciate it."

But Wolfgang, smiling wryly to himself, knew what it was to be underpaid. All this adulation of *Figaro* had not brought him one kreutzer.

This situation was remedied by a concert he was asked to give.

Every piece was of his own composition, at the audience's request, and the opera house was full. The new symphony in D Major opened the program and the orchestra played it with such devotion, the music seemed to breathe, to have sentience, as if this gift to his hosts had won their hearts.

The second half of the program was his performance of three fantasias on the pianoforte, and for the first two pieces the audience sat in an ecstatic silence, as if to applaud would be to profane the moment. Then, with the third fantasia, after he completed the written score, he improvised and preluded for half an hour with an intensity that gave the music an extra gravity. There was a wild outburst of enthusiasm. Long after he retired to his dressing room he heard the audience thundering for his reappearance. Finally, when Bondini, who had arranged this concert, told him no one would leave until he played something from *Figaro*, he returned.

He waved to Constanze, in high spirits, and started to improvise a lyrical tribute to her, and halted. There was utter silence in the entire house, and then a voice in the pit shouted, "From *Figaro*!"

Wolfgang played the theme of *Non piu andrai*, extemporizing many variations upon the aria, and now the entire audience stood and each time he paused, they shouted, "From *Figaro*!" He had to play a dozen variations of *Non piu andrai* before the audience would allow him to go.

His attendance at a performance of the opera received the same welcome, and when he conducted it several nights later, he was given an ovation.

Bondini, who entertained him afterwards, said, "Maestro, this was memorable. You caused us to hear things we never heard before."

"Thank you." He thought the Prague production not as well sung as the Vienna one; Bondini's company was not as good as the Vienna company. But their enthusiasm had compensated for most of their limitations.

"And I have five hundred gulden for you, sir. For your concert."

Wolfgang had heard that his program had taken in two thousand.

"There would have been more, Maestro, but after paying the orchestra, the attendants at the opera house, you know how it is..."

"Of course." Wolfgang took the money and turned to go.

"Your symphony was more than a gift. It was an achievement."

Wolfgang wavered. Perhaps Bondini wasn't a philistine after all.

"Maestro, I don't know whether you have been aware of our situation, but we need a new opera for next season."

"Another *Figaro*?"

"No. There can never be another *Figaro*. But when we decided

552

to do your opera, we also wrote Joseph Haydn, requesting an opera from him."

"He is a great composer. The greatest in the world."

"Haydn says the same thing about you."

"He is wrong. No one can touch the heart, make us laugh, shake us to our soul as he can. An opera from him would be a noble thing."

"But this is what he answered." Bondini handed him Haydn's letter.

"You ask me for an *opera buffa*. I am pleased by your wish to have a vocal work of mine, but if it is to be for your theater in Prague, I cannot oblige you, for all my operas have been written for my performers here at Esterházy. And it would be an even more difficult task to write a new opera for your theater, for then I would be taking a grave risk, for it is scarcely possible to stand by the side of the great Mozart.

"If I were able to impress every friend of music, especially among the great, with the deep musical intelligence of the inimitable works of Mozart – that emotion of the soul with which they affect me, and in which I both comprehend and feel them – the nations of the world would contend for the possession of such a jewel. Prague would do well to retain this wonderful man, and reward him generously, as he has rewarded us. Otherwise, the history of genius is melancholy and gives posterity little encouragement for further effort, which is the reason, alas, that many hopeful and aspiring spirits are repressed. It makes me indignant that this unique Mozart, whose *Le Nozze di Figaro* is the greatest living opera, is not yet engaged at some royal or imperial court. Forgive me if I stray from the subject, but I love the man too much."

Wolfgang said, deeply touched, "I am blessed to have such a friend."

"And I agree with Haydn. We must have another opera from you."

"To open in Prague?"

"For a hundred ducats. That is what you receive in Vienna, isn't it?"

Wolfgang nodded.

"Then we will expect a new opera from you by autumn. And we will pay the poeta, whoever you choose, the same. Do you have a subject in mind?"

"No. But I will find one."

When Wolfgang returned to Vienna after a month in Prague, he was sure he would find a subject that would please himself and the Bohemians, for their sympathy had surpassed anything he had experienced.

Constanze, who had been as happy as Wolfgang in the Czech city, didn't mind that he had hurried back to Vienna to say goodbye to his English friends who were leaving at the end of February. For while he looked sad bidding Ann Storace farewell and even promised to write her, Michael Kelly told Constanze that the original plan had been for Wolfgang to go with them alone, but that he had refused to go without "his Stanzi".

EIGHTY-ONE

═══

In Vienna, while many knew of his triumphs in Prague, Wolfgang felt suspended between hope and reality. He knew it was foolish to have felt that Prague could help him in Vienna, but he had. Only the everyday battle still confronted him. The money he had earned in Bohemia had gone to pay what he owed, and once again he was struggling to keep out of debt.

A month after he was home it was as if he had never been away. Most of his time and energy were being devoured to pay for food, rent, the maid, and even so, he was falling behind in his rent. Yet the thought of moving appalled him. He loved this house where he had composed *Figaro*.

He sat at his desk on a Sunday, the first full free day he had had to himself since he had returned, having skipped the usual musical afternoon at van Swieten's, and searched for a libretto. He had not heard from Da Ponte, and he had no intention of going to him. He must find the text himself. Constanze took his ability to create for granted, but he could not take the text for granted. After *Figaro*, he knew that much of his strength came from the libretto. But where would he find another *Figaro*?

He had been reading Molière, Goldini, Mestastasio for hours without finding anything that interested him, when Wetzlar and Da Ponte entered.

Wetzlar was worried about him. He stood in the doorway of the music room and said, "We thought you might be ill when you didn't appear today."

"I have much work to do, and this is the only free time I have."

Da Ponte leaned on his cane and said, "To save a librettist, Mozart?"

"You are very busy, I hear. With Salieri and Martín y Soler."

"Indeed! With the success of *Una Cosa Rara* everyone wants me.

I am preparing Beaumarchais' *Tarare* for Salieri. After *Figaro* I was the natural choice, and Soler insists that only I can write *L'Arbore di Diana* for him. But I am always interested in my dear friend Mozart's prospects."

"Thank you so much!" Wolfgang replied sarcastically.

Da Ponte ignored his tone. "What have you been considering for Prague?"

"What is there to consider! Metastasio writes of mythological love and heroism and is unreal and old-fashioned. Goldoni is amusing, but without substance, and Molière, while a genius at satire, does not lend himself to opera. Satire is not the most effective of musical forms."

Wetzlar asked, "What is, Wolfgang?"

"A vital human drama with characters of power and passion that people will feel deeply, whether they laugh or not."

Wetzlar said, "Lorenzo, why don't you write an original text for him?"

Da Ponte shrugged and said, "When would I have the time?"

"It doesn't have to be original," said Wolfgang, "The music will be."

"But it must please you," said Da Ponte, "whatever the poeta thinks."

Wolfgang stood up abruptly. "Thanks for the visit, Wetzlar. I appreciate your interest and concern."

"Wait a moment," said Da Ponte. "Mozart, do you want to work with me?"

"Do you want to work with me? Everyone wants you! Even Salieri!"

But none of them were a Mozart, thought Da Ponte. He asked, "If I find a libretto you like, would you be interested?"

"Lorenzo, you are a rogue. But a clever one." Wolfgang took his hand affectionately. "Of course I would prefer to work with you."

"When is the opera scheduled for Prague?"

"October."

"And this is the end of March. We have plenty of time. And if it is a success in Prague, I will persuade the Emperor to patronize it here."

"Then you do have a libretto for me, Da Ponte."

"No, no, no! But don't worry. You look for one and I will look for one, and I am sure, our genius combined, we will find what we need." He kissed Wolfgang on the cheek and added, "So *Figaro* was a sensation in Prague. I told you that you would be a success if you worked with me."

Several days later Wolfgang received a letter from Nannerl that shocked him. She wrote that Papa was quite ill, and he hurriedly answered her, offering to go to Salzburg to take care of Papa, although this was a very difficult time for him. But she replied, "That isn't necessary. I am with Papa, and everything is being done to make him comfortable."

Yet that had an ominous tone, and he had to write Papa directly. He composed this letter with great care, and with much emotion:

"Mon Très Cher Pére! I have just heard news that saddens me, especially as your previous letter said that you were in good health. Now, however, I learn that you are very ill. I am sure you know how anxiously I await and hope for consoling news from you, although I have long since accustomed myself in all things to expect and accept the worst.

"For since death, rightly considered, is the ultimate destination of our life, I have for the last few years made myself so well acquainted with this good friend of mankind, that his appearance is no longer frightening to me, but is peaceful and comforting. Now I thank God that He has given me the opportunity to know that death is the key that opens the door to our true felicity. I never lie down in bed without reflecting that – young as I am – I might not see another day. Yet no one who knows me can say that I am complaining or melancholy. For this blessing, I daily thank my Creator, and from my heart wish that it was shared by my fellow-men.

"I hope and trust that while I write you this, you are getting better, but should that not be the case in spite of all our prayers, I beg that you will not conceal it from me, but write, or let some one write me, the truth, so that I might with all possible speed rush into your arms.

"I implore you to do this by everything we esteem holy. Meanwhile, I pray that I will soon receive a more favorable letter from you.

Your ever obedient and loving son."

Nannerl read her brother's letter to Papa, who had improved a little by the time it arrived. He was surprised by his son's fatalistic tone, yet Wolfgang was right, he thought. He felt closer to Wolfgang than he had for a long time. But he still wasn't strong enough to write, which would worry his son. So he asked Nannerl to inform Wolfgang that he was better, to put it into his words and to sign his name, and to tell Wolfgang not to come – his son must get on with his new opera, whatever it was about.

While Wolfgang waited anxiously for a reply, van Swieten asked him to hear a young virtuoso. Wolfgang's impulse was to refuse. He felt too depressed to endure another would-be genius, with more desire than ability, but the Baron was insistent, adding, "I would have asked you in advance, but you didn't come Sunday," which sounded like a reproach.

Wolfgang said, "Couldn't someone else hear him?"

Van Swieten answered, "He wants only Mozart."

"He wants! Who is he, the Emperor's bastard?"

Van Swieten was surprised. Wolfgang rarely showed anger. His father must be very ill. He said, more quietly, "I am sorry to hear about your father's illness. I have some awareness of how much he means to you."

"Thank you. Unfortunately, this is not a good time for me."

"I know. Only this boy has come from Bonn just to study with you. That is, if you approve of his talent. Could you hear him today?"

"Who will pay for him?"

"I will. If his talent interests you."

Wolfgang was still skeptical about the value of this audition, but he agreed to hear the boy later in the day. But by the time van Swieten arrived with his new protégé he had forgotten about him, and he was working on a new aria for Ann, which he intended to send to her when she reached London. And he was startled and irritated by the boy's appearance.

This sixteen-year-old Ludwig van Beethoven was unprepossessing, thought Wolfgang, his skin pockmarked and swarthy yet florid, his eyes small and glittering, his features square and blunt as if they had been hewn out of a block of stone. His German had a heavy Rhenish accent, and was unmusical, almost guttural. And he stood clumsy and uncomfortable, with a kind of stupid unhappiness. Yet there was a curious air of remoteness in the boy; Wolfgang wasn't sure whether it was arrogance or awe.

Beethoven was surprised by Mozart's smallness; the Kapellmeister was even shorter than himself. He longed to feel relaxed, for ever since he had begun to study Mozart's music for the pianoforte, he had been fascinated by it, and it had made him desire to create his own pieces. Most of the music he studied he found insignificant, but not Mozart's. This was a man to study composition with; he could learn from him.

Suddenly Beethoven thrust out his hand to shake Mozart's. Like a squat young bear, thought Wolfgang, yet even as he was astonished by this gesture, he accepted the hand which was almost violent in its grasp.

Mozart's hand was small, Beethoven noticed, no wonder the Kapellmeister had a reputation for delicate playing, and his own palm seemed sweaty and coarse by comparison and he grew more self-conscious. His stronger, rougher playing would never please this fancy little man.

Van Swieten said, "Young Beethoven has a fine performing

history. He plays the pianoforte very well, the organ, the violin, the viola. . ."

"So, let him play. Beethoven, do you have any favorite sonatas?"

"One of yours," the boy blurted out. "If you don't mind."

"No, I don't," said Wolfgang. But soon he did mind the boy's lack of polish, the way he sweated over the piece, his heavy touch. The sixteen-year-old was not any better than Hummel, who was nine.

When Beethoven finished, van Swieten said apologetically, "The boy has been concentrating on the organ because of his church duties, and that has given him a somewhat heavier touch than starting on the harpsichord."

The boy frowned and said suddenly, "I played in strict time."

Wolfgang didn't answer.

"I did." Beethoven grew positive, almost defiant. "Didn't I?"

"Yes." Wolfgang had to admit that the youth's tempo had been precise.

"May I improvise, Herr Kapellmeister?"

The boy phrased it more like a demand than a question, and his manners were really deplorable, reflected Wolfgang; one moment Beethoven seemed miserable, the next the boy sat with self-appointed superiority, yet there was such an intensity in him that Wolfgang nodded, even as he doubted that this was wise.

"Give me a theme to improvise."

Wolfgang did, and Beethoven developed it with power, then with beauty. When he paused, Wolfgang motioned to go on, and now his playing was not heavy but firm. His improvisations were not meant to soothe, thought Wolfgang, but they were original, ingenious, and expressive. Best of all, they sang and had clarity. This boy was blessed after all.

Beethoven was positive that Mozart had disliked his extemporizing, Mozart sat silently, as if in another world, and he gazed at him suspiciously.

"Well?" asked an anxious van Swieten. "What do you think, Wolfgang?"

"Listen to him carefully. His music will make a fine sound in the world."

"But will you teach him? Until then?"

Wolfgang glanced at the boy, who rose abruptly from the pianoforte, his expression like a thundercloud, and as he wondered if this Beethoven would ever be capable of happiness, the boy asked, "Would you, please, sir?"

Ah, that was a concession, coming from him, thought Wolfgang. He said, "Come back a week from today, and we will arrange a schedule of lessons."

"I am more interested in composition than in playing. Anyone can

559

play with some skill, but to compose effectively, that is a man's work."

"Indeed."

"But you are my favorite composer, Herr Kapellmeister."

"I hope you still feel that way when we finish."

Wolfgang was growing sarcastic, thought van Swieten, and he said, "Perhaps, young Beethoven, you could play more variations."

"That is not necessary. Herr Kapellmeister heard what I could do."

Wolfgang said, "He is right." As he escorted him to the door he wished Beethoven wasn't so surly, it would be difficult to be friends.

But there wasn't any pupil next week, for young Ludwig van Beethoven had to return to Bonn because of the serious illness of his mother.

It was just as well, Wolfgang decided, for there was a new crisis. He had fallen back in his rent again and now his landlord was not waiting. He was told that if this back rent was not paid properly, his possessions would be seized. Wolfgang was able to borrow from Wetzlar once more to pay this debt, but he also arranged to move to the Landstrasse suburb where the rent would be one third of what he was paying at the moment.

A few days after he moved he received a more hopeful note from Papa, which he could tell Nannerl had written from the handwriting. Papa wanted to hear all the news about the Prague opera, what text had been decided on, would Da Ponte do it, and when was it scheduled for Prague?

Wolfgang didn't know how to reply, for neither he nor Da Ponte had found a subject that pleased them, and he wrote this to Papa, saying he desired a text that had tragedy in it, and asked again if he should come to Salzburg.

There was no answer for a week, then Nannerl wrote that Papa was holding his own and repeated that it was not necessary for Wolfgang to come.

Leopold felt fettered to his body. His daughter kept saying, "You have many more years to live, Papa," but he didn't want to live longer. Under the merciless scourge of pain he had no wish for infinite anguish as the price for life. Sleep was the only relief, and even it was brief, erratic.

Then he fell into a delirium, and he heard himself saying to Wolfgang, I am a reasonable man, I kept trying to tell you that poverty made a prisoner of a man, it isn't that I like money that much, but without it you are helpless. They were standing together, and Leopold was mystified, for he couldn't tell where he was, and he always knew. But the two men, the old one and the young one, gazed into each other's eyes and the same avowal shone from the eyes of each of them. A clear, boyish voice sang a serenade which rose tenderly. "It is a beautiful song," the old man said. "It is what you taught me," said the young man.

A huge teardrop seemed to rise between them. Leopold felt he was behaving irrationally now, which he disliked. And he saw Anna Maria. He recognized her clearly. But this was impossible. She was dead. He moved toward her, and she vanished. But what grieved him the most was that he could not hear her. Not a thing. Only silence.

On May 29, 1787, Wolfgang was informed by a friend of Nannerl's, Franz D'Yppold, that his father had died the day before and was to be buried on May 30 in the cemetery of St. Sebastian's church.

Numb, almost unable to accept this, Wolfgang waited to hear from his sister. He could not reach Salzburg in time to attend the funeral. The struggle had become harder rather than easier, the money had become less rather than more, and his energy had not increased in proportion to the struggle, but was dwindling alarmingly.

Papa was buried in St. Sebastian's because Nannerl's husband decided that was sensible. Papa, despite his usual foresight, had neglected to provide a cemetery plot for himself in St. Peter's, his preference, and Berchteold Sonnenburg pointed out that St. Sebastian's was less crowded than St. Peter's, yet Papa would have distinguished company. Wolf Dietrich, the most famous Archbishop that Salzburg had known, was buried here, and the great physician, Paracelsus, and Nannerl was too upset to argue, and allowed her husband to make all the arrangements.

But like her father, part of her was sharply observant. The day of the funeral she rode up the Linzergasse and thought bitterly that very few people had come. Most of his old friends had died or said they were too feeble, except for Schachtner, Bullinger, and Michael Haydn. She was angry there was no one from Colloredo's court. She felt that Papa had died without distinction, although he had brought Salzburg great distinction.

St. Sebastian's was a small church, with just fourteen pews, and as Nannerl knelt and prayed for her father's soul she wished Wolfgang could have come. She had to assemble her thoughts before she could write him, but Wolfgang should have been here, no one mattered more to Papa.

There was a red marble walk – marble from the Unsterberg – around the grave. Berchteold was right, she realized, the cemetery was not crowded. There was no one else in the graveyard but their party and all she heard was the crunch of their footsteps on the gravel path, the sound of the birds singing: Papa liked birds to sing. Papa said that a bird that didn't sing was unnatural. She wondered if any-one would care that one of the greatest teachers of music who had ever lived was buried here.

Nannerl wrote her brother that their father lay in St. Sebastian's at the start of the cemetery, in case he desired to visit the grave. She didn't add what struck her as a strange irony, that Papa was buried close to the Linzergasse on which he had led them out of Salzburg and to their triumphant tours of Europe. She said that it was a small funeral for a man who had accomplished so much in music, and that "the last few days Papa kept talking about Mamma, you know, he never really got over her death."

It was plain to Wolfgang from his sister's letter that she expected him to visit Papa's grave as soon as he could. But what was the use.

One day, however, he did walk out to a cemetery alone. It didn't matter what cemetery it was, as long as there were graves in it, and when he came to a grave which had the name Leopold on it, he paused before it, he stared at it, he prayed, he walked around it, and then, feeling that he would never be able to get to Salzburg again no matter how much he longed to see his father, he turned to his grave, marked Leopold, his eyes too filled with tears to tell what the last name was or to care and whispered, "Goodbye, Papa," but the tears did not stop.

Afterward he thought, one didn't have to go to a cemetery or to the grave of someone you loved to show that you loved them. But he realized how Papa must have felt when Mamma was buried out of reach.

A week later, when his pet starling died, he buried the little bird in the garden of his new residence in the Landstrasse suburb, and gave it a formal funeral procession, where his friends who could sing had to perform a requiem he composed for the occasion. And on the little stone he put above the starling he wrote: "Here lies a cherished fool, a starling bird. He sang so well, he was so full of life, and now he lies with all the rest."

EIGHTY-TWO

The mourning, the doubt, the questioning, the inability to work and the anxiety over debts stopped when Constanze discovered that she was pregnant again. Wolfgang was elated by the news, and in his need to be hopeful, his resilient nature saw this as a good omen. No longer able to procrasinate, when there was no word from Da Ponte the next few days, he visited the poeta at his quarters. It was several weeks after Papa's death, and as he entered Da Ponte's luxurious rooms on the Kohlmarkt, next door to where the former Imperial poeta, Metastasio, had lived, and close to the Hofburg, he suddenly felt he should have been announced.

For while it was in the middle of the day and there was ink and pens on the desk and three piles of manuscripts, it also contained liqueurs and sweetmeats, and Da Ponte himself sat on his couch clad only in a dressing gown, with a very pretty young woman on his lap. The poeta's arms were around her waist, her bodice was half undone, and he was quite pleased with himself. But the girl, who was about eighteen, jumped to her feet when she saw Wolfgang, blushed, and regarded him as an intruder.

Da Ponte however, instead of looking embarrassed was proud, and said to her, "Diana, I will see you later," and motioned for her to go.

She did, glancing at Wolfgang angrily.

Wolfgang started to say, "I'm sorry, but . . ." and Da Ponte halted him. "She'll be back. The day is young. What do you want, Wolfgang?"

"You called her Diana. But she is Austrian."

"It is the name of the heroine of the libretto I am writing for Soler. And she fancies the name. She says it is more poetic than Gretel."

"Do you really like her?"

"You are curious today!"

563

"I want to know what is keeping my librettist from finding a libretto."

"She is not the reason. I will find one. I am always enamored of someone. It is the custom. And it keeps me young."

Da Ponte, who was seven years older than himself, had assumed the manner of a vivacious youth, thought Wolfgang, yet the wrinkles remained.

"But she is a virtuous girl. She gives her affections only to me."

Wolfgang smiled cynically.

"Oh, that is true. She is madly in love with me, so why should I spoil her happiness. And she is a consolation when an idea does not come."

"And, of course, you adore her."

"At the moment. Every love affair is the sweetest of my life, until the next one. But I am always sincere. I love only one at a time."

"Why do you have three piles of manuscripts?"

"One is what I write for Salieri, one is for Soler, and one for Mozart."

"Which is the one devoted to me?"

Da Ponte indicated the third and last pile.

Wolfgang picked up the text on top. But it didn't bear Da Ponte's name; it was *Il Convitato di Pietra* by Bertati. He said, "*The Stone Guest*. Hasn't that been done as an opera recently?"

"There is a one-act *buffa* by Gassaniga, *Don Giovanni Tenorio o sia Il Convitato di Pietra*, which has been done in Venice with some success. But it doesn't have my style or wit, or your grace and melody."

"Don Giovanni could be an effective subject."

"Look at Bertati's text. It won't take you long."

Wolfgang read quickly, thinking of the situation he had found Da Ponte in, of Casanova, who Da Ponte knew, of Papa's ambition for fame, money, and position, of the joy of life and ever-present death. He was intrigued by Don Giovanni's meeting with the statue, his defiance of the devil, his descent into hell. The tragedies of the past few months seemed to explode in him with a lurid flame and he said, "*Il Dissoluto Punito Il Don Giovanni*. It could be operatic. Why don't you write such a libretto?"

"But the idea isn't original."

"Are any of your librettos?"

"Wolfgang, you know what I mean."

"I know that the character of the Don suggests a fine grand opera."

Da Ponte had rarely seen Mozart so involved. Perhaps the composer was right. He had a remarkable sense of theater, the best of any musician he knew. And the tale would be easy to adapt. There were many versions of the story, Molière, Goldoni, others. He said, "Oh, I like the idea, too."

Wolfgang knew he had convinced Da Ponte that it was a good subject, for now the poeta was acting as if the idea had originated with him.

The next few weeks Wolfgang and Da Ponte worked on the *Don*, interrupted only by the other librettos that Da Ponte was writing and occasional pieces of music that Wolfgang had to compose. One of them became vital to him when Constanze was jealous of a song he had composed for Aloysia.

He constructed this serenade in G – the first he had written in years – with loving care and arranged to present it to her as a wedding anniversary gift. And to celebrate this event he invited many friends to a party at his new rooms in the Landstrasse suburb. Nannerl had informed him that he would probably get a thousand gulden from their father's estate, which was to be divided between them, and he used this inheritance as security to borrow money to pay for the party, and rented his landlord's garden and a small orchestra.

August 4, the date of the party and their fifth wedding anniversary, felt like their good days at the Figaro house to Constanze, there was such a festive feeling in Wolfgang. And yet it contained a kind of desperation, as if he had to clutch at this happiness before it was too late.

Dinner was served in the garden where the orchestra was to play, and many friends came, and Haydn, who was in Vienna for a holiday, and Salieri, whom Wolfgang had invited at Da Ponte's suggestion.

Constanze no longer felt insignificant as Haydn insisted on sitting next to her during the concert in the garden. Wolfgang led the small orchestra with the excitement of an opening of one of his operas. In the clear Vienna twilight this serenade in G was the kind of music she loved the most, gentle, romantic, lyric, without the fierce and sometimes somber intensity that had been pervading much of his music lately. This serenade, for all of its simplicity or perhaps because of it, possessed a sweetness of tone she was certain all the other composers envied. She felt this acknowledged her in a way nothing else had. When the strings ended as perfectly as they had begun, she exclaimed, "Wolfgang, it is one of the most beautiful pieces you have ever composed."

"It is our *Eine kleine Nachtmusik*," he said lovingly.

Their son, who was sleeping upstairs, started to cry.

Constanze was upset until Haydn suggested, "Why don't you bring him down, Fräu Mozart? Maybe Karl Thomas wants to hear the music, too."

565

Constanze did, and as she put the child on the ground to walk, he toddled to Haydn, who took him affectionately into his arms.

Haydn asked, "How old is he, Wolfgang?"

"Almost three."

"Does he care for music the way you did at three?"

"I can't tell. He likes to listen, but I haven't been able to teach him."

Constanze said, "Wolfgang hasn't got the patience his father must have had." Suddenly she blushed. She hadn't talked about Leopold for weeks. She had been unable to share Wolfgang's grief, and this had caused her to feel troubled and guilty, and she had avoided the subject. Instead, she had talked about how much she enjoyed living in the country so that Wolfgang would feel better, although she missed living in the center of Vienna.

Wolfgang said, "I am not as good a teacher as my father."

Haydn said, "I was deeply sorry to hear about his death. It must have been a dreadful blow. I enjoyed meeting him very much."

Wolfgang said, "He was an honorable man, my dearest and best friend."

Karl Thomas reached for the harpsichord, where Wolfgang had conducted, and Haydn suggested, "Let him try. Let us see what will happen."

The child ignored the keys and as Wolfgang sat beside him and tried to show him how to play them, Karl Thomas began to cry. It made Wolfgang sad.

But Haydn said, "There are too many people watching. He is frightened."

Wolfgang didn't tell his dear friend that he had tried this alone with his son, and had failed. It was the one thing about the child he was unhappy about; otherwise Karl Thomas was amiable and good-natured.

Da Ponte said suddenly, provocatively, bored with this concern for a baby, "Mozart, Signor Salieri says *Don Giovanni* is a foolish idea."

Salieri protested, "I only said it has been done before."

Wolfgang, who had sat next to Salieri as a gesture of friendship, had been puzzled by the Italian's eating habits. Salieri had tried nothing, until he had tasted it first. Did his rival think he was a Borgia?

Haydn said, "I am certain that Mozart's *Don Giovanni* will be both amusing and tragic."

Salieri said, "That is what worries me. How can my good friends Mozart and Da Ponte succeed, when they have such a lecher as a hero?"

"He is a villain, yes," said Wolfgang, "but not just that."

"You admire him?" Salieri was amazed. "He is a murderer!"

"And worse, perhaps. And I am not a moralist, but a composer."

"What about public taste? Aren't you afraid of offending it?"

"I am more afraid of offending myself."

"We must also consider the Emperor's feelings. He is our Caesar."

'I respect his interest in music. But I am writing the *Don* for Prague, and myself, and for my friends."

Haydn was pained by Wolfgang's tactlessness. He said, "When our illustrious Gluck passes on, there will be a vacancy in the Imperial Kapelle."

Salieri said vehemently, "I hope Maestro Gluck lives many more years!"

Haydn didn't believe him, for with the death of Gluck, Salieri would advance. But it was Mozart he was concerned about; Wolfgang needed a royal appointment very much. He said, "We must respect our superiors."

"Oh, I do," said Wolfgang, "My father and I have written some of the most supplicating petitions to royal patrons that have ever been composed."

"It is the least we can do," said Salieri, "in gratitude to God for having blessed us with Princes wise and noble in their rule and knowledge."

Wolfgang turned to van Swieten. "Does Beethoven intend to return?"

"I don't know. His mother is very ill, and he is quite attached to her."

"The boy has genuine promise as a composer."

"Composing is the love of his life. He says nothing else really matters. He was deeply disappointed that he wasn't able to study with you."

"I wouldn't have known it from his expression."

Constanze was nudging him to say goodbye to Salieri, who was leaving, and as they bowed to each other, Salieri declared, "I was honored by your invitation, Herr Mozart, and I wish you the greatest success in Prague."

Wolfgang thanked him, not trusting a word of it, and now the party broke up, but he knew it had been a success, for Haydn said, "*Eine kleine Nachtmusik* was charming. I am sure we all wish we could have composed it."

EIGHTY-THREE

From then on, the focus was on the creating of *Don Giovanni*. Da Ponte's text, which took shape now, had some of Bertati as Wolfgang expected, and a touch of Molière, Goldoni, and Tirso, the Spanish monk who had first conceived the story, but it also included some of the poeta's own ideas.

Wolfgang saw the opera as the tragedy of the Don who had to follow his nature to its destruction, while Da Ponte was determined to write a comedy of intrigue. The poeta complicated the Don's efforts at seduction, and Wolfgang developed his clash with the Commendatore. Da Ponte felt the plot should come first, but Wolfgang stressed the characters and their emotions.

Gradually he convinced Da Ponte to create flesh-and-blood people rather than the stock figures of melodrama, and the poeta, who was enraptured with the subject, now that he considered it his own, built effective scenes.

As Wolfgang received the text he composed the music he was sure of, and which would fit any reasonable range of voice. The more he became involved with the drama of the Don, the more it fired his imagination. The story opened a treasure house of music in him. Much of what he had learned in a lifetime of music was coming to fruition in this score. There were luminous moments in the music, and demonic, primal instincts. Da Ponte continued to insist that the *Don* must be a comedy, but tragedy kept creeping in. Yet Wolfgang's sense of irony also prevailed, and his sense of the absurd. For tragic situations he wrote tragic music, and for comic situations he wrote comic music, and he was unconcerned about what kind of an opera it was supposed to be, and he concentrated on breathing musical life into the characters. However, Da Ponte declared their new work must have a style.

He titled it *Don Giovanni – Il dissoluto punito – Dramma gioscoso* in two acts, and Wolfgang accepted this. Yet while the surface of the music appeared gay, there was somberness underneath.

By October 1, when Wolfgang departed for Prague with Constanze
– they left Karl Thomas in the care of Frau Weber – he had put
down half the score on paper and much of the rest was finished in
his head. Da Ponte arrived a week later to attend the casting and to
adjust the text to the singers, and took a room in an inn opposite
Wolfgang's, so that they could consult with each other from window
to window. Wolfgang had rented fine rooms in the clean Three Lions
Inn with part of the thousand gulden he had received from Papa's
estate, and he was gratified with this inheritance.

Constanze thought he was entitled to more, for Nannerl had
appropriated many of Leopold's precious possessions without apply-
ing them to the estate.

But when she said this to Wolfgang, he became upet and answered
that he couldn't quarrel with his own sister over a few gulden.

He pointed out that the inheritance had paid for their wonderful
party, these excellent rooms, and most of his back debts. She dropped
the subject then, for as it was, he was disturbed by the casting of
the opera.

Bondini cast *Don Giovanni* without considering the composer or
the poeta, and when they questioned several of his decisions, the
impresario stated, "This is all I have. Our National Theater does not
have the resources of Vienna. Besides, this is the same company that
sang *Figaro* so well."

"But this isn't *Figaro*," said Da Ponte. "This is more difficult."

"What would you suggest," said Bondini. "Hire singers from
Vienna?"

This was obviously impossible, and Wolfgang hurried to say,
"Bassi, who is singing the Don, should be effective, and your wife
will make a lovely Zerlina, but several of the singers are limited in
their range."

Bondini stressed, "I cannot hire anyone else. We cannot afford it.
As it is, this opera is a great risk, it is so different from *Figaro*."

"Is it too heavy?" asked Da Ponte, as if he wished confirmation
of that.

"It is more tragic than I expected," answered Bondini.

"Too much?" prodded Da Ponte.

"Just enough," Wolfgang retorted sharply.

"Perhaps," said Bondini. "I have my doubts, but we will do the
best we can, and if you make enough changes, the opera might have
a chance."

That night, while Wolfgang and Da Ponte were working in The
Three Lions Inn, adjusting the libretto and the score to Bassi's strik-

ing good looks and fine bass, Da Ponte announced abruptly, "I can only stay a week."

Wolfgang was dismayed. "But there is still so much work to be done."

"Salieri insists I must be back in Vienna to work on his new opera."

"When is it scheduled to open?"

"In a month or two. I'm not sure." Da Ponte shrugged. Salieri was more important than Mozart, but he couldn't tell the latter that.

"And we have two, three weeks at the most to get ready. If you leave so soon, it will be a scandal. Prague will think you don't care."

"I'm sorry, but I have no choice in the matter. The Emperor is especially interested in Salieri's new opera and we cannot offend him."

Or, reflected Wolfgang, Salieri had confronted Da Ponte with a choice, and the poeta had decided on Salieri because he was in favor. Wolfgang longed to present Da Ponte with an ultimatum: either him or Salieri but not both. But he could not, it was not in his nature to threaten anyone.

"Mozart, you don't need me after this week. The libretto is virtually finished, and whatever alterations are necessary, you can make them."

That would be an advantage, thought Wolfgang, there were things in the text that should be improved, which would be easier to do without Da Ponte.

"The main task is with the singers, coaching them, and altering the score to suit their voices, for they are not as good as Vienna."

"At least the audience will be better."

"Some of your music is so difficult I doubt they can sing it."

"They will sing it. After I work with them."

"And the impresario's wife. You won't be able to correct her."

"I will get around her."

"With an affair?" Da Ponte smiled knowingly.

"I didn't say that." Wolfgang was annoyed.

"Everybody else uses that in the theater, why shouldn't you? I am sure she would be willing, if you give her the best arias."

"Zerlina will have what she needs, not what Signora Bondini desires."

Da Ponte sighed. "I wish you weren't so moral."

"You are the one who is moral."

Da Ponte was surprised, indignant, and denied that passionately.

"You are the one who says the Don must be punished because he is evil."

"He is!"

"But there is some of the Don in all of us. We all have a secret life, that desires more than one woman, that would love to be irresistible."

"And you give him arias of such sensuous tenderness and beauty it is almost impossible to resist him."

"Yet he becomes the seducer who doesn't succeed."

"Now you are the moralist, Mozart."

"The realist. Most Don Giovannis are more successful with the word than with the deed. That is why the opera has comedy as well as tragedy."

"I must introduce you to Casanova. He is a friend of mine, and he lives near Prague. He can fill in whatever you need."

Before Da Ponte left, he arranged for Wolfgang to meet Casanova. And he told Wolfgang, "Gluck isn't expected to live much longer. I will keep you informed. It would be useful for you to be in Vienna when Gluck passes on. There could be a place for you at court then." After having six librettos produced in 1786 and three this year, Da Ponte felt secure as the Imperial poeta. But it was always wise to protect one's position, and Mozart might just, some day, excel Salieri in the public favor.

Giacomo Casanova declared that he was honored to meet the distinguished composer, Mozart. He trusted that Herr Kapellmeister felt the same way.

"Of course," said Wolfgang, bowing in response to Casanova. The Venetian libertine's reputation was known in Vienna, and as he stood in the doorway of Wolfgang's room, even more the gallant than Da Ponte, Wolfgang was struck by his resemblance to the poeta. Both had brilliant eyes that seemed to penetrate to the heart of their listeners, a Venetian accent, hawklike features, and gestures that had an eloquent flourish.

But Casanova was much older than Da Ponte, and leaning against the door and asking to sit down, he looked worn and aged, and Wolfgang recalled Da Ponte's saying, "Casanova tires quickly now. He is sixty-two."

Casanova apologized, "I've come from Dux, outside of Prague, and years ago, I would have traveled twice as far for just a pretty smile, but today it exhausts me and I am reduced to being Count Waldstein's librarian and writing my memoirs. Da Ponte tells me that you need help with *Don Giovanni*. I have had some experiences in that world, as you may have heard."

"I have heard."

"And I am well acquainted with music. As a young man, I earned my living for a while playing the violin in a Venetian opera house."

Wolfgang grew more interested, and when Casanova said that he had heard *Figaro* in Prague and had been fascinated by it, Wolfgang gave him a copy of the libretto and took him to hear a rehearsal of the *Don.*

Casanova listened intently with a strange expression on his face, half living the Don and half disbelieving him. When it was over he said, "The scene where Leporello lists the Don's conquests, Da Ponte got from me. And the aria is like *Non piu andrai* in *Figaro.*

"Note for note?" Wolfgang was amused rather than offended.

"Naturally not. But the style is the same. That is not a sin. If it worked once, Herr Maestro, it should work again. Da Ponte's Leporello is very much like a servant I had once, Costa, a real rogue."

"And the Don?"

"My conquests were different. I enjoyed them. I am not sure the Don does. And the sextet in Act Two could be improved. I would be delighted to give you the benefit of my experiences." Wolfgang looked skeptical, and Casanova elaborated on his amorous adventures, and Wolfgang could not tell what was fact and what was false. One moment the Venetian was preening himself like a peacock as he narrated one of his lurid romances, the next he was complaining that he was being treated disgracefully by Count Waldstein's servants, who insisted on regarding him as one of them.

To conclude what had become a monologue, Wolfgang allowed Casanova to retain a copy of the libretto and to correct whatever the Venetian felt was essential, although he was not sure he would listen to him.

Several days later, Franz and Josepha Dusek, whom he had known from Salzburg, where they had toured as musicians, invited the Mozarts to stay at their country villa in the Prague suburb of Smichov, and Wolfgang accepted, although he kept the rooms in the inn, so that he could be close to the theater when it would be necessary. He had a deep respect for the Duseks as musicians as well as friends. Franz was a fine performer on the pianoforte, and an excellent teacher and instrumental composer, while Josepha was a splendid singer, with admirable artistry and taste.

The villa had a lovely garden and garden house, and Wolfgang composed in both, for the weather was mild. He was almost finished now. He had had much of the music in his head for months, and some of it had been there for years, waiting for the right moment to be used.

Casanova rewrote the sextet in Act Two and changed several of Leporello and Don Giovanni's scenes, but Wolfgang didn't care for his changes. With Da Ponte absent, he had already made his own alterations, which he liked much better. The Don was not at all like Casanova, he decided. He wrote his final scene with the Commendatore with a solemnity and terror new in his music. Don Giovanni brought to the edge of the abyss was still a passionate human being that

572

could not surrender, could not repent, and the ominous music was an oracle, full of gloom and foreboding.

The Duseks had promised privacy, but the news that Herr Mozart was staying with them brought many visitors. Ostensibly they came to play bowls in another part of the villa, but Wolfgang could hear the sound of ninepins. Once in a while he would take part in a game. And he loved their view of Prague. The villa was on a hill and commanded a sweeping vista of the baroque magnificence of the city, and the knowing that it was there even when he wasn't looking at it, was stimulating.

He was in high spirits until *Don Giovanni*, which was scheduled to celebrate the wedding trip to Prague of Prince Anton of Saxony and his wife, the Archduchess Maria Theresa, was postponed due to the illness of one of the singers. This upset Wolfgang. To perform for the royal couple was a grand opportunity, for the bride was the daughter of Leopold of Tuscany, Joseph's brother, who was to inherit the throne when Joseph died.

There was no changing Bondini's decision. Wolfgang protested, and the impresario replied that no substitute was available, that the premiere *had* to be put off. Instead, *Figaro* was performed for the royal couple.

And, thought Wolfgang, it made no difference. Any opera would have been a success with the Archduchess as long as she hadn't heard it before.

Josepha Dusek was invited to sing for the royal couple and she asked Wolfgang to compose a concert aria for her. He said, "I don't have time, I haven't done the overture yet," and she locked him in the garden house and declared, "Wolfgang, I won't let you out until you write my aria."

When he handed it to her later that day, he said, "I will tear it up unless you sing it at sight without a single mistake."

But she didn't dare make any mistakes with this aria; nothing could be finer. It was warm and tender, yet it brought out her full powers.

At the first full rehearsal of *Don Giovanni*, however, Terese Saporiti, the Donna Anna, balked at singing *Non me dir, bell'idol mio,* which he had written with a lovely lyrical gentleness. She stated that this aria was too low-keyed, that it did not express her personality as the wronged heroine or the range of her voice. He had no choice, for there was no substitute for her either. After she finished the moving *larghetto* of *Non me dir, bell'idol mio,* he added a bravura *allegretto* which finished in a cascade of high notes. He was not happy with this alteration, it was out of character, but she was very pleased. She said to Bondini, "For a little man, our Maestro can write large music."

But now Bassi, the Don Giovanni, demanded that the composer

rewrite his seduction duet with Zerlina, complaining that he had no bravura aria either, and now that Donna Anna had one, he must have one, also. Five times Wolfgang rewrote *La ci darem la mano* before Bassi would sing it.

Bassi performed with passion from then on, and in the dress rehearsal when as Don Giovanni he seized Zerlina, it was Signora Bondini as Zerlina who failed to scream at the right moment. Wolfgang asked the orchestra to play the scene without him – he had been conducting – and slipped quietly backstage and at the proper moment grasped Zerlina so forcibly that, genuinely alarmed, she screamed in real fear.

"Good," he said. "I will expect you to be as effective in performance."

Everything seemed ready but the overture was still not done. Bondini was very anxious, there was not a note of the overture on paper and the premiere was tomorrow.

After the dress rehearsal he informed the composer that the opening would have to be cancelled – how dare Mozart wait until the last moment!

"It has been in my head for weeks, but I wanted to hear the entire score before I put it on paper. The overture must contain the essential themes. Don't worry, it will be done in time. I will write it tonight."

"But it is almost midnight now. And even if you stay up all night, when can it be copied for the orchestra?"

"Have the copyists come to the inn at seven in the morning. It will be ready for them." Bondini was so apprehensive he had to be nonchalant.

Wolfgang and Constanze had returned to the inn and when they reached their living room he asked her to prepare some punch to keep him awake while he wrote the overture. He had no doubt that he would finish by morning. The overture had been finished in his head for days, except for a few alterations; he had wanted to hear how the Commendatore's scenes sounded before introducing his music thematically into the overture. And now he knew. As he sat at his writing desk he wrote quickly. But the punch made him drowsy and he began to nod, and he could only go on while Constanze was speaking. So, to stay awake, he asked her to tell him stories. This went on for several hours, but the effort to keep himself awake, the strain of nodding and dozing, then abruptly awakening at the sound of her voice was exhausting, and he began to blot the score.

She said, "Take a nap on the sofa, I will arouse you in an hour."

He slept so deeply she didn't have the heart to disturb him and suddenly at five in the morning he awoke himself, after two hours of sleep.

He did not scold her, but returned to the score refreshed. When the copyists came at seven the overture was ready for them.

They were not as quick as Wolfgang and at seven that evening, when the opera was supposed to start, the orchestra still didn't have the overture, which they had not seen or rehearsed. Bondini was frantic; the crowded theater was restive; only the sight of Herr Kapellmeister Mozart, the composer of *Figaro*, entering the pit, quieted them. He had come to tell the orchestra that the parts were on their way, that he was sure the men were capable of playing the overture without a rehearsal. He made it sound like a great compliment, but he was not that positive. A few minutes later the parts of the overture were hastily brought to the orchestra and distributed. The unrehearsed overture commenced.

During its performance, the audience listened intently and at the end applauded loudly. The curtain rose, and as the first scene of *Don Giovanni* moved smoothly, Wolfgang whispered to several of the musicians near him, "The overture went off very well on the whole, although a good many notes certainly must have fallen under the desks."

Once the overture started, dark, spirited, dramatic, it set the mood for the opera. With Wolfgang conducting the cast outdid itself, and in the ensembles seemed to sing with one voice. At the final curtain there was an ovation. The audience didn't want to let the company go. Then Bassi and Saporiti took Wolfgang by the hand and led him before the great curtains, where he stood all alone while wave after wave of applause greeted him. And Constanze sat in her box with the Duseks and wanted to cry. Wolfgang looked so tiny on the vast stage. How could so much have come from his frail self? How could anyone conceive what immense effort had gone into this opera? He had been so exhausted today.

Despite all his pretended optimism, he had been unable to sleep during the afternoon as he should have. Instead, he had been pessimistic, which was rare for him. He had sat up on the couch and had said abruptly, "Stanzi, I am afraid. I have tried things in *Don Giovanni* I have never attempted before. That is why I waited with the overture. I couldn't decide what should dominate, the dark or the light colors, until I heard the entire score. Then finally, neither did, really. What do you think? Do you think I have attempted too much? Will the *Don* please Prague as much as *Figaro*? It is such a different kind of an opera. And I couldn't make the Don an unmitigated rogue. I want to be proud of *Don Giovanni*, whatever mistakes I made."

"You did it the way you wanted," she had answered. "That is enough."

"Yet if it is a success they will say I wrote it quickly, easily, almost carelessly. They should know how many times I erase a passage in

575

my mind. But I hate to blot paper. It is simple enough for the musician to make mistakes as it is. Composing doesn't become easier with time, but harder. I want more from it, I have to have more. There is no one, Stanzi, who has studied composition harder than I have. I have studied all the good composers, Haydn, Handel, Sebastian Bach, his sons, Gluck, Sammartini, Hasse, oh, I could give you a list as long as the Don's. Do you think they will like it? I've tried to put so much into it."

And now Wolfgang was bowing and the audience was shouting, *"Evvivia Mozart! Evvivia Da Ponte! Bravo! Bravissimo!"*

And she thought how nice it would be to spend the rest of their life in Prague, without worry or debts, but applause and appreciation, a country villa like the Duseks', and many good friends, and a secure income.

Wolfgang decided to stay a few more weeks in Prague to enjoy the plaudits that accumulated with each performance of *Don Giovanni*. But Da Ponte, to whom Wolfgang wrote that their opera was a triumph, that Bondini had said to him, "All impresarios must bless Mozart and Da Ponte, for as long as they live we will never know operatic poverty!" replied, "I am happy that our work succeeded, as I expected, but you must return to Vienna at once, Gluck is on his deathbed and the instant he dies, many composers are going to clamor in the Emperor's ear for his post at court."

Gluck died the day the Mozarts returned to Vienna.

"From overeating," Da Ponte told them. "He was entertaining friends, when his wife had to leave the dining room to call his carriage for their daily drive. She had orders to watch everything he ate, and wine was forbidden. But the moment she was gone, he had servants bring wine, and when his friends refused to drink with him, out of fear for his life, he grew angry, and not only drank his glass, but theirs, too, then forced them to hide this from his wife. In the carriage he had an apoplectic seizure. Soon afterwards he was dead. He died as he lived, at the table."

"What about his successor?" Wolfgang asked eagerly and anxiously.

"I will speak to Joseph in your behalf. I will persuade him to have *Don Giovanni* done for his pleasure. He knows about our success in Prague."

Gluck's funeral was ornate, favored by Joseph's presence, witnessed by a huge crowd, and everybody wondered who would be his successor.

Three weeks later Wolfgang received a copy of the following decree:

From His Apostolic Majesty, Emperor of the Holy Roman Empire, King of Hungary and Bohemia, and Archduke of Austria. Our most gracious sovereign, concerning Wolfgang Mozart, graciously declares: that it has been His Imperial and Royal Apostolic Majesty's pleasure to do him the most signal honor of appointing him His Majesty's Kammermuiskus, in view of his capacity and knowledge in music and the approbation he has earned thereby, and to condescend to command the Imperial and Royal Treasury to assign him a salary of eight hundred gulden per annum from December 1 of this year.

In pursuance of which this Imperial resolution is herewith imparted to Wolfgang Mozart, and the present decree of the High Chamberlain's Office is drawn up at Imperial command as his guarantee.

Rosenberg
President Imperial and Royal High Chamberlain's Office.
Vienna, 7 December 1787
Johann Thorwart.

So what Papa had desired so fervently and had worked for so feverishly had finally occurred. But too late to gratify him, so many things happened too late, reflected Wolfgang. He wrote the news to Nannerl, having to tell someone in Salzburg, and using her as a substitute for Papa. However, his joy vanished when he learned that Gluck had received two thousand gulden a year. Constanze reminded Wolfgang that his eight hundred gulden was almost double what he had been paid in Salzburg, and he replied that the cost of living had risen, and that he was worth as much as Gluck.

Positive the reduction in salary was Thorwart's doing, Wolfgang angrily entered the treasurer's office, determined to get his salary raised.

Thorwart greeted him with a smile, congratulated him on his royal appointment, but when he complained that he was getting less than half of what Gluck had received, Thorwart said, "You are less than half his age."

"And with twice his ability," Wolfgang retorted defiantly.

"With half of his ability. And you mistake your position."

"I am not the Emperor's court composer now?"

"Not his first chamber composer and Kapellmeister. Gluck was the first chamber composer and Guiseppe Bonno is the court Kapellmeister."

"Bonno is seventy-eight!"

"I'm sure he had more patience when he was your age."

"What about Gluck's duties?"

"Salieri will assume them."

577

"Then what am I supposed to do?"

"Minuets for the royal balls, German dances, country dances. You are the third chamber composer, behind Bonno and Salieri. Actually, you are a lucky man, not everybody agreed with the Emperor's choice."

Most of Wolfgang's friends agreed with Thorwart about his good fortune, and Da Ponte assured him that it was his influence.

"I told Joseph about the *Don* and he is very curious about it."

"What has that to do with my appointment?"

"There have been articles in the newspapers that Herr Mozart, the distinguished composer, is thinking of moving to London or Prague. I convinced the Emperor that this would be a national calamity."

"Calamity?" Wolfgang laughed sardonically. "Joseph felt that?"

"He didn't put it in those words, but he said you would be a loss. And when the *Don* is done here, we will be paid again, which is unusual.

Unusual indeed, thought Wolfgang. *Die Entführung* had been done all over Europe, but he had not received a kreutzer. And now the same thing was occurring with *Figaro*. But he must seem grateful, however he felt. Without gratitude, he could not survive. "Thanks, Lorenzo, for all your efforts."

The money from the royal appointment enabled Wolfgang to move back to the city, and he rented a small apartment near the *Figaro* house. And when Constanze gave birth to their first daughter, whom they named Theresia after her godmother, Theresia von Trattner, he was happy. He had desired a daughter ever since the birth of Karl Thomas. He took this as a good omen and he was further cheered when Joseph ordered *Don Giovanni* to be done.

Before the opera could be produced for the Emperor, Austria and Russia declared war on Turkey, and Joseph left Vienna to lead his troops.

Wolfgang hid his disappointment, and composed battle songs for Joseph.

But finally, on May 7, 1788, *Don Giovanni* opened in Vienna at Joseph's command. At the last moment, however, he was unable to attend when he had to be with his army, which had suffered another reverse in the field.

Yet Wolfgang approached the opening with anticipation, for the Vienna company was superior to that of Prague. He knew and respected almost all of the cast. Half of the company had been in *Figaro*: Benucci, who had been such a splendid lead; Laschi, whose Countess had delighted him; Signor and Signora Bussani, each of whom had been effective in their roles. Cavalieri, the original Constanze of *Die Entführung*, was singing Donna Elvira; Aloysia

Lange was playing Donna Anna. Only the Don Giovanni, Albertarelli, and the Don Ottavio, Morella, were new to Wolfgang. And Albertarelli was bringing passion and color to the part of the Don.

As Wolfgang raised his hands to conduct the orchestra, he thought wryly, There have been only the usual difficulties. Cavalieri had demanded a new aria, and he had been gracious, he had given her a brilliant one; Morella had said his arias were impossible to sing, and he had made them easier. And he had altered the libretto on his own. He had eliminated the sextet at the end of the opera, feeling this finale was anticlimactic and moralistic, and had concluded the opera with the Don's descent into hell.

And yet from the instant the ominous opening chords of the overture sounded, the audience was restless. At the finish of the overture he could hear people starting to talk behind him. This did not halt when the singers began, but grew louder as the opera went on. He had to fight the audience for their attention. By the middle of the second act Wolfgang was disgusted. The audience had become noisy and inattentive, as if they could not endure the emotional impact of *Don Giovanni* and were interested only in the scenes that were amusing. He could hear people visiting from box to box. At the end of the opera there were more boos than bravos, although Cavalieri and Lange were cheered violently, as if each had her own claque.

He didn't want to go to the party that was being given for the company backstage, but Haydn, who was indignant at the audience's hostile reaction, said he must make an appearance and that opening night audiences were always a little foolish and the second performance would be better received.

Haydn had him by the arm and he couldn't refuse his dear friend.

Rosenberg and Thorwart were drinking, looking pleased with themselves, van Swieten and Wetzlar were with Constanze, and Aloysia was holding forth.

She stated, "What strenuous music. It is much too hard on the voice."

"Not if you use your voice correctly," replied Wolfgang.

"The music is too difficult. No wonder the public was cold, indifferent."

Her sister was wrong, Constanze thought angrily, there was more feeling in the penmanship of Wolfgang's notes than Aloysia put into her entire performance. She said, "You could have sung more attractively. You made Donna Anna sound like a shrew, with your need to show off your high notes."

"My little sister is an authority, now that she is wed to a Maestro."

"Let him compose a new opera, you will be the first to want to sing it."

Rosenberg said, "No one will want to sing it, if other audiences are as bored as tonight's was. And it could debauch the public conscience."

Thorwart added, "The Emperor wants us to keep it in repertory until he can hear it, but he won't like it. I'm sure he will find it indecent."

Salieri said, "Much of the music is melodic, but is it opera, Da Ponte?"

Da Ponte shrugged. This was not his war. He was not going to argue with the most successful composer in Vienna.

Aloysia said, "Maestro Salieri, I am sure that your new opera will be far easier to sing and far more pleasing to all of us."

Salieri bowed humbly and said, "I'm sure Herr Mozart meant well."

Wolfgang showed no visible emotion. But he was surprised by her venom. He had written some of his best arias for her, and she had sung them at every opportunity. Did she resent his indifference that much? And he was so weary of defending himself. Whatever he said would be self-serving.

Van Swieten said, "The plot is licentious, but the music is beautiful. Don't you think so, Herr Haydn?"

From the first chords of the overture Haydn knew that this opera was not like any other he had ever heard. But what was the use of telling asses like Rosenberg and Salieri, it would not change them.

Rosenberg stated, "Don Giovanni is a wicked character. Selfish, vain. He is a ridiculous hero. A year from now the opera will be forgotten."

Wetzlar and van Swieten disagreed and as voices rose high and shrill Haydn said, "Gentlemen, I cannot settle this quarrel, but this I know, Mozart is the finest composer now living, and none of us has ever heard or done anything as great as was done here tonight."

As Wolfgang tried to thank Haydn, the latter drew him aside to congratulate him on the royal appointment. "I was delighted to hear the good news. I still think Joseph will like and admire *Don Giovanni*."

"If he ever hears it. The war with Turkey goes worse and worse. There is even talk that to save money to pay for the war, he is going to eliminate the Italian Opera Company as he did the German."

"War," sighed Haydn, "it never ends. As long as I can remember, someone seems to have to be fought. The French, the Prussians, the Turks. But, at least, you have a regular income now."

"Eight hundred gulden?"

"Is that all? Gluck was given two thousand a year."

"I am being paid to compose the royal dance music. Too much for what I do, too little for what I could do."

PART ELEVEN

===

Sacred and Profane

EIGHTY-FOUR

═══

Wolfgang sat by Constanze's bed in their new rooms in the Alser-grund suburb, so he would be available if she needed anything, and was silent, for after much pain, she had fallen into a sound slumber.

Doctor Closset, who had just left, had assured him that her illness was not serious, more fatigue and sorrow from the recent death of their daughter than anything else, and that she required rest and sleep more than medication, but he could not leave her until her sister Sophie came to replace him as a nurse. It was two months after the Vienna opening of *Don Giovanni*, a perfect July day, but there was too much anguish inside him to enjoy the lovely weather. He put down his penknife, with which he had been whittling a small toy for Karl Thomas, who was staying with the Webers, and returned to a letter he had been trying to write Michael Puchberg.

He had written this fellow Mason and well-to-do merchant four times already in the past month asking for loans of money, and had gotten some.

But what more could he say? That these last few weeks had been the worst of his life? Tell Puchberg that Theresia's death and Stanzi's poor health had taken all his money? That they had been forced to move for the third time in fifteen months because he has been unable to pay the rent, and at this very moment his last land-lord was threatening to put him in jail unless he paid what he owed?

His thoughts reverted to his daughter, who had died ten days ago. Doctor Closset's diagnosis had been intestinal cramps, but he felt it had been poverty. He put the letter aside. He could not finish it until the mail arrived. That might contain some succor. The quarterly two hundred gulden from the Emperor had been due on July 1 and now it was the 8th. It could come today. Then he had a sudden fear that this money, little as it was, was being diverted to pay for the Turkish war. *Don Giovanni* was still in the repertory, but he hadn't received anything else for it, and there was talk that the Emperor, because of the expense of the war, was going to cancel all opera productions, present and future.

He was deep in this reverie when Sophie entered with Karl Thomas. The child, who had not seen him for days, ran into his arms and started to laugh with joy, and Wolfgang, alarmed that this would disturb Constanze, pushed his chair back and rose hastily to quiet his son, and the penknife, which he had left open, slipped and buried itself in his foot. Although he was very sensitive to pain, he was stoical now, motioning to Sophie and Karl Thomas to follow him silently into the living room.

Sophie said the wound was serious, but he replied that it was nothing.

But as she bandaged it, she thought that sometimes Constanze used illness as her mother did, as a weapon, yet Wolfgang didn't require such treatment, he was a devoted husband, he had such a need to love he couldn't endure living with someone he didn't care for passionately.

Sophie, whom he liked best of the Webers – she was the only one in the family whose emotion he trusted, except for Constanze – sat down beside her sister so that he could have a little time with his son.

He took Karl Thomas into the garden to see if the toy, a top, would work, and his son asked, "Papa, where is Theresia?"

"She's gone away."

"For good." This had happened before, with a baby brother.

Wolfgang nodded, too unhappy to speak.

"Where has Theresia gone, Papa?"

"Where everybody will love her, Karl."

"Will I get another baby brother or sister? You promised me one."

"I don't know." Much as he wanted a large family, the risk was becoming too great. And before Karl Thomas could ask his Papa any more questions, which he adored, for Papa, unlike his grandma and other grown-ups, always answered them, they were interrupted by the arrival of the mail.

There were a number of letters and when Wolfgang saw one with the royal seal his spirits rose. It must be his quarterly pay, he decided, and it couldn't come at a better time. Now he wouldn't have to ask Puchberg. He tore the letter open and felt he would die with disappointment.

It was from von Strack, who had been asked by the Emperor to convey his pleasure with the battle song Herr Mozart had composed for his troops in the field. *The Siege of Belgrade* had become an inspiration to his soldiers.

There was a note from van Swieten, too, inquiring if he would be interested in putting to music a one-act play of Goethe's, *Scherz,*

List und Rache. Van Swieten added that the poet was a great admirer of his work, that Goethe had written that he had been conquered by the scores of *Die Entführung* and *Figaro,* and that he would be honored by the association, only a Mozart could make his play into an opera worthy of its subject.

Ordinarily, Wolfgang, who knew Goethe's work, would have been interested in this suggestion, but now he was too depressed. And this was not a steady income, and that was what he needed more than anything else. He would have to decline; to write an opera score without a commission or a scrittura was foolishness indeed.

There was also a letter from Stephen Storace, who had just reached London, informing Wolfgang that there was a great demand for music in Europe, that Ann had earned four thousand gulden at a concert in Leipzig, and imploring Wolfgang to change his mind about joining them in London.

After he sadly wrote his refusal he read the last letter. It was from Nannerl, reproaching him for not writing her more often. But how could he? He was still owed money from the estate, but when he had said that, her husband had claimed that this money had gone to settle the estate.

And when Sophie and his son left he returned to Stanzi's side, and tried to collect his resources so he could act, as Papa would have said, sensibly.

He had planned to hold concerts in a new Casino in the Spielgasse – the Burgtheater, Trattnerhof, and Mehlgrube were no longer available to him because he could not pay in advance – but when he had tried to start a new subscription series, such as the hundred and seventy-four subscribers he had had four years ago, the only subscriber had been van Swieten.

He had written a new pianoforte concerto in D Major, as pleasing as any music he had composed, and no one wanted to hear it. Old friends had dropped away at an alarming rate, as if he had the plague. He had not even seen Da Ponte since the opening of *Don Giovanni* in Vienna. There was no alternative. He resumed writing to Puchberg. It was one of the most painful things he had ever done. He said:

"Dear Brother and most Beloved Friend! I hesitate to write you again, after already having troubled you several times the past few weeks, but I don't know where else to turn. And your past kindness gives me hope that I am not asking the impossible.

"Owing to the illness of my dear Constanze and the passing of our little Theresia, my situation has become so difficult that from the heart, I implore you, if you could lend me two hundred gulden for a short time, I will be eternally grateful. Unfortunately, my last land-lord continues to threaten me and unless I pay him at once, I will

584

be put in a dreadfully embarrassing position. And I cannot leave my dear Constanze, who is still ailing, who, at this very moment, is in bed with fever and fatigue.

"Indeed, if you could help me for a year with a thousand gulden, of course, with the proper amount of interest, it would be an immense favor. To wait for the fees that I am owed is much too uncertain and impractical. But if I had a reasonable capital to count on, I could put my situation in order. I still believe that my compositions will return to public favor, and even now, I have just completed a new symphony and expect to finish another soon. I still feel as capable as I ever have. And just today I received a letter from the Emperor thanking me for my battle song, *The Siege of Belgrade*, which, he informed me, restored the morale of his troops in the field, and he assured me of his continued approval.

"I beg you answer me as soon as possible. You will notice that I have a new address, to which I moved because it is cheaper. I hope you will forgive this plea, but you have been such a good friend. If you cannot aid me in this extremity, my credit and honor, which are precious to me, will be gone. Honorable brother, if you could advance me enough capital for a year, I will be able to be a human being again, and to live without constant anxiety, humiliation, and despair.

"In the few days I have resided here I have composed far more than I did in several months in my previous rooms, and if dreadful, ominous forebodings did not assail me so frequently, which I can exorcise only by an immense effort of my will, I would be content here. I am sending you a new trio in E Major I have just done, out of gratitude for your kindness. Your eternally grateful friend and true brother. Mozart."

Wolfgang paid a boy ten kreutzer to deliver this letter directly to Puchberg at his home in the Hohe Markt. He hoped this would bring an immediate response, but it was a week later when he heard from the textile merchant. Puchberg's reply was simple: he returned Wolfgang's letter with two hundred gulden, and a notation of the amount on the letter.

The previous landlord, who had waited, since he would not get any money if he put Mozart into jail, complained bitterly when the musician handed him a hundred gulden, but he agreed to allow him more time to pay the balance. Then Wolfgang got his quarterly two hundred gulden from the royal treasurer, and just as he was congratulating himself on climbing out of this financial hole the doctor and the cemetery demanded most of it for their services. He could not put off either of them, for Constanze's health was still uncertain, and the idea of not giving his daughter a decent burial horrified him. He put what was left, less than a hundred gulden now, away for food and other essentials, and returned to composing.

It was the only way he could turn. It was the one place where he did not feel that his world was crashing down about him. Day after day he sat by Constanze's side in the bedroom as she recuperated, and revised his last pianoforte concerto and worked on three new symphonies. The belated receipt of his pay added to his resolve to compose the symphonies while he could. Perhaps they would be done, perhaps they wouldn't – he had no feeling of surety about that any more – but they had to be written. While he still had the ideas and the emotions. Before he was used up.

He moved a small wooden table into the bedroom to have something solid to write on, and thought of Schönbrunn, Hofburg, Versailles, and a hundred other palaces he had played in. Did they echo with his music?

Then he realized this was foolishness and focused on the concerto.

He had finished it in February, but he was not satisfied with it. He liked the key, D Major, but he revised the score, stressing the singing grace and beauty of the melodic line. No one must know how unhappy he had been when he had been composing this. Music must not contain self-pity, that was maudlin. He rewrote the second movement with such delicacy the performer could create the fortissimo by lifting a finger. He refined it so that the apparent one-finger melody bore a wealth of allusion and subtlety and heart. He felt free now, free of debts and anxieties and humiliations. Yet he did not sentimentalize. He gave this music a balance between what could be and what was. The third movement became lively, elegant, authoritative. Here he was the master. The pianoforte could be a joyous, singing voice, and in this concerto that was so. As he ended the revision, he thought that this music was ideal for a coronation. But Joseph was fighting before Belgrade, and no one else desired his services.

He turned to the symphony in E Flat. He had entered it in his thematic catalogue on June 26 as a completed work, and Constanze had marveled at how quickly he had written it, but that was no great feat, much of the score had been in his mind for months; his imagination had done the vital work, it had been easy to put it down. He had composed this symphony, as he had the pianoforte concerto, with an immediate performance in view. But now there were no concerts in sight for any of his music.

The thought that he might never hear this symphony appalled him and he played it over in his mind. It was almost a month since he had completed it, and he had two new ones in his imagination, yet he could hear every note. Stanzi was talking about getting out of bed soon, and he sat at the table, staring at the composition and seeing nothing else, hearing nothing else. He didn't notice that she was sitting up for the first time in weeks. This symphony in E Flat had none of the wretchedness of the past few months. The first movement was eloquent, sonorous, and majestic. There were no blank spots and it was not too long as he had feared. Instead there was a passion and a fierce intensity that would surprise some of his friends. One had to be strong to survive – music, too – and he was pleased with the vigor he had given this symphony.

The second movement was also as he remembered it, an *Allegro* that danced, as the heart danced. He smiled with pleasure and went on to the remainder of the symphony.

It was solidly constructed, like the table he had written it on. He liked all of its four legs. Yet when he finished playing the music in his mind, he was dissatisfied. While he had been composing this symphony, he had said what he wanted to say, but now there was so much more to say.

Several days later, as he was starting the next symphony, Stanzi was sitting in the garden which brought a surge of hope to his heart and yet she was limping, her leg was very painful, and that was a new worry. And hoped-for aid had not come. His pupils had stopped for the summer and he had had to write more letters to Puchberg begging for money, and while his friend had responded, the amount sent had been less than what he had requested, just enough to subsist on. But he must not be gloomy.

He cast this symphony in G Minor, and he remembered what Haydn had said to him after hearing *Don Giovanni*. "Wolfgang, you know so much about emotion, it is as though you invented it, and then people adapted to it, and it became the human pattern." That was a generous thing for Haydn to say, whether or not it was true, and he was a dear man and a great friend, and his faith was one of the few things he trusted in this darkening world.

As he sketched the first chords, he felt it was not of earth only, but celestial, that it sang as the angels sang. And that was not enough, he knew. In the writing of this music he was involved in the struggle to make this profane thing called existence into something more than it was, something better, something sacred. In this symphony he must bring order out of the chaos into which his life had fallen, which the world was in. He had a need, a compulsion to create beauty out of ugliness, balance out of disorder. The world might be profane, but life was sacred.

So he built this symphony in G Minor with infinite care and detail and an exquisite equilibrium between poignancy and joy. He thought, if this music was ever played and that was becoming more unlikely every day, some would declare this was the saddest symphony he had ever conceived and others would say it was the most affirmative and both would be right.

He was grateful for the years of study, for his craft, for Papa who had taught him composition almost from the beginning of his consciousness. He recalled Papa saying, "I can't stress too strongly the value of technique. The ideas, the content are the culmination, but if you do not have the craft to cause them to function, they are worthless." He had to dry his eyes to keep his tears from blotting the score. He didn't want his music to cry, but there was pain in it. He finished it just a month after the symphony in E Flat, and immediately started another.

Constanze said, "Aren't you satisfied?" and he wanted to reply that he was never satisfied.

She would be hurt if he corrected her, so he said, "I have more to say."

"We're behind in our rent again. I'll die if we are evicted once more."

He had to compose this symphony in C Major before his energy ran out. He was very tired, but he couldn't halt. He was only in the thirty-third year of his life and he couldn't tell Stanzi how ill and weary he felt these days, of the terror that was overwhelming in the dread that soon he would not have the strength to compose. There was still so much music in him. The inner world of his mind and heart was richer than ever.

He worked around the clock in a race against time, against his increasing physical weaknesses. He struggled past exhaustion, past despair, past the thousand and one difficulties and doubts that plagued him, past his ailments which made him feel like Job, and wrote this new work with all the discipline at his command. He gave it dignity and majesty, and a purity of style and tone that was graceful yet vigorous. His heart was full of passion, but his music must express that with taste and subtlety. When he completed this symphony in C Major on August 10, just six weeks after he had begun the first of the three, he felt a great release. Whatever the fate of these symphonies, he had reached the goal he had set for himself. The achievement was before him, however little the world acknowledged it.

Constanze was amazed at the cleanness of his autograph of the C Major symphony. There was hardly a blot, and virtually no corrections, as if he had known with certainty from the start what to write.

"But who will do them?" she wailed, shocked by the vacuum he was in.

"I will talk to the Emperor when he returns."

"If he ever returns. He still hasn't heard *Don Giovanni*."

He felt utterly expressed, and utterly enervated. But even when he had felt like Job, no one could say he had complained. The C Major was triumphant music. He could not live without hope.

His music publisher, Pasquale Artaria, refused to offer the three symphonies for sale. Artaria begged him for more country dances. At one gulden, three kreutzer he could sell enough to pay the composer three kreutzer as his share. He was even willing to sell Mozart's sonatas, several of those for the pianoforte were popular with children and useful in teaching. He also had a pianoforte score of *Don Giovanni* in stock, which the composer had arranged, although there was no demand for this music, and wouldn't be unless the Emperor expressed approval of the opera. Unplayed symphonies were of no value, Artaria informed Wolfgang, and he advised him to compose marches, which were popular with a war going on.

Wolfgang put the three symphonies in a little safe where he kept his most precious possessions, and as he took a last look at them, as one might on a beloved friend being put into the grave, tear after tear fell on the autographs, blotting them far more than he had with ink or changes.

The next few months he did as Artaria had requested. He composed marches that sold, and the money was essential. Stanzi complained that he was being cheated, three kreutzer was less than one tenth of what Artaria was getting, but he couldn't fight with the publisher. It took energy to argue over money and he needed what little he had left to compose. And he couldn't win. As it was, Artaria acted as if he was being done a favor.

On December 15, Joseph – who had returned from the field ten days before – attended a performance of *Don Giovanni*. It was the last one scheduled and he was curious about what Da Ponte had done with the legend.

After the performance, which Wolfgang conducted, he was asked to come to the royal box. He didn't know what to expect. Bonno had died, but he hadn't been appointed in his place; the post of Imperial Kapellmeister had gone to Salieri. Da Ponte was there, ahead of him, which could be a good sign, it was the first time he had seen the poeta in months, but Rosenberg was on the Emperor's right, which could be ominous.

Joseph had aged in the field, he noticed, and looked distracted.

Joseph said, "Rosenberg tells me the *Don* does not please. That it has failed in Vienna. None of its fifteen performances have been full."

"Your Majesty," said Da Ponte. "All the operas have had some difficulties. It is the war, you know."

"I know. I would have canceled the Italian Opera season if you had not been so persuasive."

Rosenberg said, "Sir, the public didn't like *Don Giovanni* because they expected to laugh, and instead they were faced with torment and gloom. A tale about Don Juan is comic or it is nothing. But Mozart insists on trying to make it significant, and makes it scandalous and senseless."

Wolfgang asked, "Your Majesty, what do you think of the opera?"

"The music is beautiful. More beautiful than *Figaro*."

"Then you do like *Don Giovanni*, sir? Approve of it?"

"I like it, Mozart. Approve, that is a larger question."

Da Ponte said, "Your Majesty, we wrote it really for you."

"And had it done in Prague first. *Don Giovanni* is not for Vienna. Mozart, your music is not appropriate food for the teeth of the Viennese."

"Then, Sir, we must give them time to chew on it."

"No, opera is too costly. Now we must contribute to the war."

"I have tried, Your Majesty."

"Yes, your *Siege of Belgrade* has been useful to the Empire."

"What would you advise, Sire?"

"You would be more successful if you wrote simpler music, good tunes that catch the ear so the public can hum them."

"I will do my best, Your Majesty."

"Good. I am giving masked balls to lift the morale of my subjects, and if you can compose suitable dances for them, we will be pleased."

Then the Emperor was gone, with Rosenberg still by his side.

"Da Ponte, what is the real reason for his sudden distaste for opera?"

"The war goes badly. And there have been riots in France, although that has been kept quiet here, and they are blamed on his sister, and that has upset him. The French say that Marie Antoinette and her extravagance and influence on her husband has made France into an Austrian province."

"Are we going to fight for her, too?"

"It is hard to tell. But all this disturbs Joseph. Don't worry, I'll persuade him to want another opera from us."

To expect nothing had become a habit with Wolfgang, and he didn't believe Da Ponte. He never had mentioned his symphonies to the Emperor. But it did not matter, he thought. It would have been futile.

EIGHTY-FIVE

His chief source of income became the money van Swieten paid him to arrange Handel's *Acis and Galatea* and *The Messiah* for concerts given for the Society of Noblemen for the cultivation of classical music. He adapted the oratorios reluctantly, for while he still admired Handel's structure and vigor, they were less dramatic than he liked. But the money enabled him to move. As soon as Constanze was well and Karl Thomas was able to live with them again, they moved back to the center of Vienna, to be close to the musical activity. He rented the second floor of a house on the Judenplatz, next door to where they had lived with Wetzlar years ago.

And now, in early April of 1789, Wolfgang stood in the doorway of his new music room, as excited as if he had obtained a new opera scrittura, and announced to Constanze, "Prince Karl Lichnowsky has offered to take me to Berlin and to introduce me to the new Prussian King, Frederick William."

"Frederick the Great's successor? Is he musical, too?"

"Stanzi, he is a fine cellist and a passionate lover of music."

"So he gives you a commission or two. You need more help than that."

"Suppose he offers me a post as royal Kapellmeister? Lichnowsky, who knows the King, says he has spoken favorably about me."

"You would leave Vienna?"

"In a moment, if I were paid properly. And Lichnowsky tells me that Frederick William is far more generous with musicians than Joseph."

She hadn't seen him this exuberant for months. He had lost his wretched look, but she had to ask, "Aren't you afraid? With the Turks at Belgrade, riots in France? And aren't the Prussians supposed to be our enemies?"

"Not any more. Joseph admires their efficiency. And Lichnowsky is taking his own coach. It won't cost much at all. You know that his mother-in-law, Wilhelmine Thun, is one of my dearest friends."

"Where has she been these last few months when you have needed her?"

"I can't ask her for money. But this is her way of helping me."

She paused, then said, "Wolfgang, I am pregnant again."

Instead of being concerned as she expected, he kissed her with delight, and exclaimed, "Wonderful! How many months, Stanzi?"

"Three."

"Good. I'll be back long before your confinement. With enough money to take care of everything. Or with a new post where we can live in dignity. Lichnowsky intends to introduce me to Frederick William personally."

Now she didn't try to dissuade him. The idea of traveling to Dresden, Leipzig, Berlin, where he had never been, gave him new strength. He had to borrow a hundred gulden from a fellow mason, Hofdemel, to finance the trip, but he was sure this venture would bring him good fortune.

Lichnowsky was a charming companion. His fellow lodge brother and former pupil was his own age, carefree, handsome, friendly, his coach the most luxurious Wolfgang had ridden in for years. It was like the happy times when he had toured with Papa and had been the toast of Europe.

At Dresden he was invited to play at court by the Elector, Frederick August III of Saxony, which was an honor, for this sovereign rarely heard traveling musicians. His performance was enthusiastically applauded and he was given one hundred ducats and a beautiful silver snuffbox.

Then he and Lichnowsky were asked to lunch by the Russian Ambassador, Prince Belovselsky-Beloserky, who adored music. After lunch the Ambassador asked Wolfgang to compete with the leading virtuoso in Dresden, Wilhelm Hässler, on the organ and the piano-forte. Although Wolfgang had not played the organ for a long time, he could not ignore such a challenge.

Afterwards, he knew he had easily surpassed Hässler, even on the organ, for the latter's organ playing was indifferent and his pianoforte technique imitative, while he had received much more acclaim.

He heard the Ambassador saying to Lichnowsky, "Herr Mozart is a delight, witty, lively, gracious, an adornment to any court."

He approached him and suggested, "Your Excellency, I would be honored to play for your Empress. I hear that she is a connoisseur of music."

"Yes, indeed, Herr Mozart. But Catherine prefers Italian music."

Lichnowsky nudged Wolfgang that it was time to go.

In Leipzig he had to see the organ in the church of St. Thomas, where Sebastian Bach had played and composed as its Lutheran Cantor. And when the present Cantor, Johann Doles, a pupil of Bach's, heard that Wolfgang Mozart had come to pay homage to his master, he greeted him as if his visitor was a sovereign and begged him to play the organ.

"It is in perfect condition, Herr Imperial Kapellmeister! We have kept it as Bach kept it and played on it. All Leipzig and Lutheran Germany would be honored by this tribute from one great musician to another!"

Wolfgang hesitated. Despite his triumph over Hässler he had neglected the organ, and Bach was one of the few musicians he admired. But Doles was not to be denied, leading him to where Bach had sat.

As he recalled Bach's music and how much he had learned from him, he improvised on a Bach chorale, while Doles stood behind him, eyes shut, head nodding in approval, whispering with awe, "Such a masterly touch and style. It is as if Johann Sebastian has risen from the grave."

Before he left for Potsdam, Wolfgang promised Doles to return to Leipzig for a public concert of his music with himself at the pianoforte.

To his surprise and dismay, he was unable to get an audience with Frederick William. Lichnowsky assured him that would be easy, but a week passed without word from the Prussian court. Then Lichnowsky told him that he would arrange the audience in Berlin, next month, and insisted that they go back to Leipzig, that Wolfgang would earn more with a concert there. He also needed a hundred gulden, at once. "For a change of horses, so we can reach Leipzig comfortably. It is sixty-four miles."

Wolfgang couldn't say no, to refuse the son-in-law of Wilhelmine Thun was too embarrassing, but after he gave the Prince the money – the Prince did not refer to it as a loan – he had only a few gulden. And the instant they arrived in Leipzig, Lichnowsky departed for his estate in Silesia.

Afraid that he would be stranded in a strange city, Wolfgang didn't know whether to go to Berlin or return home. After getting two letters from Stanzi, he had not heard from her for several weeks and this made him anxious. Lichnowsky, before he had vanished, had told him that his worry was idiotic, a Maestro as well-known as Mozart could find mistresses along the way, but Wolfgang missed Stanzi very much and was in no mood for anyone else. He was on the verge of turning

593

back to Vienna, when Doles told him that a gala concert had been arranged for his benefit in the great Concert Hall of Leipzig. Tickets were just one gulden and Doles was positive that at such a modest price the Hall would be full.

Doles asked him to conduct the orchestra, which was also the wish of the men. As they approached the rehearsal, Wolfgang said, "Musicians think they impart fire to my work by hurrying the time, but that is a mistake. If there is no fire in the piece, it will never get it by quick playing."

Yet the composer conducted the first movement of his Haffner symphony at a very rapid rate. Then Doles realized why. Hardly twenty bars had been played and the orchestra had dragged. Suddenly Wolfgang halted them, explained what was wrong, and started again at high speed. He did everything in his power to keep the time unusually fast, and stamped on the floor with such emphasis that his handsomely wrought steel shoe buckle snapped into many pieces and scattered over the orchestra. He ignored the fragments, cried *ancora!* and resumed at the same quick tempo.

The orchestra, now thoroughly incensed with this pale little man who drove them on at such a rate, exerted themselves in earnest, and the movement went well. Doles noticed that from then on Mozart led at a moderate tempo. The composer was eager to recover the good-will of the angry orchestra, without however, compromising the effects his zeal had established. At the end of the rehearsal he praised the men, adding, "When gentlemen play in this manner, I know we will not cheat our audience."

He told Doles later, "It was not a whim on my part. I saw that most of the orchestra were elderly, that they would have dragged through the whole program if I had not put warmth into them by making them angry. Their irritation at me caused them to do their best."

At the concert the orchestra played his music as it was written, and accompanied his difficult pianoforte concertos correctly.

Wolfgang was sure the program he arranged would be liked. It consisted of the symphonies he had written for Haffner and Prague, and the pianoforte concertos in B Flat Major and the one he had just composed in D Major.

But in spite of the enthusiasm with which he was received, he noticed there was little money in the house. So, at the intermission, when he heard that many music enthusiasts were standing outside to acclaim him afterwards, but could not afford one gulden, he said, "Let them in, Doles."

After he performed the two concertos – gratified that the D Major played as well as it had sounded in the composing – and conducted for several hours, the audience wanted to hear him play alone, and he began afresh with a fantasia. The orchestra was tired, so he motioned for them to go home, but much of the audience remained, many of whom had come in free, and when he finished the fantasia they clamored for more of his music.

He announced, "I will play a little more for you, you who comprehend my music better than those who just applaud." He improvised fantasias for another hour, then suddenly he jumped up from the pianoforte and cried out to the small group who still remained, listening devotedly, "Well, are you pleased! Now you have heard Mozart for the first time!"

Wolfgang arrived in Berlin the following week. It was early evening when he reached the inn that Doles had recommended, too late to approach the court but much too soon to retire for the night.

At dinner he asked his waiter, "Is there any music here tonight?"

"Oh, yes, the German opera has just begun."

"What are they giving?"

"The Abduction from the Seraglio."

"Interesting!"

"Yes, it is a pretty piece. Let me see – who composed it. His name is. . ."

But his customer was gone.

Wolfgang hurried into the theater just as the overture was starting, and not bothering to take off his old greatcoat, he stood at the entrance to the pit, so he could listen unobserved. As the singers began he was absorbed by their performances: one moment pleased with the execution of certain passages, the next dissatisfied with their singing. Gradually, without thinking, he moved towards the orchestra, pulled by the music, humming various phrases, sometimes in a subdued tone, sometimes in a louder one, and unconsciously arousing curiosity in the audience at the eccentric behavior of this little man in the old greatcoat. He was close to the orchestra when they came to Pedrillo's aria, *Frisch zum Kampfe.*

Suddenly he realized that the stage manager had either used an incorrect score, or some one had been trying to improve the harmony, for at the frequently repeated passage, *Nur ein feiger*, the second violins played the D sharp instead of the D natural.

Unable to endure this, Wolfgang shouted, "Damn it! Play D natural!"

Everybody stared at him and some of the musicians recognized him and *"Mozart is in the house!"* ran like wildfire through the theater. This upset the singers, and Henriette Baranius, singing Blonde, refused to reappear. The conductor told this to Wolfgang, and he went backstage.

Henriette Baranius was one of the most attractive and voluptuous

595

prima donnas he had seen, and as she gazed at him seductively in her dressing room, he sensed she had used this as an excuse to meet him. He ignored her obvious coquetry and assuming the tone of a music-director, he said, "What are you afraid of, Madame? You were singing beautifully, and if you wish to give the part more color, I will study it with you myself."

He did not go backstage to congratulate her after the performance, or appear before the curtains for the ovation for him that thundered through the house. A messenger had just delivered a letter from Stanzi, which Doles had forwarded from Leipzig. Holding it lovingly, he hurried back to the inn where he could read it in the pravacy of his room.

Several days later, he was granted an audience by Frederick William, who had heard about the incident at the opera house. The King was amused by his audacity with a great prima donna such as Baranius. But Wolfgang had learned that she was the King's mistress, and he was apprehensive.

"I cannot hear you play, Herr Mozart," said the King, "but the Queen will tomorrow. She is almost as fond of music as my predecessor."

Wolfgang had heard that warrior-philosopher-composer's flute music. He didn't think much of it. But now that this King was gone, he had become Frederick the Great. The present ruler however, was drab-looking, even in a flattering hunting costume. Had he come all this distance from Vienna in vain? "Your Majesty, Prince Lichnowsky was supposed to introduce me."

Frederick William, who was in a hurry, didn't seem to know the name.

"Sir, he is wed to the daughter of the Countess Wilhelmine Thun."

"Oh, the beautiful daughter! Yes, I recall him now. Good day."

The Queen told Wolfgang that she enjoyed his playing and two days later he received a commission, signed by Frederick William, to write six easy pianoforte sonatas for their daughter, and six string quartets for the King himself. And a hundred friedrichs d'or in advance. The music was to be delivered at Herr Mozart's leisure. After he returned to Vienna.

There was no appointment to be obtained at the royal court of Prussia.

The one incident that gave him genuine pleasure the rest of his stay was Hans Hummel's concert. The boy and his father were on a three-year concert tour, stressing that the eleven-year-old child was Mozart's favorite pupil, and Wolfgang was delighted with the taste and skill with which Hans played his music. Hans and his father were greatly moved when they discovered that Wolfgang was in the audience, and their reunion was a happy one.

Papa Hummel told Wolfgang that his son was making a great deal of money.

Two months after he had left Vienna with such great expectations, he returned home with just enough money to pay back what he had had to borrow from Hofdemel to take this journey.

EIGHTY-SIX

It was too painful to admit that the expedition to Prussia had been a failure. Wolfgang gave the impression that Frederick William had offered him a post at the Prussian court but that he had refused it out of respect for Joseph. The commission he returned with gave that the aura of truth.

And a month after he was home he was in debt once more, and confronted with new debts. Constanze's foot swelled again, and Doctor Closset said, "It may be too many pregnancies or inflammation of the bone," and added that he couldn't come again unless he was paid what he was owed.

The next few days Wolfgang tried leeches, blood-letting, purges, and then ants' eggs, but Stanzi only grew sicker and developed bed sores which added to her misery. He had no choice but to write to Puchberg:

"Dear God! I would not wish my worst enemy to be in my wretched circumstances. Dearest friend and brother, if you abandon me, I am hopelessly lost, and so are my innocent ill wife and my poor child.

"Just the other day when we were together at van Swieten's concert, I yearned to reveal my heart to you, but I was afraid, and if it were not for the desperate situation I am in, I still could not write to you.

"Instead of paying what you have so generously lent me, I am asking for new help. But my wife is ill again and the doctor's bill has risen alarmingly. Now he will not come unless I pay him what I owe him. And none of the remedies I have tried have worked. Just a few days ago I sought to ease my sad condition by giving subscription concerts in my home. It was one of the reasons I moved back to the inner city, to the Judenplatz. I circulated a mailing to the many subscribers I had in the past, which reduced what little money I had, and the only one who replied was van Swieten. Cherished friend, where else can I turn!

"I am composing music for the King of Prussia, when I am not struggling to pay the doctors and the apothecaries, and if I could have just a month's peace of mind, I am certain I could finish them and receive more money from Frederick William. Then you will not have to worry about getting your money back. If you could advance me five hundred gulden, I could repay ten gulden a month, at any rate of interest you wish. My affairs are sure to improve with such aid and within a few months I will be able to repay all your kindness. I pray that you will not be upset by my confiding in you, and that you will understand that without your assistance my honor, my health, my family, and my life will be destroyed."

Wolfgang was even more frightened when Puchberg did not reply. He wrote him again and the third letter brought a hundred and fifty gulden.

He had to pay Closset in advance, and this time the doctor, who was also a Freemason, advised him to send Constanze to Baden for the cure.

"But this is impossible! It is so expensive!"

"Herr Mozart, she won't improve here."

Once again he begged Puchberg for money, explaining that the Doctor had said Baden was a matter of extreme urgency and this time he got three hundred gulden. But when Stanzi was at the health spa, a few miles outside of Vienna, he missed her poignantly and visited her often, although he couldn't afford to remain with her; as it was, her stay at Baden was reducing the money he had just borrowed at an alarming rate. However, the baths diminished her swelling, she had good color again, and she loved the atmosphere of the watering place and the sulphur springs.

When he was home he completed three of the pianoforte sonatas and one of the string quartets for Frederick William and sent them to him, but there was no more money forthcoming from the Prussian King.

At the end of the summer *Figaro* was revived at the Burgtheater by the Court theater. Da Ponte assured Wolfgang that everybody liked it now, even Joseph. Joseph, while he was upset by the fall of the Bastille and the future of his sister, who was a virtual prisoner at Versailles, had told the poeta that he liked this opera better on a second hearing.

But Wolfgang didn't believe them. Many people congratulated him on the success of *Figaro*, but it brought him no money. Yet after General Laudon – who had taken command of the army from Joseph – captured Belgrade from the Turks and with this victory

599

sealed the safety of the Empire, Joseph asked Wolfgang to appear with Da Ponte at the Hofburg.

He didn't sleep the night before, wondering what the Emperor wanted. As he entered Joseph's private audience chamber he was surprised by Joseph's appearance. The Emperor wore court dress: white silk stockings, black shoes with silver buckles, fancy silk ruffles around his neck and wrists, and the emblem of the Knight of the Garter on his chest. But Joseph's once natural rosy cheeks were faded and heavily rouged; Joseph, who had looked youthful for so long, had become an elderly man.

Da Ponte was there already and Joseph said, "I have been informed that *Le Nozze di Figaro* is returning a handsome profit. This time the public seems to find it amusing and diverting.

Wolfgang asked, "And you, sir? Have you found it to your liking?"

"I still find it frivolous. But perhaps, that is what the public needs."

Wolfgang was silent.

"We are living in difficult, anxious times. I would like to see a new opera at the Burgtheater that would be even more diverting than *Figaro*. I owe my subjects pleasant entertainment." To take their minds off the revolution brewing in France, he thought, and the cost of the Turkish war. "However, Signor poeta, it must be without *Figaro*'s social comment."

"Your Majesty, I wrote all that out!" exclaimed Da Ponte.

"And permitted *Figaro* to outwit the Count. This time I prefer an original story. Something that will suit all occasions. If it pleases, both of you will get two hundred ducats instead of the usual hundred."

That was a whole year's salary as a court composer. Wolfgang cried out, "Sir, I could supply you with such an opera each season!"

"First, let us see how this work goes. I understand that Signor poeta already has a story. Let us hope it's original, as he says."

Da Ponte began with such confidence Wolfgang was certain it wasn't original. And the librettist had gone ahead on the assumption that he would accept. Yet he couldn't refuse this opportunity. He listened carefully.

Da Ponte said, "When the elderly Don Alfonso insists that a faithful woman does not exist, his two friends, the officers Guglielmo and Ferrando, reply that their fiancées, the sisters, Fiordiligi and Dorabella, are faithful. So Don Alfonso wagers his dashing Neapolitan friends that if they follow his instructions the next twenty-four hours, he will prove that their sweethearts are unfaithful. The young officers accept his proposal. To test the constancy of their fiancées, they pretend to go off to war and return disguised as two Albanians. Attractive but unrecognizable, they court the sisters and win them. Then Guglielmo and Ferrando return as themselves and reveal that each girl has been willing to be unfaithful. But after the explanations are made, everything is forgiven."

Wolfgang had heard this tale before, it had been a well-known incident in Vienna, but when Joseph applauded, he knew he had no choice.

Da Ponte declared, as if inspired, "Sir, I will call it *Cosi fan tutte*."

"*So Do They All,*" repeated Joseph, amused. "It is a suitable title."

Da Ponte had a complete libretto ready quickly and as the people developed musically the old excitement and joy returned. Wolfgang had to care for his characters, without love and compassion they were nothing. And this was an opera devoted to love, and he wrote of devotion, parting, infidelity, and repentance with a sensuous beauty and a lyrical tenderness.

During the composing of *Cosi fan tutte*, Constanze gave birth to their fifth child, Anna Maria, who died an hour later of cramps, but he kept his sorrow and pessimism out of the score. She recovered more quickly than he expected, as if she had come to expect infant mortality with a kind of resigned inevitability, and the new opera became one of the most amorous he had written. The uglier life was, the more beautiful his music had to be. He disregarded his frequent exhaustion, the aches and chills, and pretended that only the music mattered, and wrote it from his heart.

Yet when he invited Haydn and Puchberg to hear the dress rehearsal he had qualms. They could be scandalized by the story, although he felt the music was as attractive and skillful as any he had composed.

Michael Puchberg, pot-bellied, round-faced, had no musical ability, but he was a clever merchant and a devoted musical connoisseur. He was flattered to be in the company of the two finest musicians in the Empire. He was eager to hear them discuss music, particularly their methods of composition. Instead Haydn complained about conditions at Esterházy, saying it had become a melancholy, forsaken court, while Wolfgang was telling him that Haydn was fortunate in one respect at least, Haydn had guaranteed income. They sounded more involved with money than he was.

But once the music began, Wolfgang sat like a statue while Haydn shut his eyes. Puchberg was silent, too, although he was full of questions.

When the rehearsals ended, Haydn said, "Wolfgang, your use of the vocal possibilities is extraordinary. You should be very pleased and proud."

Wolfgang beamed, but he turned to Puchberg and asked him as if his opinion was equally important. "What did you think, Michael?"

"It is music of endearment. It is full of emotion and caring despite the lightness of the text. I should think the Emperor will approve."

"If he has any sense," muttered Haydn. "Then our dear friend would have no further difficulties. But everything has to be of the moment."

"Perhaps," said Wolfgang. "Yet music has an independent life, beyond the moment, and if it is good, it will survive."

Da Ponte had just entered and he hurried to embrace Haydn as an honored guest. He nodded to Puchberg, and told Wolfgang, "The dress rehearsal went so well, it is definite that the opera will open on the 26th."

The next day, January 27, 1790, was his thirty-fourth birthday.

At the opening of *Cosi fan tutte* the Emperor informed Da Ponte and Wolfgang that he liked this *opera buffa* best of all their works. He said, "The music is delightful, and the subject is amusing and diverting."

Wolfgang believed the Emperor. For he did receive two hundred ducats for the opera. And Joseph ordered that the work be given fifteen times, and implied that he would like another of the same kind soon.

Wolfgang was elated. After all the years of struggle, he had finally convinced the Emperor of his worth as an opera composer.

Three weeks after the premiere of *Cosi fan tutte* Joseph died, and its performances were canceled to observe the period of national mourning.

EIGHTY-SEVEN

Leopold, the ruler of Tuscany and Joseph's brother, was his successor. There were many rumors about changes among the court musicians, for it was known that Leopold disapproved of most of Joseph's appointments, and Wolfgang was hopeful there might be a higher place at court for him.

When the months of mourning ended and *Cosi fan tutte* was returned to the court theater for five more performances, Wolfgang petitioned Archduke Francis – Leopold's heir and favorite, who had approved of his music in the past – for the post of assistant Kapellmeister. He stressed his experience as a composer of church music and offered his services to the royal family as a teacher. His petition was ignored.

He continued to receive his quarterly pay but it was not enough. The two hundred ducats he had received for *Cosi fan tutte* had been quickly absorbed by his debts. He tried to find pupils, but no one wanted to study with him. He composed two string quartets because Artaria said they could be sold, and so few people bought them that the sales didn't pay for the copying. Finally, he returned to Handel, composing new accompaniments for *Alexander's Feast* and *Ode for St. Cecilia* for van Swieten, and for far less gulden than he needed.

Constanze was ailing again, and only the baths at Baden helped her, and so, despite his debts, he made sure she spent the summer there. When she reproached him for being moody, he didn't tell her it was because of his own poor health and the debts. He couldn't worry her, but he was troubled that as soon as he cured himself of one ailment another occurred. He hid this from her, but he couldn't rid himself of the sadness that hung on him like a plague. Letter after letter had to be written to Puchberg begging for money. Even as he assured his friend that his prospects would improve soon, he no longer believed that himself. And the loans grew smaller. Whatever he asked for now, Puchberg sent half or less.

In September, while Stanzi and Karl were still in Baden, he sought to start a new pianoforte concerto and nothing happened. He missed them so much it was unbearable. Each time he put down a note a tear blotted it. Deciding it was the fault of their rooms, they were horribly empty without Stanzi and Karl, he rushed outside. If everything else failed, he always found a musical idea when he was walking or in motion. He stood on the Platz Am Hof and looked up at Collalto's palace, just around the corner from where he lived now, and where he had first played in Vienna. He had not performed for a Collalto in years.

When he returned to his rooms he knew he had to move. Whatever the reason, he couldn't compose in them, and without that he was lost.

The five rooms he rented on the Rauhensteingasse were more spacious, and were on the first floor, which meant less steps for Constanze to climb, and they were also near St .Stephen's and the house where he had composed *Figaro*, and where his fortunes had flourished. But the new rent was twice as high and he was even more in debt.

Leopold was to be crowned Holy Roman Emperor in Frankfurt in October, and Wolfgang decided to go there, hoping this would cause Leopold to use him.

Constanze disagreed. "Salieri already has been chosen by the court. He will certainly keep Leopold from employing you. You are foolish to take this trip. It will cost more money and you will just be an onlooker."

"Everyone of consequence will be there. The most important titles and the greatest wealth in Europe. I will surely come back with an important commission, whether or not the new Emperor uses me."

The adventure of traveling brought color to his cheeks Constanze hadn't seen since he had left for Prussia. But to pay for this expedition, for neither Puchberg nor Hofdemel would finance it, he had to pawn their silverware and silver plate. "But I will get it out the instant I return," he assured a distressed Constanze. "I am still well known in Frankfurt."

He met many old friends there, but Leopold did not use him. With Salieri in his retinue, he had no need of a Mozart, whom he regarded as a beggar. None of the music in the coronation was by Wolfgang.

He was granted permission to give a concert, after the coronation was over and most of the rich, distinguished guests had left. His two pianoforte concertos were praised, but there was no money. A second concert that had been scheduled had to be canceled for lack of interest. Although he played in Mannheim, Munich, and Mainz, and earned enough to get back to Vienna, what mattered was his reunions with the Wendlings and the Cannabichs. Yet amid all the fond reminiscences, he wondered whether he had aged as much as they had.

Wolfgang was away for six weeks. "What was accomplished?" He repeated Constanze's question on his return in November, for her implication was clear, and replied, "Everywhere I went I was honored, acclaimed, and popular, but the people were even more parsimonious than the Viennese."

There was a letter from London awaiting him. Robert May O'Reilly of the London Opera Company had written him in French: "To Monsieur Mozart Celebrated Composer: Through persons attached to His Royal Highness, the Prince of Wales, the young but eminent opera composer, Stephen Storace, and your former pupil, and the equally young but brilliant prima donna, Ann Storace, I am informed that you plan to visit England. Since I have been appointed to my position as Manager of the London Opera Company with the purpose of finding people of talent personally, I offer you, Sir, such a place as few Composers have had in England. If you could come to London by the end of December, 1790, and remain until the end of June, 1791, and compose at least two operas, serious or comic, as the management should choose, I am prepared to offer you three hundred pounds sterling. You will also be free to compose pieces for any other concert halls, only opera houses are excepted. If this proposal is agreeable to you and you are in a position to accept, please do me the favor of answering by return post, and this letter will serve you as a Contract."

Wolfgang was elated by this offer and was astonished that Constanze didn't share his feelings. He cried out, "Three hundred pounds for two operas is far more than I receive for an opera in Vienna. If there are any more operas here, which is unlikely, for Leopold doesn't like them," and she retorted, "How can you be so sure you can depend on England?"

"O'Reilly is the personal representative of the Prince of Wales."

"You think he is better than any of the others who have promised you much and given you little?"

"I was a great success in London as a child. And all the letters I have received from my English friends insist that London will welcome me with open arms."

That was the difficulty. Ann Storace was too great an admirer. But she said, "I'm afraid of the English weather. Even the Storaces say that it is too damp, and I need warm, dry weather, like Baden."

Sometimes, he thought, she was more attached to Baden than anything else. "We will be there in spring and summer, when it will be warm."

"And in December, if you wish to fulfill the contract. Why, just to cross the English channel, I hear, is a dreadful experience."

"My whole family did it without any danger."

"And were very seasick, your father said. And you went in April."

If he only had Papa now, he thought, Papa knew how to manage, knew all the pitfalls of foreign travel. "Don't you want to go, Stanzi?"

"It isn't that." It was many other things, Ann Storace, the dangers and difficulties of travel, and she didn't enjoy the adventure as he did, but feared the risks. "We can't afford it."

"I'll raise the money," he said with a confidence he didn't feel.

"You will have to. We have nothing else to pawn."

He couldn't reply. He hadn't returned with enough money to redeem their silver. And he would need at least a thousand gulden for the trip.

Nobody would lend him that much, not even Hofdemel or Puchberg. He offered a promissory note against his English salary in return for a loan of a thousand gulden and he didn't even get an answer. He was not surprised by Hofdemel's behavior, but Puchberg's shocked him.

The last two weeks he had not seen him at any of the lodge meetings, and finally, he did something he hated to do, that was very painful, he went to Puchberg's house and was told that his friend was out of Vienna on business and no one knew where the merchant had gone or when he would return.

A few days later a short, heavy-set man rushed into Wolfgang's music room and announced, "I am Salomon of London, and I am prepared to offer you whatever O'Reilly offered, and a little more. Herr Haydn has agreed to come to England, and we would want you for the next winter."

"Haydn?" Wolfgang was surprised. His friend hadn't told him.

"Yes. You know of the death of Prince Esterházy, don't you?"

He had heard about it, but in the rush of his own affairs he hadn't realized what it meant to his dear friend.

"With the death of Esterházy, Haydn is able to play wherever he desires." Johann Peter Salomon said gloatingly, "Joseph Haydn and Wolfgang Mozart, what a catch that will be. Your tour as a child is still recalled fondly."

"What about traveling expenses? I can't go on a promise."

"We would give you five hundred gulden. The same as Haydn."

"But I also have a wife and a child."

For the first time the German-born English impresario lost some of his enthusiasm. "We can't provide for an entire family. But if you

606

ınsist on taking them, I can give you another hundred gulden for travel."

"And when I am there?"

"What did O'Reilly offer? A hundred pounds an opera?"

"Three hundred pounds for two operas."

Salomon looked skeptical, but said, "I will give you two hundred pounds an opera, to be paid on the receipt of each work."

Wolfgang sighed. It was a handsome offer, and painful to decline.

"What do you say, Herr Kapellmeister? I have the contract with me."

"I will have to think it over." He couldn't go without Stanzi or Karl.

"I will have to know soon. Herr Haydn and I are leaving for England in a few days, about the middle of December."

Stanzi had a new reason for not going to England. She said, "I'm pregnant."

He started to kiss her, then paused. "But I've been home just four weeks."

"Give me a kiss," she pleaded. "Don't you trust me?"

"Is this an excuse to stay here, then go to Baden in the summer?"

"Wolfgang how could you!" She began to weep.

For once, tears didn't move him. "How can you be sure you are pregnant?"

"There are no traces of my period. And I always know when it is coming a few days in advance. Oh, I'm pregnant all right. Remember, this will be the sixth time. I know all the symptoms."

"In four weeks?"

"What are you trying to say?"

He couldn't say what he was thinking. He had been away for almost two months. And Constanze liked to flirt. She was flattered by other men's attentions. But that was not enough to be suspicious. There was a better way of judging. At the moment the vital thing was that Constanze had to be treated with great care to preserve her and the child.

Haydn spent his last day in Vienna with Wolfgang. They strolled through the inner city, so they could be alone with each other, along the Graben and on to the Kohlmarkt, passing a peasant carrying a pig under one arm and a chicken under the other, beggars willing to recite anything for a kreutzer, and finally, when the crowd grew too thick to walk in privacy, they entered a small café and sat in a corner where no one would see them.

An elderly violinist was playing music from *Cosi fan tutte* as if it belonged to him, and when he finished he went around the café for tips, and when Haydn complimented him on his choice of music, the violinist said, "You have a good ear, sir," and added, when Wolfgang gave him a gulden, "And you are a gentleman of taste, too, sir."

Haydn was more excited than Wolfgang had ever seen him. "Wolfgang, I'm free. I can go where I please, do what I please. For thirty years I have been someone's slave, but now I'm free."

"You really are, aren't you?"

"Yes." Then Haydn's voice grew solemn. "Prince Esterházy's wife died in February, almost at the same time as Joseph, and the grief-stricken Prince went into a shocking decline and passed away six months later. His son, who doesn't care for music, has released me from the Esterházy service, but with a yearly pension of fourteen hundred gulden to protect me against want. All I am required to do is to call myself, 'Kapellmeister to Prince Esterházy.' But what about your prospects. Salomon told me that he has made you a handsome offer. Why didn't you accept it?"

Wolfgang couldn't talk about his impoverished state to Papa Joseph. It would make Haydn feel guilty, Haydn would want to help him, and he couldn't put him in a precarious situation, it was bad enough that he was. He said, "There are many reasons."

"Salomon is giving me five hundred gulden to travel. If that isn't enough for you, I could help. My wants are modest, and Karl is like my own son. How much would you need?"

"No, no, no! It is not a question of money!"

"I have so many offers, Wolfgang, it is wonderful."

Wolfgang thought wryly, and I have none. What had he done wrong? He didn't consider himself Papa Joseph's superior, but they were equals.

"The moment it was known I was available the King of Naples wanted me, other courts. It is good to be a musician, good to be wanted."

"You've earned such respect and admiration." He would miss the set of Papa Joseph's jaw, long like Mamma's, the warm cadence of his speech.

"But what about yourself? You would be a great success in London."

"Perhaps I will be able to go next year. Or the year after."

Haydn shook his head sadly. "I have a feeling that if you don't go now, you never will." Wolfgang looked much older these days. His fair hair had gray in it. His once genial, lively features had an almost perpetual cast of sorrow. He was always tired. "Salomon tells me that the Storaces, who are great admirers of your work, are a huge success in London. As you would be. What is the real reason you can't go? Perhaps I can solve it."

"I wish you could. But it is not a matter of aid, but of circumstance.

Constanze is indisposed again, and you know how ill she was last year, and I just can't risk her health with such an arduous journey."

"Why don't you go alone? When you are settled you can send for her."

"She would never make the trip alone. And after our first child died when we left him in someone else's hands, I vowed that I would never leave another child with someone else, except my father, for any length of time."

Haydn was silent. He didn't agree with Wolfgang. Sometimes he sensed that Constanze used her illness to serve her own purposes, but if he suggested that to Wolfgang it would cause him too much pain. Wolfgang had to have faith in those he loved, reflected Haydn, Wolfgang had been raised in such an atmosphere of love, and his nature had blossomed in it, that no matter what else happened, love was a nourishment he couldn't exist without.

Wolfgang said, "But it is not a matter of life and death."

"I hear Salieri is resigning, that Da Ponte is talking of going to England."

"Ever since Joseph died there have been these rumors."

"It is more than rumor. Leopold simply does not care for music."

"Joseph at least, while he was not the musical expert he thought he was, had some knowledge of counterpoint, but in Leopold's chambers they play such music that his dogs would like to run away from it."

"I hope you haven't said that to anyone else."

"I haven't. But it is true. Now everything will have to be stamped with Leopold's initials. He has been appointed by God. Oh, the Hapsburgs rule by divine right, a rare gift, that they have bestowed on themselves."

"Such disrespect could ruin whatever prospects you have."

"How can I regard them as gods when I have seen them at close range all my life."

"Have you ever regretted leaving Colloredo and Salzburg?"

"Never! Not once!" Wolfgang laughed. "Salzburg still regards a musician as an ass for the Archbishop to ride on, otherwise superfluous, while Colloredo, who acts as if he is going to live forever, now has the ideal court, no theater, no opera, and actually, no music worth hearing."

"I'm taking the quartets you wrote for me. The English will like them."

"That's more than I can say for the Viennese. I composed three symphonies last summer, and I cannot persuade anyone to play them."

"Disgraceful!" Haydn was shocked.

"My music grows in the silences. That is when I hear it best."

"If I were only sure we would see each other again. . ."

Wolfgang realized that Haydn, usually sanguine, was as pessimistic as himself about their meeting again. He cried out, "I'm afraid for you, you've never travelled, you know so few languages, not a word of English, and it is a long, hard journey for a man of fifty-eight."

"I've given it a lot of thought. I must go."

As they walked back to Haydn's carriage which was waiting in front of Wolfgang's rooms, they talked about trivial things to hide the depth of their feeling, but when it came time to say goodbye, Haydn said intensely, "When it is cold and wet and I am lonesome I will dream of listening to *Figaro*, and your other masterpieces, and then I shall have such pleasure."

"Oh, Joseph, what am I going to do without you?"

"What is troubling you? That we haven't discussed?"

For a moment Wolfgang thought of telling him about Constanze and the occasional doubts whether it was his child, but no, he told himself, that was unfair, he had no proof. But there were some things he could talk about. "Perhaps God wants us to know great happiness and deep sorrow, so that we learn this is the nature of the world."

Haydn was listening intently.

"In a whole year, Papa Joseph, I have composed just two string quartets, and one string quintet. When I was eight I composed more."

"Gentle Wolfgang, except with bad music and bad musicians. Then you are merciless. Even with yourself. Good God, you have such compassion for others. Have some for yourself. You will compose again. You must."

"It would be too cruel to be forced to stop now."

"You won't. I will return from England in a year or two, or you will come yourself, and we will have many new compositions to show each other."

But now Wolfgang's premonition that he would never see Haydn again was overwhelming.

They embraced. Haydn murmured, "Goodbye. . ."

"Joseph, I'm afraid this is the last time we will see each other!"

"That would be unfair. Shameful."

But there was no putting off the parting. Then Haydn was gone.

EIGHTY-EIGHT

===

1791 began more favorably. Joseph Bähr, a clarinet virtuoso, wrote Wolfgang that he was giving a concert in Vienna and added, "I will be honored if you perform, for this concert is to be devoted to your music."

The invitation, and Haydn's faith, started him composing again. The thought of appearing before an audience once more infused him with energy, and he plunged into his first pianoforte concerto in three years. And Constanze, who was pregnant as she had told him, sat by his side as he wished, determined to prove that she was a good wife, and so that when he wanted to stop working he could chat with her. There was a letter from Haydn, notifying him of the latter's safe arrival and begging him to come to England as soon as possible, and he hoped that Wolfgang had resumed composing, for there was a demand for Mozart music in England.

"Gentle Wolfgang," Haydn had said, and he kept this in the forefront of his mind as he constructed this concerto in B Flat. The shape itself had a deceptive simplicity, with a surface that shone and sang. But the substance underneath was eloquent in its beauty and luminousness.

Which, he reflected as he composed, existed nowhere else in the world these turbulent and barbaric days. Soldiers were everywhere in Vienna now, and the Emperor was talking about saving Europe from the revolution spreading in France. Wolfgang kept informed, for if war broke out with France, it would be difficult to go to England, but he did not allow this world to master him. His concerto did not weep or lament man's fate, or summon divine guidance with grandiose chords. No one would ever know from his music how ill and despondent he had been, and often still was. There were moments when he doubted he would have any energy left for another concerto, but to think of this work as a farewell was sentimental.

Yet he loved this instrument so! What a delight it was! To lose it was unthinkable. But it was the actual hearing that was best.

The concert was given in the hall of a restaurant and he played as he always had, with a lovely sonority that refined the music to the highest elegance, and so the orchestra, pianoforte, and soloist were one.

The hall however, was half empty, although Joseph Bähr was well known and played brilliantly, and Wolfgang received just twenty-five gulden.

He felt there would be no more concerts, but he hid his pessimism, and to show the Emperor that he could be of service, too, he composed two dozen German dances, minuets, and contradances for use at the court, and did not receive an acknowledgment.

Still resolved to be practical and concealing his dismay, he wrote three little songs for children, a fantasia for a mechanical organ, two subtly wrought string quartets, and while each piece was quite different from any other, they were satisfying, for he was paid for them.

He could not stop composing now, even when there was no commission, ideas came to him in such profusion. It was as if there was not a moment to lose, he must express now whatever was in him. These impulses were so powerful he began an opera score in his head, although he had no libretto.

Da Ponte was banished from Vienna for offending the Emperor; Salieri resigned from the Imperial service; Orsini-Rosenberg was dismissed; the new first Kapellmeister became Joseph Weigl, a mediocrity.

That appointment ended whatever hope Wolfgang had had of becoming Leopold's Kapellmeister. When he heard that Leopold Hoffmann, the Kapellmeister of St. Stephen's, was ailing and might not live much longer, he applied for the post of Hoffmann's unpaid assistant.

After a period of anxious waiting – his application was turned down at first – he was given this post by decree of the Vienna city council.

Wolfgang was pleased, but Constanze reminded him that once again he was giving his services away; she read aloud the part of the decree that proved this, *"To assist the said Kapellmeister, Herr Hoffman, in his duties without compensation, substitute for him when he is unable to appear..."*

"And," interrupted Wolfgang, "if the post falls vacant, I will inherit it and the salary of two thousand gulden. More than enough to live on."

Wolfgang had a new pupil in composition, Franz Xaver Sussmayer, and the stocky twenty-five-year-old musician also became his errand boy, valet, arranger, and the affectionate butt of many of Wolfgang's jokes.

Constanze was large with child, and she said it was due in August or September, she wasn't sure, and Wolfgang was more loving than ever.

When she left for Baden early in June, with considerable self-satisfaction, as if she had the world in her hands, he was glad that she was happy. He had to write Puchberg four begging letters before he was able to borrow enough gulden to send her to Baden, and then Puchberg had sent only half of what he had requested, but he assured himself that he would manage somehow, and he wrote her tender letters almost every day and missed her very much.

For relaxation, Wolfgang went to the theater often, and at the Freihaus Theater auf der Wieden, he saw its current success, *Anton bei Hofe, oder Das Namensfest*. He thought it a dull piece, although it had been written, directed, and produced by an old friend, Emanuel Schikaneder.

But Schikaneder insisted that he sup with him after the performance.

As the two men sat in the dressing room backstage, Wolfgang sensed that his friend had a special reason for inviting him. Schikaneder was sober, realistic, without any of the false optimism that usually dominated his behavior. Yet it was natural for Schikaneder to be flamboyant, reflected Wolfgang. Five years older than himself, the actor-director-producer-librettist had had an adventurous existence. The handsome, strongly built Schikaneder had done everything from Gluck's *Orpheus*, Shakespeare's *Hamlet* and *King Lear*, Molière's *The Imaginary Invalid*, to the lowest of comedies and the most blatant pageantry. Yet while he loved playing the buffoon and was gifted at pantomime, he had a fine speaking voice – he was the best Hamlet that Wolfgang had seen – and was an effective singer and a skillful director and producer.

Wolfgang was relieved that Schikaneder didn't ask him what he thought about tonight's entertainment, but said, "As you know, Mozart, ever since I met you when I was playing in Salzburg, just before you left for Vienna, I have admired your music."

Wolfgang wondered what Schikaneder wanted. For nothing, no doubt.

"Have you ever thought of writing for the popular theater?"

At this point he would write for anything, he thought, if it would get produced, but he must sound indifferent, otherwise Schikaneder would have too great an advantage. He said, "It would depend on the libretto."

"As you may know, I have written several."

"What do you have in mind?"

"Our greatest success has been *Oberon*, with a text by Gieseke, and music by Wranitzky. But neither of them is a Schikaneder or a Mozart."

"I have heard *Oberon*. It wasn't much."

"Our audiences loved it. They love all these fairy tales. And mine, with your music, could be charming, even moving, and certainly, amusing."

Schikaneder elaborated on his idea, and Wolfgang realized that once he affiliated with him, it could be the end of ever advancing at court. The Theater auf der Wieden was not much better than a barn, while his work had been produced in the best theaters in Vienna. And Schikaneder, once he was involved in comedy, often resorted to trivia and vulgarity. But while it was impossible to know whether the charlatan or the artist would dominate, he had the capacity to do excellent work.

"What do you think, Mozart?" Schikaneder had just finished.

"It is an astonishing tale." He had missed most of the details, they had become so complicated, but perhaps Schikaneder could improve them. "Why don't you simplify it, and then we can discuss it further."

"In addition to giving you a hundred ducats for your music, you will get a share of the profits. I am a human being, not an Emperor."

Now Wolfgang was eager for a workable text of Schikaneder's idea.

The libretto that he was given several weeks later was confused and contradictory, and he was sure that much of it had been taken from other sources but it contained ideas that stirred him musically. He liked the fairy-tale tone – as a child in England he had created his own kingdom when the world had disappointed him – and now he could do it again.

Schikaneder called their work *The Magic Flute*, saying, "It is vital to have magic in the title, magic operas are the rage, and flute suggests music." And Wolfgang agreed: the musical sound of the title was effective.

Wolfgang was amused by the character of Papageno, and he liked the idealism of Sarastro and the faith of the romantic hero, Tamino. And it was an opportunity to express his own ideas without the threat of Imperial suppression. The librettist, who was a lodge brother, had given the text suggestions of Freemasonry, with its stress of tolerance, fellowship, and the brotherhood of man, and that appealed to Wolfgang. The world might be decaying into an age without honor, but when the audience heard his music it should be clear that human dignity could only be achieved by rejecting pride and behaving ethically. Yet when Schikaneder asked him what he thought of the revised text, he replied, "If this fails, don't blame me, I've never composed a magic opera in my life."

Wolfgang's concern eased Schikaneder's concern. The composer's anxiety should force him to make the score work. Schikaneder said, "I intend to open my autumn season with it. Can you have the music ready in time?" Leopold Mozart had said his son was inclined to procrastinate.

"The score will be done for the first rehearsal. Perhaps sooner."

Yet Wolfgang, every chance he got, visited Constanze in Baden, until Schikaneder provided him with a garden house where the composer could work in comfort. And where Schikaneder could watch him and prod him.

The garden house was a small, wooden, one-room cottage in the courtyard of the theater, cool and rustic, with a pianoforte to compose on, and Wolfgang was delighted with it.

He spent most of his time here, when he wasn't in Baden. The music for *The Magic Flute* came steadily, and some of the ideas that had occupied his mind the past few months were suitable. Schikaneder had given him twenty-five ducats to seal their agreement, and had promised him twenty-five more on the completion of the score, and fifty when the opera opened, but the money he had received had gone to pay for Constanze and Karl's stay in Baden, and he was still heavily in debt. He continued to hide this from her, for her confinement was approaching, although it was only July. Often his debts made him melancholy, and then he felt, as he sat at the desk that Schikaneder had supplied, that he was simply puttering. Yet gradually the subject enlarged in his mind, and from years of skillful practice the structure became defined, and the whole concept. So that he could survey it, he reflected, like a fine picture or a lovely statue, at a glance. He did not hear in his imagination the parts successively, but all at once. This reassured him. Now he knew that it didn't matter when he wrote down his ideas, that he could take them out of his bag of memory whenever he had to. The committing to paper would be done quickly enough, for once the music was finished in his imagination, it rarely differed on paper. And as this process went on, as it had in the past, he knew that whatever hodgepodge Schikaneder served him, the music would have a unity, and a unifying nature, it would be *Mozartish*.

One day while he was about to leave the Rauhensteingasse to work at the garden house, a stranger accosted him at the door. The tall, thin man regarded him gravely and asked, "You are Mozart, aren't you?"

"Yes." Wolfgang was taken aback by the stranger's appearance. He was so gaunt he looked like a scarecrow, he was garbed all in somber gray, and his gravity was frightening. "What do you want?"

"Could you write a requiem?"

"For whom?"

"He must remain anonymous."

But this was incredible. Was this stranger an emissary of the devil?

"It must be a mass for the dead." The man grew grim. "A funeral mass."

A chill went through Wolfgang. Suddenly he had a presentiment of his own death and the feeling that the stranger had come to warn him of it.

"This requiem must be composed in the utmost secrecy. No one, and certainly none of your friends, must know of this." Wolfgang was about to decline when the stranger added, "You will be paid twenty-five ducats when I return to make it official, and twenty-five when you finish."

"How do I know you will find me? I am not here much."

"I will find you," the stranger said portentously. "I always do."

Long after this mysterious gray stranger was gone, Wolfgang stood and pondered his presence. He had not felt well today. He had worked at the pianoforte many hours yesterday, trying out themes, and he had awakened this morning with swollen hands and it had been difficult and painful to move his fingers. Gradually some ease of movement had returned to them, but it had left him apprehensive about his health. The more he thought about the gray stranger's somber expression, his grim voice, his icy eyes, the more he wondered if this forbidding figure was a messenger of death.

A few days later, on July 26, Constanze gave birth to their sixth child, a son, whom they named Franz Xaver. But the date disturbed Wolfgang. He had been away from Vienna until November 10, and thus, if the infant was his, it had been born in a little over eight months.

Yet Constanze looked so happy, giving him Franz Xaver to kiss, as if the baby was her present to him, he could not charge her with anything.

But ever since he had been asked to compose the requiem, an oppressive melancholy had pervaded him. Several times since he had been visited by the mysterious stranger, his feet had swollen as well as his hands, and while, in each case, that had gone away with walking and playing, he was ashamed to let her see his heart, it was cold, as cold as ice. He felt as if he had eaten of a fatal root, and that some-how, it had poisoned him.

Perhaps he had doubted her, he told himself, because his brain was overwrought. He could not accuse her when he had no proof. It would sound pathetic, absurd. And she would never forgive him.

The infant moved so energetically in his arms he almost dropped him. This was a healthy one, he thought. This one would live.

There was no sign of the stranger the next week and Wolfgang had returned to the composing of *Die Zauberflöte*, when he received an unexpected commission. Leopold, who had been crowned Emperor of the Holy Roman Empire in Frankfurt, was now to be crowned Emperor of Bohemia at Prague. The Bohemian nobles who were arranging the coronation ceremonies and the festival opera to celebrate them, recalling Mozart' successes in Prague, asked him to compose the score of the coronation opera they had chosen.

La Clemenza di Tito shouted the praises of the Roman Emperor Titus for exhibiting clemency and magnanimity. Wolfgang found the text stilted, more spectacle than drama. But it served the purposes of the Bohemian nobles, he noted, it flattered Leopold.

Two hundred ducats came with the commission, on the assump-tion that he couldn't refuse. "And they are right," he told Constanze. "There isn't even time to hesitate. I have just twenty-eight days to compose the score, travel to Prague, rehearse the singers, and see that every note is in place." He ignored her warning that he was already overworked.

In fourteen hectic, feverish days, often working all night, he com-pleted the twenty-six numbers needed for *La Clemenza di Tito*. After leaving the children with Fräu Weber, he prepared to set out for Prague with Constanze and Süssmayer, who was to write the secco recitatives for this opera.

A few hours before he was to depart, while he was standing out-side his house to get a breath of air before collecting all the sheets of his score, the gray stranger approached him, as if this gaunt man had been waiting for him, handed him twenty-five gulden, and said, "To seal the bargain."

"How did you know that I was leaving!" exclaimed Wolfgang.

The stranger smiled mysteriously and wouldn't explain. Anton Leitgeb was performing this mission for his friend, Count Walsegg. Walsegg, who owned the mansion in which Puchberg resided, was able to keep informed of Mozart's whereabouts through Puchberg. What the Count had not told anyone except Leitgeb was that he needed a requiem to mourn the death of his wife earlier in the year. And having heard from Puchberg how desperately Mozart required

617

money, he had decided to pass off the composer's music as his own. It was a common custom. Everyone would praise his talent as a composer. Leitgeb was the ideal man to be his messenger. Leitgeb loved to be mysterious, to terrify people a little. The envoy said theatrically this would make Mozart's requiem sad, solemn, and mournful.

"And where should I deliver the requiem when it is finished?"

"I will know when it is finished. Then I will come for it."

"But I will be in Prague the next couple of weeks, and on my return I have to complete my other opera which is opening in a month."

"I know that, too." He stared at him blankly. "I trust this music will be godly and without lust. Otherwise, there could be dire consequences."

EIGHTY-NINE

The Magic Flute opened on September 30 as planned, after Wolfgang worked furiously to make that possible. But as he walked backstage to see if the cast was ready, for he was conducting the première, he wondered if Die Zauberflöte would suffer the same fate as La Clemenza di Tito. The coronation opera was still playing in Prague, but while the score was stately and eloquent as befitted the subject, the work had been received with indifference. The Emperor's Spanish-born Empress, who had disliked Figaro for what she had considered its insolence, had dismissed La Clemenza di Tito as "German garbage". This comment was widely agreed with, although Wolfgang thought the opera had some of the best music he had written.

He paused in the wings and stared at the audience, and had a terrible moment of consternation. The Theater auf der Wieden had a shabby stage, its scenery was makeshift, when the wind blew he could smell the stench from the river, and this small, cramped theater in the ugly Friehaus suburb was hard to reach. He saw Constanze in a box with van Swieten, Wetzlar, and Puchberg, but no Emperor and few nobles. This audience was different from those who had attended his other operas; they expected magic and tricks. Yet he had composed each note to fit the characters and the story as he felt it, not for any superficial theatrical effect.

Schikaneder asked him anxiously, "How does it look, Mozart?"

"It is your theater, you should be able to tell better than I can."

"They have never had this kind of music before. One moment you give them something light and gay, the next it is solemn and majestic, almost spiritual in its intention. They won't know what to think. Once an audience expects one kind of show, they become offended if you give them another kind. I hope the music won't ruin the story."

Wolfgang smiled to himself. He was not sure the story made sense, but his music did. He said, "You have a good role."

"Papageno is fine, but he is so different from Sarastro."

"It should work. I have put almost everything I know into this score." This would demonstrate he was still Mozart despite all the difficulties.

Schikaneder shrugged. He couldn't tell the composer how worried he had been that Mozart would fall ill and would be unable to complete the score. During the last week of rehearsals Mozart had taken medicine to ease his pain; often he had seemed dull and sad, yet he had worked around the clock. And now, with the opening near, his eyes glowed with animation.

But as Wolfgang knocked on Anna Gottlieb's dressing room door, he had some doubts that it was wise to visit her. After she had been cast in the role of the heroine, Pamina, she had brought him two carnations in a little flower vase. He had been touched by her gift, and she had become a pretty seventeen-year-old young lady. He had placed the flowers on his table in the garden house while he had worked on *Die Zauberflöte* the last frantic weeks. There was also an unopened bud that seemed about to sprout, and he watered the flowers carefully and placed them wherever there was sun so that they would continue to bloom and the bud would sprout. But gradually the flowers faded, then died, while the bud never bloomed. Yet her devotion had helped him compose. He knew he loved Stanzi as much as ever, but there was a sweetness about Anna Gottlieb that was almost irresistible.

Her face lit up when she saw who it was. He took a small carnation which he had bought just before coming to the theater and handed it to her, saying, "It's the bud. It blossomed finally." He hoped God would forgive this little lie, she looked so happy taking it.

Anna pressed the flower to her lips and seemed on the verge of tears. Then she glanced at him with a sudden fantastic hope – perhaps he did care for her after all, now that she was no longer a little girl.

He said, "You are my good luck piece, Anna, as you were in *Figaro*."

Her skin reddened and he had a sudden hunger to fondle it, to feel its softness against his cheeks. But he was twice her age, and it would hurt Stanzi. She said, "Your music is so moving, so expressive, Maestro. I hope and pray that I will do it justice."

"Your aria, *Ach, ich fuhl's*, is one I feel deeply and intensely."

"I do, too, Maestro!" she cried out. She held out her hand.

He ignored it. "You must always be charming and admirable."

She asked him to put the flower in a small vase on her dressing room table and said, "You were kind enough, Maestro, to say I was your good luck piece, and I will treasure that and this flower as long as I live."

Anna stood close to him, blushing and timid, with an exquisite profile, a poetic vocalist, with a voice of immaculate clarity, which she used with intelligence. He had lingered with her from tenderness and pity, and from his own need to have emotion he could trust, but suddenly, for this instant at least, he loved her. They were exactly the same height now, and as he stepped toward her and kissed her fully on the lips he felt her tremble. Then, as she stared at him with as radiant an expression as he had ever seen, he hurried out before he committed himself further.

He conducted with a buoyant enthusiasm and Anna was a lyrical joy, singing with warmth and ease. And Schikaneder's Papageno was a comic triumph. It was the one role Wolfgang was sure the audience loved. Papageno's mixture of slyness and frailty was something everyone in the audience could understand. Schikaneder's performance evoked much laughter.

Yet at the end of *The Magic Flute*, while Schikaneder was applauded loudly, the other performers were greeted only politely. Wolfgang sensed that the audience was disappointed by the seriousness of much of the music, that they had expected uninterrupted comedy, that they were not accustomed to liking what they did not expect. Stanzi was telling Puchberg that if *The Magic Flute* was a success she would be able to go to Baden again, for then Wolfgang could afford it, and he winced – now Puchberg would never lend him any more money. Wetzlar was strangely silent and when he asked what was wrong, Wetzlar said, "I have to return to the army. With the situation deteriorating in France, the Emperor is talking of attacking France to rescue his sister, and I am one of the suppliers of arms to the army." And van Swieten insisted that he read a symphony the Baron had just completed, which he took unwillingly. He never could say no, but van Swieten had no talent, and perhaps it would be better to tell him so.

The next day Wolfgang returned to the requiem, but it remained an eerie, oppressive kind of commission. He felt caught in a conflict between sun and fog. There were moments when it was as if he was composing the requiem for himself, and he shaped the first movement with resignation and a touch of rebellion instead of prayer. Then suddenly, Schikaneder paid him the fifty ducats that was still owed him for *Die Zauberflöte* and he was able to send Stanzi back to Baden, which had become her great desire. It was after the season, but she insisted that she needed the baths, and so, while he didn't want her to go, he couldn't refuse her.

He couldn't join her. In addition to the requiem he had a commission for a clarinet concerto and a small cantata for the Freemasons. *The Magic Flute* had become a popular success and Schikaneder said, "We must write another opera. Schikaneder and Mozart. I will find a libretto soon."

Wolfgang's favorite pastime became attendance at the opera and enjoying the pleasure of the audiences. One evening when Papageno was supposed to play the glockenspiel – actually this was done backstage – Wolfgang decided to play a trick. As Schikaneder paused, preparing for his supposed performance on the glockenspiel, Wolfgang played an arpeggio.

Startled, Schikaneder stared into the wings and saw Wolfgang. But now when he pretended to play the glockenspiel, Wolfgang didn't and there was a heavy silence. Then as Schikaneder stood there, Wolfgang played a few notes. Suddenly Schikaneder hit the glockenspiel and shouted, "Shut up!"

Everybody roared with laughter, and Wolfgang was gratified that many of the audience were aware for the first time that Schikaneder was not playing the instrument himself, and who had really written the music.

A week later Wolfgang, hearing that Salieri desired to hear *The Magic Flute,* invited him to be his guest. He called in a carriage for Salieri and the latter's mistress, Caterina Cavalieri, who had starred in Wolfgang's operas, and drove them to the theater and his box. And while Wolfgang was determined to be gracious, he was surprised by Salieri's generosity.

The slight, dark, animated Salieri said that he liked everything about *Die Zauberflöte*. He told Wolfgang, "The theater is charming, so intimate, so good for your opera, Maestro! It is wonderful entertainment!" He listened as if transfixed and after each number exclaimed, "Bravo!"

At the end he thanked Wolfgang for inviting him and Madame Cavalieri, and said if the Maestro could join them for supper they would be honored.

Salieri's apartments were on the Kohlmarkt, in the same section where Da Ponte, Stephanie, and Metastasio had lived. They were large, luxurious rooms, and an obvious imitation of the Hofburg. The white walls had panels of a deep red wood with gilt trimmings. There were also parquet floors, ceiling-high windows, and crystal chandeliers in each room.

Salieri said that he would supervise the repast himself – he was proud of his cooking. But Salieri ate virtually nothing, although what he served was appetizing, and he insisted that Mozart have everything. Cavalieri nibbled, but she, too, watched rather than ate.

It was very late when Wolfgang reached the Rauhensteingasse. He was in high spirits, the evening had gone very well, perhaps Salieri wasn't vicious after all. The theater had been full and Schikaneder was certain that *The Magic Flute* would run indefinitely, and had told Salieri, too, who had applauded and cried, "Fine!" But for a moment, thought Wolfgang, Salieri had looked disconcerted, worried. Then, all at once, Wolfgang wondered if he had overdone the eating. Suddenly he was dizzy, nauseous, vomiting. He was unable to sleep the rest of the night, and the pain didn't go away. By morning it had become a dull ache in his stomach and he had a feeling that Salieri had been playing a game with him. His tongue had a strange flavor. When he tried to eat breakfast he vomited again.

But he had work to do. By a tremendous effort of his will he sat at his desk and worked on the clarinet concerto. He fought with himself not to be nervous or irritable – that would harm the piece – and wrote music of an unearthly beauty.

The next time he ate he was able to keep the food down, but the dull ache in his stomach remained. He drove himself harder then, but as he was finishing the clarinet concerto he fainted. When he recovered consciousness, he was deeply frightened.

He summoned Doctor Closset, who thought the fainting was due to eye strain. "You work too much at night, Herr Kapellmeister." And when he asked, "Could I have eaten something at Salieri's that poisoned me?" the doctor smiled skeptically and replied, "Artists have vivid imaginations, you must not permit yours to run away with you. You are overworked, overwrought. You need rest more than anything else."

"But I have to compose. And it can't wait."

"It must wait. Where is Fräu Mozart?"

"In Baden. But don't write her. I will rest. I don't want to worry her." Yet he yearned so to touch someone he loved. He had a dreadful premonition again that the gray messenger was an omen of death, and that when the stranger discovered that he was ill he would come for him.

The next few days Wolfgang tried to cure himself by resting as much as possible, eating with great care, and while the pain didn't vanish, he was able to work. He conducted his new cantata at the dedication of a new Masonic lodge, and while he got dizzy and thought he would faint, he managed to finish without such a disaster.

Van Swieten, who was in the audience, was shocked by his appearance. Wolfgang was pallid, drawn, emaciated, his nose had become prominent by contrast with his shrunken face; the composer had a very distracted air.

"Are you ill?" asked van Swieten.

"A temporary indisposition. I will be better with rest."

"Have you read my symphony?"

He had, but should he tell him? Then, filled with a fatalism that it wouldn't matter, he hadn't much longer to live, he said, "Yes."

"Did you like it?"

"Dear Baron, you know I treasure your friendship."

"You didn't like it. Why?"

"Do you really want to hear the truth?"

"Of course I do. I always want my friends to be honest with me."

Wolfgang wasn't so certain, but he ventured on. "Please do not be angry, your symphony is well intended, but it is too crowded with ideas."

Van Swieten stood there, snapping his fingers, not uttering a word.

"My dear friend, I would not, for all the world, have spoken out so candidly, if I could have supposed that this would offend you."

"I'm not offended, just surprised. I worked very hard on this music."

"That is evident. The structure is sound."

"Then what is wrong with my composing?"

"Some compose correctly enough, but with other people's ideas, not possessing any themselves. Others, who have ideas of their own, do not understand how to treat them and master them. The last is your case. But please, do not be angry. In criticism, as in composing, I must show myself as I am, or I must hold my tongue and throw my pen aside."

"May I have the score. Now!"

Wolfgang could feel contempt in van Swieten as the latter surveyed his untidy rooms. Without a woman's presence, they had become disorderly. He could see the verdict in van Swieten's disapproving gaze. The Baron was a stickler for such things. Wolfgang, who had been thinking of telling van Swieten about his weariness, his fainting spells, his constant pain, said nothing. He had a feeling that instead of getting sympathy, he would be ridiculed. Yet as he handed van Swieten his symphony, he cried out, "Dear Baron, for the sake of our friendship, keep me in kind remembrance. Would to God I could have been the cause of so much joy to you, as you have been to me." Wolfgang closed the door before he broke down and wept.

Now he was not up to going to the theater. Joseph Diener, at whose tavern he ate frequently, sent his meals to him and dropped in occasionally, while he struggled with the requiem. He was living on soup and wine, which, at least, he could digest, although the pain remained. It was a problem to keep the requiem from being a piteous lament, but with great effort and all of his discipline, of which he was so proud, he kept the music under control. His God had to be a loving God.

And he had to go on working – if he paused he wouldn't be able to resume – and he wrote Stanzi loving letters, although melancholy crept into them. He knew he couldn't continue this way much longer, but he was approaching the halfway point of the requiem. Once it was half done, then if the mysterious stranger appeared he might appease him with that.

Suddenly, unexpectedly, there was a letter from Da Ponte, who had gone to Trieste after his banishment from Vienna. Da Ponte wrote: "Dear, dear Mozart: I am leaving for England shortly, and you must come with me. Together, we will be even more successful than we were in Vienna. We have many friends in England, I hear that Haydn is a great success there, and sings your praises at every opportunity. . ."

Wolfgang's eyes blurred with tears and he had to stop reading. He was in such an extreme state of sensibility that many things made him cry now. But he composed his reply with care, as calmly and honestly as he could. "My dear Da Ponte: I would love to heed your advice, but it is impossible. My head spins so I cannot see a straight path ahead, but see only darkness and the grave. I cannot rid my mind of the specter of death. I view him constantly these days: he begs me to join him, he persuades me, he says I must labor only for him. I go on working because composing exhausts me less than doing nothing. Moreover, there is little left to fear. There is such a heaviness in me that I know my hour is striking. I am near death. I am finished before I have had time to enjoy my ability. And yet life has been so beautiful, and my career started with such fortunate circumstances. But no one can alter his fate. No one can measure his days. One has to resign oneself. What Providence wills, will be done. So I have to finish my funeral song, which I cannot leave incomplete."

As he left the house to post this letter the gray stranger was waiting for him. "You are late, Mozart," he said angrily. "Where is the requiem?"

"It is almost half done."

"Only half. I can't wait much longer."

"So I'm to be your next victim."

The stranger didn't reply, but smiled grimly.

"I will try to finish it by the end of this month."

"You must. I cannot wait any longer."

After Wolfgang mailed the letter to Da Ponte, he staggered into Diener's Inn and ordered wine. But after it came he didn't touch it, sitting with his hands in front of his eyes as if to shut out what he was seeing.

Diener felt his patron's head – it was burning. He sent a waiter to the musician's sister-in-law, Sophie, who lived nearby, to notify her that Mozart was very ill, then placed him in a carriage and took him home.

And as he put him to bed, and sent for Doctor Closset, Wolfgang murmured, "Nothing to drink today, Joseph. All I need is apothecaries and doctors," and fell into a stupor. The innkeeper lit the stove. It was November, and the room was icy cold. No wonder Herr Kapellmeister had caught such a severe chill.

NINETY

When Wolfgang came out of the darkness he found Constanze and Sophie sitting by his bedside. For an instant he was annoyed that Constanze had been called – why should she be upset? – but then he was glad, for he had missed her so much. He asked, "Where are Karl and Franz?"

"With my mother," Constanze replied. "Don't be anxious about them."

Constanze had kept the children away; now he knew he was very ill.

"You have been unconscious for several days. You must rest."

He tried to sit up to kiss her, but he was too weak, and his body was swollen as well as his hands and feet. And the dull ache in his stomach was still there, but the worst thing was that he was so tired.

Constanze kissed him and said, "You should have told me, Wolfgang."

"I didn't want to upset you."

"I would have been more upset not knowing."

He went to embrace her, but because of his swollen body he could not.

"I'll make a night jacket for you, then you'll be more comfortable."

"Could I move into the front room? So I can look out on the street, and hear our canary sing? That will help my composing."

"Doctor Closset said you mustn't compose, but rest."

"I will have a very long time to rest. Can I move now?"

He couldn't stand when he sought to walk into the next room. They had a small five-room apartment and to his enervated body it had become as large as Schönbrunn. But after the bed was moved close to one of the windows facing the street, and they helped him in, he was more content. He could see the small, dark, narrow Himmelpfortgasse which came into the Rauhensteingasse at his window, and if he leaned over he could see part of Jahn's restaurant-hall where he had last performed.

The next few days he was able to work on the requiem with Süssmayer. His hands were too swollen to hold the score, but he dictated to his pupil how it should be continued. The solemn, earnest Süssmayer would never be a Mozart, thought Wolfgang, but he was conscientious.

Süssmeyer wished Herr Kapellmeister would stop talking about Salieri having poisoned him. There was no evidence, and Salieri was a great success, he didn't need to do such a stupid trick. But Mozart was so impractical. Last winter when he had been introduced to the composer, he had come upon him dancing around the room with his wife and when Mozart had been asked why, the reply had been, "We are only getting warm, it is freezing in here, and we can't afford any wood." No wonder the composer had fallen ill: Mozart was very careless with his money and worked too hard, too feverishly. During the last weeks of composing *La Clemenza di Tito* and *Die Zauberflöte*, Mozart had composed thirty-five days without a pause. He had counted them, for he had to help him; he had done so only because it would provide for his future. He might never be a Mozart, but he would never be impoverished. As Mozart's pupil and disciple he would have a considerable reputation after Herr Kapellmeister's death.

The strain of working on the requiem exhausted Wolfgang. He could hardly move, yet when Constanze came in to see if she should call the doctor, he sought to be playful to allay her fears, and he fainted.

Closset was at his side as he recovered consciousness, and suddenly he burst out passionately, "Was I poisoned, Doctor? By bad food? By Salieri?"

"Nonsense! As I told you before, you are distraught."

"But my stomach hurts so!"

"All illnesses settle in the stomach."

"It is no wonder my stomach is sick," sighed Wolfgang. "It's had to swallow all sorts of things."

"It is your fever we have to cure."

Wolfgang thought the doctor might be right. The drugs Closset gave him lessened his feverish feeling, the pain in his stomach seemed to abate – or was it that he was getting used to it? he wondered. For several nights he was able to occupy himself as he lay in bed by propping his watch against his chest, so he could tell what part of *The Magic Flute* was taking place at the theater. It was a great success, Stanzi told him, but there was no sign of Schikaneder and the ducats he had been promised. He got in the habit of looking at his watch and saying, "The overture is starting, Tamino is on now, and here is papageno," and he tried to sing the birdcatcher's first song, but his voice was not audible.

This pleasure exhausted him, also, and now he had no strength for anything. His fever grew worse, and on November 28, Doctor Closset called in Doctor von Sallaba, for consultation on his condition.

Doctor von Sallaba, who was chief of the Vienna General Hospital, surprised Wolfgang with his youth, but the much older Doctor Closset conferred with him with obvious deference.

No one would tell him what the doctors had decided, but Stanzi looked stricken. He had begun to vomit again, whatever he ate, and he felt as if he were lying with one foot in the grave.

Yet the morning of Sunday, December 4, when it was arranged for several singers to perform part of his requiem for him that afternoon, he improved a little, although he had had a terrible night.

Constanze was sure she would collapse. The doctors had informed her that Mozart's condition was hopeless. They said, "He has a heated military fever," although Süssmayer, who had dropped in to aid with the singing of the requiem, said, when she told him this, "I had a relative who died of the same symptoms as Herr Kapellmesiter, and the doctors stated it was a kidney ailment. But we had better not tell him there is anything wrong with his kidneys, or he will think he was poisoned."

"He has thought that for some time. Would you go for my sister?"

When Sophie arrived, Wolfgang was surrounded by three musicians who were performing the requiem with him. He was singing the alto part, and that seemed to lift his spirits.

But Constanze, who pulled Sophie into the next room, whispered fearfully, "Thank God, you've come. He was so weak last night I didn't think he would be alive today. Stay with me this evening, for if he gets that ill again, he will die during the night. Sit with him now, please! He likes you."

Sophie sought to control herself and went back to the bedroom. Wolfgang had stopped singing, his voice having failed him completely, and he looked as despondent as she had ever seen him. The other musicians were assuring him that they would return next Sunday to continue where they had halted, but he pushed the requiem aside and murmured, weeping, "I'm nothing, nothing. Without music I'm nothing." But when he saw Sophie, he motioned to her to sit beside him, and said, "Dear Sophie, it is good of you to come. You must stay here tonight. You must see me die."

"You're depressed. It's natural. You had a bad night."

"I already have the taste of death on my tongue. Who will look after Stanzi after I am gone?"

As night came he grew worse. Constanze begged Sophie to go to

St. Peter's and to fetch a priest. None of the priests wanted to come. They said that Mozart was a Freemason, a pagan, and Sophie couldn't accept that. Wolfgang was as godly as anyone she knew, she had never seen him in a temper, even angry. Finally, she shamed a young priest, who liked music, into coming.

By the time they reached the house, Süssmayer was at Wolfgang's side. The requiem lay on the coverlet and Wolfgang was telling his pupil how to finish it after his death. Then, asking the priest to wait a moment, he whispered to Constanze, "Don't tell anyone of my death until you can inform Albrechtsberger, so he can get my post at St. Stephen's. It belongs to him. He is a fine organist and has given them good service."

Wolfgang felt that the priest regarded him disapprovingly though he gave him extreme unction.

As Wolfgang lay in anguish, Süssmayer cried, "We must get Closset. He might relieve the pain. Frau Mozart, do you know where he is?"

Constanze was in such distress, she couldn't answer – she had to lie down in her room before she collapsed – and Wolgang said haltingly, "He is at the theater. He went to hear *Die Zauberflöte*. I gave him tickets for his calling the other doctor. He will like Papageno. He is not musical, but everybody likes Papageno. Where's Stanzi, Sophie?"

"Lying down." Süssmayer had rushed out to get Doctor Closset. "Isn't she well?"

"She needs rest. She didn't sleep much last night."

"I know," he said sadly, "I kept her up."

"No, you didn't. But you have been quite sick."

"Dying, Sophie, dying." Now that his life was finished, he wished he could start again. "There are the scores of my last three symphonies in my safe. Don't let them be destroyed. They might be played some day."

He fell into a strange world, where he didn't recognize anyone he knew, not even Papa or Mamma. He shut his eyes to eliminate this wilderness. Since he had taken to his bed he hadn't seen Puchberg, Wetzlar, or van Swieten. It didn't matter. He didn't even remember all the pieces he had composed. Life was stronger than death. His music showed that.

Then he heard Süssmayer telling Sophie – Thank God, he still had his hearing – "Doctor Closset wouldn't come until the opera was over."

"I thought he would never come," said Sophie. "Where is he now?"

"Washing his hands. He says he doesn't want to catch any infection."

"Süssmayer," murmured Wolfgang, "was *The Magic Flute* crowded?"

"Full. As always. There were many encores. And Bravo Mozarts."

Sophie thought Wolfgang smiled, but she couldn't be sure.

Süssmayer didn't add how angry the doctor had made him. Closset had refused to leave *The Magic Flute* until it was finished. The doctor was curious about the opera, and there was nothing he could do for Mozart.

Wolfgang saw Closset standing over him. The doctor was putting cold compresses on his burning head and he was on the cross. He felt it on his back, down to the marrow, to the bone. Sing clearly, love, sing clearly. Everyone said it was worse to be blind, but it was hearing that mattered the most. He hadn't been able to see clearly for some time, but he had not expected to lose his hearing. Now he knew what death was. Silence.

Closset informed Sophie that the cold compresses would ease the patient's fever and pain, but Wolfgang was shocked into unconsciousness. The doctor said, with a resigned air, "There isn't anything else that can be done," and left.

Sophie sat beside Wolfgang – Constanze was prostrate in her room and Süssmayer was tending her – and suddenly, she heard Wolfgang mumble, "What the world does to its children." Then with a convulsive effort of his mouth he sought to sound the drums in the requiem. He lifted his head, as if to make sure he heard them, and turned his face to the wall and was quiet. It was after midnight, five minutes to one, December 5, a Monday morning in 1791, and Wolfgang was dead.

NINETY-ONE

The funeral arrangements were made by Sophie, for Constanze collapsed completely and was so weak she could not stand upright. There was no money in the house, so Sophie appealed to Puchberg for money to pay for the funeral and grave, and Puchberg refused. Herr Mozart owed him many gulden as it was, which he was not asking to be repaid, but there was no sense throwing money away after what was lost already. Wetzlar was at the front of the army, which was ready to attack the convulsion going on in France, and she turned to his dearest friend, van Swieten.

The Baron was in foul humour. He had been dismissed by the Emperor from his treasured post as President of the Court Commission of Education, and although he still had a sizable fortune, it meant that his days of Imperial influence were over. And while he was distressed by Wolfgang's passing, since Wolfgang's criticism of his symphony he had not been able to care for him the same way.

But he told Sophie, "Of course I can't allow my good friend to be thrown into a pauper's grave. I will pay for a third-class funeral."

It was the cheapest funeral there was, but Sophie couldn't argue. When she completed the arrangements, van Swieten handed her the exact amount: eight gulden, fifty-six kreutzer for the funeral, and three gulden for the hearse. Wolfgang had spent that much on his pet starling's burial, thought Sophie, but Constanze was too unwell to protest.

The funeral took place the afternoon after Wolfgang died. The small coffin was carried out of the house on the Rauhensteingasse, and borne on a small cart to St. Stephen's and into the Crucifix Chapel on the north side of the cathedral. There were a few mourners, van Swieten, Salieri, Deiner, Sophie, Anna Gottlieb, Albrechtsberger, Süssmayer – Fräu Weber was staying with Constanze, who was in bed with shock. It was a quiet day and there were the usual monks and nuns from the provinces visiting this wonder of Christendom, the most famous church in the Empire, and none of them turned a head as the coffin was borne inside. Funerals were commonplace and this was that of a poor, unimportant person, that was obvious from the bare wooden box and the lack of mourners.

After the corpse was blessed, the coffin was put back on the little open cart and the driver and his horse turned toward the cemetery.

St. Marx's was just five years old, an insignificant cemetery that had been created by the parish of St. Stephen's for those who could not afford a churchyard for the mourners – that would have been an extra expense – and, by the time the cart reached the heavy cobblestones of the Landstrasse suburb, there was no one with it. The sky had grown dark, there was the threat of snow in the air, and it was very far to walk.

There was only one grave-digger in the cemetery. It was a slow day, he explained to the driver, and he was finishing the common grave.

The grave-digger was elderly, hard of hearing, and he had a number of coffins stacked in the long, narrow, straight pit. He was proud that he was neat and orderly. He didn't hear the name, but he knew it was a little man, he could tell by the smallness of the coffin, and that it was a third-class funeral. Only such a funeral would have no mourners. No one wanted to pay for anything. Not a gulden.

The driver dumped the coffin onto the ground alongside a number of other coffins, and hurried away. He detested this kind of funeral, it barely paid for the cost of the horse and the cart.

Wolfgang's body went into the common grave, stacked three deep with a hundred other corpses.

Two people did reach St. Marx's cemetery that day. Albrechtsberger, deeply touched by Wolfgang's consideration, arrived at the cemetery after the burial. He had expected carriages, and when there hadn't been any, it had taken time to hire one and to find St. Marx's. But the grave digger was gone and the caretaker said, "We have had a number of funerals today. We don't know where your friend is."

Night had fallen when Anna Gottlieb reached St. Marx's in a carriage she had been able to take because of her earnings in *The Magic Flute*.

The caretaker was nicer to her – she was such a pretty girl and she looked so sad, she must have lost her lover, he thought – and he tried to be kind. "Your friend wasn't buried in a pauper's grave. Nobody knows where they are. From what you say, he got a third-class funeral. In the large section beyond the cross. We've buried many people there."

Anna stood on ground that had been freshly dug. It extended for a long distance, and it was impossible to tell where the last grave had been spaded. Nothing had turned out the way she had expected. But she loved him, and knew she always would, whatever he had thought of her. There had never been a harsh word in him. From the moment she had met him as a child, he had been so gallant. And he knew so much about music and human feeling. Did any of his friends realize what they had lost?

She put a flower in the ground, although she knew it would die quickly in the bitter December air. There were stars in the sky now, more stars than she could count. They would shine over Wolfgang now, she thought, over his music which had given her such pleasure and happiness. Then she cried, she cried for Wolfgang, she cried for herself, she cried for all the deaths in the universe, for the disappearance of everybody. And suddenly she stopped. He hadn't disappeared. He couldn't, with his music so much a part of her. And perhaps it was fitting that he had been buried this way, she thought; his body glorified all the nameless corpses in the common grave with him, for no one knew which was his.

SOURCES

Allen, W. D., *Philosophies of Music*. 1962.

Anderson, Emily, *Letters of Mozart and His Family*, 2 v. 1966.

Anthony, Katherine, *Marie Antoinette*. 1933.

Auer, Leopold, *Violin Master Works and Their Interpretation*. 1925.
    Violin Playing as I Teach It. 1960.

Bach, C. P. E., *Essay on the True Art of Playing Keyboard Instruments*. 1949.

Badura-Skoda, Eva and Paul, *Interpreting Mozart on the Keyboard*. 1962.

Baedeker, Karl, *Austria*. 1929.
    Eastern Alps. 1911.
    Northern Italy. 1913.
    Southern Germany. 1929.

Barea, Ilse, *Vienna*. 1966.

Barrington, Daines, *Account of a Very Remarkable Young Musician*. 1770.

Barzini, Luigi, *The Italians*. 1964.

Barzun, Jacques, *Pleasure of Music*. 1951.

Bayr, Rudolf, *Salzburg – City and Province*.

Belloc, Hilaire, *Marie Antoinette*. 1909.

Benn, Christopher, *Mozart on the Stage*. 1946.

Berlioz, Hector, *Evenings with an Orchestra*. 1956.

Biancolli, Louis, *The Mozart Handbook*. (Edited and Compiled by) 1954.

Biancolli, Louis, and Bagar, Roger, *The Concert Companion*. 1947.

Blom, Eric, *Mozart*. 1963.

Bonavia, F., *Musicians on Music*. 1957.

Bourne, C. E., *The Great Composers*.

Breakspeare, Eustace, *Mozart*. 1902.

Broder, Nathan, *What Was Mozart's Playing Like?* 1959.

Brophy, Brigid, *Mozart, The Dramatist*. 1964.

Bukofzer, Manfred, *Music in the Baroque Era*. 1951.

Brion, Marcel, *Daily Life in the Vienna of Mozart and Schubert*. 1962.

Burk, John N., *Mozart and His Music*. 1959.
    Life and Works of Beethoven. 1943.

Burke, C. G., *The Collector's Haydn*. 1959.

Burney, Charles, *A General History of Music,* 4 v. 1789.
    Dr. Burney's Musical Tours in Europe. 1959.
Casanova, Giacomo, *Memoirs,* 2 v. 1922.
Castelot, André, *Queen of France.* 1957.
Cooper, Martin, *Gluck.* 1935.
Cox, Cynthia, *The Real Figaro.* 1962.
Creed, Virginia, *All About Austria.* 1950.
Davenport, Maria, *Mozart.* 1932.
Demuth, Norman, *French Opera – Its Development to the Revolution.*
Denaes, Raymond, *Versailles.* 1962.
Dent, Edward J., *Mozart's Operas.* 1947.
    Mozart – A Documentary Biography. 1965.
Deutsch, Otto Erich, *Handel – A Documentary Biography.* 1954.
    Mozart – A Documentary Biography. 1965.
    Mozart – His World in Contemporary Pictures. 1961.
Dickinson, A. E. F., *A Study of Mozart's Last Three Symphonies.* 1927.
Dolge, Alfred, *Pianos and Their Makers.* 1911.
Dunhill, Thomas, *Mozart's String Quartets.* 1927.
Durant, Will and Ariel, *The Age of Voltaire.* 1965.
    Rousseau and Revolution. 1967.
Einstein, Alfred, *Essays on Music,* 1956.
    Gluck. 1962.
    Greatness in Music. 1941.
    Mozart, His Character, His Work. 1945.
Elson, Arthur, *The Book of Musical Knowledge.* 1927.
Elson, Nina, *Love and the French.* 1959.
Erang, Robert, *Europe from the Renaissance to Waterloo.* 1939.
Ewen, David, *Encyclopedia of Musical Masterpieces.* 1949.
Ewen, David and Frederic, *Musical Vienna.* 1939.
Fay, Bernard, *Franklin, The Apostle of Modern Times.* 1929.
Ferguson, Donald N., *Image and Structure in Chamber Music.* 1964.
Flower, Newman, *Handel.* 1959.
Forster and Sandys, *History of the Violin.* 1918.
Friedell, Egon, *Cultural History of the Modern Age,* v 1, 2. 1954.
Friedenthal, Richard, *Goethe – His Life and Times.* 1965.
Funk, Addie, *Vienna's Musical Sites and Landmarks.* 1927.
Garvie, Peter, *Music and Western Man.* 1958.
Gaxotte, Pierre, *Louis the Fifteenth and His Times.* 1934.
Gay, Peter, *The Age of Enlightenment.* 1966.
Geiringer, Karl. *Haydn.* 1946.
Gheon, Henri, *In Search of Mozart.* 1934.
Girdlestone, Cuthbert, *Mozart and His Piano Concertos.* 1964.
    Jean-Philippe Rameau. 1957.

Glazer, Josef and Heinz, *A Guide to Schönbrunn*. 1965.

Gooch, G. P., *Catherine the Great and Other Studies*. 1954.

Gotwals, Vernon, *Joseph Haydn*. 1963.

Graf, Gita, *Austria – Music and Theater*. 1958.

Graf, Max, *Composer and Critic*. 1946.
    Maria Theresa and Other Studies. 1931.
    Legend of a Musical City. 1945.
    Great Styles of Furniture. 1963.

Grew, Sydney and Eva Mary, *Bach*. 1962.

Grove's Dictionary of Music. 1927.

Hadow, W. H., *Oxford History of Music – The Viennese Period*,
    v. 5. 1931.

Haggin, B. H., *The Listener's Musical Companion*. 1959.

Haldane, Charlotte, *Mozart*. 1960.

Harding, Rosamund, *The Piano-Forte*. 1933.

Helm, E. E., *Music in the Court of Frederick the Great*. 1960.

Heriot, Angus, *The Castrati in Opera*. 1956.

Holmes, Edward, *The Life of Mozart*. 1845.

Howard, Patricia, *Gluck and the Birth of Modern Opera*. 1964.

Hughes, Patrick, *Famous Mozart Operas*. 1958.

Hughes, Rosemary, *Haydn*. 1963.

Hussey, Dyneley, *Wolfgang Amade Mozart*. 1928.

Hutchings, Arthur, *A Companion to Mozart's Piano Concertos*. 1948.

Hutchinson, Ernest, *The Literature of the Piano*. 1964.

Jacob, H. E., *Joseph Haydn*. 1950.

Jahn, Otto, *The Life of Mozart*. 1882.

Jones-Pryce, Alan, *Beethoven*. 1962.

Josephson, Matthew, *Jean-Jacques Rousseau*. 1931.

Kemp, Gerald van der, *Versailles*. 1961.

Kelly, Michael, *Reminiscences*, 2 v. 1826.

Kenyon, Max, *Harpsichord Music*. 1949.
    Mozart in Salzburg. 1953.
    Mozart Letter Book. 1956.

Kerst, Friedrich, *Mozart*. 1905.
    *Mozart – The Man and the Artist Revealed in His Own
    Words*.

King, A. Hyatt, *Mozart in Retrospect*.

Kirkpatrick, Ralph, *Domenico Scarlatti*. 1953.

Knock, W. J. G., *Austria and the Hapsburgs*. 1960.

Köchel, Ludwig von, *Chronological and Classified Listing of W. A.
    Mozart's Works*. 1965.

Kolb, Annette, *Mozart*. 1956.

Landon, H. C. R., and Mitchell, Donald, *The Mozart Companion*.
    1956.
    The Symphonies of Joseph Haydn. 1955.

Lang, Paul Henry, *The Creative World of Mozart.* 1963.

Lelash, Marjorie and Peck, Robert, *Mozart's Librettos.* 1961.

Levetus, A. S., *Imperial Vienna.* 1915.

Lewisohn, Ludwig, *Goethe.* 1949.

Loesser, Arthur, *Men, Women and Pianos.* 1954.

Long, J. C., *George III.* 1961.

Loomis, Stanley, *Dubarry.* 1959.

Lowenberg, Alfred, *Annals of Opera, 1597–1940.* 1943.

Marek, George R. *Opera as Theater.* 1962.

Marks, F. H., *The Sonata: Its Form and Meaning as Exemplified in the Pianoforte Sonatas of Mozart.* 1921.

Maurois, André, *Voltaire.* 1932.

Mendel, Arthur, and David, H. T., *The Bach Reader.* 1945.

Moldenhauer, Hans, *Duo-Pianism.* 1950.

Morris, Constance Lily, *Maria Theresa.* 1937.

Mozart, Leopold, *A Treatise on the Fundamental Principles of Violin Playing.* 1951.

Musicians' World, Great Composers in Their Letters. 1966.

Nettl, Paul, *Mozart and Masonry.* 1957.

  The Other Casanova. 1950.

Neuman, Paul, *A Guide through the Imperial Palace (Hofburg) of Vienna.* 1963.

Newman, Ernest, *Essays from the World of Music.* 1958.

  Gluck and the Opera. 1895.

  Great Operas, v. 2. 1958.

Nicolson, Harold, *The Age of Reason.* 1960.

Novello, Vincent, *A Mozart Pilgrimage.* 1855.

Opel, Willi, *Masters of the Keyboard.* 1965.

Pick, Robert, *Empress Maria Theresa.* 1966.

Plumb, J. H., *The First Four Georges.* 1957.

Ponte, Lorenzo Da, *Memoirs.* 1929.

Praz, Mario, *An Illustrated History of Furnishings from the Renaissance to the Twentieth Century.* 1964.

Prezzoline, Giuseppe, *Machiavelli.* 1966.

Raynor, Henry, *Joseph Haydn.* 1961.

Rickett, Richard, *St. Stephen's Cathedral in Vienna.*

Rolland, Romain, *Beethoven the Creator.* 1929.

  Essays in Music. 1959.

  Goethe and Beethoven. 1931.

  A Musical Tour Through the Lands of the Past. 1922.

Roseberry, Eric, *W. A. Mozart.* 1960.

Rude, George, *Revolutionary Europe, 1783 1815.* 1964.

Russell, Raymond, *The Harpsichord and Clavichord.* 1959.

Sadie, Stanley, *Mozart.* 1965.

Saint-Fox, Georges de, *The Symphonies of Mozart.* 1947.

Schenk, Erich, *Mozart and His Times*. 1959.

Schlegel, Richard, *The Castle of Hohensalzburg*. 1962.

Schmiedbauer, Alois, *Salzburg*. 1956.

Schonberg, Harold C., *The Great Pianists*. 1963.

Schweitzer, Albert, *J. S. Bach*. 1923.
      Goethe – Four Studies. 1949.

Sedgwick, Henry Dwight, *Vienna*. 1939.

Shaw, Bernard, *How To Become a Musical Critic*. 1961.
      Selection from the Musical Criticism of Bernard Shaw. 1955.

Sigerist, Henry E., *The Great Doctors*. 1958.

Sitwell, Sacheverell, *Great Palaces of Europe*. 1964.
      Mozart. 1932.

Spitta, Philip, *Johann Sebastian Bach*. 1951.

Stendal (Marie Henri Beyle), *The Life of Haydn Followed by the Life of Mozart*. 1839.

Sullivan, J. W. N., *Beethoven*. 1927.

Sumner, W. L., *The Organ*. 1952.

Tenschert, Roland, *Mozart*. 1953.

Terry, Charles Sanford, *Johann Christian Bach*. 1929.

Thayer, A. W., *The Life of Ludwig van Beethoven*. 1921.

Thackeray, William M., *Miscellanies (The Four Georges)*. 1873.

Thomson, Virgil, *Music Reviewed – 1940-1954*. 1967.

Tobin, Raymond, *Mozart and the Sonata Form*.

Townson, Robert, *Travels in Hungary and Vienna*. 1797.

Turner, W. J., *Mozart, The Man and His Work*. 1938.

Valentin, Erich, *Beethoven – A Pictorial Biography*. 1958.
      Mozart – a Pictorial Biography. 1959.

Wandruszka, Adam, *The House of Hapsburg*. 1964.

Wickenburg, Erik G., *Salzburg*. 1961.

Wilder, Victor, *Mozart*, 2 v. 1906.

Williams, C. F. A., *The Story of the Organ*. 1916.

Winwar, Francis, *Jean-Jacques Rousseau*. 1961.

Zoff, Otto, *Great Composers*. 1951.

Zweig, Stefan, *Marie Antoinette*. 1933.